intel

U.S. and CANADA LITERAT

NAME: ______

COMPANY: ______

ADDRESS: ______

CITY: ______ STATE: ______ ZIP: ______

COUNTRY: ______

PHONE NO.: ( )

ORDER NO.	TITLE	QTY.		PRICE		TOTAL
			×		=	
			×		=	
			×		=	
			×		=	
			×		=	
			×		=	
			×		=	
			×		=	
			×		=	
			×		=	

Subtotal ______

Must Add Your Local Sales Tax ______

Postage: add 10% of subtotal → Postage ______

Total ______

Pay by check, money order, or include company purchase order with this form ($100 minimum). We also accept VISA, MasterCard or American Express. Make payment to Intel Literature Sales. Allow 2-4 weeks for delivery.

☐ VISA ☐ MasterCard ☐ American Express Expiration Date

Account No. ______

Signature ______

Mail To: Intel Literature Sales
P.O. Box 7641
Mt. Prospect, Il 60056-7641

International Customers outside the U.S. and Canada should use the International order form or contact their local Sales Office or Distributor.

For phone orders in the U.S. and Canada
Call Toll Free: (800) 548-4725

Prices good until 12/31/90.

Source HB

intel

INTERNATIONAL LITERATURE ORDER FORM

NAME: ______________________________

COMPANY: ______________________________

ADDRESS: ______________________________

CITY: ____________________ STATE: ________ ZIP: ________

COUNTRY: ______________________________

PHONE NO.: (   ) ______________________________

ORDER NO.	TITLE	QTY.		PRICE		TOTAL
			X		=	
			X		=	
			X		=	
			X		=	
			X		=	
			X		=	
			X		=	
			X		=	
			X		=	
			X		=	

Subtotal ________

Must Add Your
Local Sales Tax ________

Total ________

PAYMENT

Cheques should be made payable to your local Intel Sales Office (see inside back cover.)

Other forms of payment may be available in your country. Please contact the Literature Coordinator at your local Intel Sales Office for details.

The completed form should be marked to the attention of the LITERATURE COORDINATOR and returned to your local Intel Sales Office.

i486™ PROCESSOR HARDWARE REFERENCE MANUAL

1990

Additional copies of this manual or other Intel literature may be obtained from:

Intel Corporation
Literature Sales
P.O. Box 7641
Mt. Prospect, IL 60056-7641

CUSTOMER SUPPORT

INTEL'S COMPLETE SUPPORT SOLUTION WORLDWIDE

Customer Support is Intel's complete support service that provides Intel customers with hardware support, software support, customer training, consulting services and network management services. For detailed information contact your local sales offices.

After a customer purchases any system hardware or software product, service and support become major factors in determining whether that product will continue to meet a customer's expectations. Such support requires an international support organization and a breadth of programs to meet a variety of customer needs. As you might expect, Intel's customer support is quite extensive. It can start with assistance during your development effort to network management. 100 Intel sales and service offices are located worldwide – in the U.S., Canada, Europe and the Far East. So wherever you're using Intel technology, our professional staff is within close reach.

HARDWARE SUPPORT SERVICES

Intel's hardware maintenance service, starting with complete on-site installation will boost your productivity from the start and keep you running at maximum efficiency. Support for system or board level products can be tailored to match your needs, from complete on-site repair and maintenance support to economical carry-in or mail-in factory service.

Intel can provide support service for not only Intel systems and emulators, but also support for equipment in your development lab or provide service on your product to your end-user/customer.

SOFTWARE SUPPORT SERVICES

Software products are supported by our Technical Information Service (TIPS) that has a special toll free number to provide you with direct, ready information on known, documented problems and deficiencies, as well as work-arounds, patches and other solutions.

Intel's software support consists of two levels of contracts. Standard support includes TIPS (Technical Information Phone Service), updates and subscription service (product-specific troubleshooting guides and; *COMMENTS Magazine*). Basic support consists of updates and the subscription service. Contracts are sold in environments which represent product groupings (e.g., iRMX® environment).

CONSULTING SERVICES

Intel provides field system engineering consulting services for any phase of your development or application effort. You can use our system engineers in a variety of ways ranging from assistance in using a new product, developing an application, personalizing training and customizing an Intel product to providing technical and management consulting. Systems Engineers are well versed in technical areas such as microcommunications, real-time applications, embedded microcontrollers, and network services. You know your application needs; we know our products. Working together we can help you get a successful product to market in the least possible time.

CUSTOMER TRAINING

Intel offers a wide range of instructional programs covering various aspects of system design and implementation. In just three to ten days a limited number of individuals learn more in a single workshop than in weeks of self-study. For optimum convenience, workshops are scheduled regularly at Training Centers worldwide or we can take our workshops to you for on-site instruction. Covering a wide variety of topics, Intel's major course categories include: architecture and assembly language, programming and operating systems, BITBUS™ and LAN applications.

NETWORK MANAGEMENT SERVICES

Today's networking products are powerful and extremely flexible. The return they can provide on your investment via increased productivity and reduced costs can be very substantial.

Intel offers complete network support, from definition of your network's physical and functional design, to implementation, installation and maintenance. Whether installing your first network or adding to an existing one, Intel's Networking Specialists can optimize network performance for you.

PREFACE

This manual describes the basic mechanisms of the hardware interface to the i486™ processor and gives design examples of systems using the processor. The manual is written for designers who have moderate to advanced experience in microprocessor-based systems.

The chapters include:

- Chapter 1, "Introduction to the Processor." Introduces the functions and features of the i486 processor and its system components. Lists microprocessor products which are object-code compatible with the i486 processor. Shows block diagrams of basic system architecture and applications.
- Chapter 2, "Internal Architecture." Describes the i486 processor's internal instruction pipelining and the nine internal functional units: the bus interface, caches, instruction prefetch, instruction decode, integer (datapath), floating point, segmentation, and paging units.
- Chapter 3, "Processor Bus." Describes the signals on the i486 processor pins, including their uses and timing. Describes memory and I/O space. Describes data transfers, bus control, cache control, and floating-point error control.
- Chapter 4, "Performance Considerations." Describes the i486 microprocessor performance issues.
- Chapter 5, "Memory Subsystem Design." Describes the DRAM subsystem implementation for i486 microprocessor. It discusses the tested example. Appendix B contains PLD codes and schematics example of this design.
- Chapter 6, "Cache Subsystem." Describes the second-level cache implementation for the i486 microprocessor. It also covers the 82C6 cache controller specifics and general caching issue.
- Chapter 7, "Peripheral Subsystem." Describes the techniques for connection peripheral devices to the i486 microprocessor.
- Chapter 8, "System Design." Describes the i486 microprocessor-based system in general and cover the basics of i486 EISA chip set.
- Chapter 9, "MULTIBUS II System Interface."
- Chapter 10, "Physical Design and System Debugging."
- Appendix A, "Introduction to Intel 86 Family Architecture." Compares hardware characteristics of the 8086, 80286, 386™, and i486 processors. Describes how the hardware architecture of the Intel 86 family of processors has evolved.
- Appendix B, "PLD Codes and Schematics." This contains schematics and PLD codes for i486 DRAM design.

TIMING DIAGRAM NOTATION

In the timing diagrams for this manual, the beginning and end of bus cycle are illustrated with heavy, vertical, dashed lines. The beginning of data-transfer bus cycles is marked by the assertion of the address-status (ADS#) output, as shown in the following sample timing diagram. Signals which are "don't care" are cross hatched as in the RDY# signal shown in the following diagram. Signals which are not valid contain the words "not valid" as in the BLAST# signal. Signals which are valid are shown as high or low (as in the ADS# signal), or as both high and low (as in the PCHK# signal, indicating that the signal is in one or the other valid state).

DATA STRUCTURE NOTATION

The i486 processor is a "little endian" machine; this means the bytes of a word are numbered starting from the least significant byte. Pictures of data structures in memory show the smallest addresses at the bottom and the highest addresses at the top. Bit positions are numbered from right to left. The following diagram illustrates these conventions. The numerical value represented by a bit that is set (1) is equal to two

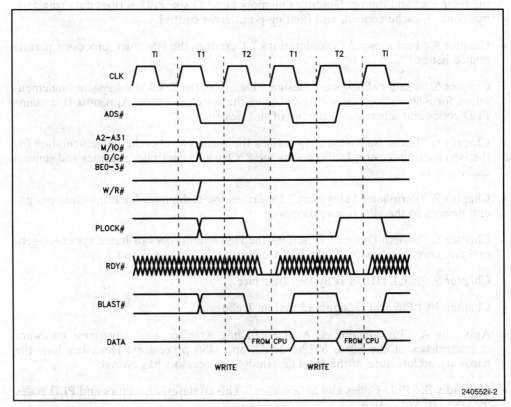

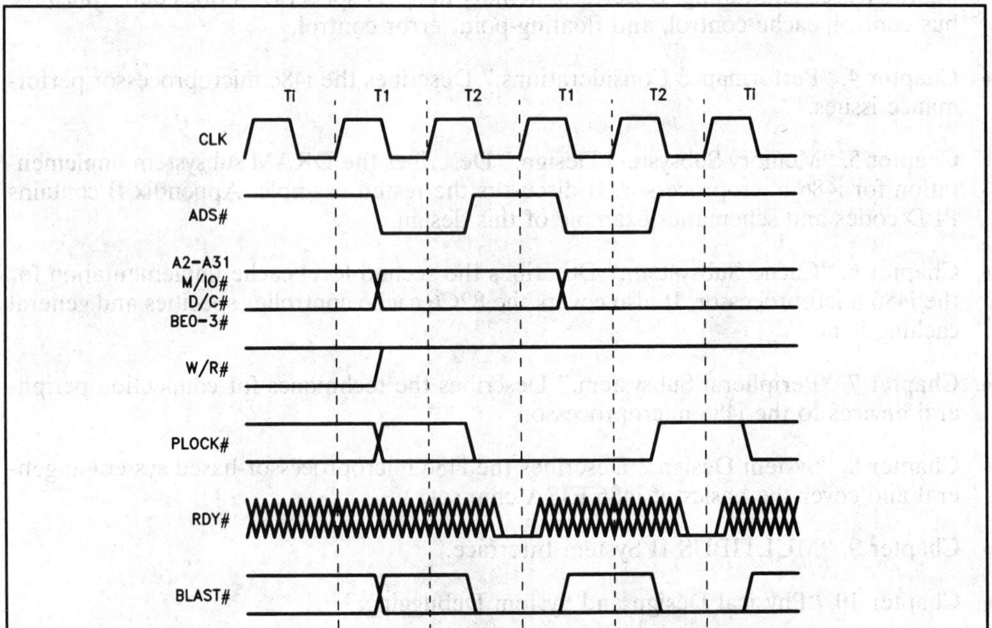

Timing Diagram Notation

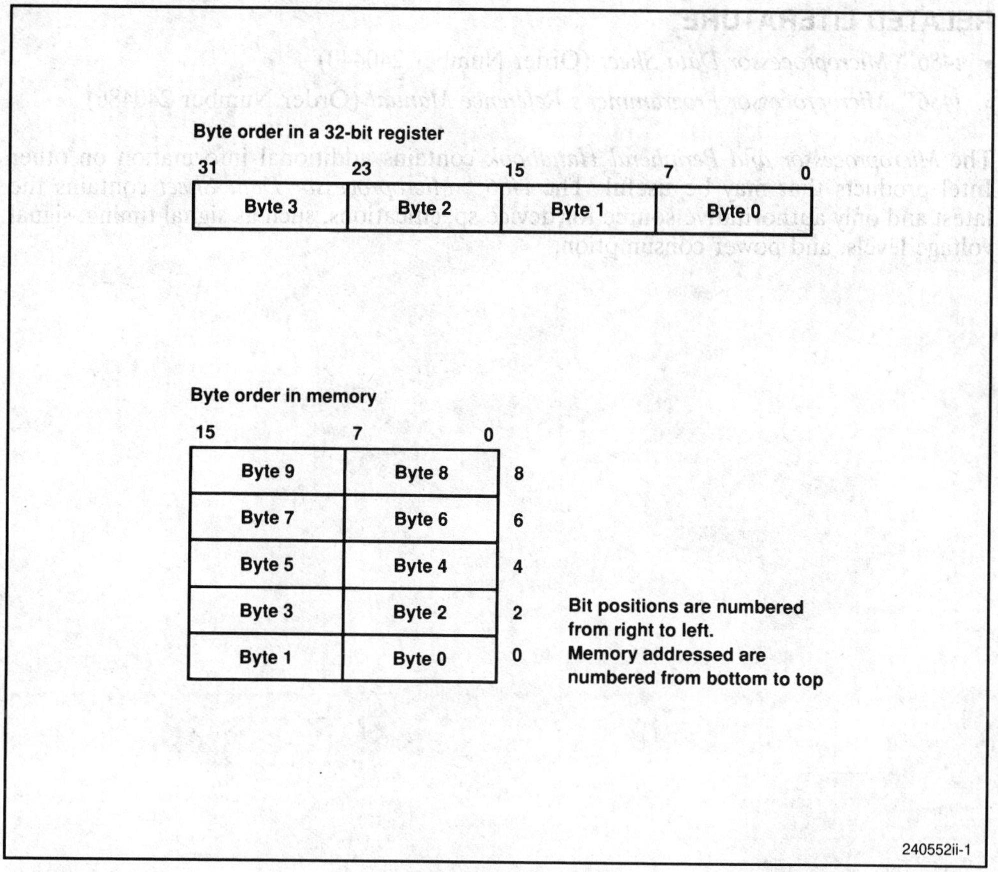

Bit and Byte Order

raised to the power of the bit position. The bit notation in a 32-bit register corresponds directly to the bit notation on the data bus when 32-bit data items are aligned to 32-bit boundaries in memory.

When bits are marked as undefined or reserved, it is essential for compatibility with future processors that software treat these bits as having a future, though unknown, effect. Programs that read registers with undefined bits must mask off those values. Programs that write to registers with undefined bits must first read the register and then change only the desired defined bits before writing back to the register.

NOTE

Depending upon the values of reserved register bits will make software dependent upon the unspecified manner in which the i486 processor handles these bits. Depending upon reserved values risks incompatibility with future processors. ***AVOID ANY DEPENDENCE UPON THE STATE OF RESERVED REGISTER BITS.***

RELATED LITERATURE

- *i486™ Microprocessor Data Sheet* (Order Number 240440)
- *i486™ Microprocessor Programmer's Reference Manual* (Order Number 240486)

The *Microprocessor and Peripheral Handbook* contains additional information on other Intel products that may be useful. The *i486™ Microprocessor Data Sheet* contains the latest and only authoritative source for device specifications, such as signal timing, signal voltage levels, and power consumption.

TABLE OF CONTENTS

Figures

Figures

Figures

Figures

Figures

Tables

Tables

Introduction to the Processor 1

CHAPTER 1
INTRODUCTION TO THE PROCESSOR

The Intel i486™ processor is the highest-performance member of the Intel 386™ family of processors. The i486 processor executes DOS, Windows, OS/2 operating system, UNIX System V/386, iRMX® operating system, and iRMX kernel applications faster than any other processor. It is upward binary compatible with the 8086, 8088, 80186, 80286, 386 DX processor, and 386 SX processors. The i486 processor brings mainframe power to PC architectures.

1.1 ARCHITECTURE

The i486 processor includes an integer processing unit, floating-point processing unit, memory-management unit, and cache. With these units together on a single chip, many inter-unit signals remain on-chip, running at the speed of VLSI silicon rather than the speed of printed circuit boards. The increased level of integration also reduces board space, which lowers cost and simplifies design.

The i486 processor can give a two- to four-fold performance improvement over the 386 processor, depending on the clock speeds used and the specific application. Like the 386, the i486 processor includes both segment-based and page-based memory protection schemes. Instruction processing time is reduced by on-chip instruction pipelining. By performing fast, on-chip memory management and caching, the i486 processor relaxes requirements for memory response for a given level of system performance.

The i486 processor bus is significantly faster than the 386 processor (local) bus. Both buses are 32 bits wide, but the i486 processor bus introduces the use of a single-frequency (1x) clock and support for parity checking, burst cycles, cacheable cycles, cache invalidation cycles, and 8-bit data buses. There are two major advantages to using a 1x clock. First, it simplifies system design by cutting in half the clock frequency required by external devices. Second, elimination of the 2x clock used on the 386 processor reduces RF emission at the higher speed of the i486 processor and simplifies clock generation.

The i486 processor can use burst cycles for read transfers which require multiple bus cycles. Burst cycles are done at the continuous rate of one 32-bit (doubleword) transfer per clock cycle. In the 386 processor, by comparison, data transfers require at least two clock cycles per transfer. External cache, interleaved memory banks, or DRAMs with static-column addressing may be used to achieve zero wait-state memory performance during a burst.

Instructions can be executed in fewer clock cycles than with the 386 processor. In the i486 processor, streamlined instruction pipelining supports a continuous execution rate of one clock cycle per instruction for most instructions. The internal cache supports a continuous rate of one processor request per clock cycle. To support efficient task switching in real-time multitasking and multiuser systems, the i486 processor, like the 386 processor, allows a single instruction or an interrupt to perform a complete task switch.

Device testing is supported by a built-in self-test. Results of the built-in self-test are available in an internal register. Assembly-language testing of the cache and translation lookaside buffer are also supported.

Chapter 2 describes the processor's internal architecture. Chapter 3 describes the processor bus. The rest of this section highlights features of particular interest to system designers.

1.1.1 Features

The i486 processor offers the following features:

- *Compatibility*—The processor is binary-compatible with the 8086, 8088, 80186, 80286, 386 processor, and 386 SX processor.
- *Full 32-bit integer processor*—The processor performs a complete set of arithmetic and logical operations on 8-, 16-, and 32-bit data types using a full-width ALU and eight general-purpose registers.
- *Separate 32-bit Address and Data Paths*—Four gigabytes of physical memory can be addressed directly.
- *Single-Cycle Execution*—Many instructions execute in a single clock cycle.
- *On-Chip Floating-Point Unit*—The 32-, 64-, and 80-bit formats specified in IEEE Standard 754 are supported. The unit is binary-compatible with the 8087, 80287, 387™ DX coprocessor, and 387 SX coprocessor.
- *On-Chip Memory Management Unit*—Address-management and memory-space protection mechanisms maintain the integrity of memory. This is necessary in multitasking and virtual-memory environments, like those implemented by the UNIX and OS/2 operating systems. Both memory segmentation and paging are supported.
- *On-Chip Cache, with Cache Consistency Support*—The internal write-through cache can hold 8K bytes of data or instructions. Cache hits are as fast as read accesses to a processor register. Bus activity is tracked to detect alterations in the memory which internal cache represents. The internal cache can be invalidated or flushed, so that an external cache controller can maintain cache consistency in multi-processor environments.
- *External Cache Control*—Write-back and flush controls over an external cache are provided so that the processor can maintain cache consistency in multi-processor environments.
- *Instruction Pipelining*—The fetching, decoding, execution, and address translation of instructions is overlapped within the i486 processor. This results in a continuous execution rate of one clock cycle per instruction, for most instructions.

- *Burst Cycles*—Burst transfers allow a new doubleword to be read from memory each clock cycle. With this capability the internal cache and instruction prefetch buffer can be filled very rapidly.
- *Write Buffers*—The processor can continue operations internally after a write, without waiting for the write to be executed on the processor bus.
- *Bus Backoff*—If another bus master needs control of the bus during a i486 processor-bus cycle, the i486 processor will float its bus signals, then restart its cycle when the bus again becomes available.
- *Instruction Restart*—Programs can continue execution following an exception generated by an unsuccessful attempt to access memory. This feature is important for supporting demand-paged virtual memory applications.
- *Dynamic Bus Sizing*—External controllers can dynamically alter the effective width of the data bus. Bus widths of 8, 16, or 32 bits can be used.

1.1.2 Operating Modes and Compatibility

The i486 processor can run programs in modes which give it object-code compatibility with software written for the 8086, 80286, and 386 processor families. The operating mode is set in software as:

- *Real Mode:* When the processor is reset or powered up, it is initialized in Real Mode. This mode has the same base architecture as the 8086 processor but allows access to the 32-bit register set of the i486 processor. The address mechanism, maximum memory size (1 Mbyte), and interrupt handling are identical to the Real Mode of the 80286 processor. Nearly all of the i486 processor instructions are available, but the default operand size is 16 bits; in order to use the 32-bit registers and addressing modes, override instruction prefixes must be used. The primary purpose of Real Mode is to set up the processor for Protected Mode operation.
- *Protected Mode (also called Protected Virtual Address Mode):* The complete capabilities of the i486 processor become available when programs are run in the Protected Mode. In addition to segmentation protection, paging can optionally be used in Protected Mode. Linear address space is four gigabytes and virtual memory programs of up to 64 terabytes can be run. All existing 8086, 80286, and 386 processor software can be run under the i486 processor's hardware-assisted protection mechanism. The addressing mechanism is more sophisticated in Protected Mode than in Real Mode.

  Virtual 8086 Mode, a sub-mode of Protected Mode, allows 8086 programs to be run with the segmentation and paging protection mechanisms of Protected Mode. This mode offers more flexibility than the Real Mode for running 8086 programs. Using this mode, the i486 processor can execute 8086 operating systems and applications simultaneously with an i486 operating system and both 80286 and i486 processor applications.

The hardware offers additional modes which are described in Chapter 2 of this manual. For more information on operating modes, see the *i486™ Microprocessor Data Sheet* and the *i486™ Programmer's Reference Manual*.

1.1.3 Memory Management

The memory management unit supports both segmentation and paging. Segmentation provides several independent, protected address spaces. This is a security feature which limits the damage a program error can cause. For example, a program's stack space should be prevented from growing into its code space. The segmentation unit maps the separate address spaces seen by programmers into one unsegmented, linear address space.

Paging provides access to data structures larger than the available memory space by keeping them partly in memory and partly on disk. Paging breaks the linear address space into units of 4K bytes called *pages*. When a program makes its first reference to a page, the program can be stopped, the new page copied from disk, and the program restarted. Programs tend to use only a few pages at a time, so a processor with paging can simulate a large address space in RAM using a small amount of RAM, plus storage on a disk.

1.1.4 On-Chip Cache

A software-transparent 8K-byte cache stores recently accessed information on the processor chip. Both instructions and data can be cached. If the processor needs to read data which is available in the cache, the cache responds and a time-consuming external memory cycle is avoided. This allows the processor to complete transfers faster and reduces traffic on the processor bus.

The cache uses a write-through protocol; all writes to the cache are immediately passed on to the external memory which the cache represents, rather than stored for future memory updating (write-back). To reduce the impact of writes on performance, the processor can buffer write cycles; an operation which writes data to memory can finish before the write cycle is actually performed on the processor bus.

The processor performs a cache line fill to place new information into the on-chip cache. This operation reads four doublewords into a cache line, the smallest unit of storage which can be allocated in the cache. Most read cycles on the processor bus result from cache misses, which cause cache line fills.

Mechanisms are provided to maintain cache consistency between memory and cached data in multiple bus master environments. The mechanisms protect the i486 processor from reading invalid data from its own internal cache or from external caches. For example, when the i486 processor attempts to read an operand from memory that is also held in the cache of another bus master, the other bus master must be forced to write its cached data back to memory before the i486 processor can complete its read from memory. This is done because the cached version of the data may have been updated, and so may now be different from the version stored in memory.

Most memory systems optimize the speed of access on a read cycle. This is because the large majority of all memory accesses in a typical system are read accesses. The i486 processor's internal cache changes this ratio. Most read requests will result in cache hits, so most memory accesses on the processor bus will be write cycles. Memory optimization should be done with this in mind.

1.1.5 Floating-Point Unit

The internal floating-point unit performs floating-point operations on the 32-, 64- and 80-bit arithmetic formats specified in IEEE Standard 754. Like the integer processing unit, the floating-point unit architecture is binary-compatible with the 8087, 80287 coprocessors. The architecture is 100% compatible with the 387 DX coprocessor, and 387 SX coprocessor.

Floating-point instructions are executed fastest when they are entirely internal to the processor. This occurs when all operands are in the internal registers or cache. When data needs to be read from or written to external locations, burst transfers minimize the time required and a bus locking mechanism ensures that the bus is not relinquished to other bus masters during the transfer. Bus signals are provided to monitor errors in floating-point operations and to control the processor's response to such errors.

1.2 SYSTEM COMPONENTS

Intel offers several chips which are highly compatible with the i486 processor. These components can be used to design high-performance systems with a minimum of effort and cost. For components not directly connectable to the i486 processor bus, industry-standard interfaces can be used, such as the MULTIBUS II system bus.

For Ethernet interfacing, the 82596 32-bit LAN coprocessor off-loads network data management and physical-layer LAN functions to a single chip. The 82320-family 32-bit MCA system peripherals provide efficient, low-cost interfacing to Micro Channel expansion buses for PS/2 systems. The 82350-family 32-bit EISA system peripherals provide efficient, low-cost interfacing to EISA expansion buses. Several other components are currently in development.

Table 1-1 lists the components which interact directly with the i486 processor bus. Chapter 9 gives more details on many of these system peripherals. Chapter 10 describes MULTIBUS II system bus interfacing.

1.2.1 i486 Processor

The i486 processor provides all of the integer and floating-point CPU functions plus many of the peripheral functions required in a typical computer system. It executes the complete instruction set of the 386 processor and 387 DX numerics coprocessor, with some extensions. The processor eliminates the need for an external memory management unit, and the on-chip cache minimizes the need for external cache and associated control logic.

Table 1-1. System Components

Component	Name	Description
32-Bit General-Purpose CPU	i486™ CPU	General-purpose processor with floating-point arithmetic, memory management, and cache.
32-Bit LAN Coprocessor	82596CA	Local-area network communications coprocessor supporting CSMA/CD protocol.
32-Bit MCA System Peripherals	82320	Functional support for Micro Channel (PS/2) expansion buses and boards. Seven chips in the set.
32-Bit EISA System Peripherals	82350	Functional support for EISA expansion buses and boards. Four chips in the set.
485Turbocache Module for i486 microprocessor	485Turbocache Module	Second-level cache module.

Chapters 2 through 7 of this manual focus on the details of the i486 processor's architecture, hardware functions, and interfacing. For more information on the architecture and software interface, see the *i486™ Processor Programmer's Reference Manual.*

1.2.2 LAN Coprocessor

The 82596CA LAN coprocessor is a 32-bit multitasking local-area network communications processor that supports 80-Mbyte/second transfers at 25 MHz. It implements the carrier-sense, multiple-access and collision-detect (CSMA/CD) link access protocol and interfaces the i486 processor to a wide variety of networks and functions, including:

- IEEE 802.3 networks (Ethernet, HDLC, Cheapernet, StarLAN, and others).
- IBM PC networks (baseband and broadband).
- Proprietary CSMA/CD networks.
- HDLC frame delimiting.

The 82596 LAN coprocessor is typically used in desktop computers, file servers, and gateways. It provides a high-performance front-end controller for heavy data traffic, and it permits extensive protocol-layer software implementations. A complete hardware interface to Ethernet networks, for example, can be implemented with the 82596 LAN coprocessor and the 82C501AD Ethernet serial interface device. The i486 processor and 82596 LAN coprocessor communicate by means of a memory-based mailbox, command system and buffer system. The coprocessor fetches and executes high-level commands from shared memory to control all time-critical network functions. It performs command chaining and inter-processor communication. It is object-code compatible with the 82586 LAN coprocessor, with extensions which simplify software drivers.

Because the 82596 LAN coprocessor can execute commands directly from main memory and operate on data buffers without processor intervention, supervision from the i486 processor is minimized. In large networks, the high performance of the i486 processor in executing control and protocol software minimizes the need for host intervention.

1.2.3 485Turbocache Module

The 485Turbocache Module is a high-performance, optional, write-through, second-level cache designed specifically for the i486 microprocessor. It consists of the 82485 cache controller and 4 to 8 custom SRAMs for a complete cache solution in one package.

The 485Turbocache Module is a performance upgrade for 25-MHz or 33-MHz i486 microprocessor systems. One module provides 64K or 128K bytes of external cache memory. Up to four modules may be cascaded for up to 512K bytes of external cache memory. The module is optional, that is a single socket allows three price/performance options: no cache, a 64K cache, or a 128K cache.

The module is organized as two-way, set-associative with a line size of 16 bytes. The interface to the i486 microprocessor is simple since all CPU timings and bus cycles are supported. The module also supports Burst Mode, BOFF# cycles, and the same invalidation cycles as the processor.

While performance benefits are extremely application sensitive, the module typically provides from 5% to 30% performance improvement. The 485Turbocache Module provides the best price-performance ratio for 25- and 33-MHz i486 microprocessor designs. Chapter 6 discusses the 485Turbocache Module in detail.

1.2.4 EISA Chip Set

The 82350 family of peripherals interfaces the i486 processor to an extended industry standard architecture (EISA) bus. The chip set includes three motherboard peripherals (bus controller, integrated system peripheral, and bus buffers) and one peripheral for EISA-bus expansion boards (a bus master interface chip). The EISA standard maintains full compatibility with the existing ISA (also known as AT) standard. The EISA expansion board connector is a superset of the ISA expansion board connector, allowing existing 8- and 16-bit ISA boards to be installed in EISA slots. This is discussed in detail in Chapter 8.

The EISA bus controller performs data path translation, bus timing, and centralized bus arbitration. The improvements over the ISA standard are provided transparently, even to existing ISA DMA devices.

The EISA integrated system peripheral contains most of the EISA-specific peripheral functions, including DMA controller, 2 eight-channel interrupt controllers, 4 counter modules, EISA bus arbiter, and DRAM refresh address generator. The peripheral operates in a tightly coupled environment with the EISA bus controller to generate control signals for the DMA transfers. A master on any of the buses can communicate in parallel with both devices. Transfers between buses of varying sizes or transfers with misaligned addresses are performed correctly.

The EISA bus-master interface controller is the primary interface between local functions on an EISA expansion board and the EISA bus on the i486 system motherboard. The primary function of the controller is to support burst transfers between the expansion board and main memory. Data transfer rates of up to 33 Mbytes/second are supported—the fastest available on an EISA bus. With the controller, an EISA expansion board can be implemented with simple logic similar to that used in traditional ISA DMA designs. The general-purpose command and status interface allows a variety of software control protocols by a local expansion-board processor. Data transfers on the local processor bus are similar to traditional DMA transfer protocols. Local processors are supported with the ability to access individual locations in system memory or I/O space.

1.2.5 High-Performance PLDs

Programmable Logic Devices (PLDs) have become a vital factor in systems design. Intel manufactures a line of CMOS PLDs that meet the performance requirements of high-speed systems while reducing power consumption and heat dissipation. Some of these devices, such as the 85C220 (20-pin general-purpose PLD), 85C224 (24-pin general-purpose PLD), and 85C508 (28-pin address decoder PLD), are shown in this manual.

The 85C220 and 85C224 PLDs are both supersets to commonly used bipolar and CMOS alternatives (16x8 and 20x8 type devices). Both Intel PLDs are available at clock speeds to support fast state-machines in i486 systems. The 85C508 is a 28-pin address decoder PLD with integral transparent latches on its eight outputs.

1.3 SYSTEM ARCHITECTURE

The i486 processor can be the foundation for systems ranging from single-processor to multiprocessor. A single-processor system might be a personal computer, updated to use the i486 processor. A system design of this type offers higher performance through the integration of floating-point processing, memory management, and caching. More complex systems may use multiple processors which provide, at chip-level, the equivalent of board-level functions. Designs of this type are typically used in multiuser machines, scientific workstations, and engineering workstations.

A typical system, something between a single-processor design and a more complex multiprocessing design, is shown in Figure 1-1. This example uses a single i486 processor with external cache and the 82596 LAN coprocessor. Other examples of system design are illustrated in the figures that follow.

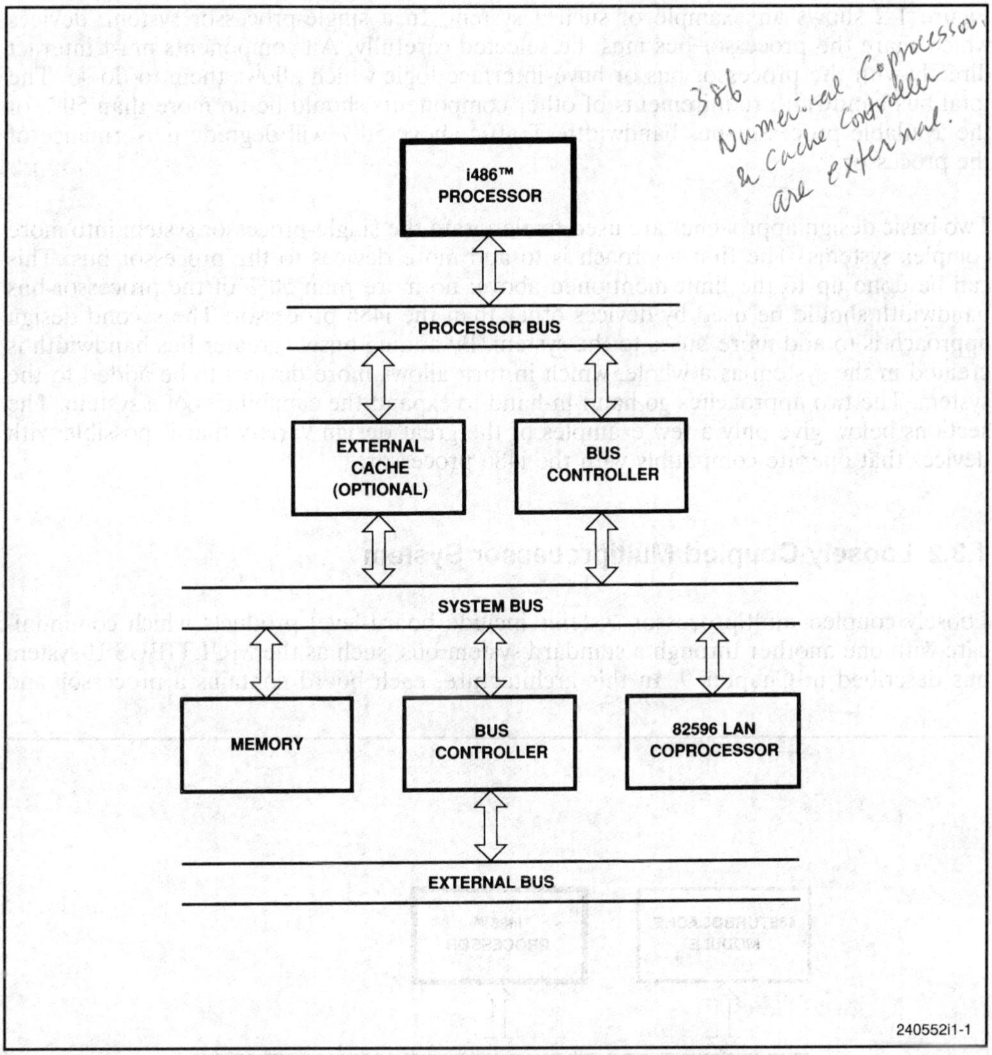

Figure 1-1. A Typical i486™ Processor System

1.3.1 Single Processor System

In single-processor systems, the processor handles all peripheral resources and intelligent devices, and executes all software. The i486 processor does this in a more efficient way and for a wider range of task complexity than earlier processors. Single-processor systems offer small size and low cost in exchange for flexibility in upgrading or expanding the system. Typical applications include personal computers, small desktop workstations and embedded controllers. Such applications are implemented as a single board, usually called a motherboard; the processor bus does not extend beyond the board occupied by the i486 processor.

Figure 1-2 shows an example of such a system. In a single-processor system, devices which share the processor bus must be selected carefully. All components must interact directly with the processor bus or have interface logic which allows them to do so. The total bus bandwidth requirements of other components should be no more than 50% of the available processor-bus bandwidth. Traffic above 50% will degrade performance of the processor.

Two basic design approaches are used to elaborate the single-processor system into more complex systems. The first approach is to add more devices to the processor bus. This can be done up to the limit mentioned above: no more than 50% of the processor-bus bandwidth should be used by devices other than the i486 processor. The second design approach is to add more buses to the system. By adding buses, greater bus bandwidth is created in the system as a whole, which in turn allows more devices to be added to the system. The two approaches go hand-in-hand to expand the capabilities of a system. The sections below give only a few examples of the great design variety that is possible with devices that operate compatibly with the i486 processor.

1.3.2 Loosely Coupled Multiprocessor System

Loosely coupled multiprocessor systems include board-level products which communicate with one another through a standard system bus, such as the MULTIBUS II system bus described in Chapter 9. In this architecture, each board contains a processor and

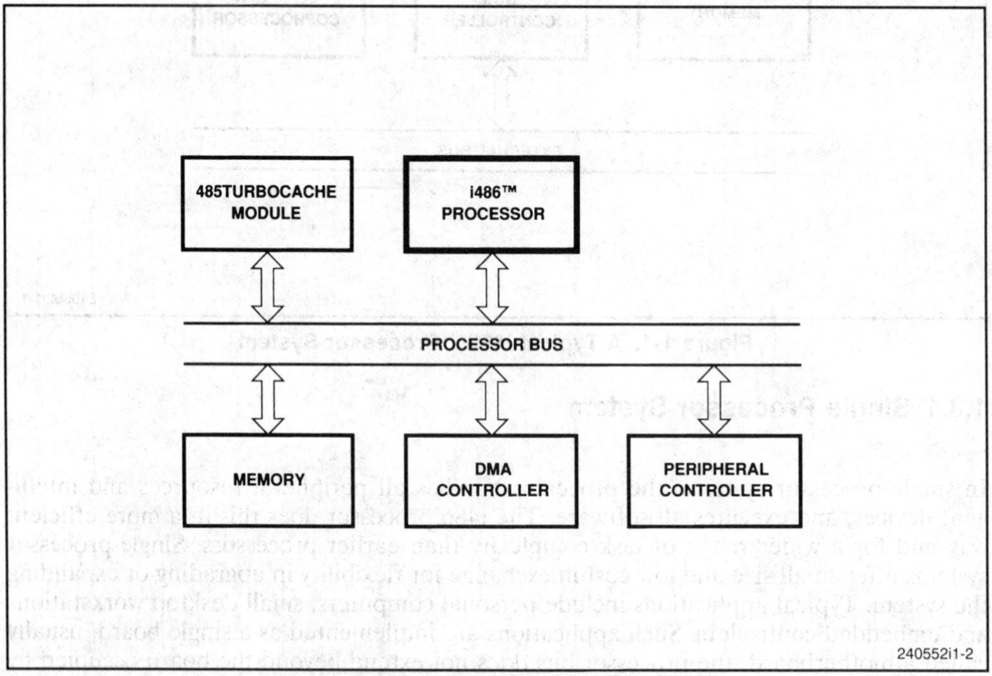

Figure 1-2. Single-Processor System

associated logic. There is typically only one processor per board. Components within each board communicate on either a processor bus or on the buffered system bus. The system bus provides extra bandwidth beyond the processor bus.

A typical system is shown in Figure 1-3. Such system-bus boards typically occur in higher-end personal computers and systems which allow for modular expansion. A typical design would include a coprocessor or LAN interface board in a personal computer, or a network-interface board in a file server or gateway. Systems built from these boards can contain a mix of processor types. Devices attached to the processor bus on a given board make demands which may affect system performance. For example, the 82596 LAN coprocessor may use up to 3% of the bus bandwidth to handle 10-Mbit/second Ethernet traffic.

1.3.3 External Cache

External cache allows a system to achieve maximum performance. This cache is essential in tightly coupled multi-processor systems. The external cache should consist of cache memory (usually fast SRAM) and cache control logic.

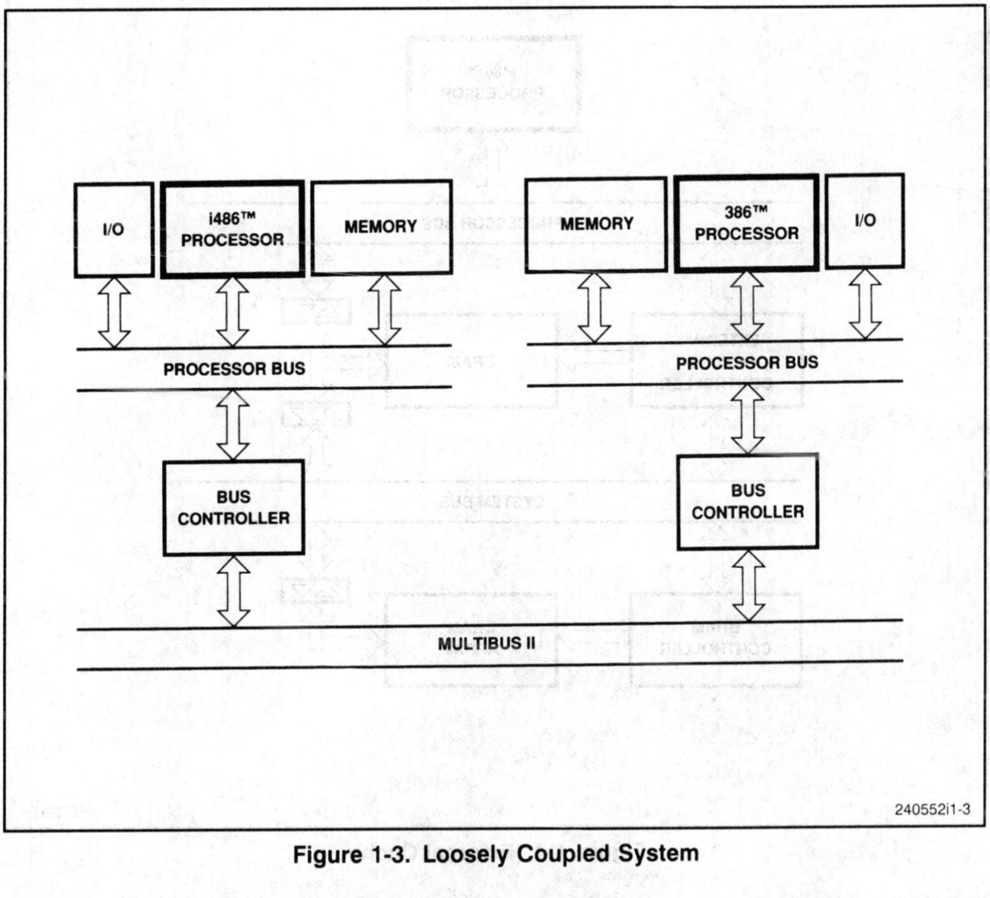

Figure 1-3. Loosely Coupled System

External cache systems typically provide access to the cache from both the processor and the system buses. This is shown in Figure 1-4. These caches typically monitor processor memory accesses, optimal mix of data and instructions, processor access time, and consistency between cache and memory.

1.4 System Applications

A majority of i486 processor systems can be grouped into these types:

- Personal Computers
- Minicomputers and Workstations
- Embedded Controllers

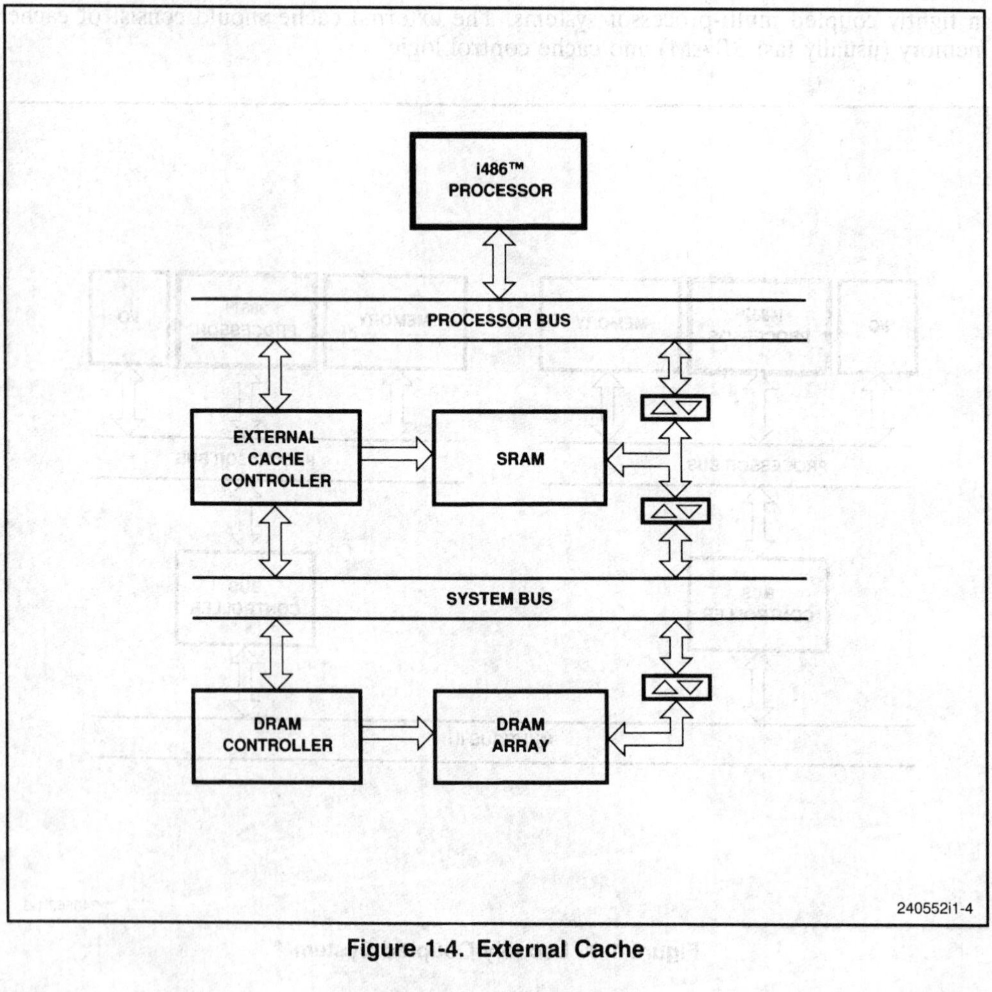

Figure 1-4. External Cache

Each type of system has distinct design goals and constraints, as described in the following sections. Software running on the processor, even in standalone embedded applications, should use a standard operating system such as DOS, Windows, OS/2 operating system, UNIX System V/386, iRMX operating system, or iRMX kernel for ease of debugging, documentation, and transportability.

1.4.1 Personal Computers

In single-processor systems, the processor will interact directly with I/O devices and DRAM memory. Other bus masters, such as the 82596 LAN coprocessor, typically reside on the system bus; conventional personal computer architecture puts most peripherals on separate plug-in boards. Expansion is typically limited to memory boards and I/O boards. A standard I/O architecture such as MCA or EISA is used. System cost and size are very important. Figure 1-5 shows an example of a personal computer application.

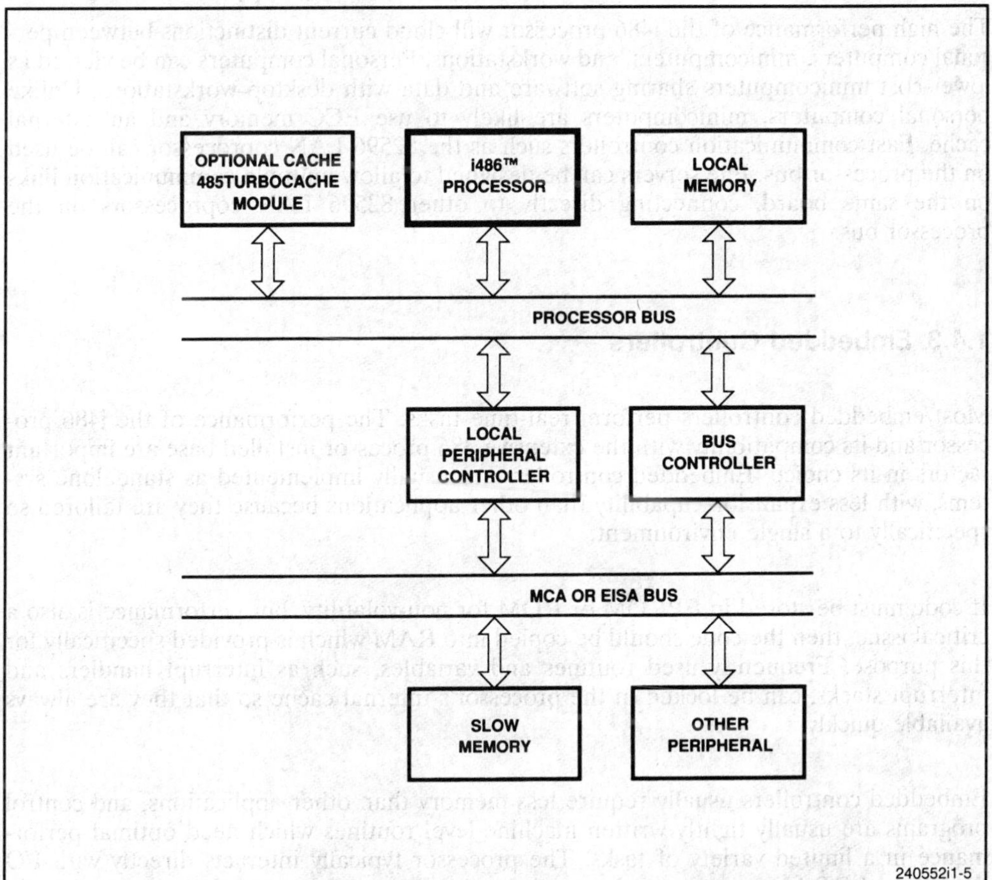

Figure 1-5. Personal Computer Example

External cache is optional in such environments, particularly if system performance is not a critical parameter. Where an external cache is used, memory-access speed will improve only if the cache is designed as a write-back system and memory access has zero to one wait states.

1.4.2 Minicomputers and Workstations

Minicomputer and workstation systems can be implemented with a loosely coupled architecture. These typically allow expansion of the number of CPUs, memory modules, and I/O devices. Standard system buses like the MULTIBUS II system bus are used. Minicomputers and workstations are more performance oriented and less cost oriented than personal computers. Higher-performance systems may need a tightly coupled architecture. Due to the variety of architectures in which minicomputers and workstations are implemented, no representative design example can be given.

The high performance of the i486 processor will cloud current distinctions between personal computers, minicomputers, and workstations. Personal computers can be viewed as lower-cost minicomputers sharing software and data with desktop workstations. Unlike personal computers, minicomputers are likely to use ECC memory and an external cache. Fast communication controllers such as the 82596 LAN coprocessor can be used on the processor bus. File servers can be designed to allow multiple communication links on the same board, connecting directly to other 82596 LAN coprocessors on the processor bus.

1.4.3 Embedded Controllers

Most embedded controllers perform real-time tasks. The performance of the i486 processor and its compatibility with the extensive 386 processor installed base are important factors in its choice. Embedded controllers are usually implemented as standalone systems, with less expansion capability than other applications because they are tailored so specifically to a single environment.

If code must be stored in EPROM or ROM for non-volatility, but performance is also a critical issue, then the code should be copied into RAM which is provided specifically for this purpose. Frequently used routines and variables, such as interrupt handlers and interrupt stacks, can be locked in the processor's internal cache so that they are always available quickly.

Embedded controllers usually require less memory than other applications, and control programs are usually tightly written machine-level routines which need optimal performance in a limited variety of tasks. The processor typically interacts directly with I/O devices and DRAM memory. Other peripherals connect to the system bus, as shown in Figure 1-6.

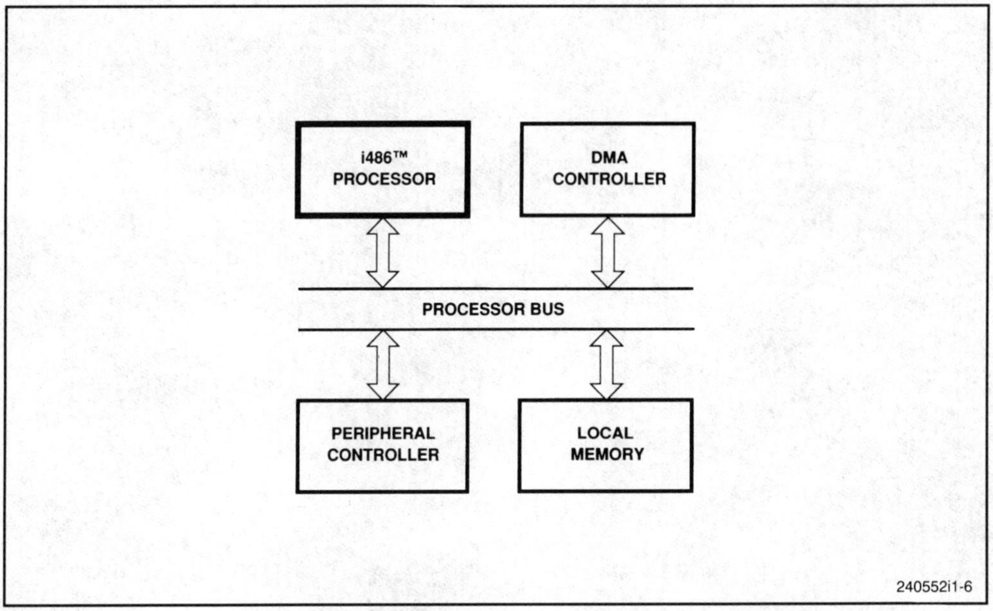

Figure 1-6. Embedded Controller Example

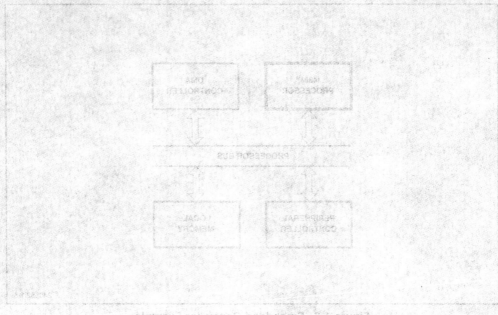

Internal Architecture 2

CHAPTER 2
INTERNAL ARCHITECTURE

Internally, the i486™ processor has nine functional units which operate in parallel. Figure 2-1 shows the nine internal units:

- Bus Interface
- Cache
- Instruction Prefetch
- Instruction Decode
- Control
- Integer and Datapath
- Floating-Point
- Segmentation
- Paging

The internal architecture is very much like that of the 386 processor, except for the new on-chip cache and floating-point units.

Signals from the external 32-bit processor bus reach the internal units through the bus interface unit. On the internal side, the bus interface unit and cache unit pass addresses bidirectionally through a 32-bit bidirectional bus. Data is passed from the cache to the bus interface unit on a 32-bit data bus. The closely coupled cache and instruction prefetch units simultaneously receive instruction prefetches from the bus interface unit over a shared 32-bit data bus, which is also used by the cache to receive operands and other types of data. Instructions in the cache are accessible to the instruction prefetch unit, which contains a 32-byte queue of instructions waiting to be executed.

When internal requests for data or instructions can be satisfied from the cache, time-consuming cycles on the external processor bus are avoided. The bus interface unit is only involved when an operation needs access to the processor bus. Many internal operations are therefore transparent to the external system.

The instruction decode unit translates instructions into low-level control signals and microcode entry points. The control unit executes microcode and controls the integer, floating-point, and segmentation units. Computation results are placed in internal registers within the integer or floating-point units, or in the cache. Internal storage locations (datapaths) are kept in the integer unit.

The cache shares two 32-bit data buses with the segmentation, integer, and floating-point units. These two buses can be used together as a 64-bit interunit transfer bus. When 64-bit segment descriptors are passed from the cache to the segmentation unit, 32 bits are passed directly over one data bus and the other 32 bits are passed through the integer unit, so that all 64 bits reach the segmentation unit simultaneously.

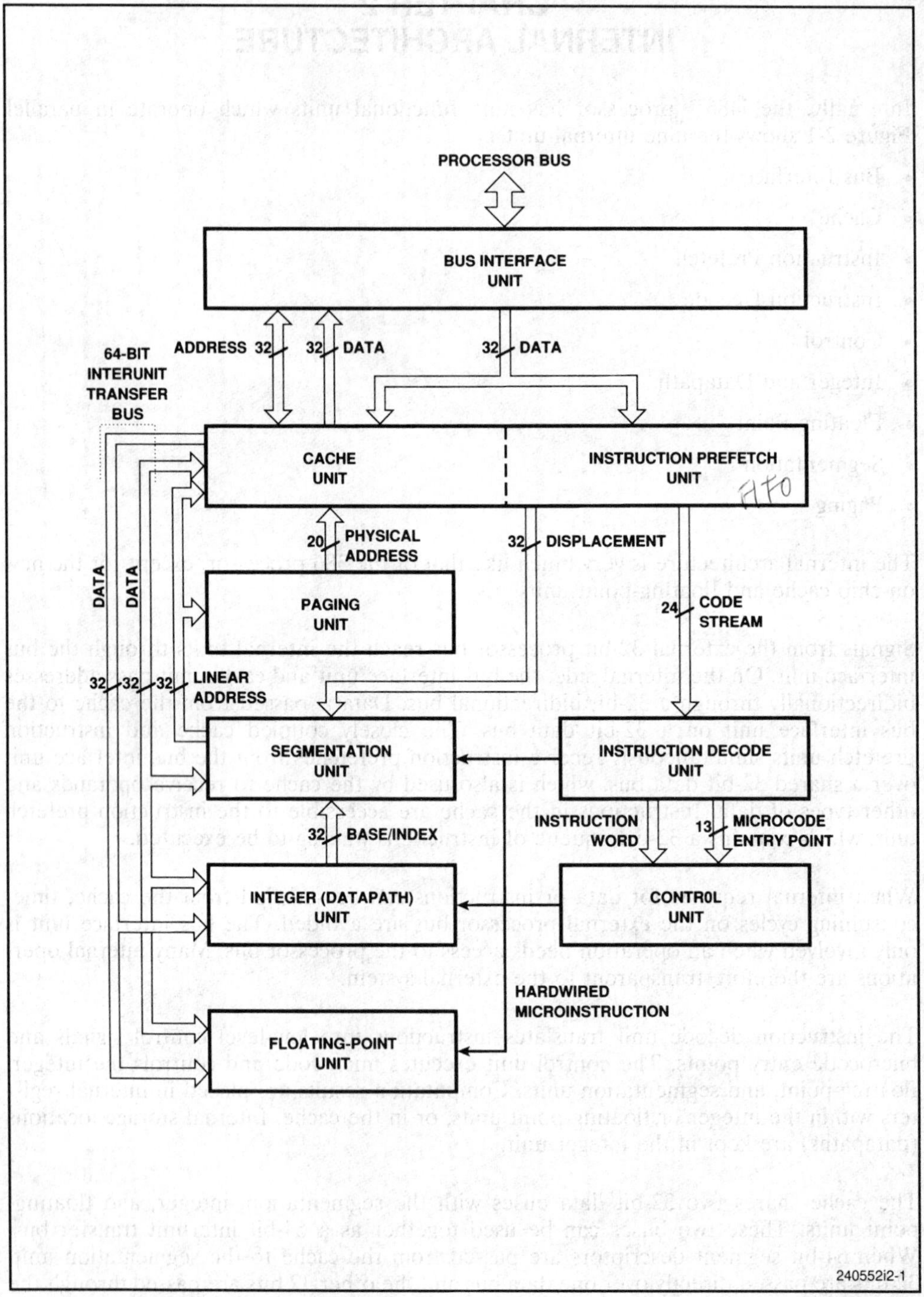

Figure 2-1. Internal Architecture

Address generation is performed by the segmentation and paging units. Logical addresses are translated by the segmentation unit and passed to the paging and cache units on a 32-bit linear address bus. The paging unit translates linear addresses into physical addresses, which are passed to the cache on a 20-bit bus.

The next section describes the internal instruction pipelining method. Following that, Sections 2.2 through 2.10 describe each of the nine internal units.

2.1 Instruction Pipelining

Not every instruction involves all internal units. When an instruction needs the participation of several units, each unit operates in parallel with others on instructions at different stages of execution. Although each instruction is processed sequentially, several instructions are at varying stages of execution in the processor at any given time. This is called *instruction pipelining*. Instruction prefetch, instruction decode, microcode execution, integer operations, floating-point operations, segmentation, paging, cache management, and bus interface operations are all performed simultaneously. Figure 2-2 shows some of this parallelism for a single instruction: the instruction fetch, 2-stage decode, execution, and register write-back of the execution result. Each stage in this pipeline can occur in one clock cycle.

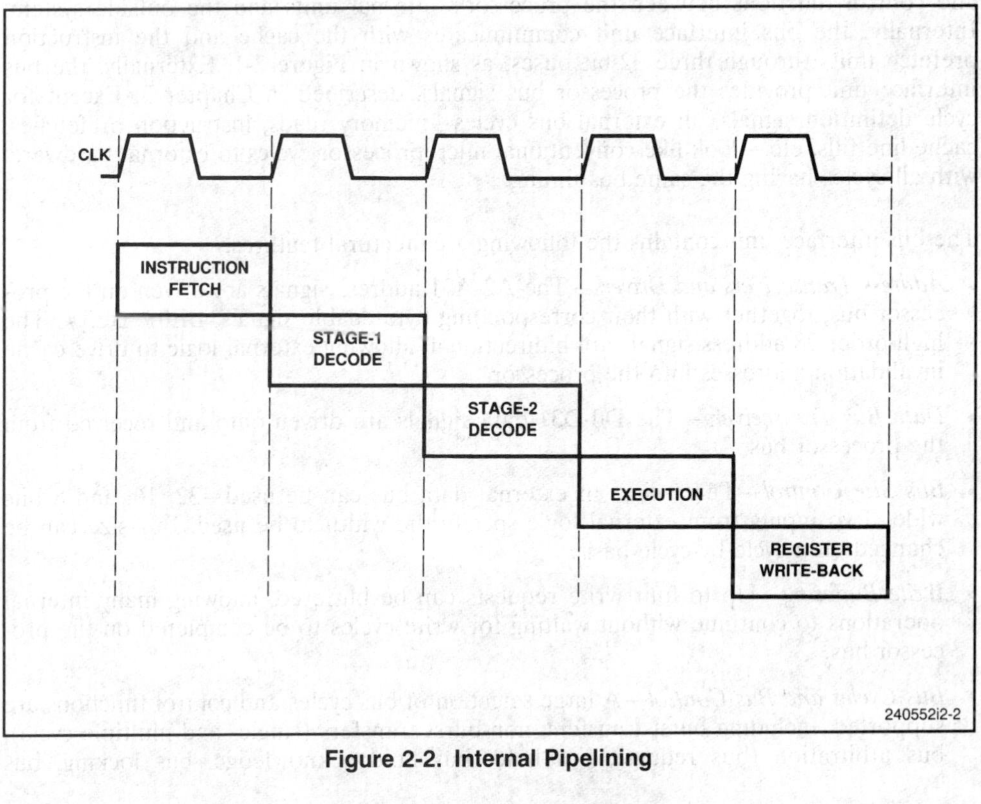

Figure 2-2. Internal Pipelining

The internal pipelining on the i486 processor offers an important performance advantage over many single-clock RISC processors: in the i486 processor, data can be loaded from the cache with one instruction and used by the next instruction in the next clock. This performance advantage results from the stage-1 decode step, which initiates memory accesses before the execution cycle. Because most compilers and application programs follow load instructions with instructions which operate on the loaded data, this method optimizes the execution of existing binary code.

The method has a performance tradeoff: an instruction sequence which changes register contents and then uses that register in the next instruction to access memory takes three clocks rather than two. This tradeoff is only a minor disadvantage, however, since most instructions which access memory use the stable contents of the stack pointer or frame pointer, and the additional clock is not used very often. Compilers often place an unrelated instruction between one which changes an addressing register and one which uses the register. Such code is compatible with the 386 processor, and the i486 processor provides special stack increment/decrement hardware and an extra register port to execute back-to-back stack push/pop instructions in a single clock.

2.2 Bus Interface Unit

The bus interface unit prioritizes and coordinates data transfers, instruction prefetches, and control functions between the processor's internal units and the outside system. Internally, the bus interface unit communicates with the cache and the instruction prefetch units through three 32-bit buses, as shown in Figure 2-1. Externally, the bus interface unit provides the processor bus signals, described in Chapter 3. Except for cycle definition signals, all external bus cycles – memory reads, instruction prefetches, cache line fills, etc. – look like conventional microprocessor cycles to external hardware, with all cycles having the same bus timing.

The bus interface unit contains the following architectural features:

- *Address Transceivers and Drivers* – The A2-A31 address signals are driven on the processor bus, together with their corresponding byte-enable signals, BE0#-BE3#. The high-order 28 address signals are bidirectional, allowing external logic to drive cache invalidation addresses into the processor.
- *Data Bus Transceivers* – The D0-D31 data signals are driven onto and received from the processor bus.
- *Bus Size Control* – Three sizes of external data bus can be used – 32, 16, and 8 bits wide. Two inputs from external logic specify the width to be used. Bus size can be changed on a cycle-by-cycle basis.
- *Write Buffering* – Up to four write requests can be buffered, allowing many internal operations to continue without waiting for write cycles to be completed on the processor bus.
- *Bus Cycles and Bus Control* – A large selection of bus cycles and control functions are supported, including burst transfers, non-burst transfers (single- and multiple-cycle), bus arbitration (bus request, bus hold, bus hold acknowledge, bus locking, bus

pseudo-locking, and bus backoff), floating-point error signalling, interrupts, and reset. Two software-controlled outputs enable page caching on a cycle-by-cycle basis. One input and one output are provided for controlling burst read transfers.

- *Parity Generation and Control*—Even parity is generated on writes to the processor and checked on reads. An error signal indicates a read parity error.
- *Cache Control*—Cache control and consistency operations are supported. Three inputs allow the external system to control the consistency of data stored in the internal cache unit. Two special bus cycles allow the processor control the consistency of external cache.

2.2.1 Data Transfers

To support the cache, the bus interface unit reads 16-byte cacheable transfers of operands, instructions, and other data on the processor bus and passes them to the cache unit. When cache contents are updated from an internal source, such as a register, the bus interface unit writes the updated cache information to the external system. Non-cacheable read transfers are passed through the cache to the integer or floating-point units.

During instruction prefetch, the bus interface unit reads instructions on the processor bus and passes them to both the instruction prefetch unit and the cache. The instruction prefetch unit may then obtain its inputs directly from the cache.

2.2.2 Write Buffers

The bus interface unit has temporary storage for buffering up to four 32-bit write transfers to memory. Addresses, data, or control information can be buffered. Single I/O-mapped writes are not buffered, although multiple I/O writes may be buffered. The buffers can accept memory writes as fast as one per clock. Once a write request is buffered, the internal unit which generated the request is free to continue processing. If no higher-priority request is pending and the bus is free, the transfer is propagated as an immediate write cycle to the processor bus. When all four write buffers are full, any subsequent write transfer will stall inside the processor until a write buffer becomes available.

The bus interface unit can re-order pending reads in front of buffered writes. This is done because pending reads can prevent an internal unit from continuing, whereas buffered writes need not have a detrimental effect on processing speed.

Writes are propagated to the processor bus in the same first-in-first-out order in which they are received from the internal unit. However, a subsequently generated read request (data or instruction) may be re-ordered in front of buffered writes. As a protection against reading invalid data, this re-ordering of reads in front of buffered writes will only occur if all buffered writes are cache hits. Because an external read will only be generated for a cache miss, and will only be re-ordered in front of buffered writes if all such buffered writes are cache hits, any read generated on the external bus with this protection will never read a location which is about to be written by a buffered write.

This re-ordering can only happen once for a given set of buffered writes, because the data returned by the read cycle could otherwise replace data about to be written from the write buffers.

To ensure that no more than one such re-ordering is done for a given set of buffered writes, all buffered writes are re-flagged as cache misses when a read request is re-ordered ahead of them. Buffered writes thus marked are propagated to the processor bus before the next read request is acted upon. Invalidation of data in the internal cache also causes all pending writes to be flagged as cache misses. Disabling the cache unit disables the write buffers, which eliminates any possibility of re-ordering bus cycles.

2.2.3 Locked Cycles

The processor can generate signals to lock a contiguous series of bus cycles. These cycles can then be performed without interference from other bus masters, if external logic observes these locking signals. One example of a locked operation is a semaphor read-modify-write update, where a resource control register is updated. No other operations should be allowed on the bus until the entire locked semaphor update is completed.

When a locked read cycle is generated, the read is not attempted from the internal cache. All pending writes in the buffer are completed first. Only then is the read part of the locked operation performed, the data modified, the result placed in a write buffer, and a write cycle performed on the processor bus. This sequence of operations ensures that all writes are performed in the order in which they were generated.

2.2.4 I/O Transfers

Transfers to and from I/O locations have some restrictions to ensure data integrity:

- *Caching*– I/O reads are never cached.
- *Read Re-Ordering*– I/O reads are never re-ordered ahead of buffered writes to memory. This ensures that the processor will have completed updating all memory locations before reading status from a device.
- *Writes*– Single I/O writes are never buffered. Thus, when processing an OUT instruction, internal execution stops until all buffered writes and the I/O write are completed on the processor bus. This allows time for external logic to drive a cache invalidate cycle or mask interrupts before the processor executes the next instruction. The processor will have completed updating all memory locations before writing to the I/O location. However, repeated OUT instructions may be buffered.

I/O device recovery time; is determined by the write buffers and the cache unit. In the 386 processor, back-to-back write recovery time; could be guaranteed to exceed a certain value by inserting a jump to the next instruction that writes to the I/O device. This forced an instruction prefetch cycle which could only be performed after the preceding write was completed. This technique is not used in the i486 processor because a prefetch can be satisfied internally by the cache and recovery time may be too short. The same effect is achieved in the i486 processor by explicitly generating a read to an area of memory that is not cacheable. Because the i486 processor does not buffer single I/O writes, such a read will not be done until the I/O write is completed.

2.3 Cache Unit

The cache unit stores copies of recently read instructions, operands, and other data. When the processor requests information already in the cache—called a *cache hit*—no processor-bus cycle is required. When the processor requests information not in the cache—called a *cache miss*—the information is read into the cache in one or more 16-byte cacheable data transfers, called *cache line fills*. When an internal write request is generated to an area currently in the cache, two things happen: the cache is updated, and the write is also passed through the cache to memory. This is called *cache write-through*.

The cache transfers data to other units on two 32-bit buses, as shown in Figure 2-1. The cache receives linear addresses on a 32-bit bus and the corresponding physical addresses on a 20-bit bus. The cache and instruction prefetch; units are closely coupled. 16-byte blocks of instructions in the cache can be passed quickly to the instruction prefetch unit. Both units read information in 16-byte blocks.

The cache can be accessed as often as once each clock. The cache acts on physical addresses, which minimizes the number of times the cache must be flushed. When both the cache and the cache write-through functions are disabled, the cache may be used as a high-speed RAM.

2.3.1 Cache Structure

The cache has a *four-way set associative* organization. There are four possible cache locations to store data from a given area of memory. Four-way association is a compromise between the speed of a direct-mapped cache during cache hits, and the high cache-hit ratio of fully associative cache. As shown in Figure 2-3, the 8-Kbyte data block is divided into four data *ways*, each containing 128 16-byte *sets*, or *cache lines*. Each cache line holds data from 16 successive byte addresses in memory, beginning with an address divisible by 16.

Cache addressing is performed by dividing the high-order 28 bits of the physical address into three parts, as shown in Figure 2-3. The 7 bits of the *index field* specify the set number, one of 128, within the cache. The high-order 21 bits are the *tag field*; these bits are compared with tags for each cache line in the indexed set, and they indicate whether a 16-byte cache line is stored for that physical address. The low-order 4 bits of the physical address select the byte within the cache line. Finally, a 4-bit valid field, one for each way within a given set, indicates whether the cached data at that physical address is currently valid.

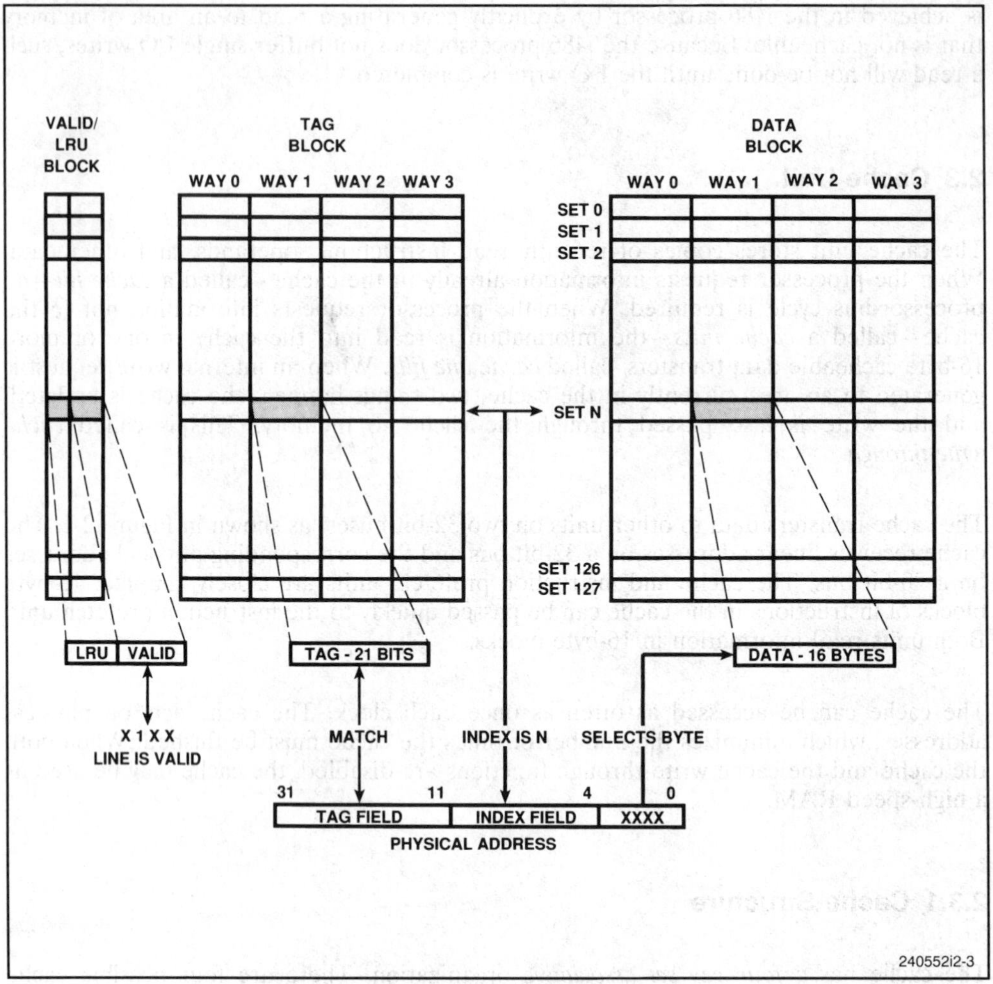

Figure 2-3. Cache Organization

2.3.2 Cache Updating

When a cache miss occurs on a read, the 16-byte block containing the requested information is written into the cache. Data in the neighborhood of the required data is also read into the cache, but the exact position of data within the cache line depends on its location in memory with respect to addresses divisible by 16.

Any area of memory is cacheable, but any page of memory can be declared not cacheable by setting a bit in its page table entry. When a read from memory is initiated on the bus, external logic can indicate whether the data may be placed in cache, as discussed in Chapter 3. If the read is cacheable, the processor attempts to read an entire 16-byte cache line.

The unit is a write-through cache. Cache line fills are performed only for read misses, never for write misses. When the processor is enabled for normal caching and write-through operation, every internal write to the cache (cache hit) not only updates the cache but is also passed along to the bus interface unit and propagated through the processor bus to memory. The only conditions under which data in the cache differs from the corresponding data in memory occur when a processor write cycle to memory is delayed by buffering in the bus interface unit, or when an external bus master alters the memory area mapped to the internal cache.

2.3.3 Cache Replacement

Replacement in the cache is handled by a pseudo-LRU (least recently used) mechanism. This mechanism maintains three bits for each set in the valid/LRU block, as shown in Figure 2-3. The LRU bits; are updated on each cache hit or cache line fill. Each cache line (four per set) also has an associated valid bit which indicates whether the line contains valid data. When the cache is flushed or the processor is reset, all of the valid bits are cleared. When a cache line is to be filled, a location for the fill is selected by simply finding any cache line which is invalid. If no cache line is invalid, the LRU bits select the line to be overwritten. Valid bits are not set for lines which are only partially valid.

Cache lines can be invalidated individually by a *cache line invalidation* operation on the processor bus. When such an operation is initiated, the cache unit compares the address to be invalidated with tags for the lines currently in cache and clears the valid bit if a match is found. A *cache flush* operation is also available. This invalidates the entire contents of internal cache unit.

2.3.4 Cache Configuration

Configuration of the cache unit is controlled by two bits in the processor's machine status register (CR0). One of these bits enables caching (cache line fills). The other bit enables memory write-through. The four configuration options are shown in Table 2-1. Chapter 3 gives details.

When caching is enabled, memory reads and instruction prefetches are cacheable. These transfers will be cached if external logic asserts the cache enable input in that bus cycle, and if the current page table entry allows caching. During cycles in which caching is disabled, cache lines will not be filled on cache misses. However, the cache remains active even though it is disabled for further filling. Data already in the cache will be used if it is still valid. Only when all data in the cache is flagged invalid, as happens in a cache flush, will all internal read requests be propagated as bus cycles to the external system.

When cache write-throughs are enabled, all writes, including those which are cache hits, are written through to memory. Invalidation operations will remove a line from cache if the invalidate address maps to a cache line. When cache write-throughs are disabled, an internal write request which is a cache hit will not cause a write-through to memory, and cache invalidation operations are disabled. With both caching and cache write-through

Table 2-1. Cache Configuration Options

Cache Enabled	Write-Through Enabled	Operating Mode
no	no	Cache line fills, cache write-throughs, and cache invalidations are disabled. This configuration allows the internal cache to be used as high-speed static RAM.
no	yes	Cache line fills are disabled, and cache write-throughs and cache invalidations are enabled. This configuration allows software to disable the cache for a short time, then re-enable it without flushing the original contents.
yes	no	INVALID
yes	yes	Cache line fills, cache write-throughs, and cache invalidations are enabled. The is the normal operating configuration.

disabled, the cache can be used as a high-speed static RAM. In this configuration, the only write cycles which are propagated to the processor bus are cache misses, and cache invalidation operations are ignored.

2.4 INSTRUCTION PREFETCH UNIT

When the bus interface unit is not performing bus cycles to execute an instruction, the instruction prefetch unit; uses the bus interface unit to prefetch instructions. By reading instructions before they are needed, the processor rarely needs to wait for an instruction prefetch cycle on the processor bus.

Instruction prefetch cycles; read 16-byte blocks of instructions;, starting at addresses numerically greater than the last-fetched instruction. The starting address is generated by the prefetch unit, which has a direct connection (not shown in Figure 2-1) to the paging unit. The 16-byte prefetched blocks are read into both the prefetch and cache units simultaneously. The prefetch queue; in the prefetch unit stores 32 bytes of instructions. As each instruction is fetched from the queue, the code part is sent to the instruction decode unit and (depending on the instruction) the displacement part is sent to the segmentation unit where it is used for address calculation. If loops are encountered in the program being executed, the prefetch unit gets copies of previously executed instructions from the cache.

The prefetch unit has the lowest priority for processor bus access. Assuming zero wait-state memory access, prefetch activity never delays execution. However, if there is no pending data transfer, prefetching may use bus cycles that would otherwise be idle. The prefetch unit is flushed whenever the next instruction needed is not in numerical sequence with the previous instruction – for example, during jumps, task switches, exceptions, and interrupts.

The prefetch unit will never access beyond the end of a code segment and it will never access a page that is not present. However, prefetching may cause problems for some hardware mechanisms. For example, prefetching may cause an interrupt when program execution nears the end of memory. To keep prefetching from reading past a given address, instructions should come no closer to that address than one byte plus one aligned 16-byte block.

2.5 INSTRUCTION DECODE UNIT

The instruction decode unit; receives instructions from the instruction prefetch unit and translates them in a two-stage process into low-level control signals and microcode entry points, as shown in Figure 2-1. Most instructions can be decoded at a rate of one per clock. Stage 1 of the decode, shown in Figure 2-2, initiates a memory access. This allows execution of a two-instruction sequence which loads and operates on data in just two clocks, as described above in Section 2.2.

The decode unit simultaneously processes instruction prefix bytes, opcodes, modR/M bytes, and displacements. The outputs include hardwired microinstructions to the segmentation, integer, and floating-point units. The unit is flushed whenever the instruction prefetch unit is flushed.

2.6 CONTROL UNIT

The control unit interprets the instruction word and microcode entry points received from the instruction decode unit. The control unit has outputs with which it controls the integer and floating-point processing units. It also controls segmentation because segment selection may be specified by instructions.

The control unit contains the processor's microcode. Many instructions have only one line of microcode, so they can execute in an average of one clock cycle. Figure 2-2 shows how execution fits into the internal pipelining mechanism.

2.7 INTEGER (DATAPATH) UNIT

The integer and datapath unit identifies where data is stored and performs all of the arithmetic and logical operations available in the 386 processor's instruction set, plus a few new instructions. It has eight 32-bit general-purpose registers, several specialized registers, an ALU, and a barrel shifter. Single load, store, addition, subtraction, logic, and shift instructions are executed in one clock.

Two 32-bit bidirectional buses connect the integer and floating-point units. These buses are used together for transferring 64-bit operands. The same buses also connect the processing units with the cache unit. The contents of the general purpose registers are sent to the segmentation unit on a separate 32-bit bus for generation of effective addresses.

2.8 FLOATING-POINT UNIT

The floating-point unit; executes the same instruction set as the 387 math coprocessor. The unit contains a push-down register stack and dedicated hardware for interpreting the 32-, 64-, and 80-bit formats specified in IEEE Standard 754. An output signal passed through to the processor bus indicates floating-point errors to the external system, which in turn can assert an input to the processor indicating that the processor should ignore these errors and continue normal operations.

2.9 SEGMENTATION UNIT

A segment is a protected, independent address space. Segmentation is used to enforce isolation among application programs, to invoke recovery procedures, and to isolate the effects of programming errors.

The segmentation unit translates a segmented address issued by a program, called a *logical address*, into an unsegmented address, called a *linear address*. The locations of segments in the linear address space are stored in data structures called *segment descriptors*. The segmentation unit performs its address calculations using segment descriptors and displacements (offsets) extracted from instructions. Linear addresses are sent to the paging and cache units. When a segment is accessed for the first time, its segment descriptor is copied into a processor register. A program can have as many as 16,383 segments. Up to six segment descriptors can be held in processor registers at any one time. Figure 2-4 shows the relationships between logical, linear, and physical addresses.

2.10 PAGING UNIT

The paging unit allows access to data structures larger than the available memory space by keeping them partly in memory and partly on disk. Paging divides the linear address space into 4-Kbyte blocks called *pages*. Paging uses data structures in memory called *page tables* for mapping a *linear address* to a *physical address*. Physical addresses are used by the cache and/or put on the processor bus. The paging unit also identifies problems, such as accesses to a page which is not resident in memory, and raises exceptions called *page faults*. On a page fault, the operating system has a chance to bring the required page into memory from disk. If necessary, it can free space in memory by sending some other page out to disk. If paging is not enabled, the physical address is identical to the linear address.

The paging unit includes a *translation lookaside buffer* (TLB) which stores the most recently used 32 page table entries. The TLB data structures are shown in Figure 2-5. The paging unit looks up linear addresses in the TLB. If the paging unit does not find a linear address in the TLB, the unit generates requests to fill the TLB with the correct physical address contained in a page table in memory. Only when the correct page table entry is in the TLB does the bus cycle take place. When the paging unit maps a page in

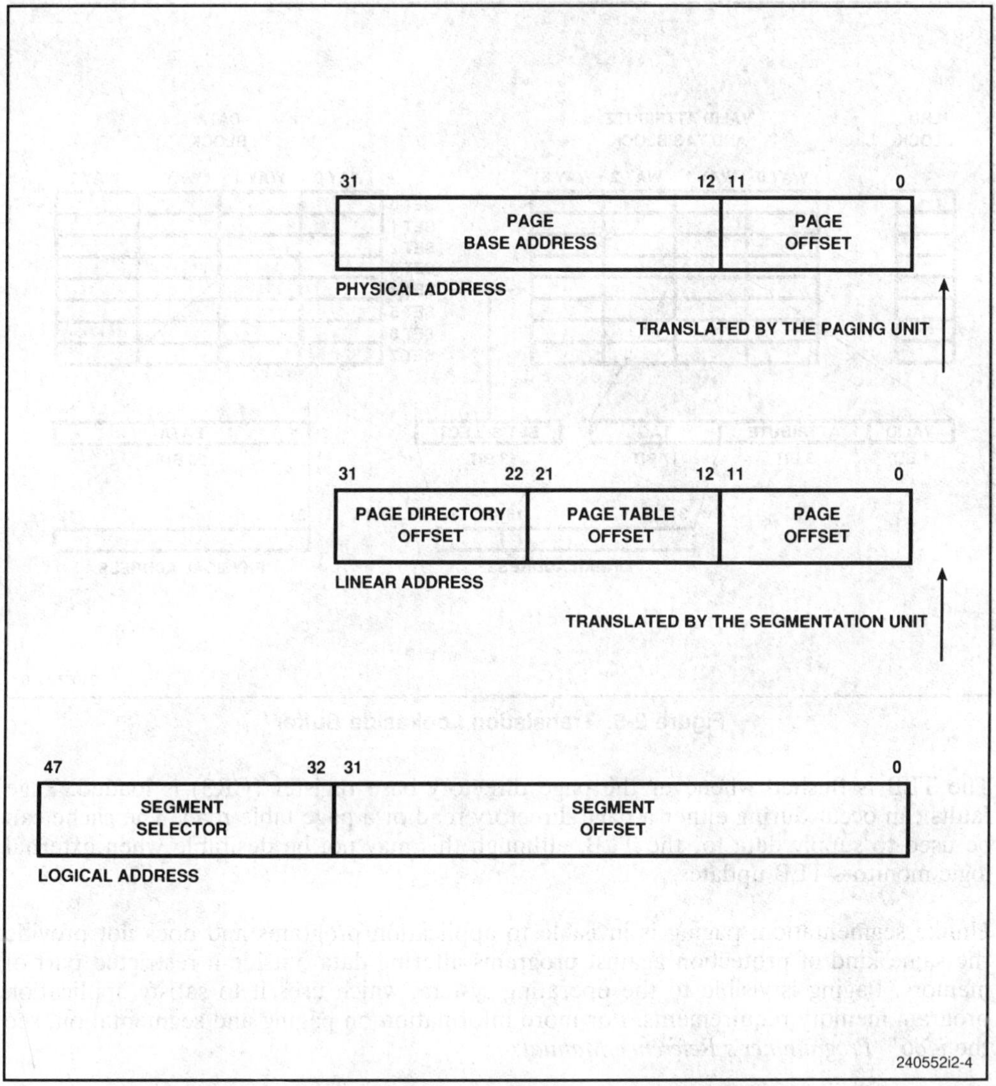

Figure 2-4. Segmentation and Paging Address Formats

the linear address space to a page in physical memory, it only maps the upper 20 bits of the linear address. The lowest 12 bits of the physical address come unchanged from the linear address.

Most programs access only a small number of pages during any short span of time. When this is true, the pages stay in memory and the address translation information stays in the TLB. In typical systems, 99% of the requests to access the page tables are satisfied by the TLB. The TLB uses a pseudo-LRU algorithm, similar to the cache, as a content-replacement strategy.

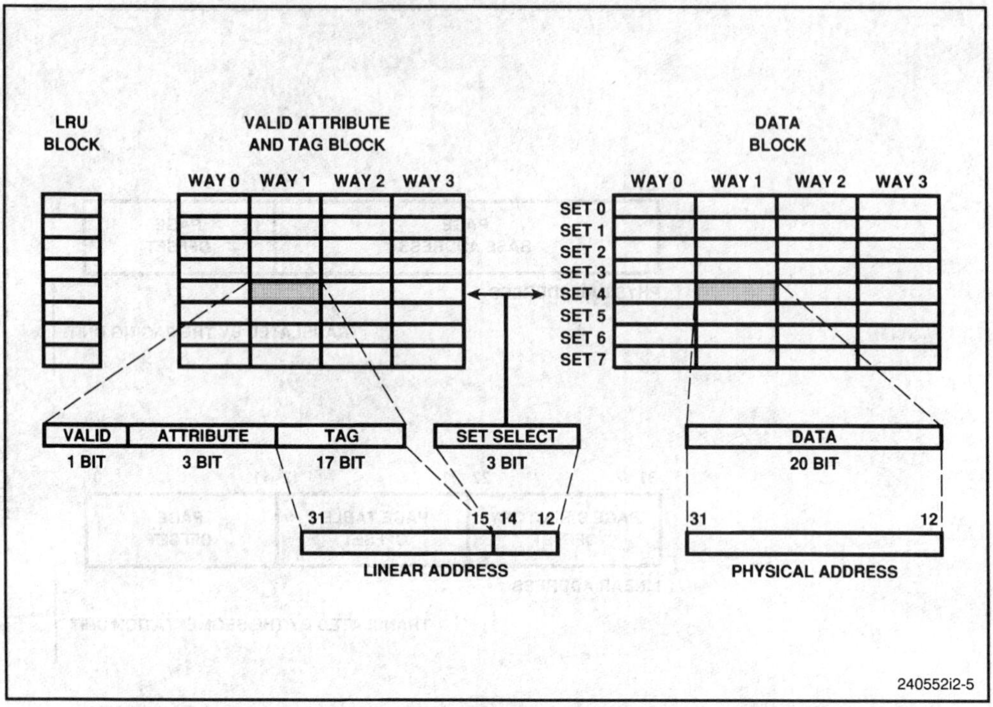

Figure 2-5. Translation Lookaside Buffer

The TLB is flushed whenever the page directory base register (CR3) is loaded. Page faults can occur during either a page directory read or a page table read. The cache can be used to supply data for the TLB, although this may not be desirable when external logic monitors TLB updates.

Unlike segmentation, paging is invisible to application programs and does not provide the same kind of protection against programs altering data outside a restricted part of memory. Paging is visible to the operating system, which uses it to satisfy application program memory requirements. For more information on paging and segmentation, see the *i486™ Programmer's Reference Manual*.

Processor Bus 3

CHAPTER 3
PROCESSOR BUS

3.1 OVERVIEW OF THE BUS

The processor bus is the set of pinout signals on the i486™ processor chip. It is the bus through which the processor communicates with other devices in the system. The signals on the bus are classed by their functions, which include bus control and arbitration, bus cycle definition and control, address and data, cache control, and floating-point error control.

The features of the processor bus include:

- Non-multiplexed 32-bit address and data buses.
- Single-frequency (1x) clock.
- Bus hold operations.
- Bus locking and pseudo-locking operations.
- Burst transfers (up to 16 bytes).
- Cacheable transfers.
- Support for internal and external cache consistency.
- Floating-point error handling.
- Maskable and non-maskable interrupts.
- Support for 16- and 8-bit peripherals.
- Support for 1-Mbyte 8086 address wrap-around.
- Parity generation and checking.

The way in which system designs use the processor bus has an important effect on performance. Typically, only a few devices are located on the bus – those which need fast communication with the processor, share compatible signals, and observe the basic constraint on use of bus bandwidth: at least 50% of processor-bus bandwidth should be reserved for the i486 processor. Devices placed on the bus might include a LAN coprocessor, an external (second-level) cache controller, or other similar device. In most systems, the processor bus interfaces with one or more system buses. This distributes bus traffic across greater bus bandwidth and provides greater flexibility for system expansion. The design of external buses need not conform to the signal set of the processor bus. Chapter 8 describes general approaches to system design, Chapter 7 describes system peripherals, and Chapter 9 describes interfaces to the MULTIBUS II backplane.

Write cycles dominate i486 processor bus activity. This is unlike most other systems in which read cycles dominate bus activity and can keep the processor waiting. With the i486 processor's internal cache, instruction prefetch unit, and support for burst transfers, any memory subsystem capable of sustaining a rate of one data transfer per clock cycle can form the basis of a high-performance system. Most of the processor's immediate needs for instructions and data will then be satisfied quickly from the internal cache and instruction prefetch queue, without having to perform cycles on the processor bus.

The processor bus can support multiple external caches. Cache consistency can be maintained between the processor's internal cache, external caches, and main memory. External cache can be requested to write its contents back to memory, or it can be flushed; individual cache lines in the internal cache can be selectively invalidated, or the entire internal cache can be flushed.

The 386 processor used address pipelining on the processor bus to minimize processor waiting time. In the i486 processor, burst reads into the on-chip cache are used, rather than address pipelining on the bus, to achieve high performance. This, together with the simpler 1x bus clock and more latitude in bus-cycle scheduling, results in simpler system logic.

Two processor inputs dynamically control bus size for interfacing 8- and 16-bit devices to the processor's data bus. There are no restrictions on byte or word alignment within doubleword boundaries, although data that is not aligned to doubleword boundaries requires more than the minimum number of bus cycles to transfer. The bus supports an emulation of the 8086 processor's 1-Mbyte address wrap-around.

The sections below first summarize, and later elaborate on, the use of processor bus signals, how the signals work together during bus cycles, and other matters relating to the processor bus.

3.1.1 Bus Cycles

Bus cycles implement the processor's interactions with the external system. The processor can drive two basic groups of bus cycles.

- *Data Transfer Cycles:*
  Prefetch (read) instructions from memory.
  Read data from memory.
  Read data from I/O.
  Write data to memory.
  Write data to I/O.
- *Other Cycles:*
  Interrupt acknowledgement.
  Halt (a special bus cycle).
  Shutdown (a special bus cycle).
  Cache flush (a special bus cycle).
  Cache write-back and flush (a special bus cycle).

Some of the cycles driven by the processor are, or can be, locked or pseudo-locked. External hardware can exercise a bus hold operation and drive its own cycles on the processor bus, including cache invalidation cycles into the processor.

From the viewpoint of external hardware, data can be transferred as doublewords, words, or bytes, depending on the bus size specified. From the processor's viewpoint, all transfers use the 32-bit data bus but some transfers have only certain bytes enabled. Bus cycles which transfer data are of two basic types:

- *Non-Burst Cycles*—These cycles transfer up to four bytes at a maximum rate of two clocks per data item (doubleword, word, or byte). When a single data item is transferred, it is a *single-transfer cycle*. When these single cycles are repeated in a series, they form a *multiple-cycle sequence*.
- *Burst Cycles*—The fastest way to transfer more than one item of data is with a burst cycle. These cycles transfer up to 16 bytes at a rate of one data item per clock cycle. They are designed for cacheable reads (each internal cache line holds 16 bytes) but they can also be used for long floating-point reads, segment table descriptor reads, and other types of transfers.

Transfers internal to the processor, such as reads from the internal cache, do not appear on the processor bus. However, writes to the cache always appear on the bus because the cache uses a write-through policy: all writes go to memory and they will only go to the internal cache if the addressed data is already stored in the cache.

The remaining types of bus cycles, aside from the data transfers discussed above, include interrupt acknowledgement and four special bus cycles. The details of interrupt acknowledgement cycles are given in Section 3.3.2. The four special bus cycles are described in Sections 3.3.3 (halt and shutdown), 3.4.4 (cache flush cycle), and 3.4.5 (cache write-back and flush cycle).

3.1.2 Overview of Signals and Control Cycles

Table 3-1 lists the signals on the processor bus. Tables 3-2 and 3-3 provide additional perspectives on the signals. Table 3-3 shows that certain input signals have internal pullup or pulldown resistors. These resistors will cause current to flow in these inputs, but the resistors should not be relied upon as the sole connection for an input. All unused inputs should be connected to an external pullup or pulldown.

Some signals on the processor bus have a dual use, one for normal operations and another for device testing; only their normal function is described here. The power supply pins are not included. The *i486™ Microprocessor Data Sheet* contains full details on the timing and electrical characteristics of all signals. This data sheet is the only authoritative source for timing and electrical information. The classification of signals in the data sheet differs somewhat from the classification shown in Figure 3-1—the signals, of course, are the same, but the viewpoint each reader may have of their functions can differ.

The text immediately following the tables summarizes the function of each signal. It also includes descriptions of the five bus cycles (halt, shutdown, cache flush, cache write-back, and interrupt acknowledge) that perform control functions very much like signals. The data transfer cycles, for which the bus fundamentally exists, are then described in Section 3.2.

Table 3-1. Processor Bus Signals

Class	Signal	Type	Description
Address and Data Buses	A4-A31	I/O	Address
	A2-A3	O	Address
	A20M#	I	Address-bit 20 mask
	D0-D31	I/O	Data
	BE0#-BE3#	O	Byte-enable (also Special Bus Cycle selection)
	BS8#	I	8-bit data bus size
	BS16#	I	16-bit data bus size
	DP0-DP3	I/O	Data parity
	PCHK#	O	Parity error
Cycle Definition and Control	ADS#	O	Address status
	M/IO#	O	Memory or I/O
	D/C#	O	Data or control
	W/R#	O	Write or read
	RDY#	I	Non-burst data ready
	BRDY#	I	Burst data ready
	BLAST#	O	Last burst cycle
	KEN#	I	Internal-cache enable
Bus Control	CLK	I	Clock (386: 2x Clock used)
	RESET	I	Reset
	NMI	I	Non-maskable interrupt
	INTR	I	Maskable interrupt
	BREQ	O	Bus request
	HOLD	I	Bus hold request
	HLDA#	O	Bus hold acknowledgement
	BOFF#	I	Bus backoff
	LOCK#	O	Bus lock
	PLOCK#	O	Bus pseudo-lock
Cache Control	PCD	O	Page cache disable (internal and external)
	PWT	O	Page cache write-through or write-back (external)
	EADS#	I	Cache invalidation (internal)
	AHOLD	I	Address-bus hold (internal)
	FLUSH#	I	Cache flush (internal)
Floating-Point Error Control	FERR#	O	Floating-point error
	IGNNE#	I	Ignore floating-point error

3.1.2.1 ADDRESS AND DATA BUSES

The address and data buses are the paths on which bus cycles implement data transfers. The signals include:

- *Address Bus*—The A2-A31 address signals (Figure 3-1) are a mixture of bidirectional and output signals. A4-A31 are bidirectional. A2-A3 are output only. As outputs, the A2-A31 signals carry the 30-bit physical address of a doubleword in the memory or I/O space. As inputs, A4-A31 specify addresses in the internal cache to be invalidated during a cache invalidation cycle controlled by external hardware. The A0-A1 bits

Table 3-2. Output and Bidirectional Signals

Signal	Type	When Floated
A4-A31	I/O	Bus Hold and Address Hold
A2-A3	O	Bus Hold and Address Hold
D0-D31	I/O	Bus Hold
BE0#-BE3#	O	Bus Hold
DP0-DP3	I/O	Bus Hold
ADS#	O	Bus Hold
M/IO#	O	Bus Hold
D/C#	O	Bus Hold
W/R#	O	Bus Hold
BLAST#	O	Bus Hold
LOCK#	O	Bus Hold
PLOCK#	O	Bus Hold
PCD	O	Bus Hold
PWT	O	Bus Hold
PCHK#	O	(never)
BREQ	O	(never)
HLDA	O	(never)
FERR#	O	(never)

only exist internally; they generate the four byte-enable signals, BE0#-BE3#, described below. The processor is a little-endian machine; the least significant byte of a doubleword is the lowest-addressed byte of that doubleword, while the most significant byte is the highest-addressed byte of the doubleword.

- *Address-Bit 20 Mask* – The A20M# input emulates the address wrap-around which occurs at 1 Mbyte on the 8086 processor. The input causes the i486 processor to mask (clear to zero) physical address bit 20 when performing an internal-cache lookup and when writing to memory on the processor bus. During normal operation, the signal should be asserted only when the processor is in Real-Address Mode, which emulates the 8086 processor. During reset, A20M# plays a role in testability, as explained in the data sheet.

- *Data Bus* – The D0-D31 bidirectional signals (Figure 3-2) can carry a doubleword of data. D0-D7 is the least significant byte; D24-D31 is the most significant byte. The valid bytes on the 32-bit bus are specified by the byte-enable signals, BE0#-BE3#. The parity bit for each byte is specified by the DP0-DP3 signals.

- *Byte Enables* – The BE0#-BE3# outputs (Figure 3-2) indicate which bytes on the data bus are valid. The byte-enable signals should be ignored for the first transfer of cacheable cycles. In addition to their byte-enable functions for the data bus, these signals perform two additional functions: they can be decoded to generate A0, A1, and BHE# signals used in addressing 16- and 8-bit systems (see Section 3.2.3), and they encode special bus cycles (see Section 3.3.3).

- *Bus Size* – The BS8# and BS16# inputs (together with the address of data being accessed) control the sequence in which the byte-enable signals are driven. BS8# and

Table 3-3. Input Signals

Signal	Internal Resistor	Timing with Respect to CLK
CLK	–	–
NMI	–	Asynchronous
IGNNE#	Pullup	Asynchronous
A20M#	Pullup	Synchronous
BS8#	Pullup	Synchronous
BS16#	Pullup	Synchronous
RDY#	–	Synchronous
BRDY#	Pullup	Synchronous
KEN#	Pullup	Synchronous
RESET	–	Synchronous
INTR	–	Synchronous
HOLD	–	Synchronous
BOFF#	Pullup	Synchronous
EADS#	Pullup	Synchronous
AHOLD	Pulldown	Synchronous
FLUSH#	Pullup	Synchronous

BS16# cause the processor to run multiple bus cycles to satisfy data transfers for 8- and 16-bit devices. Doubleword transfers are converted to the appropriate number of word or byte transfers. BS8# and BS16# must be driven for each data transfer.

- *Data Parity*–The DP0-DP3 bidirectional signals (Figure 3-2) carry the parity bit of each byte on D0-D31. Even parity is used. To use parity checking, external logic must latch these signals in the write direction and provide parity inputs in the read direction. Only enabled bytes are checked for parity.

- *Parity Check*–The PCHK# output indicates a parity error in one or more of the four bytes sampled during the last clock of a read transfer. Only enabled bytes are checked for parity. The processor continues with normal operations after such errors. External hardware must take any action required.

3.1.2.2 CYCLE DEFINITION AND CONTROL

The cycle definition and control signals specify the type and direction of cycles (as shown in Table 3-4), the points in time at which data becomes valid or invalid, and the cacheability of the cycle. The signals in this class include:

- *Address Status*–The ADS# output indicates that a valid address (or addresses) and a valid cycle definition are being driven on the processor bus. The assertion of this signal marks the beginning of a bus cycle. In non-burst bus cycles, each address is

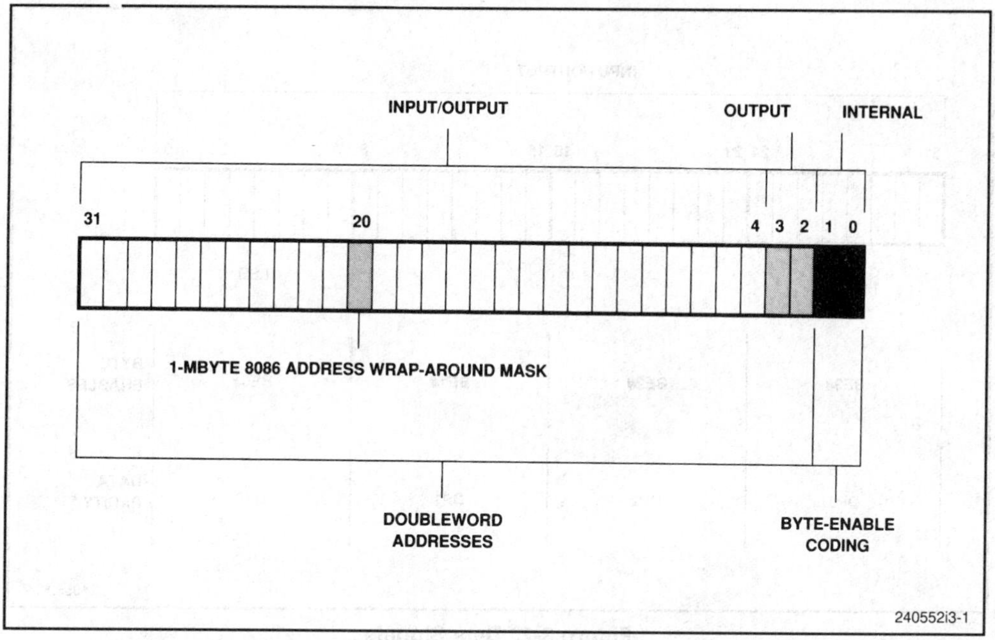

Figure 3-1. Address Signals

marked by a separate assertion of ADS# and a single data transfer. In burst bus cycles, one assertion of ADS# marks the beginning of a sequence of addresses and corresponding data transfers.

- *Memory or I/O* – The M/IO# output differentiates memory space from I/O space. It is used for bus cycle definition. For halt and shutdown cycles, the encoding of this signal is reversed from that used in the 386 processor.
- *Data or Control* – The D/C# output differentiates data cycles from all other cycles. It is used for bus cycle definition.
- *Write or Read* – The W/R# output indicates whether the cycle is a write or read. It is used for bus cycle definition.
- *Ready (non-burst)* – The RDY# input indicates that an external device has presented valid data on the data bus, or that the external device has accepted the processor's data. Slow devices can withhold RDY#, adding wait states until data is stable, so that transfers can be made at a sustainable pace. RDY# always terminates the current bus cycle, even if the signal is asserted in the middle of a burst cycle.
- *Burst Ready* – The BRDY# input is used instead of RDY# during a burst transfer. The signal is analogous to RDY#, although it does not terminate a burst cycle in progress. The processor responds to BRDY# by expecting the next clock cycle to be another data transfer. A maximum of 16 bytes can be transferred during the burst, at the rate of one doubleword, word or byte per clock. The assertion of BLAST# ends the burst.

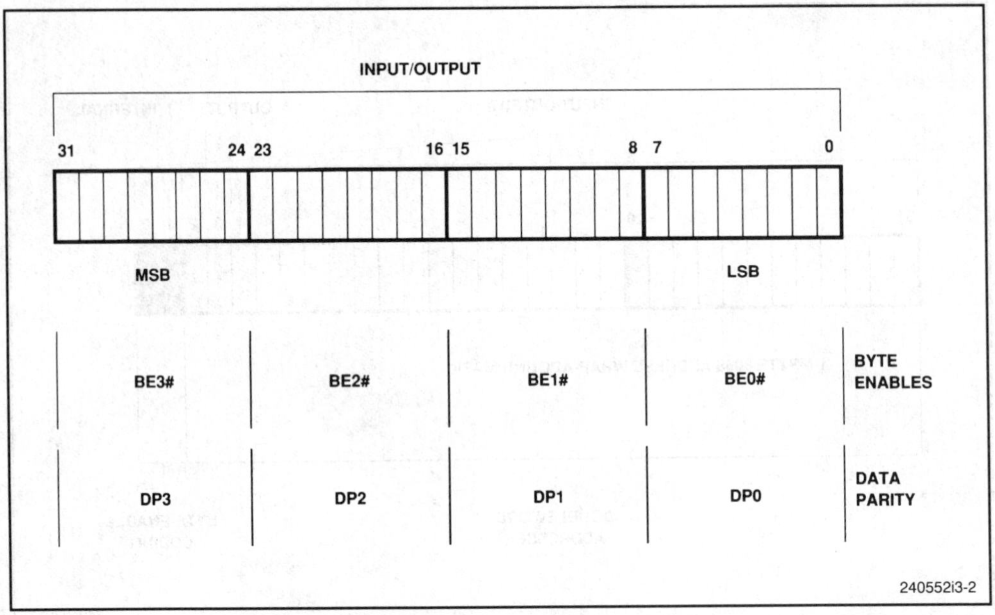

Figure 3-2. Data Signals

Table 3-4. Bus Cycle Definitions

M/IO#	D/C#	W/R#	Transfer Type
0	0	0	Interrupt acknowledge
0	0	1	Special bus cycles (see also BE0#-BE3#)
0	1	0	Read data from I/O
0	1	1	Write data to I/O
1	0	0	Prefetch (read) instructions from memory
1	0	1	(reserved)
1	1	0	Read data from memory
1	1	1	Write data to memory

- *Burst Last*—The BLAST# output indicates the last transfer of *any* data transfer cycle (burst or non-burst), from the processor's viewpoint. When BLAST# is asserted, the next BRDY# returned to the processor has the same effect as a RDY# input. If BLAST# is de-asserted, additional transfers are needed to complete the cycle. These additional transfers may be made in a burst cycle, if the external memory is capable of bursting, or they may be made in a multiple-cycle sequence.

- *Cache Enable*—The KEN# input enables the internal cache. Almost any read cycle, whether non-burst or burst, can be cached. When KEN# is asserted properly, the current read cycle will be transformed into a cache-line fill and 16 bytes will be read. The processor will run as many contiguous bus cycles as are required to fill the 16-byte cache line. KEN# is ignored during write cycles; data written by the processor will only be put in the cache if data from that address is currently in the cache.

Section 3.2 describes data transfer cycles. Special bus cycles are described in Section 3.3.3.

3.1.2.3 BUS CONTROL

Bus control signals, interrupt acknowledgement, and special bus cycles affect basic timing of, access to, and emergency actions for the processor bus. In the following list, these signals and cycles are grouped under two headings: (1) those which apply to all systems, and (2) those which apply only to multiple bus-master systems.

The signals and cycles used in all systems include:

- *Clock*—A single CLK input controls the timing of the processor and the bus. All timing parameters are specified with respect to the rising edge of this clock, which uses TTL logic levels.
- *Reset*—The RESET input forces the processor to initialize itself to a known state. The reset can initialize all registers or only non-floating-point registers, and it can run various tests, depending on the assertion of other signals during reset.
- *Maskable Interrupt*—The INTR input, if it is not masked by software, interrupts the processor and causes it to acknowledge the interrupt by reading an interrupt vector (number) from an external interrupt controller.
- *Interrupt Acknowledge Cycle*—The processor does not have a separate output for acknowledgement of maskable interrupts, as do earlier Intel 8086-family processors. Instead, the processor executes a unique interrupt-acknowledgement bus cycle that reads an interrupt vector from external hardware. This is described in Section 3.3.2.
- *Non-Maskable Interrupt*—The NMI input interrupts the processor and causes it to execute a specific interrupt service routine, without reading a vector from external logic. These interrupts indicate conditions which require immediate attention, such as loss of power.
- *Halt Cycle*—This special bus cycle indicates that the processor has suspended its operations. The cycle is generated by the execution of a HLT instruction.
- *Shutdown Cycle*—This special bus cycle indicates that the processor has terminated all of its operations. The cycle is generated by multiple protection exceptions.

The signals used in multiple bus-master systems include:

- *Bus Request*—The BREQ output indicates that the processor needs access to the bus, or that it is currently using the bus. The signal is used by external logic to arbitrate bus access among multiple bus masters. BREQ is always generated when the processor has a cycle pending, whether or not the processor is currently driving the bus. The signal is never floated. Thus, BREQ can be asserted during bus hold (HOLD), bus backoff (BOFF#), or address hold (AHOLD).
- *Bus Hold*—The HOLD input causes the processor to release the bus. It is used by other bus masters to gain access to the bus. In response, the processor floats most of its signals after completing its current bus cycle (or sequence of locked cycles) and asserts HLDA. Bus hold is distinct from address hold, which is described later. Bus hold will be recognized during a reset.

- *Bus-Hold Acknowledge*—The HLDA output indicates that the processor has floated most of its bus signals in response to a HOLD input. During bus hold, the processor continues execution internally; the internal cache and instruction prefetch unit will satisfy most of its bus requests. If the processor needs the bus, it will assert BREQ.
- *Bus Lock*—The LOCK# output allows the processor to complete multiple bus cycles without interruption via the HOLD input. The signal is generated by read-modify-write operations, interrupt acknowledge cycles, and segment descriptor loads. Among other things, it is asserted during semaphor updates. Locked read cycles are not cacheable. In systems with external cache, locked cycles should always cause a system-bus cycle. During locked cycles, the processor will not recognize a HOLD request, but will recognize a BOFF# or AHOLD request.
- *Bus Pseudo-Lock*—The PLOCK# output, like LOCK#, allows the processor to complete multiple bus cycles without interruption via the HOLD input. PLOCK# is asserted for all multiple-cycle sequences in which the transferred data is aligned to quadword boundaries. This includes transfers of 64-bit floating-point operands and cache line fills. BLAST# and PLOCK# have a complementary relationship—when BLAST# is de-asserted and valid, PLOCK# is asserted—except during the first transfer of a 64-bit write. During pseudo-locked cycles, the processor will not recognize a HOLD request, but will recognize a BOFF# or AHOLD request.
- *Bus Backoff*—The BOFF# input indicates that another bus master needs to complete a bus cycle in order for the processor's current cycle to complete. It is used to avoid a "deadly embrace" where neither the processor nor the other bus master can complete its operation, since each is waiting for some action by the other. BOFF# is recognized at any time. The processor's response to BOFF# is similar to that of HOLD, but more immediate; when BOFF# is asserted, the bus is always released in the next clock and no acknowledgment is given. When BOFF# is de-asserted, the processor will reliably restart the same bus cycle that was aborted. If RDY# or BRDY# is asserted simultaneously with BOFF#, only BOFF# will be recognized.

Section 3.3 describes bus control in detail.

3.1.2.4 CACHE CONTROL

Cacheable reads are stored in the processor's internal 8-Kbyte cache when the KEN# input is asserted and other conditions are met, as described in Section 3.2. Cache control maintains consistency between the internal cache, main memory, and any external cache during cycles that update any of the three.

Each 4-Kbyte page of memory locations can have its cacheability and write-through or write-back policy controlled on a cycle-by-cycle basis. The two outputs which implement page-based controls are:

- *Page Cache Disable*—The PCD output indicates whether the current page is cacheable. The information is taken from the page table entries, used by the internal cache, and can be used to control external caching.
- *Page Write-Through (or Write-Back)*—The PWT output, when asserted, applies a write-through caching policy for the current page (in which updates to external cache will immediately be written through to memory). When de-asserted, the signal allows

the possibility of a write-back caching policy (in which updates to cache will written back to memory only when specifically requested). This signal, also derived from the page table entries, is only useful to external cache; internal cache is always write-through.

Three inputs cause partial or complete invalidations of the internal cache:

- *Address Hold*—The AHOLD input causes the processor to float its address bus in the next clock cycle. This allows an external device to drive an address into the processor for internal cache-line invalidation. The address is strobed by the EADS# input. Only the address bus is floated: the remainder of the bus remains active. No address-hold acknowledgement is given. During reset, AHOLD plays a role in testability, as explained in the data sheet.

- *Internal Cache-Line Invalidation*—The EADS# input indicates that an address for a 16-byte cache line has been driven into the processor and is valid. This causes immediate invalidation of the cache line at that address, if the address matches an area that is cached. EADS# is used together with AHOLD. In most cases, the processor can accept one invalidation every clock cycle. Multiple invalidations can occur in a single address hold operation.

- *Internal Cache Flush*—The FLUSH# input forces the processor to flush the entire contents of its internal cache. Since the internal cache is write-through, the cache contents will already have been written to memory. During reset, FLUSH# plays a role in testability, as explained in the data sheet.

Two special bus cycles control invalidation and write-back for both internal and external cache:

- *Cache Flush Cycle*—This special bus cycle does two things: (1) invalidates the entire contents of the internal cache, and (2) requests an external cache to invalidate its entire contents. External cache should not write its contents back to memory before the flush. The cycle is initiated by the INVD instruction.

- *Cache Write-Back and Flush Cycle*—This special bus cycle does three things: (1) invalidates the entire contents of the internal cache, (2) requests an external cache to write its entire valid contents back to memory, and (3) requests the external cache to invalidate its entire contents after the write-back. The write-back function is not used with internal cache, which is write-through. The cycle is initiated by the WBINVD instruction.

Section 3.2 describes cacheable transfers. Section 3.3.3 describes special bus cycles. Section 3.4 describes cache control.

3.1.2.5 FLOATING-POINT ERROR CONTROL

Two signals are used to maintain compatibility with DOS floating-point error reporting. One signal alerts the system to errors within the processor's floating-point unit and the other signal tells the processor what to do if errors occur. The mechanism is compatible with floating-point error control in other Intel 8086-family processors and with DOS environments:

- *Floating-Point Error*–The FERR# output indicates that an unmasked floating-point error has occurred. The signal is similar to the ERROR# output on the 287 and 387 coprocessors. For DOS-compatible error reporting, the signal is routed back to the processor's INTR input.
- *Ignore Floating-Point Errors*–The IGNNE# input directs the processor to ignore floating-point errors and continue execution. If IGNNE# is de-asserted when a floating-point error is detected, the processor will either stop and wait for an interrupt, or it will jump to the floating-point interrupt location (vector 16), depending on the state of a control register bit.

Section 3.5 gives more detail on this mechanism, including a description of the software bit and a design example for DOS-compatible error reporting.

3.1.3 Timing and Clock Generation

The i486 processor uses a single-frequency (1x) clock input. All operations across the bus (except for the two asynchronous inputs, NMI and IGNNE#) are timed with respect to the rising edge of the CLK input.

There are two major advantages to using a 1x clock, as opposed to the 2x clock used in the 386 processor. First, the 1x clock simplifies system design by cutting in half the clock frequency required by external devices. Second, it keeps RF emission to a minimum and simplifies clock generation. A 25 MHz clock can be used to achieve high performance.

3.1.3.1 BUS STATE DIAGRAM

The bus can pass through five states during the operations described earlier in this chapter. A transition between states is made in every clock cycle, even when the transition is back to the immediately preceding state. The states are listed in Table 3-5. A state diagram is given in Figure 3-3.

When no bus cycle is executing, or when HOLD or BOFF# is asserted, the bus continuously loops in the Ti idle state. The bus passes to the T1 state when a new bus cycle is started and there is no bus hold or backoff. The bus passes to T2 if BOFF# is not asserted during the single T1 clock. The bus loops in T2 until RDY#, or the final BRDY# of a burst cycle, or BOFF# is asserted.

The bus returns to the T1 state if BRDY# or RDY# is received for a non-burst transfer or if the final BRDY# or RDY# is received for the last transfer of a burst cycle, provided that a new bus cycle is pending and HOLD, AHOLD and BOFF# are all de-asserted. If HOLD or AHOLD is asserted, or if no new bus cycle is pending, while BOFF# is de-asserted, the bus returns to the Ti idle state.

Table 3-5. Bus States

State	Description
Ti	Bus is idle. Address and status signals may be driven to undefined values, or the bus may be floated to a high-impedance state.
T1	First clock cycle of a bus cycle. Valid address and status are driven and ADS# is asserted.
T2	Second and subsequent clock cycles of a bus cycle. Data is driven if the cycle is a write, or data is expected if the cycle is a read. RDY# and BRDY# are sampled.
T1b	First clock cycle of a restarted bus cycle. Valid address and status are driven and ADS# is asserted. Externally, this state cannot be distinguished from T1.
Tb	Second and subsequent clock cycles of an aborted bus cycle.

If BOFF# is asserted while the bus is in T1 or T2, the bus goes to Tb, the backoff state. It remains in that state while HOLD, AHOLD or BOFF# is asserted. When HOLD, AHOLD and BOFF# are all de-asserted, the bus proceeds to T1b, ready to restart the cycle which was aborted. The bus proceeds to T2 on the next clock if BOFF# remains de-asserted. Otherwise, the bus goes back to Tb.

Table 3-6 shows the six conditions under which the processor will float its bus signals, including its address bus.

3.1.3.2 CLOCK TIMING AND GENERATION

The processor uses only a TTL-level CLK input for all internal timing. The CLK input is used at its undivided rate (1x). The processor can operate over a wide frequency range, but the frequency of CLK cannot change rapidly while RESET is inactive. See the i486 Microprocessor Data Sheet for details on the clock waveform.

3.1.3.3 BASIC READ TIMING

Non-burst data transfers take at least two clock cycles. During the first clock, the address of the source or destination of the data is placed on the address signals and the address status signal ADS# is asserted. At the same time, the transfer type and direction are defined by the M/IO#, D/C# and W/R# signals. In a data read from memory, for example, M/IO# is high, D/C# is high, and W/R# is low. In the second clock, data is transferred into the processor at the end of the cycle if the RDY# input is asserted. Otherwise, the processor waits for RDY# to be asserted.

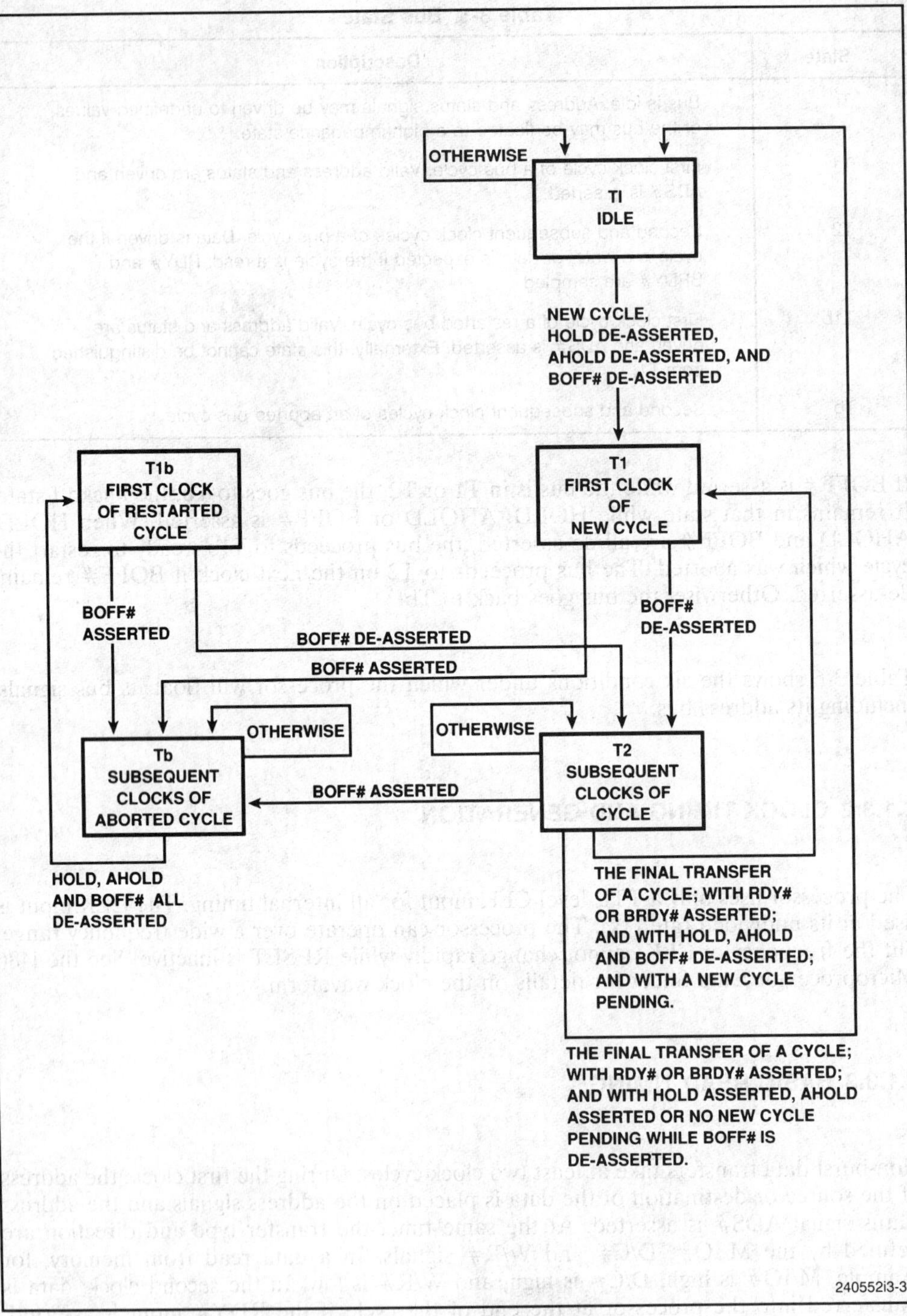
OTHERWISE
TI
IDLE
NEW CYCLE,
HOLD DE-ASSERTED,
AHOLD DE-ASSERTED, AND
BOFF# DE-ASSERTED
T1b
FIRST CLOCK
OF RESTARTED
CYCLE
T1
FIRST CLOCK
OF
NEW CYCLE
BOFF#
ASSERTED
BOFF# DE-ASSERTED
BOFF# ASSERTED
BOFF#
DE-ASSERTED
OTHERWISE
OTHERWISE
Tb
SUBSEQUENT
CLOCKS OF
ABORTED CYCLE
BOFF# ASSERTED
T2
SUBSEQUENT
CLOCKS OF
CYCLE
HOLD, AHOLD
AND BOFF# ALL
DE-ASSERTED
THE FINAL TRANSFER
OF A CYCLE; WITH RDY#
OR BRDY# ASSERTED;
AND WITH HOLD, AHOLD
AND BOFF# DE-ASSERTED;
AND WITH A NEW CYCLE
PENDING.
THE FINAL TRANSFER OF A CYCLE;
WITH RDY# OR BRDY# ASSERTED;
AND WITH HOLD ASSERTED, AHOLD
ASSERTED OR NO NEW CYCLE
PENDING WHILE BOFF# IS
DE-ASSERTED.
240552i3-3

Figure 3-3. Processor-Bus States

Table 3-6. Conditions for Floating the Processor Bus

When...	The processor...
HOLD is asserted during the Ti (idle) state...	Floats the bus and asserts HLDA in the next clock.
HOLD is asserted in the Tb (backed off) state...	Stays in Tb. The bus is not floated.
HOLD is asserted, RDY# is asserted, and BOFF# is de-asserted in the T2 state...	Floats the bus and asserts HLDA in the next clock.
HOLD is asserted, BRDY# is asserted, and BOFF# is de-asserted in the T2 state either for the last transfer of a burst or a non-burst transfer...	Floats the bus and asserts HLDA in the next clock.
BOFF# is asserted	Floats the bus in the next clock, without asserting HLDA.
AHOLD is asserted.	Floats A2-A31 in the next clock.

3.1.4 Memory and I/O on the Bus

The instruction set supports an address space for memory that is separate from the address space for I/O ports, as in other Intel 8086-family processors. Up to four gigabytes of memory (2^{32} bytes, 00000000H-FFFFFFFFH) and up to 64 kilobytes of I/O (2^{16} bytes, 00000000H-0000FFFFH) can be addressed. Both memory and I/O address space has hardware support for protection and multi-tasking.

3.1.4.1 DATA BUS STRUCTURE

To the programmer, memory locations and I/O ports are accessible as 8-bit bytes, 16-bit words, 32-bit doublewords, and a variety of other data structures. A word is any two consecutively addressed bytes. A doubleword is any four consecutively addressed bytes. However, in hardware, memory and I/O on the data bus are viewed as a sequence of doublewords (2^{30} 32-bit memory locations and 2^{14} 32-bit I/O ports, maximum). From the processor's viewpoint, each doubleword location has four individually addressable bytes at consecutive memory addresses. Each 32-bit memory location starts at a physical address that is a multiple of four.

The least significant byte of a doubleword is transferred on bits D0-D7 of the data bus; the most significant byte of the doubleword is transferred on bits D24-D31. Also, the least significant byte of a doubleword is the lowest addressed byte of that doubleword, while the most significant byte is the highest addressed byte, as illustrated in Figure 3-4.

Memory and I/O address space should be implemented as four sections in hardware. Each section connects to a byte on the data bus (D0-D7, D8-D15, D16-D23, and D24-D31). When the processor reads a doubleword, it accesses one byte from each section.

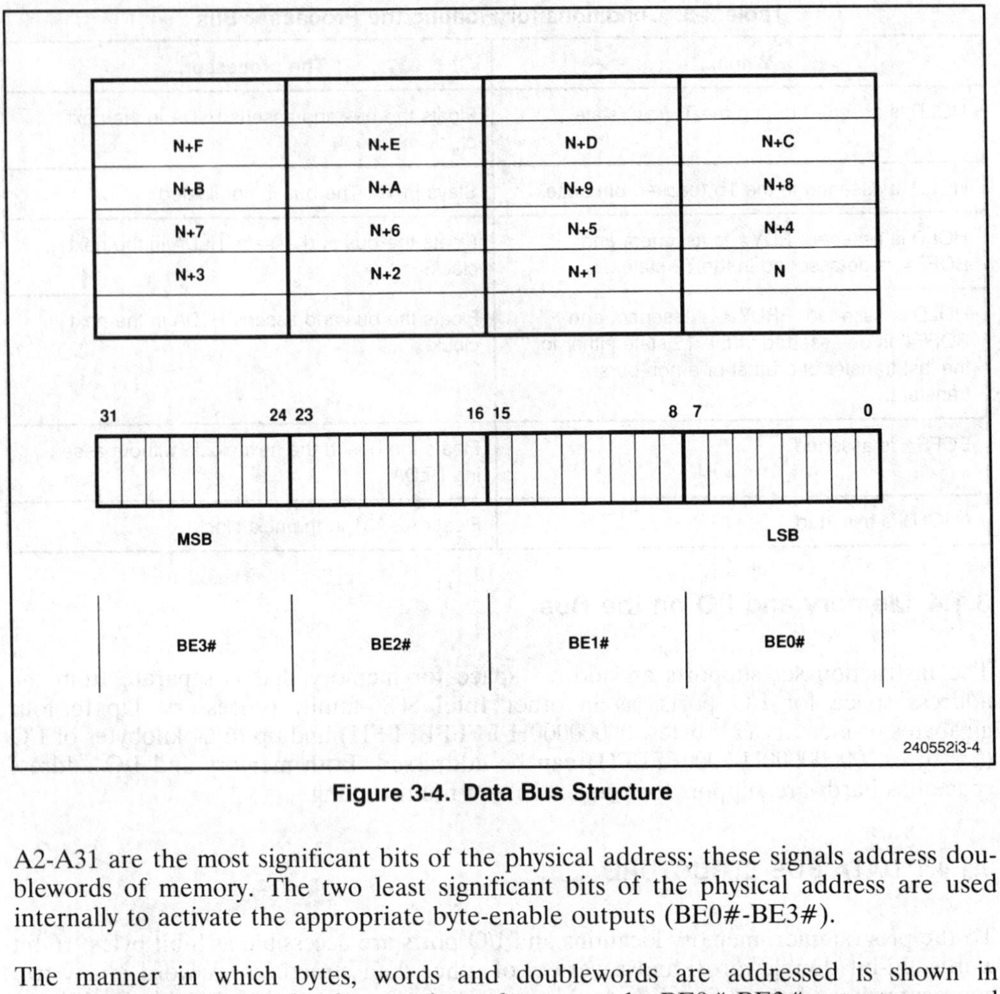

Figure 3-4. Data Bus Structure

A2-A31 are the most significant bits of the physical address; these signals address doublewords of memory. The two least significant bits of the physical address are used internally to activate the appropriate byte-enable outputs (BE0#-BE3#).

The manner in which bytes, words and doublewords are addressed is shown in Figure 3-5. In implementing four sections of memory, the BE0#-BE3# outputs are used as chip selects for the sections, with each section passing data on one byte of the processor's data bus.

3.1.4.2 DATA ALIGNMENT

Software normally considers data to be aligned if its address is an even multiple of its data width, in bytes. However, the processor hardware views alignment less strictly. Transfers on the processor's full 32-bit data bus are *aligned* if their data does not overlap doubleword boundaries. A word is aligned if it can be read from one of three possible positions within the doubleword space, as shown in Table 3-7 and Figure 3-6.

Data alignment is an important performance consideration: transfers of aligned words and doublewords take one bus cycle; transfers of unaligned words and doublewords take two bus cycles.

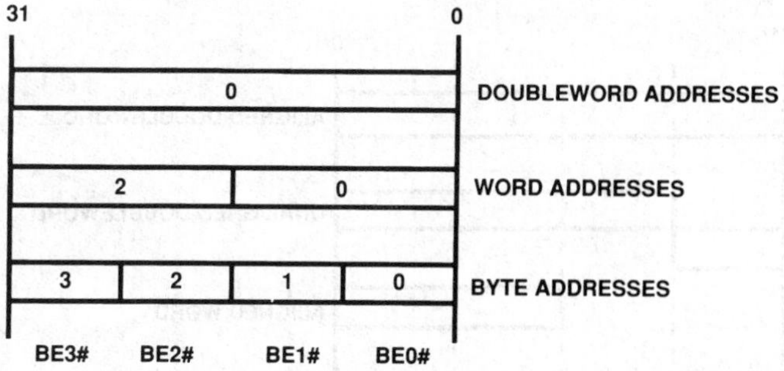

Figure 3-5. Addressing Bytes, Words and Doublewords

Table 3-7. Possible Transfers in a Single 32-Bit Bus Cycle

Bytes Transferred	Bytes Enabled
4 bytes	3-2-1-0
3 bytes	3-2-1 2-1-0
2 bytes	3-2 2-1 1-0
1 byte	3 2 1 0

An aligned doubleword has an address which is clear in its lowest two bits. An aligned word can have any address except one which is set in both of its lowest two bits. If the addressed word is in the middle of a doubleword boundary (bytes 1 and 2 enabled, but not bytes 0 and 3), the word is aligned from the hardware viewpoint – it will be transferred in a single bus cycle on the full 32-bit bus – even though it will generate an alignment check fault in software.

Figure 3-7 shows an example of reading a misaligned doubleword at memory location n+2. The operation takes two bus cycles instead of one. The first cycle accesses the upper word of the doubleword at address n+4 and n+5, with BE1# and BE0# asserted. The second cycle accesses the lower word at address n+2 and n+3, with BE3# and BE2# asserted.

For maximum software compatibility with hardware environments, programmers should keep word data aligned to two-byte boundaries, doubleword data aligned to four-byte

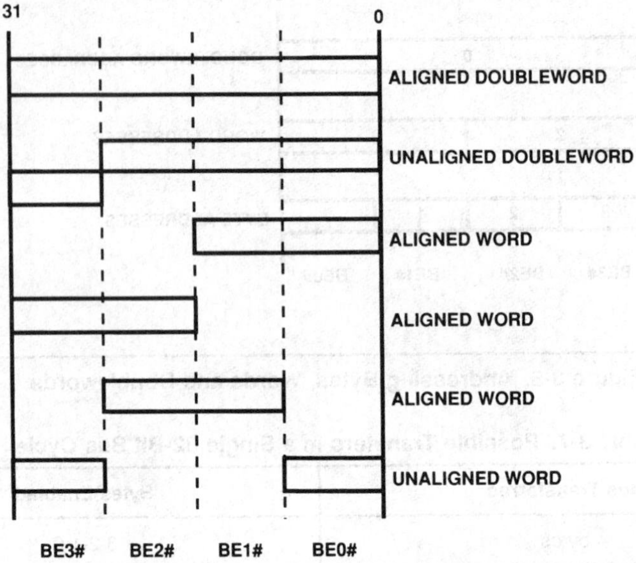

Figure 3-6. Data Alignment on 32-Bit Data Bus

boundaries, and quadword data (such as floating-point operands and segment-table descriptors) aligned to 8-byte boundaries. Quadword alignment is useful because the processor can do a quadword-aligned read from its internal cache in one clock cycle. Quadword alignment also anticipates development of future Intel processors which may have 64-bit data buses.

A software mechanism is provided for flagging misaligned data. The mechanism checks for word data for word operands, doubleword data for doubleword operands, and quadword data for quadword operands. It will execute interrupt 17 if:

- The alignment check (AC) bit in the machine status register (CR0) is set (one).
- The alignment check (AC) bit is not masked.
- The data being checked is for user level 3.

As mentioned above, aligned words which have bytes 1 and 2 enabled (but not bytes 0 and 3) will generate an alignment check fault but will nevertheless be transferred in a single bus cycle.

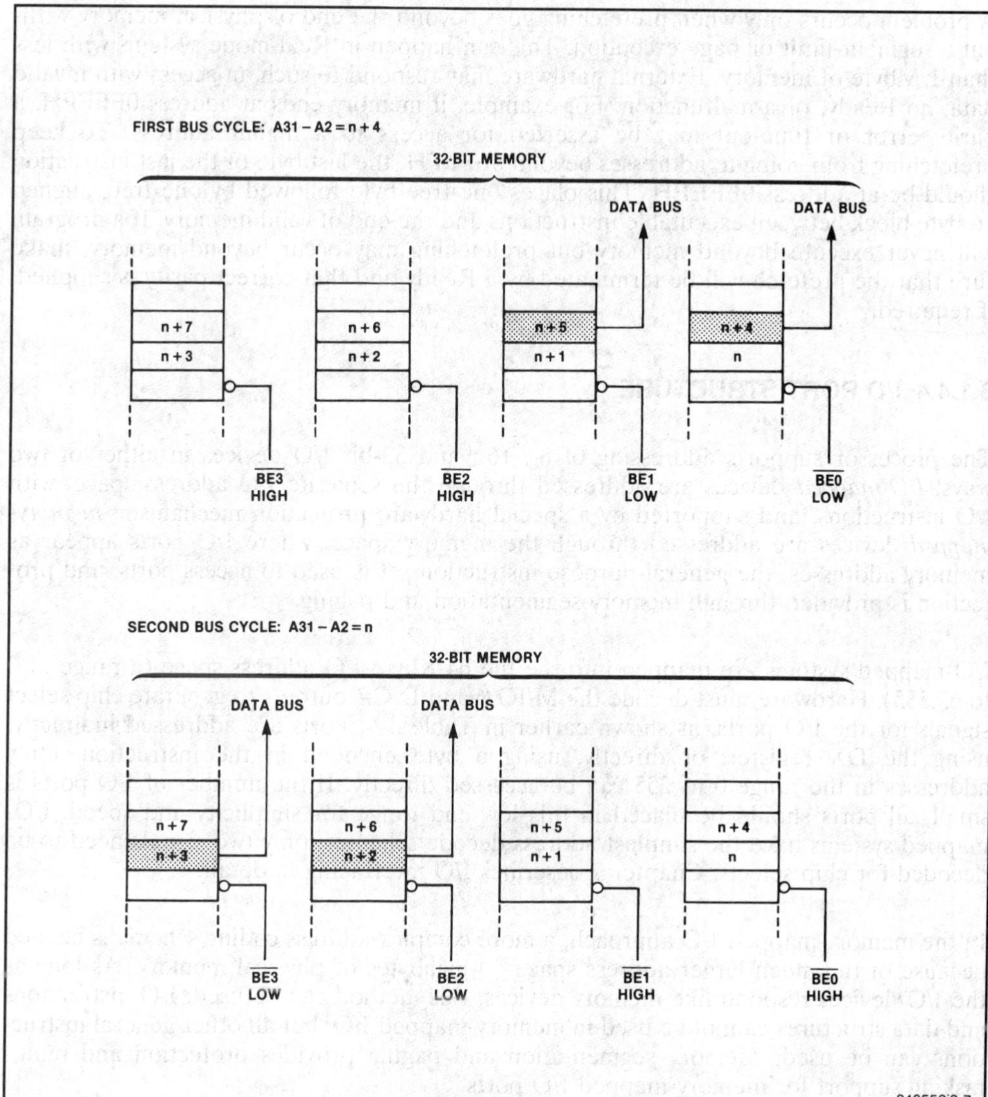

Figure 3-7. Misaligned Doubleword Transfer

3.1.4.3 INVALID INSTRUCTION PRE-FETCHING

The processor may perform instruction prefetching to memory addresses not anticipated by programmers. For example, prefetching may access addresses beyond the end of the program in memory. The prefetcher will never read past the end of an instruction segment or access a page which is not present. An exception is generated when attempting to execute a subsequent instruction which would violate the segment limit or access a page which is not present.

A problem occurs only when prefetching goes beyond the end of physical memory without a segment-limit or page exception. This can happen in Real-mode systems with less than 1 Mbyte of memory. External hardware may respond to such an access with invalid data, no Ready, or a malfunction. For example, if memory ends at address 0FFFFH, a parity error or time-out may be asserted for access to a higher address. To keep prefetching from going to addresses beyond 0FFFFH, the last byte of the last instruction should be at address 0FFEEH. This places one free byte followed by one free, aligned 16-byte block between executable instructions and the end of valid memory. If a program will never execute beyond memory but prefetching may occur beyond memory, make sure that the prefetch will be terminated by a Ready and that correct parity is supplied, if required.

3.1.4.4 I/O PORT STRUCTURE

The processor supports addressing of 8-, 16-, and 32-bit I/O devices in either of two ways: *I/O-mapped* devices are addressed through the separate I/O address space, with I/O instructions, and supported by a special hardware protection mechanism; *memory-mapped* devices are addressed through the memory space, where I/O ports appear as memory addresses, the general-purpose instruction set is used to access ports, and protection is provided through memory segmentation and paging.

I/O-mapped systems are mapped into the the 64-Kbyte I/O address space (a range of 0 to 65,535). Hardware must decode the M/IO# and D/C# outputs to generate chip select signals for the I/O ports, as shown earlier in Table 3-4. Ports are addressed indirectly, using the DX register, or directly, using a byte encoded in the instruction. Only addresses in the range 0 to 255 can be accessed directly. If the number of I/O ports is small, all ports should be placed in this low-end range for simplicity and speed. I/O-mapped systems have the simplest address decode schemes; only two signals need to be decoded for chip selects. Chapter 7 describes I/O interfacing in detail.

In the memory-mapped I/O approach, a more complex address coding scheme is needed because of the much larger address space – 4-gigabytes of physical memory. As long as the I/O devices respond like memory devices, this method can be used. I/O instructions and data structures cannot be used in memory-mapped I/O, but all other general instructions can be used. Memory segmentation and paging provides protection and multitasking support for memory-mapped I/O ports.

Like words in memory, 16-bit I/O ports should be aligned to even addresses so that all words can be transferred in a single bus cycle. Like doublewords in memory, 32-bit ports should be aligned to addresses which are multiples of four. The processor supports data transfers to unaligned ports, but an extra bus cycle must be used. A port which crosses a doubleword boundary, whether it is I/O mapped or memory mapped, is first accessed in its high doubleword.

I/O hardware should not rely on the byte order the processor uses to access memory, except for the order specified for burst transfers. Intel reserves the right to change the byte order of non-burst bus cycles.

PCHK# is generated for both memory and I/O cycles. If I/O ports do not return parity on reads, the PCHK# output may need to be masked during I/O access if irrelevant interrupts are to be avoided. This is true whether I/O-mapped or memory-mapped I/O is used. The PCHK# signal is masked internally to prevent parity errors from being reported for interrupt-acknowledge and special bus cycles. The i486 processor handles I/O cycles in a special way with regard to the write buffers. See Chapter 7 for details.

3.1.4.5 16-BIT AND 8-BIT PERIPHERALS

The BS16# and BS8# inputs allow the external system to specify, on a cycle-by-cycle basis, whether an addressed peripheral can only supply 8 or 16 bits of data on the processor bus. If the peripheral cannot return all the bytes requested, the processor will run enough bus cycles to complete the transfer. Data must be presented across the processor's entire 32-bit bus width, even though this cannot be done simultaneously. Chapter 7 describes the logic needed to connect the peripheral's data and address buses to the processor's 32-bit data and address buses.

If 8- or 16-bit memory devices support cacheable transfers to the processor, external logic must detect the first transfer of a cacheable cycle and properly prioritize the bytes placed on the processor's data bus during this first transfer. Section 3.2.3.4 and Table 3-11, describe this byte ordering during cacheable cycles. Chapter 6 covers memory interfacing in detail.

3.2 DATA TRANSFERS

Data transfers, also called *data cycles*, move instructions, operands, and other data across the processor bus. Each item of data (doubleword, word, or byte) is identified by an address and by the byte-enable signals.

Bus cycles control data transfers through a series of signal changes on the bus. The beginning of data-transfer bus cycles is marked by the assertion of the address-status (ADS#) output. In the timing diagrams for this manual, the beginning and end of bus cycle are illustrated with heavy, vertical, dashed lines.

A single bus cycle may involve more than one data transfer; for example, burst cycles transfer several items of data in a single cycle. The converse is also true for 8- or 16-bit bus sizes: one 32-bit data transfer involves multiple bus cycles.

Data transfers can be made in the following ways:

- *Non-Burst Cycles.*
  Non-cacheable memory or I/O reads or writes.
  Cacheable memory reads (including instruction prefetching).
- *Burst Cycles.*
  Non-cacheable memory or I/O reads or (for small bus sizes) writes.
  Cacheable memory reads (including instruction prefetching).

Non-burst cycles that transfer a single data item are called *single-transfer cycles*. A continuous series of non-burst single-transfer cycles is called a *multiple-cycle sequence*. *Cacheable cycles* provide the processor with internal copies of recently read instructions, operands, and other data. When the processor generates a read request, it first checks its cache for the data being addressed. If data at that address had previously been read into the cache and is still valid (a *cache hit*), no bus cycle is required. If such data is not present or not valid (a *cache miss*), the processor will read from memory. During memory reads which result from a cache miss, the processor transfers 16 bytes into the cache (a *cache line fill*), if caching is enabled. Only memory reads are convertible into cache line fills; write data will only be put into the cache if data at the address of the write is currently cached.

Burst cycles are the fastest way to transfer more than one item of data. They are the most important type of cycle for high-performance systems. Burst cycles transfer up to 16 bytes of contiguous, aligned data at a maximum rate of one data item per clock cycle. They are designed primarily for 16-byte cache line fills, but they can also be used for non-cacheable transfers involving fewer bytes.

Table 3-8 shows the restrictions on burst cycles and cacheable cycles.

3.2.1 Non-Burst Cycles

A non-burst transfer that passes a single data item is called a single-transfer cycle. The minimum single-transfer read or write cycle takes two clocks. It is called a "2-2" bus cycle, because read cycles and write cycles each take two clocks. If external logic is unable to respond within the second clock, a 2-2 bus cycle can be converted into a "3-3" cycle, in which read cycles and write cycles each take three clocks. A continuous series of non-burst single-transfer cycles is called a multiple-cycle sequence. Of the non-burst cycles, only multiple-cycle sequences can be cacheable. Each of these non-burst cycles is described in the subsections below.

3.2.1.1 NON-CACHEABLE 2-2 CYCLES

Figure 3-8 shows the timing for 2-2 non-cacheable single-transfer cycles—the fastest non-burst bus cycle that the processor supports. The cycle begins with the appearance of a stable address and the processor's assertion of ADS# at the rising edge of the first

Table 3-8. Restrictions on Burst Cycles and Cacheable Cycles

Cycle Type	Restrictions
Burst Cycles	Only memory or I/O reads that *require more than one data transfer* can be bursted. Instruction prefetches are burstable. Burst writes can only be done on 16- or 8-bit data buses, for a maximum of 4 bytes.
Cacheable Cycles	Only memory reads (including instruction prefetches) can be cached. Locked reads, I/O-mapped reads, and interrupt acknowledge reads cannot be cached.

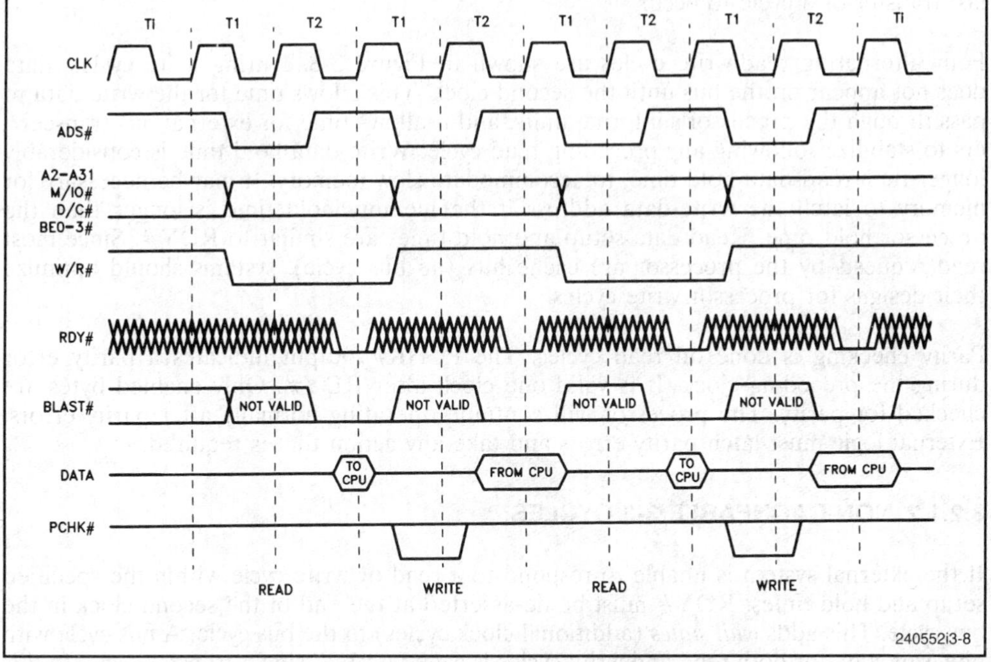

Figure 3-8. Non-Burst, Non-Cacheable 2-2 Cycle

clock. ADS# indicates that the bus-cycle definition and address signals are available. The first clock is used only to pass the address and bus cycle definition. It allows time for external devices to decode and prepare data in the case of a read cycle.

During the second clock, ADS# is de-asserted, but the address bus and other bus cycle definition signals are held stable. To complete the transfer, external logic must assert RDY# just before the end of the second clock. The processor samples RDY# on the rising edge of the third clock. RDY# indicates either that the external device is able to receive data during a write or return stable data during a read. Setup and hold times are specified in the *i486™ Microprocessor Data Sheet*.

RDY# is ignored at the end of the bus cycle's first clock. During the second clock, the assertion of RDY# does more than indicate the acceptance or validity of data; it also enables a subsequent ADS# signal, if more data transfers are needed. BRDY# (used to invoke a burst transfer) may be in any state throughout the bus cycle, as long as RDY# is asserted properly. RDY# always takes precedence over BRDY# when the two signals are sampled on the rising edge of the second clock. If the external system is unable to respond in time, it must keep RDY# (and BRDY#) de-asserted until a valid response is possible. The next section, on 3-3 cycles, discusses the details of adding these wait states.

The processor asserts BLAST# during the final (second) clock of the bus cycle, as shown in Figure 3-8. This indicates that the transfer is complete after a single cycle.

While BLAST# is designed primarily for use with burst cycles (explained later), the processor asserts the signal in all bus cycles to indicate when the processor expects the last transfer of a cycle to occur.

Four alternating read/write cycles are shown in Figure 3-8. During write cycles, data does not appear on the bus until the second clock. This allows time for the write data to pass through the processor's internal units, and it allows time for external bus transceivers to stabilize following any preceding read cycle. Write-data hold time is considerably longer than read-data hold time, to accommodate slow memory. It may be necessary for memory to latch the write-data address if the memory hold time is longer than the processor hold time. Read-data setup and hold times are similar to RDY#. Since most read requests by the processor are cache hits (no bus cycle), systems should optimize their designs for processor write cycles.

Parity checking is done on read cycles. The PCHK# output indicates a parity error during the preceding clock. It is valid one clock after RDY#. Only enabled bytes are checked for parity. The processor will continue operating normally after parity errors. External logic must latch parity errors and take any action that is required.

3.2.1.2 NON-CACHEABLE 3-3 CYCLES

If the external system is unable to respond to a read or write cycle within the specified setup and hold times, RDY# must be de-asserted at the end of the second clock in the bus cycle. This adds *wait states* (additional clock cycles) to the bus cycle. A bus cycle with one wait state for both read and write cycles is called a "3-3" single-transfer cycle. In this cycle, reads and writes each take three clocks, as shown in Figure 3-9. One wait state is added for each clock that RDY# is withheld, so there can be "4-4" cycles, and so on. Any number of wait states can be added, and external logic can add a different number of wait states to read cycles than are added to write cycles.

The address bus, cycle definition, and data bus outputs remain stable during wait states. However, BRDY# must be de-asserted on all clock edges where RDY# is de-asserted. If this is not done, the processor may initiate a burst cycle. As with all data transfer cycles, BLAST# is asserted during the final (in this case, third) clock of a 3-3 bus cycle.

Parity checking is the same as for 2-2 cycles. Where high performance is important, systems should avoid wait states in favor of 2-2 cycles, described above, and burst cycles, described below.

3.2.1.3 NON-CACHEABLE MULTIPLE-CYCLE SEQUENCES

A non-cacheable multiple-cycle sequence is a series of single-transfer cycles. A sequence can be caused by internal requests from the processor or external requests from the memory system. They are used when more than one doubleword of data needs to be transferred. For example, the processor can cause the non-burst, non-cacheable sequences by reading 128-bit instructions, 64-bit floating-point operands, or an unaligned 32-bit doubleword. The external memory system can cause the sequences when it reads or writes 32- bit data over an 8- or 16-bit data bus.

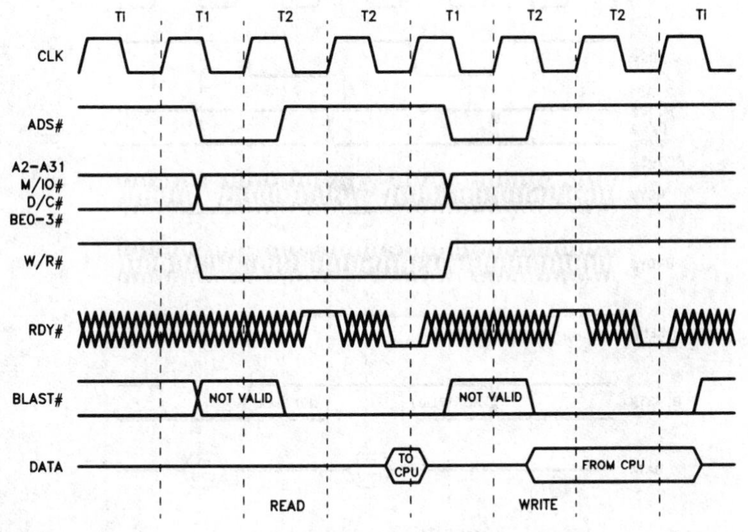

Figure 3-9. Non-Burst, Non-Cacheable 3-3 Cycle

Figure 3-10 shows such a multiple-cycle sequence; this one reads two data items in a sequence of two bus cycles. The sequence begins exactly like a 2-2 cycle, with the assertion of ADS# when the address and cycle definition signals are valid. The processor then indicates that this is a multiple-cycle sequence by de-asserting BLAST# at the end of the second clock of the first bus cycle. The external system asserts RDY#, completing the first bus cycle. Each subsequent bus cycle in the sequence begins with the assertion of ADS# and ends with the return of RDY#. The sequence ends when RDY# is asserted while BLAST# is asserted.

If the data read or written in a multiple-cycle sequence is aligned to the width of the data transferred (32, 64, or 128 bits), the PLOCK# signal is asserted as described below in Section 3.3.6. Parity checking is the same as for 2-2 cycles.

3.2.1.4 CACHEABLE MULTIPLE-CYCLE SEQUENCES

Cacheable multiple-cycle sequences are used to fill a cache line in the processor's internal cache. Only read sequences are cacheable. The cache does not support allocate-on-write, and the KEN# input is not sampled during write cycles. Whenever a write is internally generated, the processor will only put the data in its cache if data at the address of the write is currently cached.

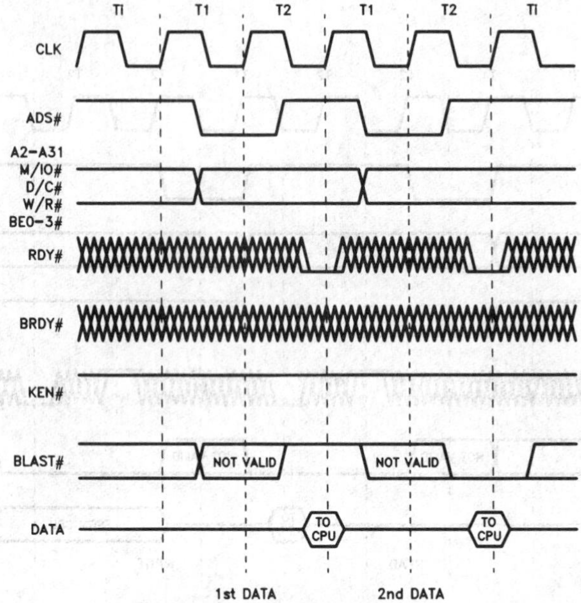

Figure 3-10. Non-Burst, Non-Cacheable Multiple-Cycle Sequence

Cacheable read sequences are like the non-cacheable multiple-cycle sequences described immediately above, except for the following conditions:

- *KEN#*—The cache enable input must be asserted both at the beginning and the end of the cache line fill.
- *Cacheability*—Only memory reads and instruction prefetches are cacheable. Locked reads, interrupt acknowledge cycles, and I/O-mapped reads are not cacheable.
- *Page Cache Disable Bit*—The PCD bit in the page directory base register, CR3, must be clear (zero).
- *Cache Enable Bit*—The CE bit in the machine status register, CR0, must be set (one).

If the conditions listed above are fulfilled, the processor will change a memory-read request that could be satisfied by a single-transfer cycle into a cacheable multiple-cycle sequence. KEN# must be asserted by the external system at the end of the first clock, before RDY#. When this is done, the processor will continue to read an entire 16-byte cache line. Figure 3-11 shows a sequence in which four doublewords are transferred in four bus cycles, with no wait states. The processor will read all data by running between 4 and 16 contiguous bus cycles, depending on the bus size selected by BS16# or BS8#.

BLAST# is invalid and should be ignored during the first clock of the sequence. In response to the assertion of KEN# in the first clock, the processor de-asserts BLAST# one clock later. KEN# must also be asserted one clock before RDY# is returned for the

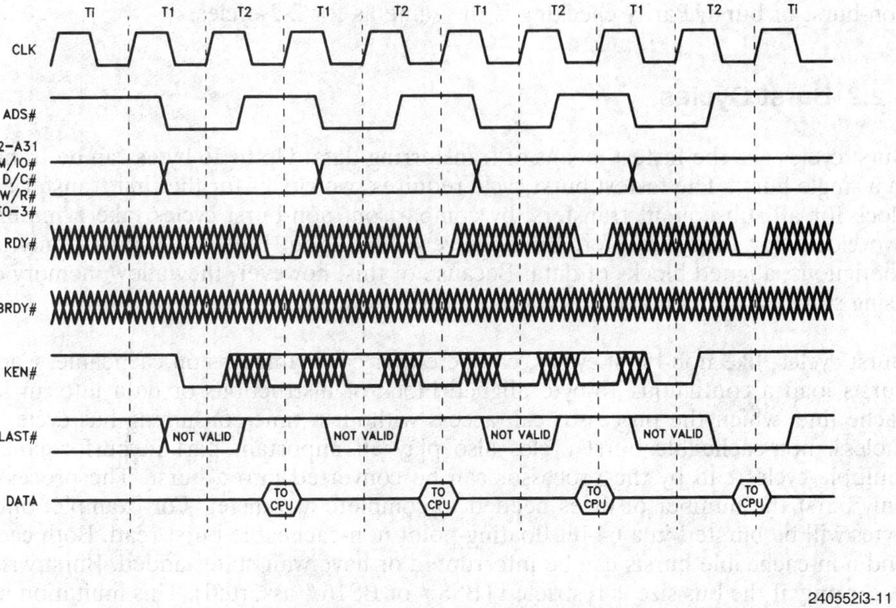

Figure 3-11. Non-Burst, Cacheable Multiple-Cycle Sequence

final transfer of the sequence. This second assertion of KEN# causes the data to actually be placed in the internal cache; without this second assertion of KEN#, the data read into the processor will not be written into the cache.

The processor samples the KEN# input every clock. The value sampled in the clock before RDY# determines (1) whether a bus cycle should be transformed into a cache line fill, and (2) whether a transformed bus cycle should be loaded into the cache after it is fully read. Between its first and second assertions, KEN# is don't care except at each clock edge, when it must meet setup and hold times. KEN#, BS8#, and BS16# are synchronous inputs. BS8# and BS16# are also sampled each clock to determine whether additional bus cycles are needed to complete a transfer. Like KEN#, BS8# and BS16# must meet setup and hold times at each clock edge.

Whenever a bus cycle is first converted to a cache line fill, the processor expects valid data across its entire data bus. Thus, the BE0#-BE3# outputs (although valid) should be ignored during the first transfer in a cache line fill, and the memory system should supply valid data as if BE0#-BE3# were all asserted. The data expected is that addressed by the A2-A31 signals. After the first transfer of the cache line fill, the byte-enable signals should be used for all subsequent transfers in the cache line fill. This is true for both non-burst and burst cache line fills. Section 3.2.2.8 describes how to distinguish the first transfer of a cacheable cycle. Data sequencing for burst cycles (which can be cacheable or non-cacheable) has additional considerations described in the next section.

KEN# can change state several times before a single-transfer cycle is converted into a cacheable multiple-cycle sequence, as described later in Section 3.2.2.4 and Figure 3-15. Section 3.2.2.5 describes data alignment and sequencing of cacheable cycles, whether non-burst or burst. Parity checking is the same as for 2-2 cycles.

3.2.2 Burst Cycles

Burst cycles are the fastest means of transferring data. Up to 16 bytes can be transferred in a single burst. The fastest burst cycle requires two clocks for the first transfer and one clock for all subsequent transfers; by comparison, non-burst cycles take a minimum of two clocks for every transfer. Bursts have a limitation: they can transfer only address contiguous, aligned blocks of data. Because of this, however, they allow memory devices using static column decode to be accessed very quickly.

Burst cycles, like non-burst cycles, can be either cacheable or non-cacheable. Cacheable bursts load a contiguous 16-byte aligned block of instructions or data into an internal cache line, which the processor can access without a time-consuming bus cycle. Nevertheless, non-cacheable burst cycles also play an important part in performance. Any multiple-cycle read by the processor can be converted into a burst. The processor will only burst the number of bytes needed to complete a transfer. For example, only eight bytes will be bursted in a 64-bit floating-point non-cacheable burst read. Both cacheable and non-cacheable bursts can be interrupted or have wait states added. Burst writes can occur only if the bus size is restricted (BS8# or BS16# asserted). This limitation may not apply to future Intel processors, and designers should allow for longer burst writes in the future. To allow for upward compatiblity in the future, the i486 processor always asserts BLAST# during writes if BS8# or BS16# are de-asserted.

Parity checking is the same as for non-burst cycles. The PCHK# output indicates a parity error on a data read during the preceding clock. It is valid one clock after BRDY#. Only data signals which actually return data are checked for parity. The processor will continue program execution after parity errors. External logic must latch parity errors and take any action that is required.

The following text covers non-cacheable bursts first, then cacheable bursts. The basic timing methods used in both types of burst are described in the non-cacheable burst section, so it is important to read this even though your primary interest may be in cacheable bursts.

3.2.2.1 NON-CACHEABLE BURSTS

The conditions for a non-cacheable burst cycle are:

- *BRDY#*—The burst ready input must be asserted instead of RDY#, with the same timing as RDY#.
- *Burstability*—Memory and I/O reads that require more than a single data transfer are burstable. Instruction prefetches are burstable. Interrupt acknowledge cycles and write cycles (except writes of up to four bytes on 16-bit or 8-bit bus sizes) are not burstable.

- *Contiguous Data Alignment*—Addresses of all data must fall within a contiguous aligned area. The number of bytes transferred will be the number of bytes needed for the specific operation.

Figure 3-12 shows a non-cacheable burst cycle; in this example, two doublewords are transferred in three clocks. The burst begins with the processor driving an address and asserting ADS#, in the same manner as for non-burst cycles. In addition, however, the processor indicates that more than one data item is needed or can be accepted by holding BLAST# de-asserted at the end of the second clock. Simultaneously, the external system indicates its preparedness for a burst by asserting BRDY# and de-asserting RDY#. The BRDY# input has the same effect as RDY#; it indicates that the external system has presented valid readable data or has accepted written data, and that the next transfer in the cycle can begin.

While BLAST# is de-asserted at the end of the second clock in non-cacheable bursts, the state of BLAST# should not be used by external logic to determine whether the current burst is being cached. The de-assertion of the signal is governed by the state of other signals, such as KEN#.

Thereafter, ADS# is no longer asserted. The addresses change for each data transfer, after BRDY# is returned for the prior transfer. A4-A31 change only at the beginning of the burst cycle, but A2-A3 and the byte enables signals change at the beginning of each data transfer within the burst cycle.

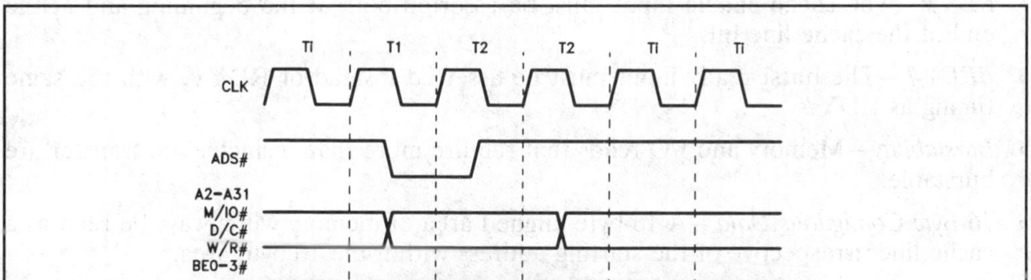

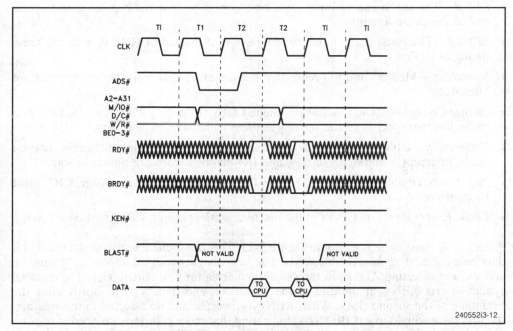

Figure 3-12. Non-Cacheable Burst Cycle

For non-cacheable bursts, addresses will always increment after each data item is returned. (This is not necessarily true for cacheable bursts, as described later in Section 3.2.2.5.) In Figure 3-12, for example, two doublewords are sequentially addressed. BLAST# behaves exactly as it does in non-burst cycles. It is de-asserted at the end of the second clock in the first data transfer, indicating that more transfers are needed to complete the data transfers in the bus cycle. In the last transfer, BLAST# is asserted, indicating that the end of the cycle will coincide with the next BRDY#.

For transfers which the processor cannot burst (interrupt acknowledge and all write cycles that use the full 32-bit data bus width), the assertion of BRDY# has an effect identical to RDY#. BRDY# is ignored if RDY# is returned in the same clock. Memory areas that cannot perform bursting must terminate cycles with RDY#. If RDY# is returned at any time during a burst cycle, bursting will stop and, if BLAST# is not asserted (indicating that more transfers are needed to complete the cycle), the processor will continue with non-burst transfers until all the data has been transferred.

3.2.2.2 CACHEABLE BURSTS

Cacheable burst cycles are the most important data transfer method for high-performance systems. They are the fastest method for filling internal cache lines, the internal cache is the processor's fastest source of read data, and reading data is one of the processor's most time-consuming tasks.

To use cacheable burst cycles, these conditions for both burstability and cacheability must be met:

- *KEN#*—The cache enable input must be asserted both at the beginning and at the end of the cache line fill.
- *BRDY#*—The burst ready input must be asserted instead of RDY#, with the same timing as RDY#.
- *Burstability*—Memory and I/O reads that require more than a single data transfer are burstable.
- *16-Byte Contiguous Data*—A 16-byte aligned area of memory will always be read as a cache line, irrespective of the starting address within the 16-byte area.
- *Cacheability*—Only memory reads and instruction prefetches are cacheable. Locked reads, interrupt acknowledge cycles, and I/O-mapped reads are not cacheable.
- *Page Cache Disable Bit*—The PCD bit in the page directory base register, CR3, must be clear (zero).
- *Cache Enable Bit*—The CE bit in the machine status register, CR0, must be set (one).

A cacheable burst cycle is shown in Figure 3-13. This is a cache line fill on the full 32-bit data bus; it transfers four doublewords. The burst begins with the processor driving an address and asserting ADS#, in the same manner as for non-burst cycles. The external system asserts KEN# at the end of the first clock and de-asserts it shortly after the beginning of the second clock. When KEN# is asserted and de-asserted in this manner, the processor will de-assert BLAST#, indicating that more transfers are needed to complete the cycle. The processor will then attempt to read all four doublewords. At the end

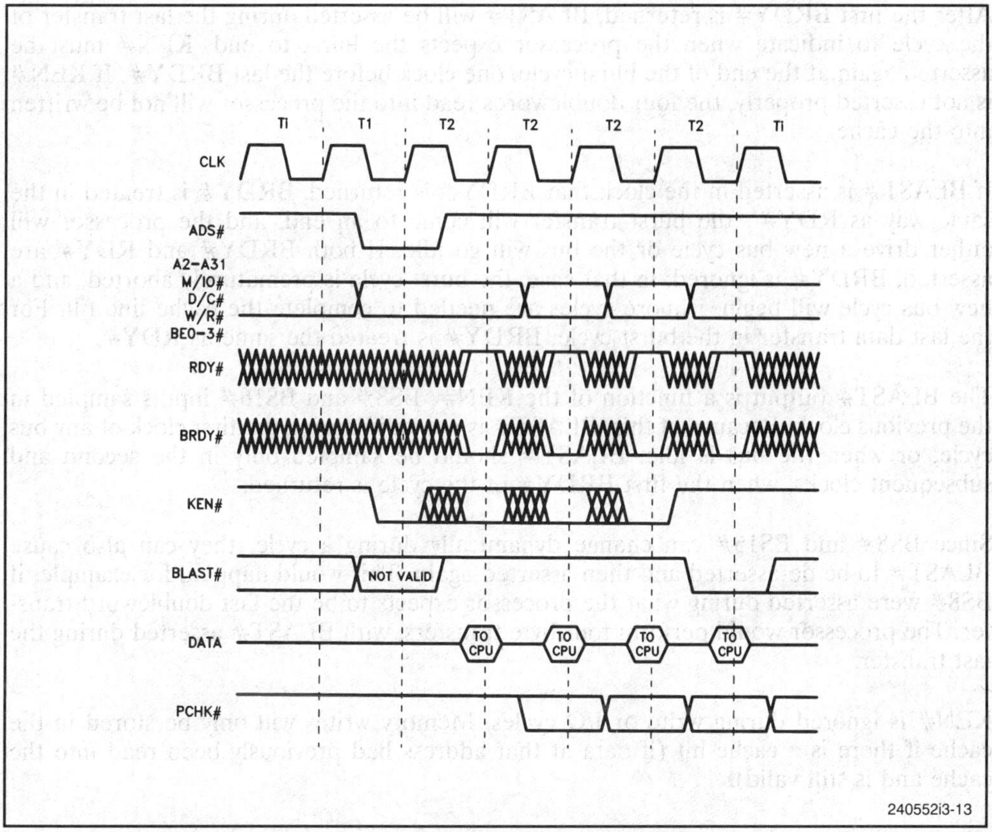

Figure 3-13. Cacheable Burst Cycle

of the second clock, the external system strobes in the first doubleword and indicates its preparedness for a burst by asserting BRDY# and de-asserting RDY#. BRDY# is sampled in each clock and, if asserted, the data will be strobed into the processor.

The last three doublewords are transferred without ADS# being asserted; however, addresses will change with each transfer to reflect the next item of data expected by the processor. For the first transfer in the cache line fill, the processor expects valid data across its entire data bus. During this first transfer, the BE0#-BE3# byte-enable outputs (although valid) should be ignored and the external system should supply valid data as if BE0#-BE3# were all asserted. The data expected is that addressed by the A2-A31 signals. The byte-enable signals for all subsequent cycles in the cache line fill can then be used normally. Addresses will always fall within the same 16-byte aligned area, corresponding to an internal cache line. Such an area begins at location xxxxxxx0 and ends at location xxxxxxxF. Given the first address in the burst, external hardware can easily calculate the addresses of subsequent transfers in advance. The sequence of addresses depends on the first address sent out, as described below in Section 3.2.2.5.

After the first BRDY# is returned, BLAST# will be asserted during the last transfer of the cycle to indicate when the processor expects the burst to end. KEN# must be asserted again at the end of the burst cycle, one clock before the last BRDY#. If KEN# is not asserted properly, the four doublewords read into the processor will not be written into the cache.

If BLAST# is asserted in the clock that BRDY# is returned, BRDY# is treated in the same way as RDY#'; the burst transfer will come to an end, and the processor will either drive a new bus cycle or the bus will go idle. If both BRDY# and RDY# are asserted, BRDY# is ignored; in that case, the burst cycle is prematurely aborted, and a new bus cycle will begin, if more cycles are needed to complete the cache line fill. For the last data transfer in the burst cycle, BRDY# is treated the same as RDY#.

The BLAST# output is a function of the KEN#, BS8# and BS16# inputs sampled in the previous clock. Because of this, BLAST# is not valid during the first clock of any bus cycle, or when the bus is idle. BLAST# should be sampled only in the second and subsequent clocks, when the first BRDY# of the cycle is returned.

Since BS8# and BS16# can change dynamically during a cycle, they can also cause BLAST# to be de-asserted and then asserted again. This would happen, for example, if BS8# were asserted during what the processor expects to be the last doubleword transfer. The processor would perform four byte transfers, with BLAST# asserted during the last transfer.

KEN# is ignored during write or I/O cycles. Memory writes will only be stored in the cache if there is a cache hit (if data at that address had previously been read into the cache and is still valid).

3.2.2.3 ADDING WAIT STATES

Burst cycles need not return data on each clock. The processor will only strobe burst data in when BRDY# is asserted. Thus, keeping BRDY# de-asserted will delay the transfer by adding wait states. This type of cycle, where each data transfer takes two clocks, is shown in Figure 3-14.

3.2.2.4 CHANGING KEN# DURING A CACHEABLE CYCLE

KEN# can change several times at the beginning of a burst cycle, as long as it settles in the clock before BRDY# or RDY# is asserted. This is shown in Figure 3-15, in which wait states are added. The timing of BLAST# follows that of KEN# by one clock. In the first clock of this example, KEN# is asserted by the external system and the processor responds by de-asserting BLAST# in the next clock. In the second clock, KEN# is de-asserted and, since neither BRDY# (for cacheable burst cycles) nor RDY# (for cacheable non-burst cycles) are asserted, the cycle is converted back to a single-transfer cycle. The processor responds by asserting BLAST# in the next clock. Finally, in the third clock, KEN# is asserted again, converting the cycle back to a cache line fill, and BLAST# is de-asserted in the next clock. BRDY# or RDY# is asserted in the fourth clock, thereby starting the cache line fill.

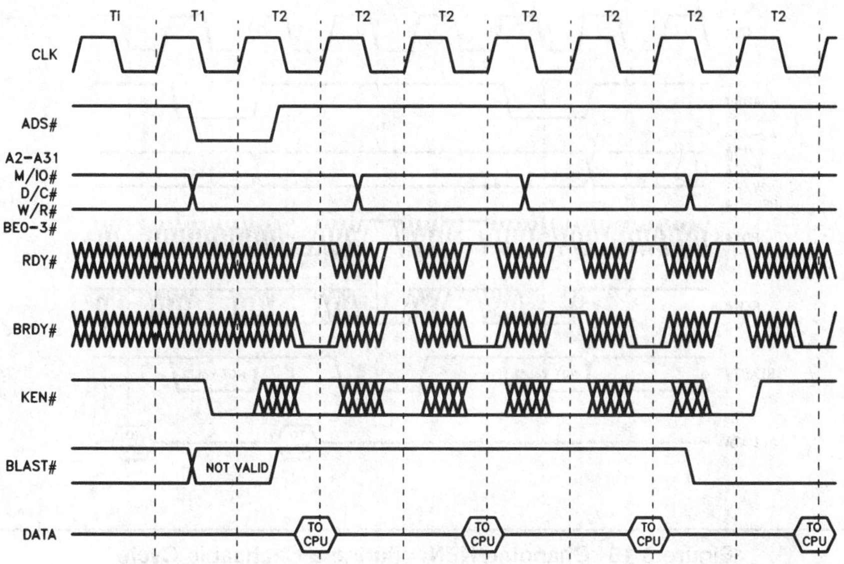

Figure 3-14. Slow Cacheable Burst Cycle

3.2.2.5 DATA ALIGNMENT AND SEQUENCING

The processor presents each request for data in an order determined by the first address in the transfer, as shown in Table 3-9. The sequence accommodates either 64-bit or 32-bit buses and applies to all burst cycles, regardless of whether their purpose is to fill a cache line, do a 64-bit read, or do a 16-byte instruction prefetch. Given the current address, external logic can easily calculate in advance the addresses of subsequent transfers.

Data transferred with burst cycles is expected on the same data signals as for non-burst cycles. Data transfers can take place using 8- or 16-bit bus sizes. When either of these smaller bus sizes is used, more transfers are needed to complete operations than would be needed on the full 32-bit bus. If either BS8# or BS16# is asserted, the processor completes the transfer of the current doubleword before proceeding to the next. Within each doubleword, the high-order word is transferred first. Within each word, the high-order byte is transferred first. For example, a cacheable cycle beginning at address 104 while BS16# is asserted would generate a burst address sequence of 104, 106, 100, 102, 10C, 10E, 108, 10A. This is shown in Figure 3-16.

If either BS8# or BS16# is asserted during a cacheable burst cycle, the burst could stretch to as many as 16 data transfers (16 bytes on an 8-bit bus). The sequencing of addresses and the location of data on the data bus are different in this case. For the first

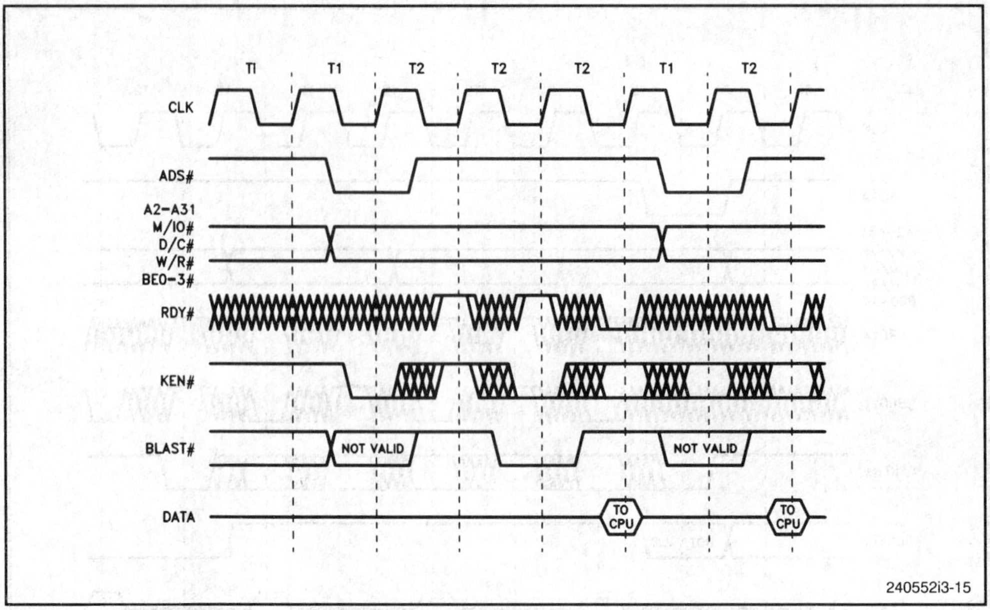

Figure 3-15. Changing KEN# during a Cacheable Cycle

Table 3-9. Burst Address Sequencing

First Address	Second Address	Third Address	Fourth Address
0	4	8	C
4	0	C	8
8	C	0	4
C	8	4	0

transfer in the cache line fill, the processor expects valid data across its entire data bus. The byte-enable outputs, BE0#-BE3#, should be ignored and the external system should supply valid data as if BE0#-BE3# were all asserted. Both BS8# and BS16# are sampled during the clock before each BRDY# is returned. Thus, the bus size inputs should be held asserted throughout the entire burst, unless the addressed device can dynamically alter its bus size during the cycle.

3.2.2.6 INSTRUCTION PREFETCH

Instruction prefetches are burstable data transfers which read, in advance of execution, an aligned block of 16 bytes of instructions into the processor's internal cache and instruction prefetch units. The read is done with a burst transfer from sequentially higher addresses. The instruction prefetch unit generates the addresses. Instruction prefetch cycles have a unique encoding of the M/IO#, D/C# and W/R# signals, as shown in Table 3-4.

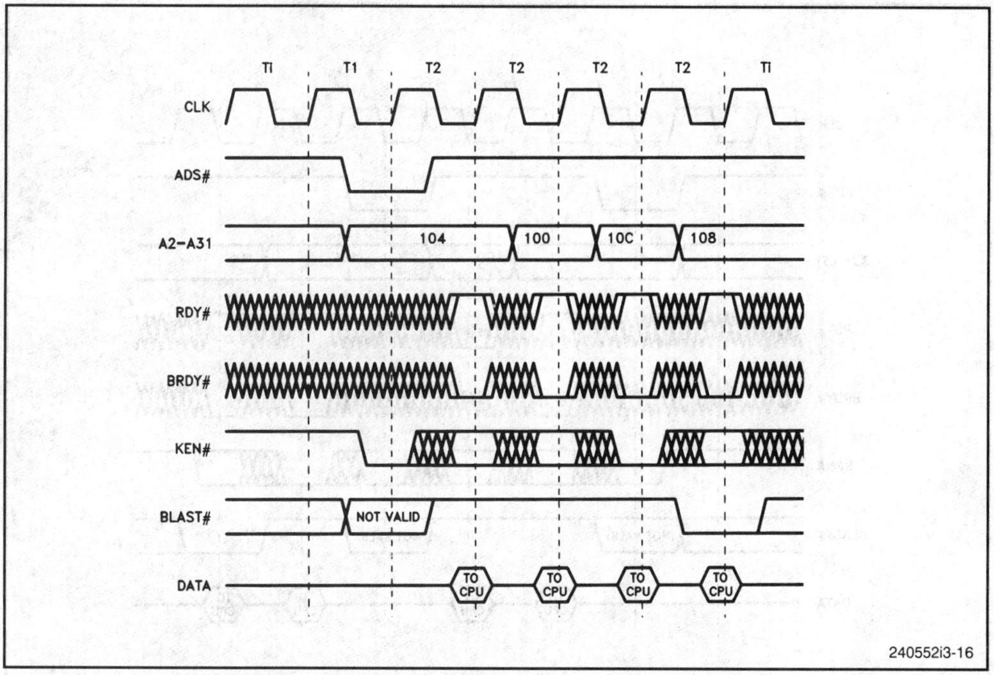

Figure 3-16. Burst-Cycle Order of Addressing

3.2.2.7 INTERRUPTED BURSTS

Some memory systems may not be able to respond with burst cycles in the address sequence described in the previous section. To support such systems, the burst cycle may be interrupted by asserting RDY# instead of BRDY#. After being interrupted, the processor will automatically generate another normal burst cycle to complete the transfers required. The external system can respond to an interrupted burst cycle with another burst cycle.

Figure 3-17 shows a cacheable burst cycle being interrupted and converted to two burst cycles. After RDY# is asserted, the processor immediately asserts ADS# to initiate a new burst cycle. BLAST# is de-asserted one clock after ADS# begins in the second burst cycle, indicating that the transfer is not complete. KEN# need not be asserted in the first transfer of the second burst cycle, after the interruption. The operation will be recognized as a cache line fill due to the assertion of KEN# during the burst preceding the interrupt. The second part of the operation can itself be a burst.

Within the normal limits of burst transfers, there is no restriction on the number of transfers that must be made with BRDY# before RDY# is asserted. If RDY# is asserted and the processor indicates that the number of transfers required has not yet been reached by continuing to de-assert BLAST#, then the processor immediately generates non-burst cycles using ADS# to complete the transfers.

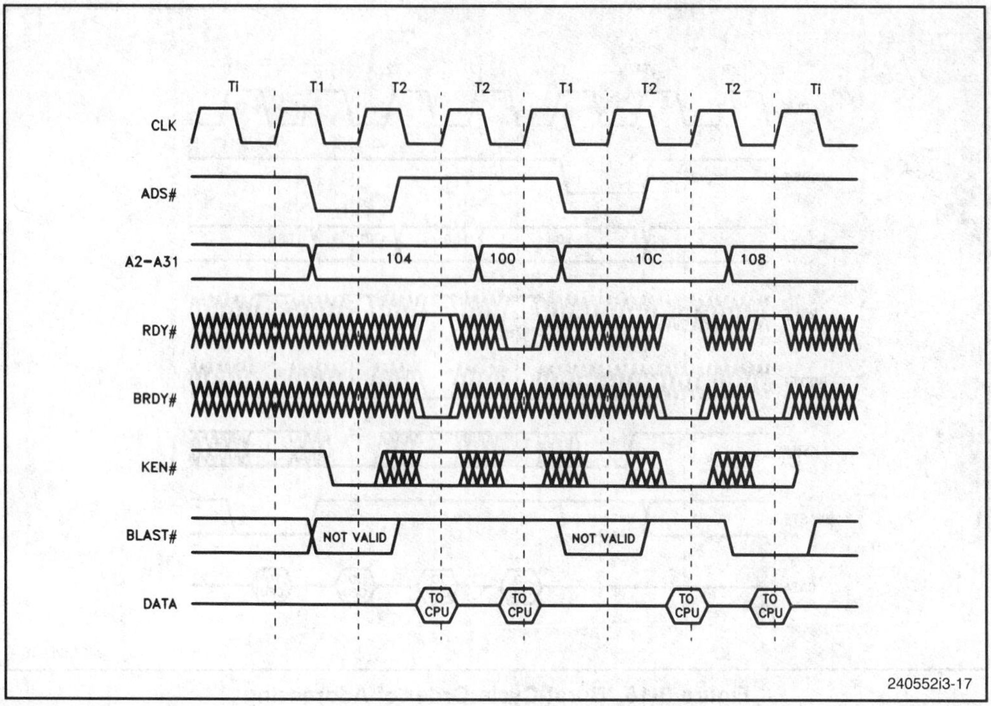

Figure 3-17. Interrupted Burst Cycle, Example #1

The order in which the processor addresses data during an interrupted burst cycle is determined by Table 3-9. Mixing RDY# and BRDY# does not change this order. Figure 3-18 shows such an example, where the order of addresses may not be obvious. The processor initially requests and receives the data at address 104. Then, the system asserts RDY# instead of BRDY#. The processor begins a non-burst cycle by strobing address 100 with the ADS# signal. If BRDY# is asserted during the next clock, the processor will expect address 10C to follow. The correct order is therefore determined by the address during the first transfer of the entire operation. This may not be the same as the address for the first transfer of the burst.

3.2.2.8 IDENTIFYING THE FIRST TRANSFER OF A CACHEABLE CYCLE

The byte-enables signals (BE0#-BE3#) are valid in any cycle or transfer except the first transfer of a cacheable cycle. During such a transfer, BE0#-BE3# should be ignored and the external system should supply valid data as if BE0#-BE3# were all asserted.

To determine the first transfer of a cacheable cycle, sample BLAST#, RDY#, and BRDY#. If BLAST# is asserted with the immediately preceding RDY# or BRDY#, then the next cacheable transfer will be the first transfer of a cacheable cycle.

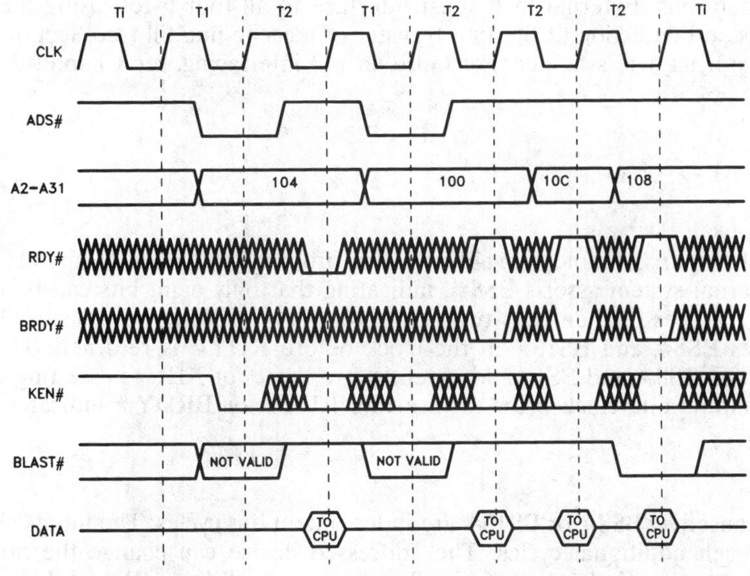

Figure 3-18. Interrupted Burst Cycle, Example #2

3.2.3 Bus Size

Two sets of signals work together to control the flow of cycles across 8- and 16-bit data buses:

- *Bus Size*—The BS8# and BS16# inputs.
- *Byte Enables*—The BE0#-BE3# outputs.

The bus-size inputs are useful for interfacing to I/O or ROM. The BS8# and BS16# inputs allow the external system to specify, on a cycle-by-cycle basis, whether the external device being addressed can supply 8 or 16 bits of data. BS8# and BS16#, together with the address of data being accessed, control the sequence in which the BE0#-BE3# outputs are driven. BE0#-BE3# tell the external device which of the bytes on the full 32-bit data bus are valid in any cycle or transfer. The only exception to this is in the first transfer of a cacheable read cycle (cache line fill), when BE0#-BE3# should be ignored and the external system should supply valid data as if BE0#-BE3# were all asserted.

Without BS8# or BS16# asserted, the data bus size is 32 bits. BS8# and BS16# can be used in non-burst or burst cycles. If both BS8# and BS16# are asserted, only BS8# will be recognized. Asserting BS8# or BS16# can cause the processor to run additional bus cycles to complete a transfer.

This interface to smaller bus sizes is quite different from that used in the 386 processor. Unlike the 386 processor, the i486 processor expects to find data on all four addressed bytes of the data bus. External logic must interface to all four bytes, using the BE0#-BE3# outputs and detection of the first transfer of a cache line fill (see Section 3.2.2.8) to steer the external byte swapper. For more on I/O interfacing, see Chapter 7.

3.2.3.1 TIMING

Figure 3-19 shows an example using BS8#. The processor requests 24 bits of information. The external system asserts BS8#, indicating that only eight bits can be supplied per cycle. The processor then runs two extra cycles to complete the transfer. The processor samples BS8# and BS16# in the clock before RDY# is returned. The timing requirements for BS8# and BS16# are identical to those for KEN#; asserting either of the bus-size inputs one clock prior to asserting RDY# or BRDY# indicates the bus width.

Extra cycles caused by BS8# or BS16# are independent bus cycles. The inputs should be asserted for each additional cycles. The addressed device can change the number of bytes it returns on a cycle-by-cycle basis. The processor will keep BLAST# de-asserted until the last cycle of the transfer.

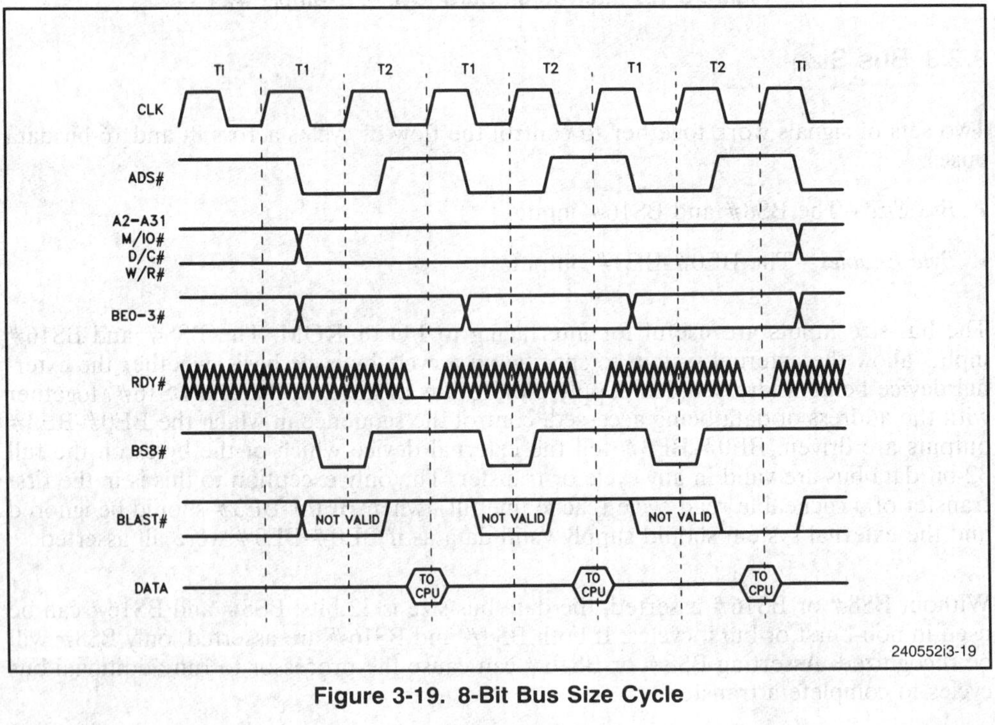

Figure 3-19. 8-Bit Bus Size Cycle

3.2.3.2 DATA ALIGNMENT

Because the processor operates on only bytes, words, and doublewords, certain combinations of BE0#-BE3# are never produced. For example, a bus cycle is never performed with only BE0# and BE2# active; such a transfer would be an operation on two non-contiguous bytes at the same time. A single 3-byte transfer will never occur, but a 3-byte address or data transfer followed or preceded by a 1-byte transfer can occur for misaligned doubleword transfers.

The processor does not automatically align data on the processor bus from 16-bit or 8-bit buses. Systems with 16- or 8-bit devices must use external logic to align their bytes on the processor bus, as described in Chapter 7. Such devices are usually I/O, where the extra delay is not a significant factor in overall performance.

While BS8# and BS16# are sampled every clock, only the state sampled in the clock prior to the assertion of RDY# or BRDY# is used. If memory is running with no wait states, the bus size inputs must be asserted in the same clock as the ADS# output. The bus size inputs can be driven by static logic levels only if the entire physical memory and I/O spaces use the same bus size.

3.2.3.3 MULTIPLE-CYCLE SEQUENCES

A single bus cycle may be converted to multiple bus cycles if the BS8# or BS16# inputs are asserted. For example, a non-burst doubleword transfer will be converted to four byte transfers if BS8# is asserted. Each of the four byte transfers will have the same value on the A2-A31 address bus. The processor will attempt to read as many bytes as possible. After the first byte of a doubleword is read, the processor will enable the three remaining bytes on the second cycle. If BS8# is again asserted, the processor enables the two remaining bytes on the third cycle. If BS16# is asserted in place of BS8#, the two remaining bytes will be read during the third cycle, and the doubleword transfer will be complete.

Table 3-10 shows the states of the byte-enable signals for the first and second bus cycles of a multiple-cycle sequence in which either BS8# or BS16# are asserted.

3.2.3.4 CACHEABLE MEMORY READS

On small bus sizes, only memory reads can be cached, not I/O reads. In any cacheable memory read, BE0#-BE3#, although valid, should be ignored during the first transfer of a cacheable cycle. When a normal read cycle is promoted to a cacheable cycle by the assertion of KEN#, the entire doubleword addressed by A2-A31 is read by the processor, even though only a few bytes may have been enabled. If an 8-bit bus size is selected, the processor reads the lowest byte of this doubleword in the first cycle of the cache line fill, even though the original bus cycle might not have selected this byte for reading. If a 16-bit bus size is selected, the processor reads the low word. On the second and following transfers of the cache line fill, the BE0#-BE3# outputs correctly reflect which bytes the processor expects.

Table 3-10. Byte-Enable Signals With BS8# and BS16#

First Cycle				Second Cycle, BS8#				Second Cycle, BS16#			
BE3#	BE2#	BE1#	BE0#	BE3#	BE2#	BE1#	BE0#	BE3#	BE2#	BE1#	BE0#
1	1	1	0	none	none	none	none	none	none	none	none
1	1	0	0	1	1	0	1	none	none	none	none
1	0	0	0	1	0	0	1	1	0	1	1
0	0	0	0	0	0	0	1	0	0	1	1
1	1	0	1	none	none	none	none	none	none	none	none
1	0	0	1	1	0	1	1	1	0	1	1
0	0	0	1	0	0	1	1	0	0	1	1
1	0	1	1	none	none	none	none	none	none	none	none
0	0	1	1	0	1	1	1	none	none	none	none
0	1	1	1	none	none	none	none	none	none	none	none

The processor might not use all of the enabled bytes when the BS8# or BS16# inputs are asserted. Table 3-11 shows which bit positions are used by the processor for all of the valid combinations of the byte-enable signals and for all bus sizes. The implied rule is: when multiple bytes are enabled, return only the lowest byte(s) that the device on the data bus can provide.

3.2.3.5 BURST CYCLES

Burst read cycles can be returned on 8- or 16- bit data buses. In this case, the burst cycle could stretch to 16 transfers (16 bytes in a cache line fill). The sequencing of addresses and data is the same as for non-burst cycles. A single 32-bit non-cacheable processor

Table 3-11. Data Bus Signals and Bus Size

BE3#	BE2#	BE1#	BE0#	No selects (32-Bit Bus)	BS16# (16-Bit Bus)	BS8# (8-Bit Bus)
1	1	1	0	D0-D7	D0-D7	D0-D7
1	1	0	0	D0-D15	D0-D15	D0-D7
1	0	0	0	D0-D23	D0-D15	D0-D7
0	0	0	0	D0-D31	D0-D15	D0-D7
1	1	0	1	D8-D15	D8-D15	D8-D15
1	0	0	1	D8-D23	D8-D15	D8-D15
0	0	0	1	D8-D31	D8-D15	D8-D15
1	0	1	1	D16-D23	D16-D23	D16-D23
0	0	1	1	D16-D31	D16-D31	D16-D23
0	1	1	1	D24-D31	D24-D31	D24-D31

read or write could be done in four 8-bit burst cycles. An example of a burst write is shown in Figure 3-20. Burst writes can occur only if BS8# or BS16# is asserted.

When running a burst cycle, the processor samples BS8# and BS16# in the clock before each BRDY# is returned. Thus, the bus size inputs should be driven active throughout the entire burst, unless the addressed device can change the number of bytes returned in each cycle.

3.2.3.6 DECODING A0, A1 AND BHE#

If the system needs the low-order addresses A0-A1 and a byte-high enable BHE#, these can be generated from the byte-enable outputs, as shown in Table 3-12. Such signals may be necessary in systems using earlier Intel processors.

In Table 3-12, the check marks (✔) indicate all combinations of the byte enable signals that are generated for cache line fills. As described earlier for cacheable cycles, the processor expects valid data across its entire 32-bit data bus when a cycle is first converted to a cache line fill. Thus, for the first transfer in a cache line fill, the byte-enable outputs (BE0#-BE3#) should be ignored and the memory or I/O system should supply valid data as if BE0#-BE3# were all asserted. The data expected is that addressed by

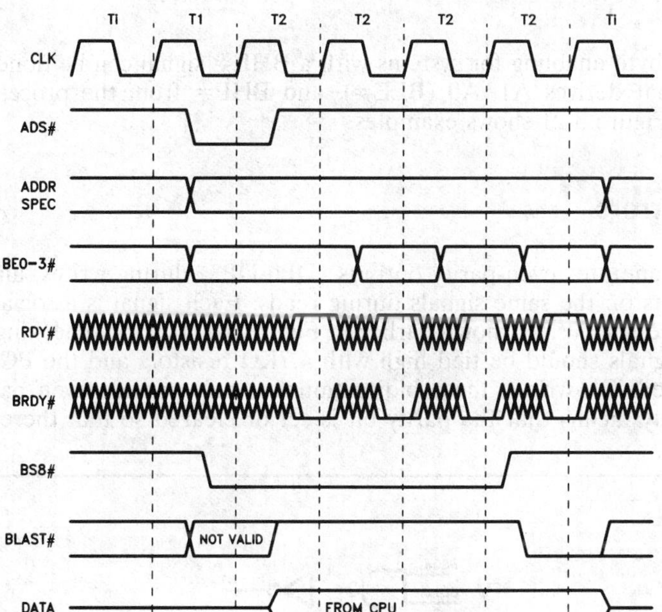

Figure 3-20. Burst Write on 8-Bit Bus

Table 3-12. Decoding A1, A0 (BLE#), and BHE# from Byte-Enables

	Processor Outputs				First Transfer in a Cache Line Fill			Any Other Transfer		
	BE3#	BE2#	BE1#	BE0#	A1	A0	BHE#	A1	A0	BHE#
	1	1	1	0	–	–	–	0	0	1
	1	1	0	0	–	–	–	0	0	0
	1	0	0	0	–	–	–	0	0	0
✓	0	0	0	0	0	0	0	0	0	0
	1	1	0	1	–	–	–	1	0	0
	1	0	0	1	–	–	–	1	0	0
✓	0	0	0	1	0	0	0	1	0	0
	1	0	1	1	–	–	–	0	1	1
✓	0	0	1	1	0	0	0	0	1	0
✓	0	1	1	1	0	0	0	1	1	0

✓ Marks all combinations of byte enable signals that will be generated after a cycle has been converted to a cache line fill.

the A2-A31 signals. The processor will then generate the appropriate byte-enable signals for all subsequent cycles in the cache line fill. This is true for both non-burst and burst cache line fills.

Addressing and byte enabling for systems with a BHE# signal can be done with simple external logic that derives A1, A0 (BLE#), and BHE# from the processor's BE0#-BE3# outputs. Figure 3-21 shows examples.

3.2.4 Parity Errors

The processor generates even-parity outputs (DP0-DP3) during writes, and checks for even-parity inputs on the same signals during reads. Each signal is associated with one byte on the processor bus, as shown earlier in Figure 3-2. If parity-checking is not used, each of these signals should be tied high with 4.7KΩ resistors and the PCHK# output should be ignored. On writes, these bidirectional signals provide even parity for each byte. (Even parity means that the parity bit is set or cleared so that there are an even

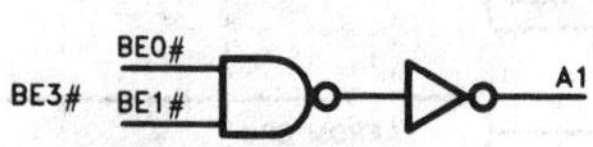

240552i3-21

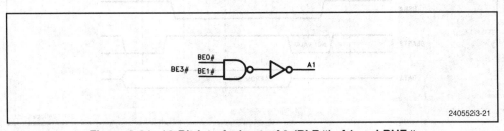

Figure 3-21. 16-Bit Interfacing to A0 (BLE#), A1 and BHE#

number of high bits in the 9 byte-plus-parity bits.) The timing of these signals is the same as the timing of the data bus. Additional memory required for parity may be implemented by widening the memory array from 32 bits to 36 bits, but byte addressability must be maintained.

When the processor detects odd parity during a read, it asserts the PCHK# output. When either the BS8# or BS16# input is asserted, parity is checked only for the enabled bytes. Parity is valid on all bytes which are selected by the byte-enable outputs BE0#-BE3#, except during the first transfer of a cache line fill, in which case parity is valid on all four bytes of the full 32-bit data bus.

PCHK# is valid only during the clock immediately following the clock in which RDY# is returned, as shown earlier in Figure 3-8. PCHK# is never floated and is de-asserted at all times other than the clock following RDY#. External logic must latch parity errors, if the information is to be used; the processor continues program execution when a parity error occurs.

A parity error is usually considered to be an unrecoverable condition, since the data or instruction which is read is invalid. In these cases, a program which receives a parity error should be terminated. Data read into the internal cache should be invalidated or the entire cache must be flushed with the FLUSH# input. If the operating system receives a parity error, the system may need to be shut down and restarted. The PCHK# output is normally fed back to the processor to cause an interrupt and initiate recovery or shutdown procedures.

If I/O ports do not support parity, the PCHK# output must be masked by a signal which indicates access to an I/O port. This is true whether I/O-mapped or memory-mapped I/O is used. The PCHK# signal is masked internally to prevent parity errors from being reported for interrupt-acknowledge cycles.

3.3 BUS CONTROL

The bus control signals and special cycles govern access to the bus and handle extraordinary conditions, like interrupts and reset. The controls are of two types:

- *Signals and special bus cycles used in all systems:*
  Reset (RESET).
  Interrupts (INTR and NMI).
  Halt and Shutdown (special bus cycles).

- *Signals used only in systems with more than one bus master:*
  Bus Hold (HOLD).
  Bus Lock (LOCK#).
  Bus Pseudo-Lock (PLOCK#).
  Bus Backoff (BOFF#).

3.3.1 RESET

The RESET input starts or restarts the processor. During reset, various tests can be invoked. The *i486™ Microprocessor Data Sheet* gives complete information on reset and testing. The discussion below is only an overview of how reset uses or affects the signals on the processor bus.

When the processor detects a low-to-high transition on RESET, it terminates all activities. When RESET goes low again, the processor's registers are initialized to a known internal state, and the processor begins reading instructions from the reset address. The RESET input is normally provided by the external clock generator, thereby ensuring a stable reset signal common to the entire system.

If only the RESET input is asserted, only the processor's non-floating-point states will be initialized. The internal floating-point registers are undefined after RESET, with one exception: if both Vcc and CLK are kept within specification during the entire cycle in which RESET is asserted, the registers will be in the same state as they were on the rising edge of RESET.

With RESET asserted, testing options are specified by asserting one or more of the following three inputs, which are sampled on the falling (inactive) edge of RESET:

- *AHOLD*—If this input is asserted while RESET is asserted, the built-in self test (BIST) will be invoked, and all processor states, both floating-point and non-floating-point, will be initialized. Without the assertion of AHOLD, only the processor's non-floating-point states will be initialized. No bus cycles will be run until the BIST is finished, although the bus signals will be driven.

- *A20M#*—This signal must be sampled asserted while RESET is asserted.

- *FLUSH#*—If this input is asserted while RESET is asserted, the high-impedance (float) test mode will be invoked. All outputs and bidirectional signals are floated, including signals normally driven during a hold (HLDA, BREQ, FERR# and PCHK#). After RESET is de-asserted, the processor bus enters the idle state, Ti. Outputs after RESET are shown in Table 3-13.

RESET must be kept asserted for the time shown in the data sheet. Upon power-up, RESET must be held asserted for the specified period after Vcc and CLK stabilize to allow the processor's internal clock generator to synchronize with CLK.

Table 3-13. Processor Outputs after RESET

State	Signals
High	LOCK#, ADS#, PCHK#
Low	HLDA, BREQ
High Impedance	D0-D31, DP0-DP3
Undefined	A2-A31, BE0#-BE3#, W/R#, M/IO#, D/C#, PLOCK#, BLAST#, PCD, PWT , FERR#

Before its first instruction fetch, the processor makes no requests for the bus and will relinquish bus control if it receives a HOLD request. INTR and NMI are not recognized before the first instruction fetch. Although maskable interrupts are disabled, it is not possible to disable NMI. External hardware should ensure that an NMI does not occur before the interrupt descriptor table (IDT) is built and the stack is initialized.

3.3.2 Interrupts

Interrupt requests are of three types: maskable hardware interrupts (INTR), non-maskable hardware interrupts (NMI), and software interrupts (the INT instruction or software exceptions). INTR and NMI are asynchronous to the clock. The processor will not recognize an interrupt during a reset operation, and it will recognize only a single NMI during a bus hold operation. The setup and hold times for NMI and INTR de-assertion and subsequent assertion are given in the *i486™ Microprocessor Data Sheet*. For details on the algorithmic response to interrupts and on the INT instruction, see the *i486™ Processor Programmer's Reference Manual.*

To service an interrupt, the processor completes its execution of the current instruction, and saves its current state on the stack, along with task information if a task switch is required. The processor then services the interrupt by transferring execution to one of the 256 possible interrupt service routines defined in software. Entry-point descriptors to the service routines are stored in an interrupt descriptor table (IDT) in memory. Not all 256 entry-point descriptors are available for general use; the first 32 are reserved by Intel. To access a particular service routine, the processor needs an interrupt vector, or index number, to the IDT location that contains the corresponding entry-point descriptor. The source of the interrupt vector depends on the type of interrupt. Only INTR interrupts cause the processor to query external hardware for the interrupt vector; NMI interrupts always use same vector, and software interrupts specify the vector as an operand within the instruction or exception.

3.3.2.1 NON-MASKABLE INTERRUPTS

Assertion of the NMI input typically indicates a catastrophic event which requires immediate attention, such as imminent power loss, bus-transfer parity error, or memory-data parity error. The input has a two-clock-cycle synchronizer to ensure stability. NMI is edge-triggered; the rising edge of the signal, after internal synchronization with the clock, is used to generate the interrupt request. NMI must first be de-asserted for at least two clocks and then asserted. The request need not remain active until the interrupt is serviced; NMI need only be active for a single clock, if it meets the setup and hold requirements. NMI will also operate properly if it is held active for an arbitrary number of clocks. In order for a second non-maskable interrupt to be latched while an earlier one is being serviced, the NMI input must again be de-asserted for at least two clocks before its second assertion. Only one NMI can be latched and held pending; all others will be lost.

Interrupt acknowledgement cycles are not performed to obtain the interrupt vector. Instead, a recognized NMI always causes the processor to execute the service routine referenced by the entry-point descriptor at location 2 in the interrupt descriptor table.

To prevent recursive NMI calls, NMI is internally masked whenever the NMI routine is entered, until the IRET instruction is executed. During NMI interrupts in the Real-Address Mode, the processor disables INTR requests, although these can be re-enabled in the service routine. In Protected Mode, the disabling of INTR requests depends on the gate in location 2 of the IDT.

3.3.2.2 MASKABLE INTERRUPTS

Unlike NMI, the INTR input is level-sensitive; INTR must be held asserted until the processor services the interrupt. Like NMI, the INTR input has a two-clock-cycle synchronizer to ensure stability. A valid INTR input will be seen by the internal instruction execution unit two clocks after it appears at the pin. INTR is sampled at the beginning of every instruction.

INTR must first be de-asserted and then asserted continuously until it is acknowledged. Setup and hold times are given in the data sheet. The interrupt will be serviced, unless the signal is masked by the IF (bit 9) flag in the EFLAGS register. This flag is cleared automatically when an interrupt operation is initiated; it prevents successive interrupts from arriving too closely. INTR will be ignored for as long as the flag is clear. The flag should be set by software at an appropriate point in the interrupt service routine.

The processor acknowledges INTR by performing two locked read cycles which request external logic to provide the interrupt vector. The entire interrupt-acknowledgement operation is shown in Figure 3-22. Interrupt-acknowledge transfers are the same as normal data transfers, except for the A2 signal. For interrupt acknowledgement, the principal signal configuration is:

- *ADS#*—driven low to indicate the start of each transfer.
- *M/IO#, D/C#, W/R#*—driven low to indicate interrupt acknowledgement.
- *LOCK#*—driven low to block any hold operations during both transfers.
- *A31-A3 and BE0#*—driven low during both transfers.
- *A2*—driven high during the first transfer and low during the second.
- *BE3#, BE2# and BE1#*—driven high during both transfers.

During the first read cycle shown in Figure 3-22, all data on the bus is ignored. As with normal transfers, RDY# must be returned to the processor to terminate the cycle. BRDY# can also be returned, although interrupt acknowledgement cycles are not burstable. The processor then inserts four idle clocks before starting the second read cycle. During the second read, the data on the lowest byte of the data bus (D7-D0) is assumed to be the interrupt vector. Wait states can be added by withholding RDY#.

Maskable interrupts can be nested until the stack overflows. Nesting will occur if an interrupt is recognized and the interrupt flag is set while a previous interrupt operation has not yet completed. The latest interrupt to be recognized will be the first one serviced. If both NMI and INTR are recognized simultaneously, NMI takes precedence.

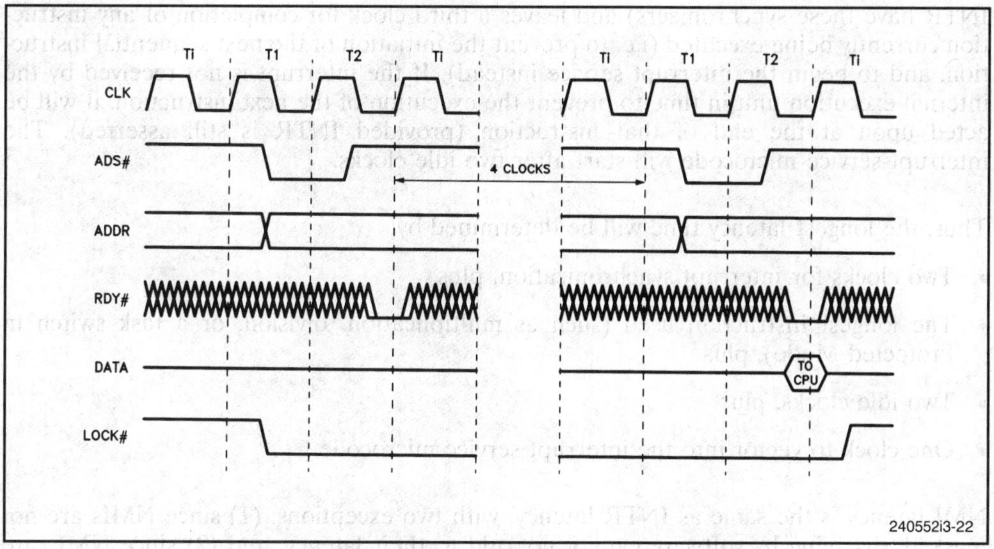

Figure 3-22. Interrupt Acknowledgement Timing

3.3.2.3 INTERRUPT LATENCY

The time that elapses before an interrupt request is serviced (interrupt latency) varies according to the following factors:

- *NMI*—If a non-maskable interrupt is being serviced, another incoming NMI will not be serviced until the processor executes an IRET instruction.
- *INTR*—If INTR interrupts are masked, they will not be serviced until they are re-enabled.
- *Instruction Execution*—If the processor is currently executing an instruction, the instruction will usually be completed. Interrupts are serviced only at instruction boundaries, except that (1) iterated string instructions can be interrupted at iteration boundaries, and (2) transcendental floating-point instructions can be interrupted at various points.
- *Register Loads and Saves*—Interrupts are not serviced when the contents of registers are being saved. During task switching, registers must be saved and restored before interrupts are recognized. If an instruction loads the stack segment register or sets the interrupt flag, interrupts are not processed until after the next instruction.

The internal instruction execution unit will only act on an NMI or INTR interrupt at instruction boundaries or (in the case of string-move instructions) at instruction-iteration boundaries. The longest latency can be expected when a request is received during execution of a long instruction, such as multiplication.

For an interrupt to be acknowledged at the end of a specific instruction, the interrupt must be asserted at least three clocks before the end of the instruction execution. This allows the interrupt to pass through the two-clock-cycle synchronizer (both NMI and

INTR have these synchronizers) and leaves a third clock for completion of any instruction currently being executed (i.e. to prevent the initiation of the next sequential instruction, and to begin the interrupt service instead). If the interrupt is not received by the internal execution unit in time to prevent the execution of the next instruction, it will be acted upon at the end of that instruction (provided INTR is still asserted). The interrupt-service microcode will start after two idle clocks.

Thus, the longest latency time will be determined by:

- Two clocks for interrupt synchronization, plus
- The longest instruction used (such as multiplication, division, or a task switch in Protected Mode), plus
- Two idle clocks, plus
- One clock to vector into the interrupt service microcode.

NMI latency is the same as INTR latency, with two exceptions: (1) since NMIs are not masked, disabling by software cannot not add to their latency, and (2) since NMIs are automatically disabled whenever their interrupt service routine is executed, the length of the NMI routine itself will contribute to maximum NMI latency.

3.3.2.4 THE 8259A INTERRUPT CONTROLLER

Maskable interrupts to the processor can be handled directly by the 8259A interrupt controller. This device can coordinate the interrupt requests of up to eight devices and can be cascaded with other 8259As to handle as many as 64 devices. The 8259A is controlled by commands from the i486 processor and appears as a series of I/O ports to the processor. These ports are used to configure masks and priorities for the interrupt input signals.

When a device signals an interrupt request, the 8259A determines its priority relative to other requests, and asserts INTR to the processor. When this signal is serviced, the processor allows the 8259A sufficient recovery time to provide the 8-bit interrupt vector during the second acknowledgement cycle. System logic may be required to delay the RDY# signals during the transfers in order to comply with the minimum pulse-width requirements of the 8259A.

3.3.3 Special Bus Cycles

Special bus cycles are initiated by the processor in the same way as data transfers, except that the cycle-definition signals have the values shown in Table 3-14. One of four operations is specified by the BE0#-BE3# outputs normally used for byte enabling on the data bus. Special bus operations use the same bus-signal protocol as data transfers, including the assertion of either the RDY# or BRDY# signals to acknowledge completion of the operation.

Table 3-14. Special Bus Cycles

M/IO#	D/C#	W/R#	BE3#	BE2#	BE1#	BE0#	Operation
0	0	1	1	1	1	0	Shutdown
0	0	1	1	1	0	1	Cache Flush
0	0	1	1	0	1	1	Halt
0	0	1	0	1	1	1	Cache Write-Back and Flush

Shutdown and halt are described immediately below. The coding of the M/IO# signal is reversed from that in the 386 processor for halt and shutdown. The cache flush cycle and the cache write-back and flush cycle are discussed later in Section 3.4.

3.3.3.1 HALT

Halt occurs upon execution of a HLT instruction. The instruction can be used as a response to an unrecoverable error, such as a parity error, or to a program error. Halt can also be used to indicate that the processor has failed the built-in self test invoked on reset. The appropriate response depends on the details of system implementation.

Externally, a halt differs from a shutdown only in the resulting address-bus outputs and in the processor's ability to acknowledge a bus hold while in the halt condition. The processor will remain in the halt condition until one of three inputs is asserted:

- INTR
- NMI
- RESET

3.3.3.2 SHUTDOWN

Shutdown occurs when the processor is handling a double fault and encounters a protection fault. This indicates an error in operating-system data structures, such as task-state segment descriptors (if tasks are used for exception handling), segment descriptors, or page-table entries. It may be desirable to invoke an NMI interrupt handler to record diagnostic information.

While in shutdown mode, the processor cannot perform any bus operations. The processor will remain shut down until one of two inputs is asserted:

- NMI
- RESET

3.3.4 Bus Hold

Bus masters other than the processor take control of the bus by causing the assertion of the HOLD input. When HOLD is asserted, the processor completes the current bus operation or sequence of locked or pseudo-locked cycles, floats most of its outputs to high impedance, and asserts the HLDA acknowledgement. The bus stays in the hold state until HOLD is de-asserted. During bus hold, the processor continues operation with the information in its internal cache and instruction prefetch unit, until it needs access to the bus again; then it asserts BREQ.

Bus hold uses the same hold-acknowledge protocol found in earlier Intel 8086-family processors. The HLDA, BREQ, PCHK# and FERR# outputs are not floated and can be asserted during bus hold. The processor will recognize and respond to HOLD during reset; none of the outputs that are floated in response to HOLD are provided with internal pullup resistors. During bus hold, the AHOLD, EADS#, and BOFF# inputs are recognized. The AHOLD (address hold) input is not associated with the bus hold operation; it is used for cache invalidation, as described in Section 3.4.

The following operations are completed before a bus hold is acknowledged:

- The current bus cycle in progress (whether burst or non-burst) or the current sequence of bus cycles for which BLAST# is de-asserted in all but the last data transfer.
- Pseudo-locked cycles—i.e., multiple-cycle sequences during which PLOCK# is asserted.
- Locked cycles.

Multiple processors can be in bus hold, and an external arbitration unit can use their bus request signals to see which processors are ready to perform bus cycles.

3.3.4.1 TIMING

When HOLD# is asserted, the processor stops driving the following outputs:

- A2-A31.
- D0-D31.
- DP0-DP3.
- BE0#-BE3#.
- PWT, PCD.
- M/IO#, D/C#, and W/R#.
- LOCK#.
- PLOCK#.
- ADS#.
- BLAST#.

The processor's acknowledgement consists of floating all address and data bus signals and asserting HLDA, as shown in Figure 3-23. LOCK#, M/IO#, D/C#, W/R#, ADS#, A2-A31, BE0#-BE3# and D0-D31 are held in the high-impedance condition. Some signals such as ADS# and LOCK# may require external pull-up resistors to guarantee that they remain inactive during transitions between bus masters.

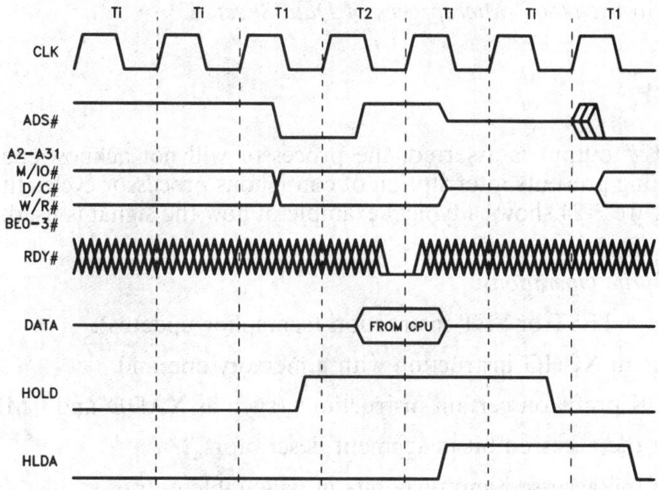

Figure 3-23. Bus Hold Timing

Since BREQ, HLDA, PCHK# and FERR# are not floated, they must not be driven by any other bus master. The processor will remain in the hold state until after HOLD is de-asserted. The requesting bus master must maintain HOLD asserted until it is ready to pass control back to the processor.

During hold, the processor continues to execute from the internal instruction prefetch unit and cache until it needs access to the bus. The processor can generate and store up to four write cycles, until bus access is again granted, as discussed in Chapter 2. In a read cycle, an instruction fetch that misses in the internal cache, or more than four write cycles are needed, execution stops until the bus is available.

During hold, the processor monitors only HOLD, RESET, NMI, and INTR. One NMI request will be recognized and latched for acknowledgement after the end of the hold operation. While INTR is monitored during hold, the input must be held asserted until the interrupt acknowledge cycle is run, after the end of the hold operation.

Once HOLD is de-asserted, the processor drives the bus and de-asserts HLDA on the next clock. If a bus cycle is pending in the processor, the bus cycle will begin on that clock.

3.3.4.2 HOLD LATENCY

Maximum HOLD latency is determined by the maximum duration of locked cycles. Asserting AHOLD may prevent the processor from recognizing HOLD. For example, asserting AHOLD during the third of four BS8# cycles will prevent HOLD from being recognized.

For details on LOCK# latency, see Section 3.3.5 immediately below. Other details and values are given in the *i486™ Microprocessor Data Sheet*.

3.3.5 Bus Lock

When the LOCK# output is asserted, the processor will not acknowledge a bus hold request. Bus locking prevents interruption of contiguous processor cycles that need to be kept integral. Figure 3-24 shows a typical example of how the signal is used. The signal is generated by:

- *Read-Modify-Write Operations*:
  - Executing a TEST or SET instruction (semaphor updates).
  - Executing an XCHG instruction with a memory operand.
  - The LOCK prefix on certain instructions (such as XADD and CMPXCHG).
  - Updating the accessed bit in segment descriptors.
  - Updating the accessed and dirty bits in page table entries.
  - Setting the busy bit in a task state segment (TSS) descriptor.
  - Setting the access bit in a segment descriptor.
- *Interrupt Acknowledge Cycles*.

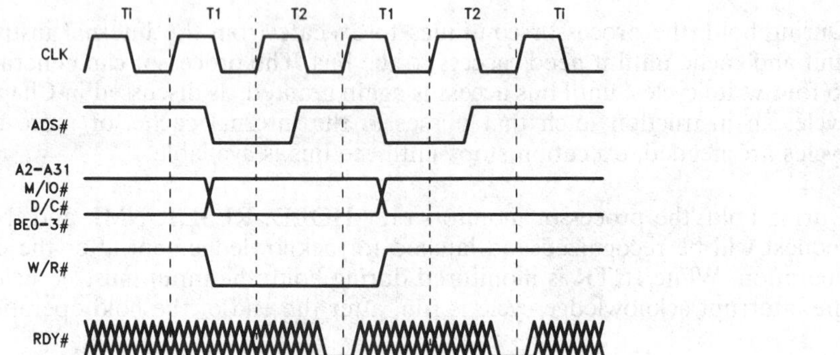

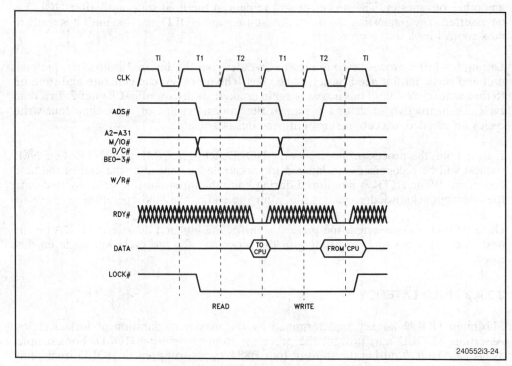

Figure 3-24. Locked Bus Cycles

Locked read cycles are not cacheable. In systems with an external cache between the processor bus and a system bus, locked cycles should always cause a system-bus cycle. This will ensure consistent synchronization between multiple agents on the system bus. During locked cycles, the processor will not recognize a HOLD request, but it will recognize BOFF# and AHOLD requests.

3.3.5.1 TIMING

Figure 3-24 shows a sequence of locked cycles. The LOCK# output is asserted on the rising clock edge of the first locked bus cycle, at the same time as ADS#, and it is de-asserted after RDY# is asserted at the end of the last bus cycle to be locked. Maximum duration of the LOCK# signal affects the maximum HOLD request latency because HOLD is not recognized until LOCK# is de-asserted. The duration of LOCK# depends on the instruction being executed and the number of wait states per cycle.

In Real Mode, the longest duration of LOCK# is two bus cycles plus approximately two clocks. This occurs during the XCHG instruction and during locked read-modify-write operations. In protected mode, the longest duration of LOCK# is five bus cycles plus approximately 15 clocks. This occurs when a hardware or software interrupt occurs and the processor performs a locked read of the gate in the interrupt descriptor table (8 bytes), a read of the target descriptor (8 bytes), and a write of the accessed bit in the target descriptor. The insertion of wait states will affect the length of the required bus cycles.

3.3.5.2 SEMAPHOR APPLICATIONS

LOCK# is used for read-modify-write operations on memory-based semaphors, as shown in Figure 3-25. The value of a semaphore indicates a condition, such as the availability of a resource. If the processor reads a semaphore, determines that a resource is available, and writes a new value to the semaphore to indicate that it intends to take control of the resource, the read and write cycles should be locked to prevent another bus master from reading or writing the semaphore between the processor's two bus cycles.

3.3.5.3 LOCK LATENCY

Execution of the LOCK instruction causes the assertion of the LOCK# output for two bus cycles (each of which may split into multiple cycles for misaligned data or for 8- or 16-bit bus sizes), plus four clocks for ALU computation.

References to the global descriptor table (GDT) or the local descriptor table (LDT) will lock the bus to set the accessed (A) bit for memory descriptors (if not already set). Descriptors are read without LOCK# asserted. If the A bit is not set, the descriptor is re-read with LOCK# asserted (two 4-byte read cycles), the A bit is set, and then four bytes are written to store the updated half of the descriptor. This keeps LOCK# asserted for three bus cycles (two reads, then one write), plus eight clocks. Once the

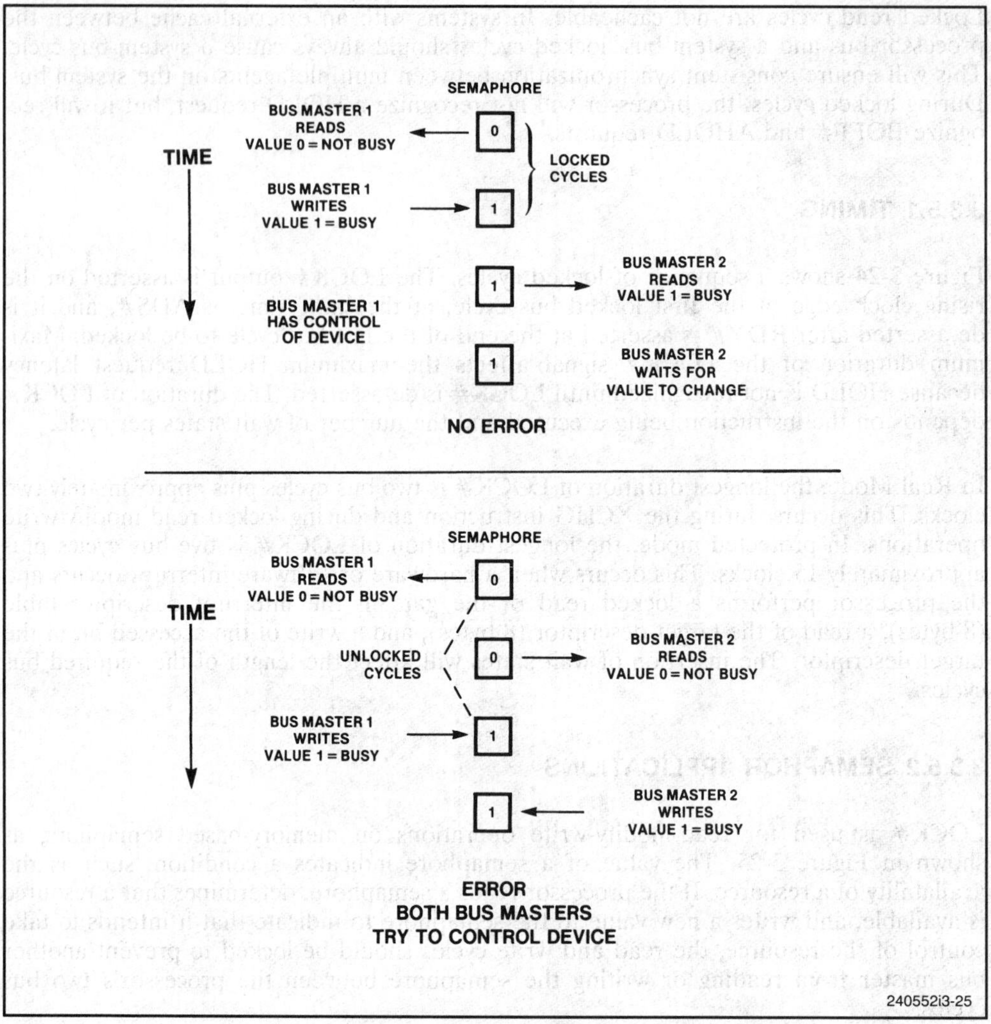

Figure 3-25. Semaphor Passing with Non-Locked Cycles

accessed bit is set, subsequent reads of the same descriptor will use unlocked cycles. Operating system software can minimize LOCK# duration by aligning descriptor tables to 8-byte boundaries and storing these tables in 32-bit memory, avoiding use of BS8# and BS16#.

Page table references will assert LOCK# to set the dirty (D) and/or accessed (A) bits in the page-directory or page-table entries. First, the entry is read with LOCK# de-asserted. If either bit is clear, the entry is re-read, with LOCK# asserted, the appropriate bit is set, and then the entry is written back to memory. LOCK# is asserted for two bus cycles plus four clocks. Page table entires are always aligned, but again, storage in 32-bit memory will avoid the possibility of BS8# or BS16# lengthening the lock latency.

The worst-case lock latency occurs when reading a descriptor table entry: it takes 8 clocks, plus 2 read cycles, plus 1 write cycle. The worst-case use of the LOCK instruction prefix occurs with a locked BTS, BTC, or BTR instruction: these take 4 clocks, plus 1 read cycle, plus 1 write cycle (each of which may split into multiple cycles for misaligned data or for 8- or 16-bit bus sizes).

3.3.6 Bus Pseudo-Lock

The PLOCK# output offers a new protection, not available in the 386 processor. The signal performs a function identical to that of LOCK#—the processor will not acknowledge a bus hold request while PLOCK# is asserted, thereby preventing interruption of contiguous processor cycles that must be kept integral—but PLOCK# is asserted under circumstances which are different than LOCK#. Pseudo-locking protects transfers of aligned data that are longer than 32 bits. It is asserted only for cycles in a single direction (read cycles or write cycles, but not read-modify-write cycles). Figure 3-25 shows a typical example of how the signal is used. During pseudo-locked cycles, the processor will not recognize a HOLD request, although it will recognize a BOFF# or AHOLD request.

The PLOCK# output is generated by:

- Any data transfer longer than 32 bits, in which the data is aligned to boundaries equal to the data-structure size—i.e., any multiple-cycle sequence with aligned data.
- Whenever BLAST# is de-asserted (this case overlaps with the one above).
- During the first cycle of 64-bit floating-point writes.

Pseudo-locked cycles include 128-bit cache line fills, 64-bit floating-point operand reads or writes, and doubleword transfers on an 8- or 16-bit bus. In 80-bit floating-point operands, only the first 64 bits are pseudo-locked. PLOCK# is asserted predictably only if the transferred data is aligned to boundaries equal to the data-structure size: 32-bit data must be aligned to 4-byte boundaries, 64-bit data must be aligned to 8-byte boundaries, and 128-bit cache line fills must be aligned to 16-byte boundaries. Otherwise, additional transfers will be necessary, and the additional transfers may not be pseudo-locked to the normally required transfers.

The processor bursts read cycles longer than 32 bits whenever it can. In burst cycles, all of the data is transferred in a single bus cycle. PLOCK# is only useful to external logic in transfers which need more than one bus cycle. In systems which do not interrupt burst cycles with BOFF#, no special provision for examining PLOCK# is needed during burst reads. However, the system must examine PLOCK# during 64-bit writes, which need at least two data transfers. In 64-bit writes, BLAST# is asserted at the end of each data transfer but PLOCK# is asserted at the end of the first transfer and into the first part of the second transfer. The assertion of PLOCK# indicates that another data transfer is pending. Figure 3-26 shows the timing of PLOCK# in a 64-bit write. Access to 80-bit operands use pseudo-locked bus cycles; however, only the 64 bits at the lowest addresses are transferred in pseudo-locked bus cycles.

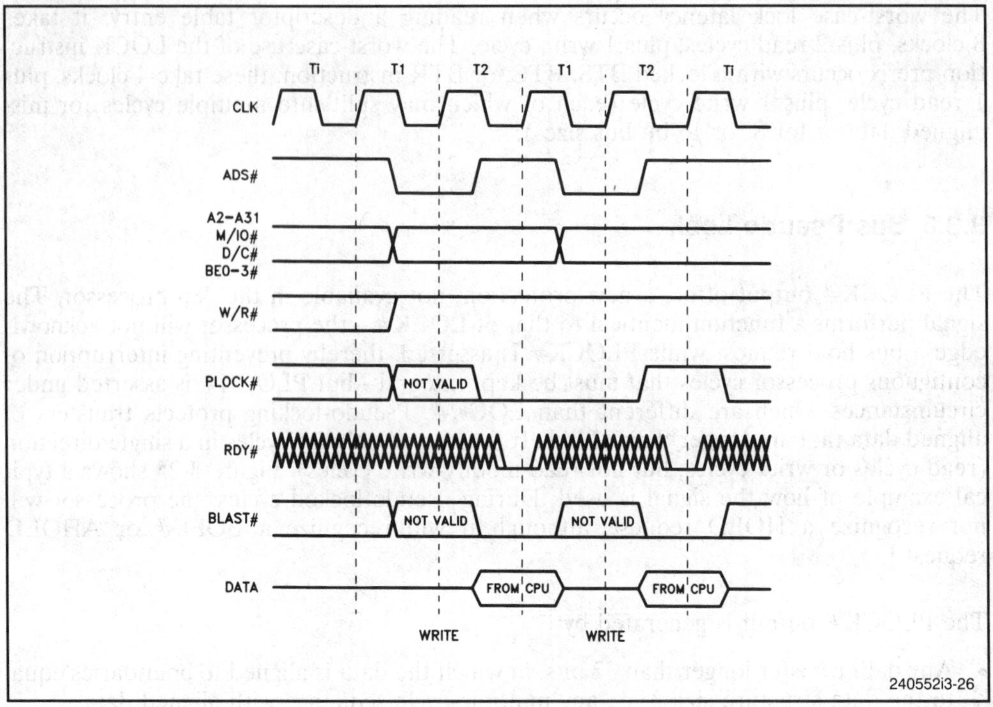

Figure 3-26. Pseudo-Locked 64-Bit Write Cycle

PLOCK# should be sampled only in the clock in which RDY# or BRDY# is asserted, as shown in Figure 3-26. Assertion of PLOCK# indicates that the next cycle is pseudo-locked to the current cycle. PLOCK# and BLAST# are always the inverse of each other, except during the first transfer of a 64-bit floating-point write. PLOCK# is a function of the KEN#, BS8#, and BS16# inputs. PLOCK# may change state during a cycle, but it is stable in the clock in which RDY# or BRDY# is asserted.

In systems with an external cache between the processor bus and a system bus, pseudo-locked cycles (unlike locked cycles) would not typically cause a system-bus cycle on external cache hits. The pseudo-locked cycle should be confined to the processor bus and the external cache controller should not allow system-bus activity to intervene with pseudo-locked cycles on the processor bus.

There are some situations in which both PLOCK# and LOCK# will be asserted simultaneously—for example, during 64-bit segment descriptor loads, which are operands longer than 32 bits (thus, protected by PLOCK#) but which are also specifically protected by LOCK#.

3.3.7 Bus Backoff

Some bus cycles initiated by the processor may require, for their completion, an external bus master to complete bus cycles of its own. For example, access to data which is held in the external cache of another processor may require the other processor to write-back the cached data to memory. Bus backoff is used to avoid this "deadly embrace," where neither the processor nor the other bus master can complete its operation, since each is waiting for something from the other. The BOFF# input indicates that another bus master needs to complete a bus cycle in order for the processor's current cycle to complete. The processor's response to bus backoff is similar to the bus hold operation, but more immediate; the processor releases the bus in the next clock, and no acknowledgment is given. When BOFF# is de-asserted, the processor will reliably restart the same bus cycle that was aborted.

Bus backoff is also known as *bus cycle restart* because any cycle in progress when BOFF# was asserted will be restarted when BOFF# is de-asserted. The restarted cycle will begin with a new assertion of ADS# but the transfer will continue from its state at the clock in which BOFF# was asserted. Any transfer complete before BOFF# was asserted will be assumed correct and will not be repeated.

Chapters 6 and 8 contain more information on how BOFF# is used in a system design.

3.3.7.1 TIMING

BOFF# is sampled in every clock cycle. When the signal is asserted, the processor stops driving the following outputs:

- A2-A31.
- D0-D31.
- DP0-DP3.
- BE0#-BE3#.
- PWT, PCD.
- M/IO#, D/C#, and W/R#.
- LOCK#.
- PLOCK#.
- ADS#.
- BLAST#.

Bus backoff takes effect more immediately than bus hold: the processor floats the signals listed above in the clock following the assertion of BOFF#. Burst cycles and other types of cycles may be stopped and held pending for the duration of the backoff operation. Bus backoff continues until the clock following the de-assertion of BOFF#, as shown in Figures 3-27 and 3-28. If BOFF# is asserted during a write cycle, the processor will float its data bus in addition to the signals listed above.

On assertion of BOFF#, the current bus cycle is suspended in a state which allows reliable restarting after BOFF# is de-asserted. Any data returned during the cycle in which BOFF# was recognized, or while BOFF# is asserted, is ignored. If RDY# or BRDY# is asserted simultaneously with BOFF#, only BOFF# will be recognized. If BOFF# is asserted after the processor has already begun a bus cycle, it may be necessary for the device which asserts BOFF# to wait for the assertion of RDY# or BRDY#

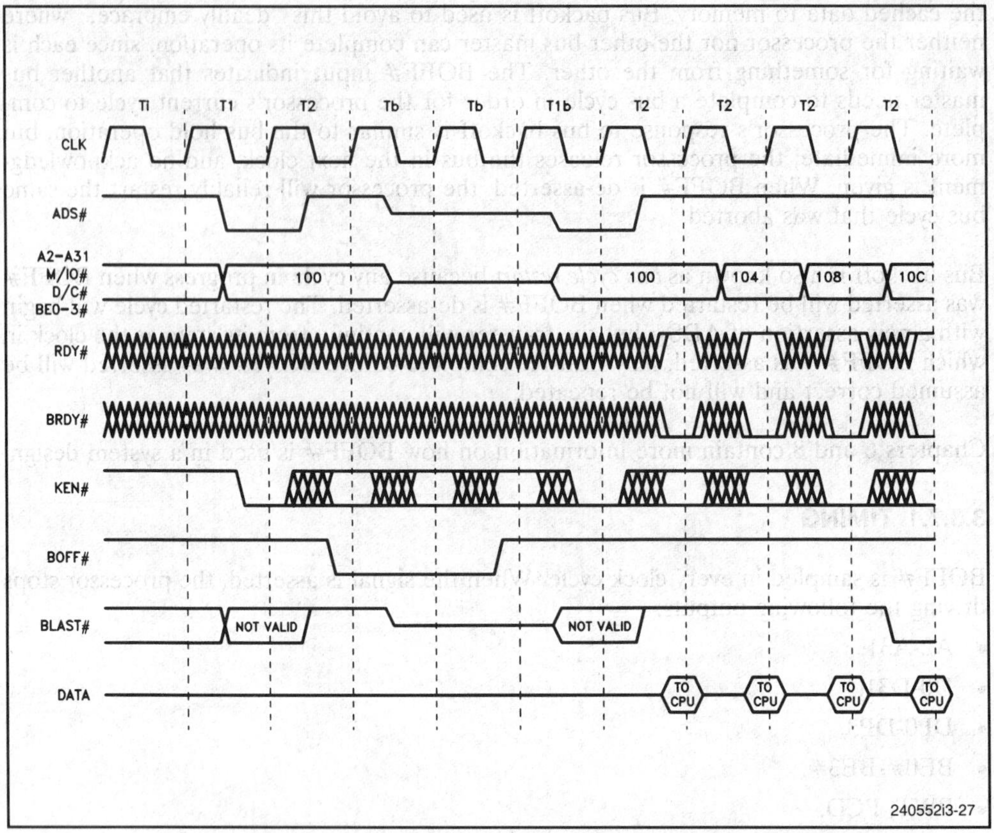

Figure 3-27. Bus Backoff and Restart during a Read Cycle

before starting a new cycle. This verifies that the memory system is ready to accept another bus cycle. If BOFF# is asserted while the bus is idle, the processor will go into bus hold in the next clock. Thus, the signal can prevent a subsequent bus cycle from starting.

RDY# and BRDY# need not be asserted if the processor is not performing a data transfer at the time bus backoff occurs. A state machine used to track the operation of the bus can indicate when a bus cycle is in progress. During backoff, the processor floats the same signals as during a hold operation, but HLDA is not asserted. The data bus is floated if BOFF# is asserted during a write cycle. Each turnaround of the bus between bus masters takes two clocks to ensure that there is no overlap of control on the bus.

3.3.7.2 CAUTIONS

If bus backoff occurs during a burst transfer, instruction prefetch, or cache line fill, any cycles which have been completed with assertion of RDY# or BRDY# are not

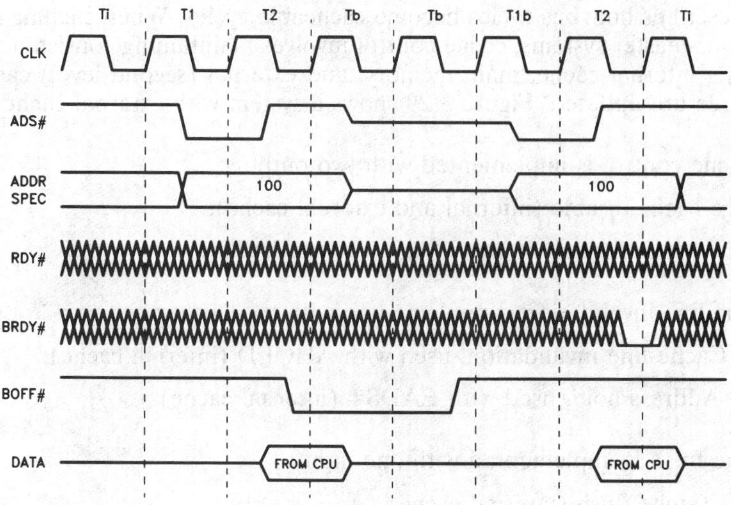

Figure 3-28. Bus Backoff and Restart during a Write Cycle

restarted. Data obtained in these cycles is assumed to be good. The burst transfer, instruction prefetch, or cache line fill continues with its next transfer after BOFF# is de-asserted.

If BOFF# is asserted during a burst cycle or when BS8# or BS16# is asserted, the processor will be forced to ignore data returned for that cycle only; data from previous cycles must still be valid. For example, if BOFF# is asserted on the third RDY# of a burst cycle, the processor assumes that the data returned with the first and second RDY# is valid, and it restarts the burst beginning with the third cycle. The same thing happens with transfers that are broken into multiple cycles when BS8# or BS16# are asserted.

A problem may occur if BOFF# is asserted in the same clock the processor asserts the ADS# output. Bus masters see the beginning of a bus cycle, which is then terminated abnormally. One approach is to have all bus masters recognize bus backoff. Another approach is to add an additional clock cycle before bus backoff is used. Asserting the AHOLD input in this additional clock will keep the processor from issuing a new address; it prevents assertion of the ADS# output in the next clock.

Care should be taken if BOFF# is asserted during an I/O cycle because the processor will restart the I/O cycle after it regains control of the bus. Either BOFF# occurs before the I/O device sees the I/O command, or the I/O device must understand that the cycle is restarting, or the system should not assert BOFF# during I/O cycles.

3.4 CACHE CONTROL

Section 3.2 describes how bus cycles become cacheable cycles. When caching is enabled for multiple-bus-master systems, cache control involves maintaining consistency between the processor's internal cache, main memory, and external (second-level) caches when any of the three are updated. Figure 3-29 shows a system with external cache.

Page-level cache control is implemented with two outputs:

- *PCD*—Page cache disable (internal and external cache).
- *PWT*—Page write-through or write-back (external cache).

Internal cache-line invalidation is implemented with two inputs:

- *EADS#*—Cache-line invalidation, used with AHOLD (internal cache).
- *AHOLD*—Address hold, used with EADS# (internal cache).

Internal cache flush is implemented with one input:

- *FLUSH#*—Cache flush (internal cache).

Cache flush and cache flush/write-back are implemented for both internal and external cache with two special bus cycles:

- *Cache Flush Cycle*—Initiated by the INVD instruction (internal and external cache).
- *Cache Write-Back and Flush Cycle*—Initiated by the the WBINVD instruction (external write-back, and internal and external cache).

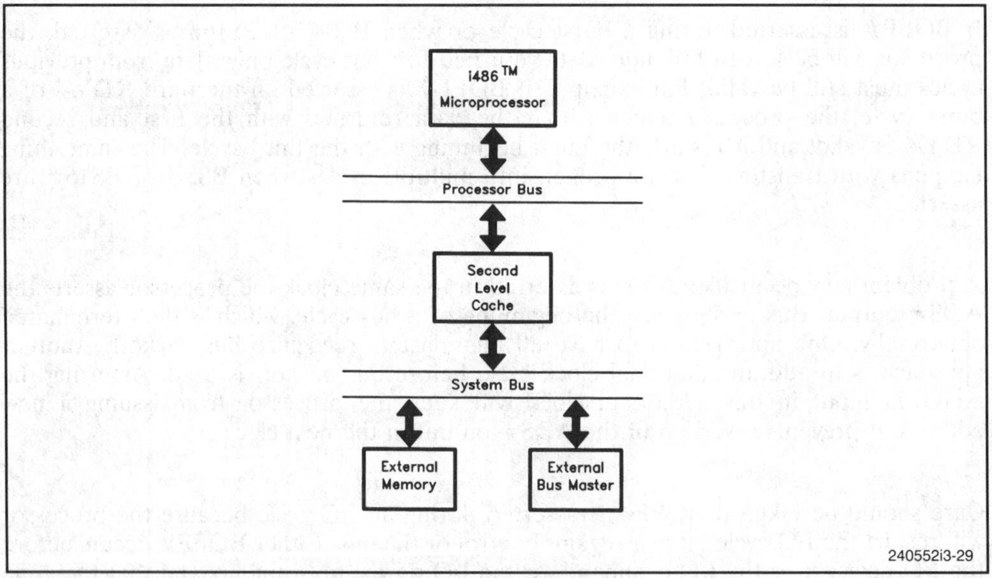

Figure 3-29. External (Second-Level) Cache

The sections below describe each cache control in detail. Section 3.3.3 describes special bus cycles.

3.4.1 Page-Level Cache Controls

Caching and memory updating are page-based: each 4-Kbyte page of contiguous memory locations can have its cacheability and write-through or write-back policy controlled on a cycle-by-cycle basis. Two software-controlled outputs, PCD and PWT, are used for page-level cache control on a cycle-by-cycle basis.

- *PCD*—The page cache disable output controls cacheability for the current page, assuming that all other conditions for caching are satisfied. When the corresponding bit is cleared in software, the output is de-asserted and caching is enabled for the internal cache. The output can be used to enable external cache. When asserted, internal caching is disabled even if the KEN# input is asserted; the PCD control bit is internally ANDed with KEN#.
- *PWT*—The page write-through output is only useful for external cache; internal cache is always write-through. When asserted, the signal applies a write-through caching policy for the current page; updates to cache will be written through to memory. When de-asserted, the signal allows the possibility for external caches to use a write-back policy for the current page. Future Intel parts which incorporate write-back caches will use PWT as described here.

When paging is enabled (PG = 1 in the machine status register, CR0), the PCD and PWT outputs reflect the page-table entry of the current page that are stored in the translation lookaside buffer (TLB), described in Section 2.8.2. The outputs are driven when the page mapped by the TLB entry is referenced. For normal memory cycles with paging enabled, PCD and PWT are taken from the second-level page-table entry. During TLB refresh cycles, PCD and PWT are taken from CR3.

When paging is disabled (PG = 0 in the machine status register, CR0), or for cycles which bypass paging, such as I/O-mapped references, interrupts and halts, the processor drives PWT and PCD to the state of the corresponding bits in the CR3 register. These are cleared at reset, but can be given any value by level-0 software. See the *i486™ Processor Programmer's Reference Manual* for more information.

3.4.2 Internal Cache-Line Invalidation

The processor's address bus, unlike those of previous Intel 8086-family processors, is bidirectional. Addresses can be driven into the i486 processor for the purpose of invalidating any cache line at that address. The system should provide address-bus latches; this will prevent loss of the address information when the address bus is turned around to provide a cache-line invalidation address. Cache invalidations can be done at any time. Because the address bus is not used during a burst transfer, cache invalidation can be done simultaneously with burst transfers. During non-burst single-transfer cycles with wait states, invalidation can also be performed during wait states if the address of the invalidation is latched externally.

Cache-line invalidation starts with the assertion of AHOLD by external logic. In the next clock the processor floats A2-A31, allowing the external bus master to drive the address of a 16-byte cache line into the processor. No address-hold acknowledgement is given. The A3, A2, and BE0#-BE3# signals should not be driven, because the smallest unit of storage in the cache is four doublewords. External logic then asserts EADS# to request the cache invalidation. Multiple addresses may be invalidated by asserting EADS# multiple times while asserting AHOLD. Normal operation of the bus resumes with the de-assertion of AHOLD.

AHOLD is always recognized, even during reset, although invalidations during reset are superfluous because reset invalidates the entire cache. During address hold, data can be returned for a single previously initiated bus cycle; the processor floats only its address bus. The processor will not initiate another bus cycle (which starts with ADS#) during address hold. Locked and pseudo-locked sequences can be interrupted.

Other cache operations, such as satisfying an internal request for cache contents, are delayed while the cache invalidation is performed. Unnecessary cache invalidation cycles reduce performance. Cache invalidation should not be attempted at the end of a cache line fill. During the clock in which the line is actually written into the cache – either the last clock of the fill or the first one following – EADS# is ignored. This is the only circumstance in which EADS# is not recognized.

Figure 3-30 shows an internal cache invalidation cycle.

3.4.2.1 RATE OF INVALIDATION

The processor samples EADS# every clock and can accept cache-line invalidations at the rate of one every clock, except in the last clock of a cache line fill. This rate of invalidation can be maintained, if EADS# is de-asserted during one or both of the following times:

- The clock in which RDY# or BRDY# is asserted for the last time in a transfer.
- The clock immediately following the one in which RDY# or BRDY# is asserted for the last time in a transfer.

These conditions allow two distinct types of systems. A simple cache system can restrict invalidations to every other clock, and need not track bus activity. Systems which require invalidation once every clock must monitor the processor bus for the above conditions of RDY# and BRDY#.

3.4.2.2 INVALIDATION CONCURRENT WITH LINE FILLS

In systems with external (second-level) cache and two buses allowing concurrent activity, precautions are needed to prevent caching invalid data in the processor. In such systems it is desirable to run invalidation cycles concurrently with other processor bus activity. This is possible because the two buses allow a device to be writing to main memory while the processor is retrieving data from the external cache. When such a write occurs, the cache line must be invalidated if it exists in the processor's internal cache, and the

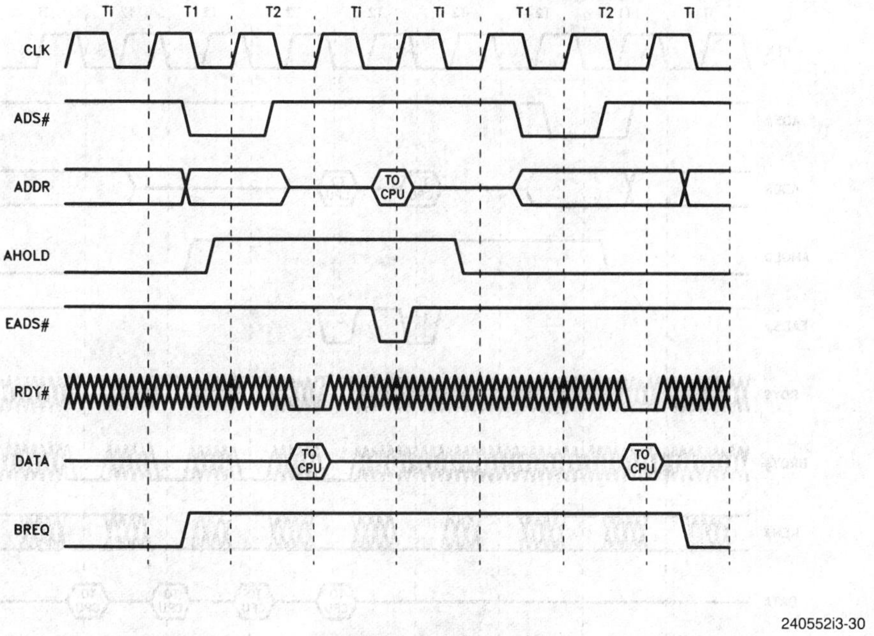

Figure 3-30. Internal Cache Invalidation Cycle

external cache must be invalidated or updated. However, since the write to main memory and the read from external cache can occur at any time relative to one another, the order in which the invalidation is requested and data is returned to the processor becomes important. A simple rule to ensure consistency in such cases is described below and shown in Figure 3-31.

If the processor is doing a cache line fill, and a cache-line invalidation is requested in the first clock in which cache-line data is returned to the processor, or in any subsequent clock, the processor will invalidate that line, even if it is the same cache line that the processor is currently filling. That is, if EADS# is asserted in the same clock that the first RDY# or BRDY# is asserted, or if it is asserted in a later clock, the processor will invalidate the data even if the data pertains to the cache line that is being filled. During an invalidation, the invalidated cache line is simply marked invalid; however, the processor will still use the data for the original purpose of the read (as a memory operand, for example).

If an invalidation occurs before the first data is transferred to the processor, the processor assumes that the data subsequently transferred is valid. Invalidation operations cannot be done on data that the processor has not yet received. Thus, the system is responsible for the validity of data passed to the internal cache. The responsibility for invalidating data is passed along with the data itself: an external cache controller must

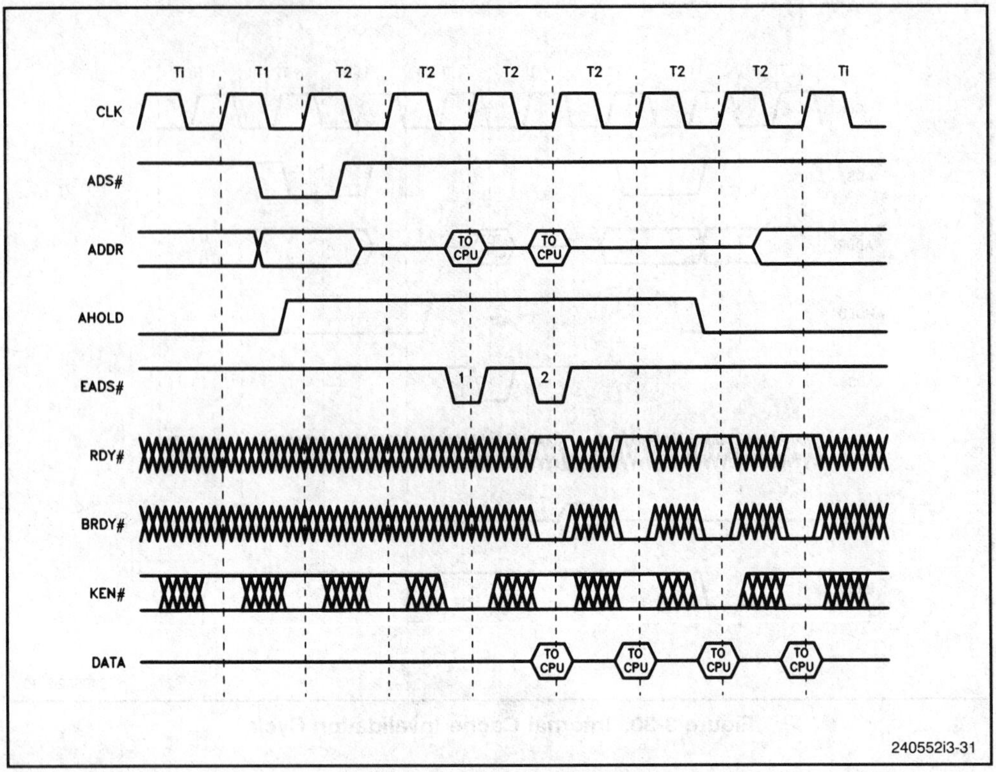

Figure 3-31. Concurrent Cache Invalidation and Line Fill

keep its copies of data consistent with memory; but when data is copied from the external cache to the processor's internal cache, the processor will keep its copy of that data consistent with memory.

3.4.3 Internal Cache Flush

This cycle invalidates the entire internal cache. When the address of modified data is not available, a partial invalidation cannot be performed, and a cache flush is the only alternative. Changes to address mapping information require a cache flush. Assertion of the FLUSH# input for one clock causes a cache flush, as shown in Figure 3-32.

In addition to flushing, which clears the entire cache but allows it to begin storing new data in the next clock, the cache can also be disabled. Cache disabling is a two-step process: (1) set the PCD and PWT bits in CR3, and (2) flush the cache.

3.4.4 Cache Flush Cycle

This special bus cycle is invoked by executing the INVD instruction, which causes the assertion of BE1# and the de-assertion of BE0#, BE2#, and BE3#, as shown in Table 3-14.

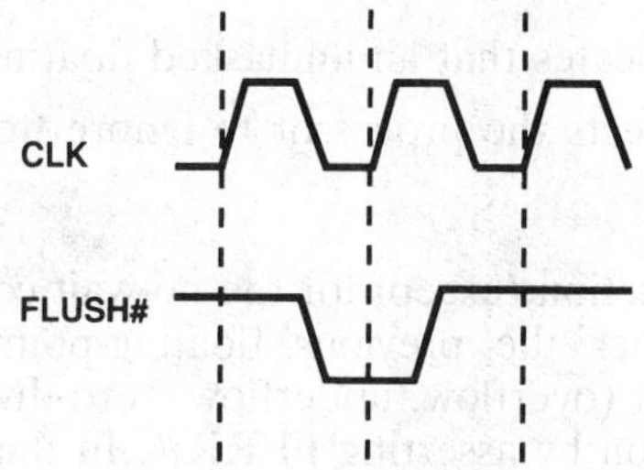

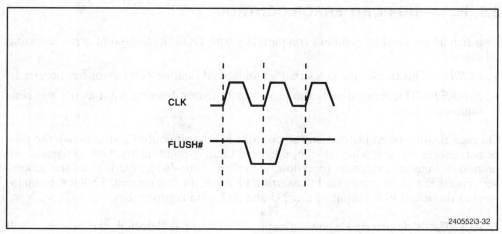

Figure 3-32. Internal Cache Flush

When the INVD instruction is executed, it will (1) force the internal cache to invalidate its entire contents. External logic should decode this cycle to (2) cause external cache to invalidate its entire contents (the external cache should not write its contents back to memory before the flush).

A combination of software and hardware design must define the behavior of signals used to control the internal and external cache. For example, in a system with multiple processors on the system bus, hardware should propagate the external cache flush indications to all of the other processors.

3.4.5 Cache Write-Back and Flush Cycle

This special bus cycle, shown in Table 3-14, is like the cache flush cycle except that it adds a write-back function for external caches. The cycle is invoked by executing the WBINVD instruction, which causes the assertion of BE3# and the de-asserted of BE0#-BE2# during a special bus cycle.

When the WBINVD instruction is executed, it will (1) force the internal cache to invalidate its entire contents. External logic should decode this cycle to (2) cause external cache to write its entire contents back to memory, and then (3) cause external cache to invalidate its entire contents.

Unlike the processor's internal write-through cache, a write-back cache does not immediately update memory with data received during a write cycle. Instead, each block of the cache has a bit set in the tag field if the cache contains data more recent than the corresponding memory area. Only if this block is about to be overwritten is the data it currently contains written out to memory. This reduces bus activity.

3.5 FLOATING-POINT ERROR CONTROL

Two signals are used to maintain compatibility with DOS floating-point error reporting schemes:

- *FERR#*—This output indicates that an unmasked floating-point error has occurred.
- *IGNNE#*—This input directs the processor to ignore floating-point errors and continue execution.

On each floating-point instruction (except for the no-wait control instructions), the processor checks to see whether the previous floating-point instruction generated an unmasked numeric exception (overflow, underflow, zero-divide, etc.). If so, the processor reports the error condition by asserting FERR#. In this respect, FERR# is analogous to the ERROR# output of the 287 and 387 math coprocessors.

If IGNNE# is de-asserted when a floating-point error is detected, the processor will either stop and wait for an interrupt, or it will jump to the floating-point interrupt location (vector 16), depending on the state of the NE bit in the machine status register (CR0). These two methods of invoking exception handlers are the same as in systems using the 286 processor and 287 math coprocessor, and in systems using the 386 processor and 387 math coprocessor.

- If the NE bit in CR0 is set, the processor raises interrupt 16, the floating-point error interrupt.
- If NE is clear, the processor stalls and waits for an external interrupt. NE is cleared at RESET. This is the default.

The default mechanism (NE clear) emulates error-reporting in 8086/8087 systems, and is supported for DOS compatibility. It requires an external interrupt controller, such as that shown in Figure 3-33, to monitor the FERR# output and generate the necessary interrupts (normally to the INTR input). The interrupt controller can allow execution of floating-point instructions before the error condition is cleared (i.e., within the interrupt handler), by asserting the IGNNE# input of the processor. When IGNNE# is asserted (and NE is clear), the processor executes floating-point instructions in spite of pre-existing error conditions. The IGNNE# input can be asynchronous to the processor's clock.

See the *i486™ Processor Programmer's Reference Manual* for detailed discussion of floating-point instructions, numeric exceptions, and exception handlers.

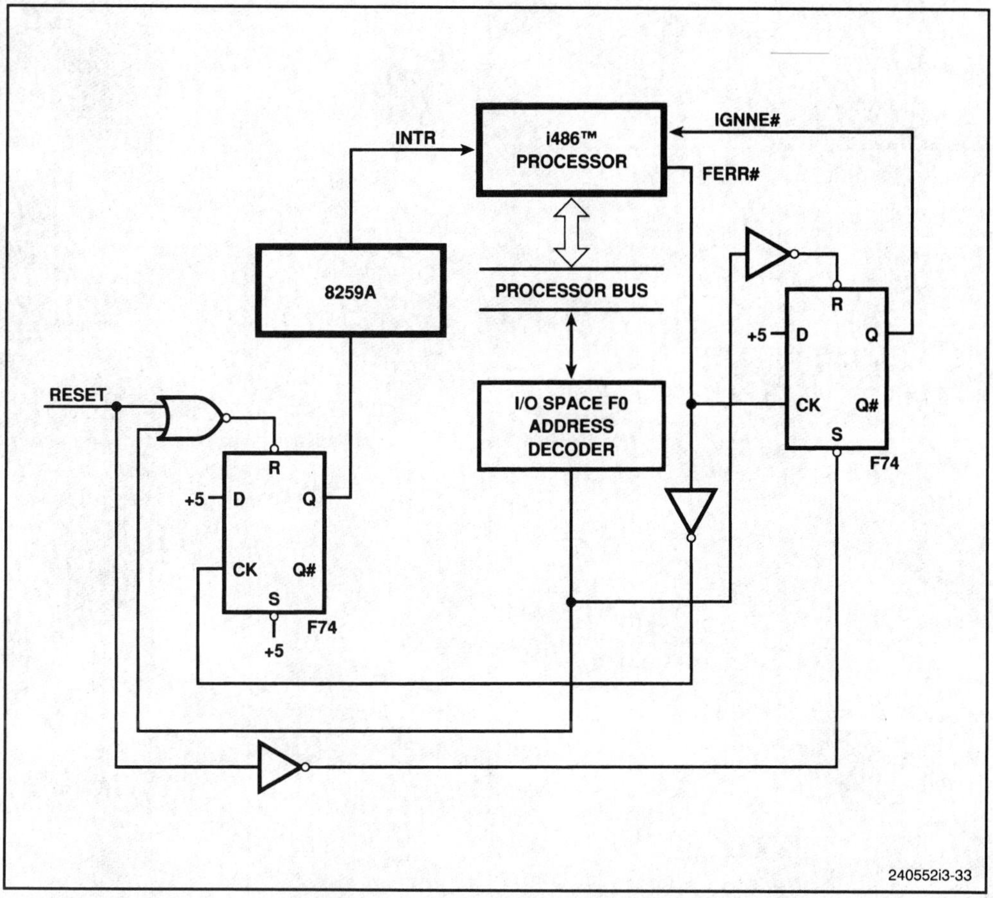

Figure 3-33. DOS-Compatible Logic for Floating-Point Error Interpretation

Performance Considerations 4

CHAPTER 4
PERFORMANCE CONSIDERATIONS

4.1 INTRODUCTION

System performance is a key attribute of any computer system. How quickly a program is run is the common measure of performance. Program performance is a function of many parameters: CPU speed, clock speed, memory latency, memory data transfer rate, memory size, disk access time, disk data transfer rate, video access time, compiler efficiency, operating system efficiency, program algorithms, etc. This chapter will focus on the memory system parameters that affect performance. External caches will also be examined as a means of improving memory system performance. Later chapters will give specific examples of memory and cache designs. To see how other factors affect performance, see the *i486™ CPU Benchmark Report*, February 1990.

Memory system design is important. The i486 microprocessor is faster than any practical memory system. It contains a significant amount of logic (e.g., caches, write buffers, prefetcher) to allow the execution logic to keep operating even with slow external memories. The on-chip caches and data bandwidth requirements of the i486 microprocessor are different than earlier microprocessors. Memory system design should be approached differently as well. This chapter will describe the memory requirements and bus usage characteristics of the i486 microprocessor.

4.1.1 Memory Performance Factors

The ideal memory subsystem would operate without wait states. All bus cycles on the i486 microprocessor would complete in only two clocks for single access and five clocks for cache fill. This is impractical for almost all applications since they would require huge amounts of 15 ns memory to run at 33 MHz. Practical systems use DRAM of 60-100 ns access times. The i486 microprocessor is designed to effectively use DRAM. This chapter examines memory system design using DRAM.

There are many different performance options in the design of the memory subsystem for the i486 microprocessor. The CPU clock speed sets the maximum possible performance. Higher is faster, but it then requires faster memories to keep the whole system performance scaling at the frequency rate. The i486 CPU is designed to allow overall performance to increase up to a point with higher clock speed and constant memory speed.

The most common attribute of memory design is the number of wait states if any required to read a data item. At 33 MHz, a read operation requires 15 ns memories. For slower memories with wait states, add 30 ns each to the access time at 33 MHz. Wait states will exist in practical memory system design. This chapter will examine how they affect i486 microprocessor performance.

The i486 microprocessor adds a new metric to memory design, read transfer rate. It is important for filling the internal cache of the i486 microprocessor. The i486 CPU can transfer data from memory on every clock for most read transfers. This is twice the rate of individual memory cycles. Memory systems supporting this high speed transfer rate increase performance 10-20% over those without.

A third important attribute is write cycle time. The i486 CPU write-through cache generates approximately twice as many writes as reads. Write performance is especially important for 16-bit programs which generate more writes than 32-bit programs. The cycle time of the write can limit system performance as the total bus usage approaches the maximum allowed.

A common method of improving memory system performance is a cache. The i486 microprocessor has an on-chip cache. It handles most of the read requests. The performance gain of an external cache for the i486 microprocessor is less than for the 386™ microprocessor. The performance gain is highly dependent on the application. Some applications benefit less than 5% with an external cache. Most benefit 10-15% while a few benefit as much as 40%. An external cache is not required for many i486 microprocessor applications.

A high-performance i486 microprocessor design needs to consider all of these issues in the memory design. The following sections provide more detail on the activity of the i486 CPU during typical program execution. The memory activity of the CPU needs to be understood to best design the memory subsystem.

4.2 INSTRUCTION EXECUTION PERFORMANCE

The i486 CPU was designed to execute instructions in fewer clocks than earlier Intel386™ family microprocessors. The reduced clock counts increase performance relative to earlier products. This section will review how the i486 microprocessor accomplishes this and compare it to earlier Intel microprocessors.

The instruction execution rate and internal design is important to understand when designing memory systems. It accounts for the heavy write traffic on the i486 CPU as compared to earlier microprocessors. It also explains how memory bandwidth and latency affect performance.

4.2.1 i486 Microprocessor Execution Times

The i486 microprocessor uses several techniques to execute many frequent instructions in a single clock. The chip has an on-chip code/data cache, five stage pipelined execution unit, decodes many simple instructions directly into hardware actions, and uses write buffers to match the execution rate to memory bus speed.

One high-level way to examine the impact of these techniques is to compare the execution time of a typical application. To do so, Intel has measured a set of applications for the frequency of instruction usage. Based on this we can compare the individual instruction execution times of the i486 and 386 microprocessors. For each instruction we multiply the frequency times the clocks required to execute. The sum of the products then yields the typical number of clocks required to execute an instruction.

Table 4-1 shows such a comparison. The i486 microprocessor requires 1.95 clocks for a typical instruction while the 386 microprocessor requires 4.919 clocks. This is a 2.5x improvement for integer programs. The floating-point instructions have an even larger improvement as discussed later. The numbers in Table 4-1 do not include effects of cache misses for the i486 CPU.

One implication of these numbers is that the i486 CPU cannot sustain that rate of execution with the cache disabled. The bus bandwidth required for the i486 CPU with cache disabled would be 2.5× that of the 386 CPU. The i486 CPU bus has 60% more data bandwidth for reads than the 386 CPU, but the same bandwidth for writes. The

Table 4-1. Typical Instruction Mix and Execution Times for the i486™ CPU and the 386™ CPU

Instruction	Percentage Utilization	i486™ CPU Clocks	i486 Accum. Clocks	386™ CPU Clocks	386 Accum. Clocks
Move R,M	16.2%	1.16	0.188	5	0.810
Move M,R	6.9%	1	0.069	2	0.138
Push R	6.1%	1	0.061	2	0.122
Move R,R	5.7%	1	0.057	2	0.114
Move R,I	5.5%	1	0.055	2	0.110
JCC taken	4.6%	3.4	0.156	9.25	0.426
JCC fail	4.5%	1	0.045	3	0.135
ALU2 R,R	4.3%	1	0.043	2	0.086
POP R	4.0%	1.16	0.046	5	0.200
JMP M	2.9%	3.4	0.099	9.25	0.268
ALU2 R,M	2.9%	2.16	0.063	7	0.203
ALU2 M,I	2.9%	3.16	0.092	8	0.232
Call	2.8%	3.4	0.095	9.25	0.259
Shift R	2.8%	2	0.056	3	0.084
ALU2 R,I	2.8%	1	0.028	2	0.056
RET	2.7%	5.56	0.150	15.25	0.412
String	2.6%	3.16	0.082	8	0.208
ALU1 R	2.0%	1	0.020	2	0.040
LDS	1.4%	12	0.168	22	0.308
ALU2 M,R	1.3%	3.16	0.041	8	0.104
ALU1 M	1.2%	3.16	0.038	8	0.096
Push M	1.1%	2.16	0.024	7	0.077
NOP	1.1%	1	0.011	2	0.022
Others	11.7%	2.25	0.263	3.5	0.410
Average clocks per instruction			1.95		4.919

on-chip cache of the i486 CPU handles most (90-95%) of the read requests. The external bus must handle all of the writes. A later section will examine bus utilization and on-chip cache hit rates in more detail.

4.2.2 Application Programs Used in Analysis

For the bus utilization and cache statistics presented later, a series of five programs were used. Each was traced to record the address access pattern. These patterns were then used in a cache simulator to measure how many accesses could be handled in the on-chip cache of the i486 CPU. The cache simulator is an accurate representation of on-chip cache. External bus traffic was also measured to give bus utilization statistics. An external DRAM controller and external cache can also be simulated to measure their effect on program execution.

The programs represent different types of work. Each was run in the UNIX environment. Some are 16-bit DOS applications run under a DOS emulator. Each had 16 million memory references recorded.

4.3 INTERNAL CACHE PERFORMANCE ISSUES

The i486 processor is capable of very high speed operations, as fast as 1 CPI for many common instructions. Since external memory cannot provide data for the CPU every clock, an on-chip cache that can be accessed very quickly is necessary to enhance the overall performance. The cache eases the bandwidth differences between the external bus and the CPU. The size, organization, write policy, miss replacement, and busing of the i486 CPU on-chip cache were chosen to support a broad range of applications.

4.3.1 On-Chip Cache Organization Issues

The i486 processor contains an 8-Kbyte cache on-chip cache. The cache is unified (containing both code and data), and is organized as 4-way set-associative, with four 2-Kbyte sets. Each set contains 128 lines. Cache lines are 16 bytes long. Lines in the cache are either valid or not valid. There is no provision for partially valid lines.

Read requests are generated either by program flow (data request) or an instruction prefetch (code request). The great majority of the time, these requests are usually satisfied by the on-chip cache. However, if a cache miss occurs, an external bus request is generated. For reads to non-cacheable areas of memory, the read is completely normal. If, however, the read request is to a cacheable portion of memory, then the CPU initiates a cache bus line fill. Cache line fills require the execution of additional bus cycles in order to read the remainder of the 16-byte line into the CPU.

Cache line size can impact system performance. If the line size is too large, then the number of blocks that can fit in the cache is reduced. In addition, as the line length is increased the latency for the external memory system to fill a cache line increases, reducing overall performance.

However, the i486 processor bus is optimized for a line size of 16 bytes. Since the i486 processor can access four bytes in each bus cycle and the cache lines are 16 bytes long, four bus cycles are necessary to fill a cache line. To reduce latency of reading cache lines, the CPU allows for burst cycles. During burst cycles, four bytes of data can be read into the CPU every clock. With the use of burst cycles, a 16-byte cache line can be read into the CPU in as few as five clock cycles. Static column DRAMs can be implemented to support burst cycles to the CPU.

During writes, the main memory update method utilized is the write through policy. All writes from the i486 CPU will initiate an external bus cycle. In addition, the internal cache is updated if the address written to is contained in the cache. This policy ensures consistency between the on-chip cache and the external memory.

4.3.2 Performance Effect of the On-Chip Cache

If all program operations use on-chip resources, the fastest possible execution is achieved, as the on-chip registers and cache satisfy all requests. However, on cache read misses or any memory write operation, the external bus has to be accessed reducing system performance.

A hit rate of approximately 95% is realized from the on-chip cache, depending on the application. The high level of cache hits has three main effects.

1. Performance is improved. The i486 CPU can access data from its on-chip cache every clock. This high bandwidth allows the execution unit of the i486 processor to execute many common instructions in one clock.

2. The bus utilization decreases. As a high percentage of reads are satisfied by the cache, the i486 processor is idle a large percentage of the time. Additional bus masters can reside in a system without bus saturation and the resulting performance degradation.

3. The ratio of writes to reads is increased on the external bus. The number of reads is decreased but the amount of writes remains constant. Therefore, main memory systems should have low latency on write operations.

Internally, two separate 128-bit wide prefetch buffers interface to the cache unit. These can be filled with data fetched from the on-board cache or the external memory in one clock cycle. Because the wide prefetch buffers satisfy multiple prefetches, the usual degradation caused by a combined code cache and data cache scheme is avoided.

To optimize performance during cache line fills, a technique called bypassing is used. The first cycle of a cache line fill satisfies the original request. Data read in during the first cycle is sent directly to the requesting unit. Because of this, it is not necessary to wait for the entire cache line to fill before the requested data can be used.

Figure 4-1 shows the on-chip hits rates for prefetch and read operations when running the programs shown in Table 4-2.

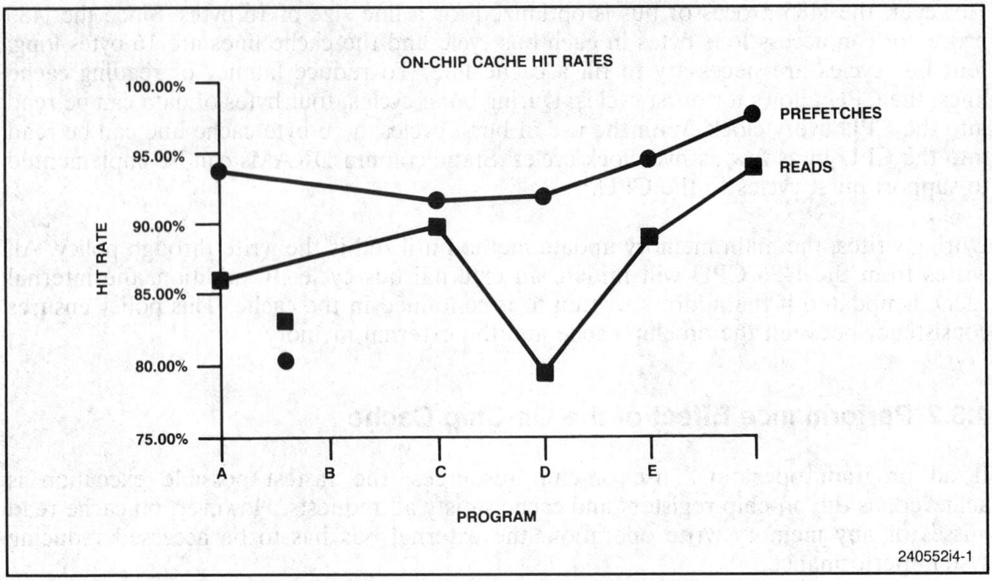

Figure 4-1. Cache Hit Rate for Various Programs

Table 4-2. Programs Used

	Name	Description
A	FRAME	Desktop publishing package
B	PHONGS4	Small benchmark program
C	SUNVIEW	Window manager
D	INVFRAME	Desktop publishing package
E	TPASCAL	Pascal compiler
F	TROFF	Text formatter

4.3.3 Bus Cycle Mix with and without an On-Chip Cache

Microprocessors that lack an on-chip cache must devote a significant portion of execution time to external bus accesses. Code prefetches and data reads must come from the external memory system; subsequently a high percentage of bus accesses are reads. This is shown in Figure 4-2 for the 386 DX CPU. Traditional memory systems are optimized for reads because of this mix of bus cycles.

With the i486 processor's on-chip cache, however, the high hit rate reduces the number of external reads. As the on-chip cache implements a write-through policy, the number of writes to the bus is not reduced. As a result, external bus read cycles are now a minor portion of the overall bus cycles, as shown in Figure 4-3. For best performance, memory systems that use the i486 processor should be optimized for write cycles.

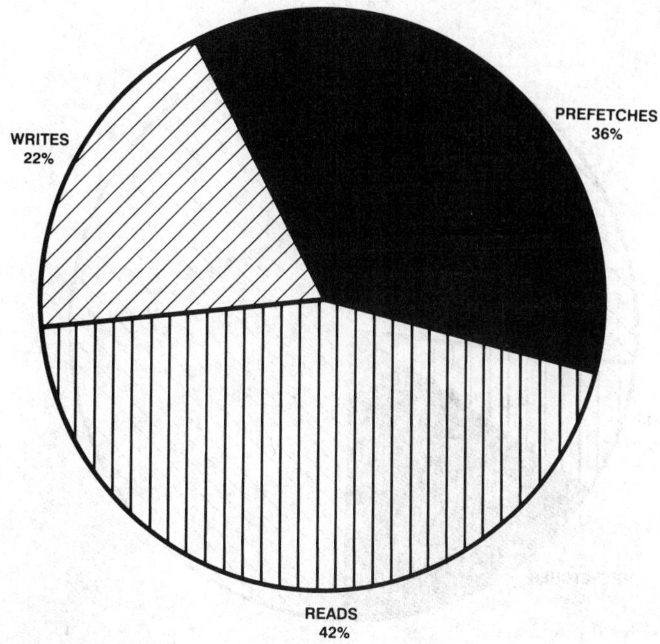

Figure 4-2. 386™ DX CPU Bus Cycle Mix without On-Chip Cache

4.4 ON-CHIP WRITE BUFFERS

As previously discussed, low write latency is more critical for i486 CPU systems than in previous processors. The i486 processor has four write buffers to allow CPU execution without latency for write operations. The buffers can be filled at the rate of one per clock cycle until all four are filled.

When all four write buffers are empty and the bus is idle, then a write request propagates to the external bus bypassing the write buffers directly. If the bus is not available when the write cycle is generated internally, then the write is buffered and propagated as soon as the bus is available. If a cache hit occurs on a write, then the on-chip cache is updated immediately.

Writes are normally executed on the external bus in the same order in which they are received by the write buffers, as in a FIFO. Under certain conditions a memory read can take priority, and the sequence of external bus cycles can be reordered, even though the writes occurred earlier in program execution.

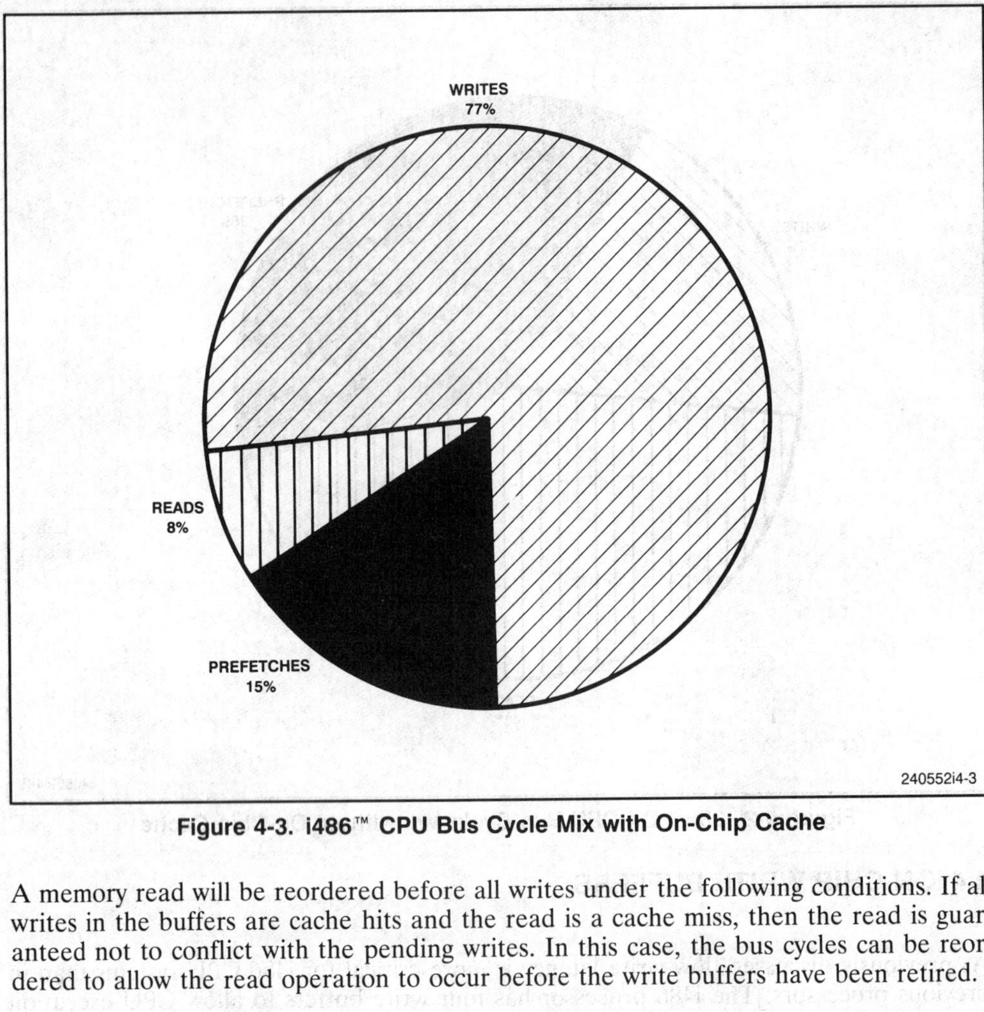

Figure 4-3. i486™ CPU Bus Cycle Mix with On-Chip Cache

A memory read will be reordered before all writes under the following conditions. If all writes in the buffers are cache hits and the read is a cache miss, then the read is guaranteed not to conflict with the pending writes. In this case, the bus cycles can be reordered to allow the read operation to occur before the write buffers have been retired.

i486 CPU performance is enhanced because of both the write buffers and bus cycle reordering. The write buffers decouple the internal execution unit from the bus. Program execution can continue without delay of write latency. In addition, reordering allows program execution to continue in some cases even if some write buffers are filled.

4.5 EXTERNAL MEMORY CONSIDERATIONS

4.5.1 Introduction

A well-designed external memory system is needed to achieve high-performance i486 processor system performance. A system can be designed using different combinations of SRAMs and DRAMs to provide different price-performance levels. SRAMs have faster access times and do not require precharging between accesses or refresh cycles. DRAMs offer higher densities and are less expensive, but they require refresh circuitry, and require the addition of wait states due to the longer access times.

The overall system performance of a high-performance microprocessor system is directly related to the performance of the memory subsystem. The great majority of bus cycles are used to access memory for instructions and data. As processor speeds increase, so does the demand for higher-speed memories because a high-performance processor that is coupled with a low performance memory offers no better throughput than a low-performance processor.

The cost of using only fast memories in a system may be prohibitive. Yet as slower devices are added to lower the overall cost, the performance penalty of added wait states increases. At frequencies of 25 MHz or more, optimum memory performance can only be achieved with use of very fast memory devices. However, using only fast memory devices is uneconomical. Building a system out of slower devices lowers the cost, but the penalty is lower performance.

The cost performance tradeoff can be compromised by partitioning functions and using a combination of both fast and slow memories. The most frequently used functions are placed in a faster memory. A common use of faster memory devices is implementation of an external cache, built of fast SRAM devices.

Fast SRAM devices have high enough bandwidth to achieve optimum performance. For high performance and ease of design, the Intel 485Turbocache Module can be used. Performance of the 485Turbocache Module will be discussed later in this chapter. In addition, Chapter 6 covers external (second level) cache concepts.

Regardless of the use of an external cache, the external memory system consists of a combination of EPROM and DRAM devices. EPROM devices tend to have a long access time. Being nonvolatile, EPROMs are used primarily for initialization routines. After initialization EPROMs are accessed infrequently. Thus, system performance is not dependent upon EPROM latency. If a high-level of performance is desired EPROM contents may be copied to the DRAM memory array. This technique is called shadowing.

Organization of the DRAM memory array is more critical to system performance. DRAM optimization techniques can be used to reduce the average latency of accesses to DRAM devices. Techniques such as static column and interleaving will be discussed.

Several of the memory design concepts described in this chapter depend on the principle of locality for high performance. The locality principle basically states that when a program references a particular location in memory, there is a high probability that nearby locations will then also be referenced. Caches and paged memory DRAM design techniques offer high performance because of locality.

4.5.2 Wait States in Burst and Non-Burst Modes

The i486 processor can execute non-burst cycles in as little as two clocks. These cycles are called 2-2 cycles, as read and write cycles take two cycles each. The first 2 refer to read cycle time and the second 2 to write cycle time. Accesses to devices which cannot respond by the end of the second clock require the addition of wait states. If a wait state must be added to write cycles, then a 2-3 system is created. The external system generates RDY# and the RDY# signal is sampled at the end of the second clock. If it is asserted (low) at the sample time, it indicates that the external system has placed valid data on the pins for reads, or that the system has accepted the data for writes. Wait states are inserted by driving RDY# inactive (high) at the end of the second clock.

The i486 non-burst cycles are very similar to non-pipelined 386 DX CPU cycles. In the 386 DX processor, the read and write accesses can be as fast as two cycles each. Thus, adding a wait state increases the bus cycle time by 50 percent of the zero wait state bus cycle time. Overall performance does not degrade in direct proportion to the bus cycle increase.

To enhance read performance, the i486 processor supports burst cycles. The i486 processor bus can burst successive words from memory into the cache every clock. Most memory reads can be performed in bursts as indicated by the BLAST# pin. The i486 processor keeps the BLAST# output inactive in the second clock of the cycle, indicating that it is able to perform a burst cycle. The external system indicates that it will initiate a burst cycle by asserting BRDY#. If BRDY# is not asserted at the second clock, wait states will be inserted. If a system executes non-burst reads in 2 clocks, burst reads in 1 clock, and writes in 3 clocks, a 2-1-3 system is indicated.

Because of the on-chip cache, the addition of external wait states affects the i486 processor's performance less than previous processors. A wait state in a 386 DX system incurs a performance degradation of about 20 percent. The i486 processor achieves optimum performance through a 2-1-2 cycle, zero wait state bus cycle. Adding one wait state in an i486 processor system causes a performance degradation of only about 6 percent.

The i486 processor can execute an external bus cycle in as little as two clock cycles. For achieving the optimum system performance, memory accesses must also execute in two cycles to eliminate wait states. At higher frequencies, however, it is impractical and cost-prohibitive to implement zero wait states for all of memory.

At 25 MHz, a wait state adds 40 ns to the available access time. While an operation with one wait state increases the bus cycle time by 50 percent, system performance does not degrade in direct proportion. The amount of degradation incurred is application dependent and varies with instruction mix, external cache size, and the number of memory references.

Several DRAM design techniques can reduce wait states and keep system performance at a high level using slower memory devices. Three of these techniques, page mode design, static column and interleaving and their impact on performance are discussed in Section 4.7.

4.5.3 Impact of Wait States on Performance

There are many benchmarks used to evaluate the performance of microprocessor systems. Figure 4-4 demonstrates the performance of i486 processor systems using different bus cycle implementations. The 100 percent performance level is an i486 processor with an external memory that operates a 2-1-2 cycle. The 2-1-2 cycle achieves the highest level of performance while a 5-1-4 cycle achieves the lowest.

Note that the performance effect of the four on-chip write buffers is apparent. Since more than 75% of external cycles are writes, write latency due to slower external memory should impact overall performance more than read latency. However, the on-chip write buffers reduce the dependence on write latency.

4.5.4 Bus Utilization and Wait States

Figure 4-5 demonstrates external bus utilization versus systems with different wait state configurations. The percentage figures were calculated by dividing the number of bus cycles in which the processor required the bus by the total number of bus cycles. A smaller percentage is better because it indicates that the external bus is accessed less frequently. In the benchmarks used in this demonstration, the percentages varied from 39 percent for a 2-1-2 cycle system to 90 percent for a 5-1-4 cycle system.

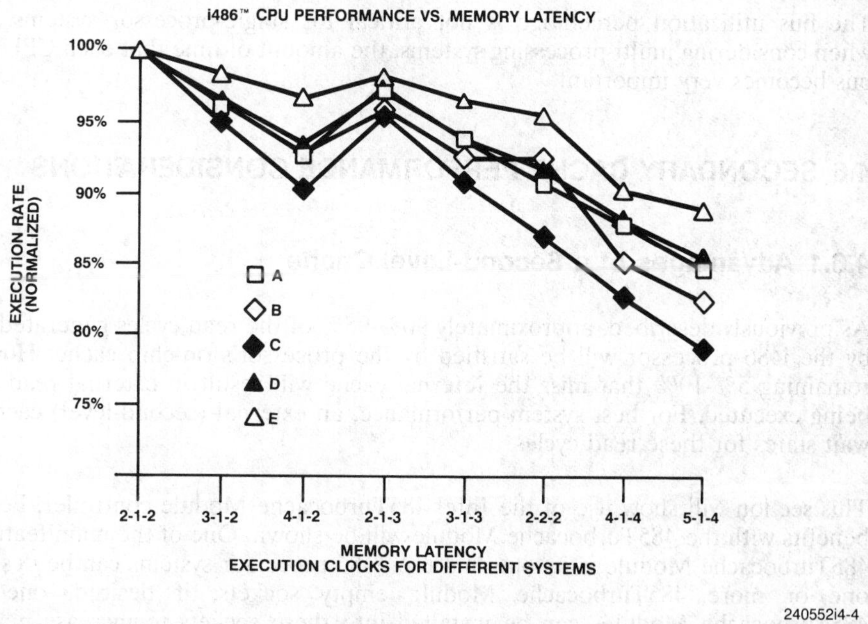

Figure 4-4. Effect of Wait States on Performance

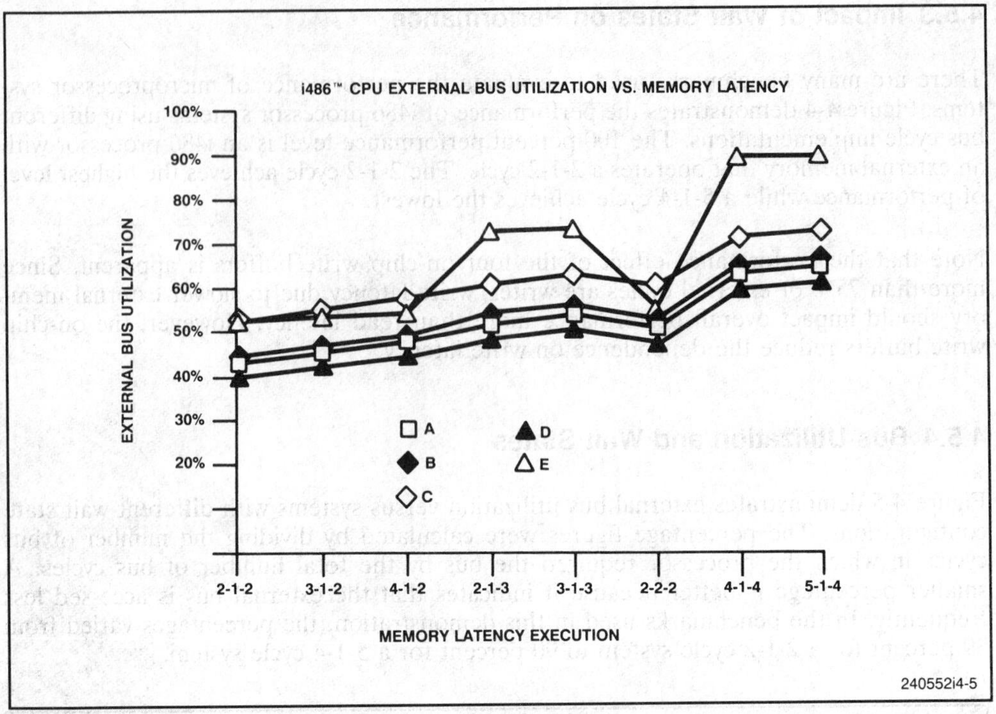

Figure 4-5. Effect of External Bus Utilization versus Wait States

The bus utilization percentage is not critical for single-processor systems. However, when considering multi-processing systems, the amount of time that each CPU needs the bus becomes very important.

4.6 SECONDARY CACHE PERFORMANCE CONSIDERATIONS

4.6.1 Advantages of a Second-Level Cache

As previously described, approximately 90%-95% of the read cycles generated internally by the i486 processor will be satisfied by the processor's on-chip cache. However, the remaining 5%-10% that miss the internal cache will result in external read bus cycles being executed. For best system performance, an external (second-level) cache reduces wait states for these read cycles.

This section will show use of the Intel 485Turbocache Module controller. Performance benefits with the 485Turbocache Module will be shown. One of the main features of the 485Turbocache Module is its optional use. i486 processor systems can be designed with one or more 485Turbocache Module empty sockets; if desired, one or more 485Turbocache Modules can be installed into these sockets to increase performance. Chapter 6 will discuss the 485Turbocache Module design in detail.

Different applications and operating environments will experience varying performance benefits from use of the 485Turbocache Module. Hit rates for second level caches depend on the application being executed and the randomness with which the application addresses memory. Systems which make extensive use of multitasking should see a very beneficial gain in system performance with use of the 485Turbocache Module.

4.6.2 The 485Turbocache Module Second-Level Cache

The 485Turbocache Module is a high-performance cache designed for the i486 processor, which provides 64- or 128-Kbytes of cache depth. Multiple 485Turbocache Modules can be cascaded to give 256 Kbyte or 512-Kbyte cache depths. The 485Turbocache Module is organized as a 64- or 128-Kbyte, 2-way set-associative memory. Like the processor, the 485Turbocache Module has a line size of four doublewords. On a cache read operation the address is presented to the 485Turbocache Module, and the tags are compared. If they match, a hit condition has occurred and the data is bursted to the i486 processor. Data can be sent over in two cycles for the first word, and one cycle for each of the subsequent three doublewords. This implies the fastest read cycle time for cache hits on the 485Turbocache Module. For cache misses, the data is fetched from the main memory, and then sent to both the i486 processor and the 485Turbocache Module. On write operations, the 485Turbocache Module operates like the i486 processor's cache by updating write hits and not updating write misses. The main memory is updated on all writes, because of the write-through policy.

4.6.3 System Performance with the 485Turbocache Module

The performance of the 485Turbocache Module is shown in Figure 4-6. The 1.0 level of performance reflects an i486 processor system that operates with 2-1-2 memory accesses. For example, a system which has 4-2-4 cycles for page hits and 7-2-5 cycles for page misses results in less than .6 of optimum (2-1-2) performance with no cache. Adding 256K of external cache and 1 level of write buffering to this system increases the performance level to greater than .9 optimum performance.

4.6.4 Impact of Secondary Cache on Bus Utilization

A secondary cache reduces the number of processor reads to main memory, lowering external system bus utilization. The benefit is more bandwidth available to other bus master devices like DMA or LAN controllers. Systems with multiple CPUs are sensitive to the amount of bus bandwidth used by each CPU. Note that with a write-through cache the minimum bus bandwidth is the number of writes performed.

4.7 DRAM DESIGN TECHNIQUES

An efficient DRAM memory design is needed for a high-performance i486 CPU system. For some applications, the principle of locality will not be as applicable. A common technique used to improve performance with DRAMs uses the commonly seen attribute

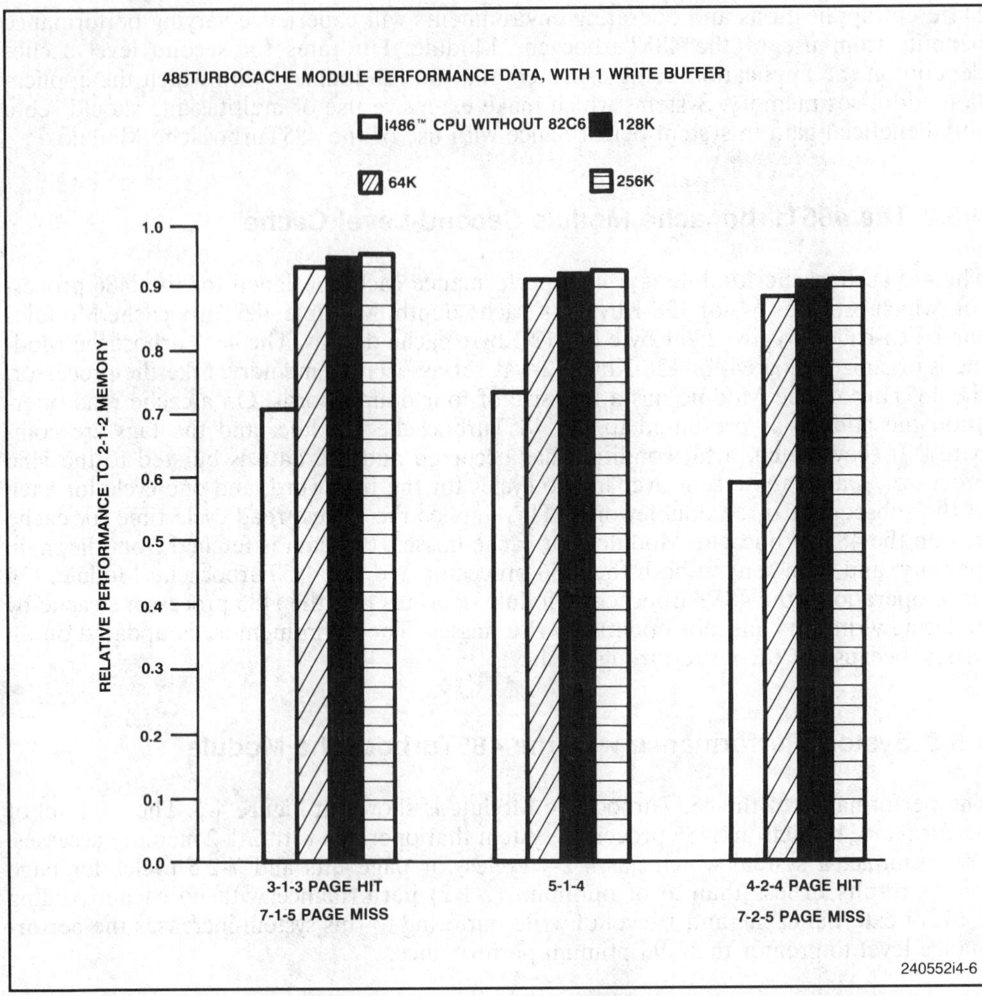

Figure 4-6. 485Turbocache Module Performance Data with 1 Write Buffer

of locality of reference in programs. This works well with the fast access modes offered by DRAMs using the same row address. As a result, system performance will be more dependent upon DRAM latency.

Normally, a DRAM access is made by first asserting RAS# (Row Address Strobe) to latch the presented row address into the DRAM device. As the DRAM devices have multiplexed address pins, the address must then be externally switched to present the column address. Finally, the CAS# (Column Address Strobe) is asserted to latch the column address and enable the DRAM output buffers. Refer to the Memory Design chapter for specific details of memory accessing.

The simplest DRAM design offers a fixed number of wait states for each access. As an example, a system could be designed such that all DRAM accesses occur in six clocks.

However, many DRAMs offer special modes of operation based on the policy of updating the row address which have higher performance. Some of these modes and their impact on performance are discussed below.

4.7.1 Static Column Design

A static column design partitions a DRAM array into physical pages of memory. Each page corresponds to a series of column addresses using the same row address. The memory page size depends on size of the memory used, and its row addresses. The first access into a page occurs as a normal access, with RAS# asserted followed by CAS# asserted. If the next access occurs to the same page in memory, then it is not necessary to update the row address. The previous row address remains latched in the DRAM. As the CPU drives a new address for the next access, the column address changes and the DRAM data outputs are driven with the corresponding data. It is not necessary to negate and reassert the CAS# signal for DRAMs that support static column design.

The use of static column DRAMs is particularly useful for high-speed burst cycles. As burst cycles will always be to the same memory page, designs may be implemented with static column DRAMs to provide one clock burst cycle.

Static column designs may use multiple banks of memory. For example, Figure 4-7 shows a static column memory map with four banks. The banks use the same RAS# signal, and the page size is effectively quadrupled. Consecutive accesses within the same row address to any bank results in high-speed accesses.

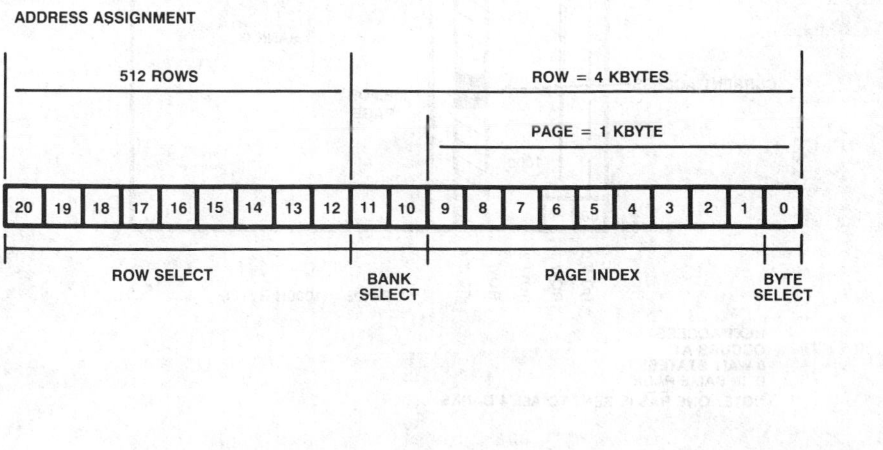

Figure 4-7. Static Column Memory Map (Part 1 of 2)

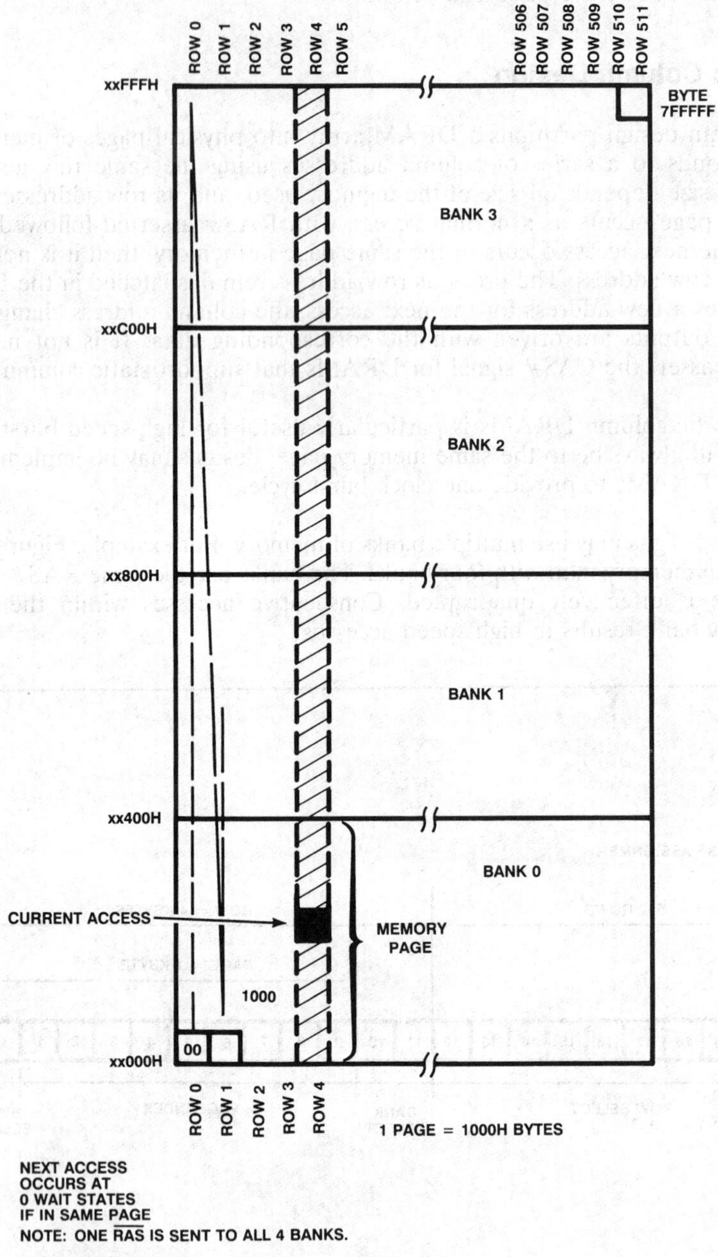

Figure 4-7. Static Column Memory Map (Part 2 of 2)

Note that i486 processor systems which use page memory techniques will experience lower page hit percentages than similar designs on the 386 CPU. Because of the on-chip cache of the i486 processor, the external bus cycles which occur will tend to be more randomly distributed throughout memory, reducing page hit percentage. However, writes will continue to show the same degree of locality as in a 386 SX microprocessor system.

4.7.2 Interleaving

A more complicated DRAM design technique is called interleaving. Interleaving is possible when more than one memory bank is used. Effective implementation of interleaving brings higher performance to a design. Specific memory design issues will be discussed in Chapter 5.

Interleaving controls each bank separately. As an access is occurring, the other (non-accessed) banks are being readied for their next access. Interleaving can help provide fast burst accesses for designs. In addition, another use of interleaving is to hide the RAS# precharge time, which is incurred on page misses for paged memory designs. As the number of banks is increased, the chances for hiding the precharge time is increased. As a result, the performance is increased with additional banks.

Figure 4-8 demonstrates the performance differences between an interleaved system supporting one clock bursting and a non-interleaved system in two applications. The

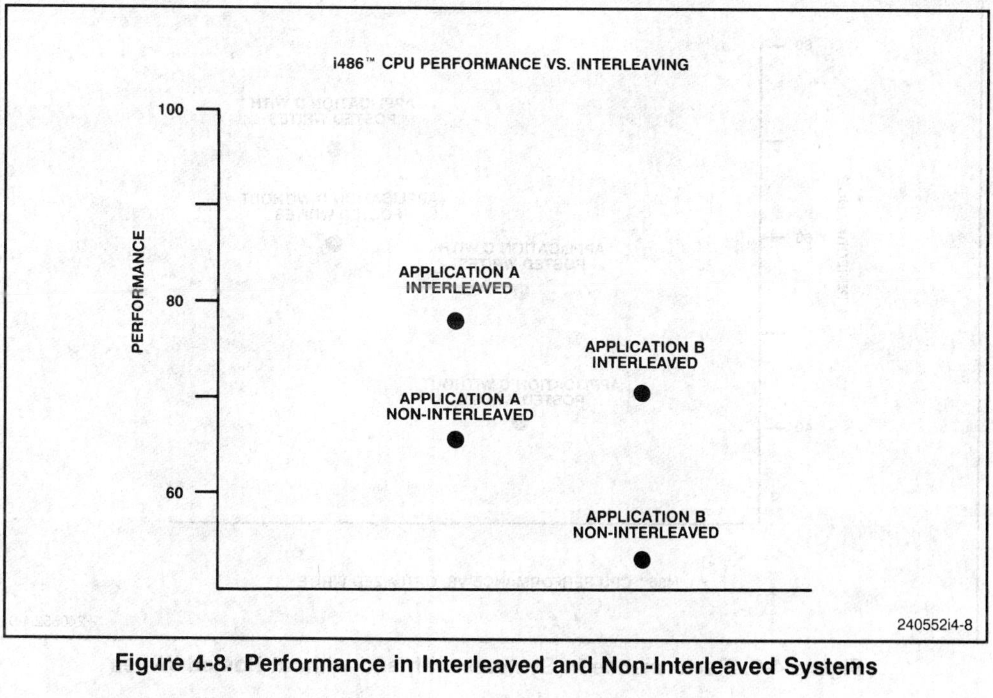

Figure 4-8. Performance in Interleaved and Non-Interleaved Systems

performance levels are measured with respect to a zero wait state (2-1-2 bus). Interleaving can add as much as 15% to system performance.

4.7.3 Impact of Performance for Posted Write Cycles

In an i486 processor system, the on-board cache reduces the external read cycles so that as much as 77 percent of the external bus cycles are write cycles. In program execution, writes occur in strings of two, about 60 to 70% of the time. Writes occur in strings of 3, 40-50% of the time. The DRAM subsystem must be optimized for write strings; one method is to support posted writes with write buffers. Posting writes means that RDY# is returned to the CPU before the write transaction is completed. This avoids the CPU depending on the write latency time. This is discussed further in the Memory Subsystem chapter. Figure 4-9 demonstrates the performance in two different applications and shows the improvement gained by using posted writes.

4.8 FLOATING-POINT PERFORMANCE

4.8.1 Floating-Point Execution Sequences

The floating-point unit on the i486 processor contains the logic to execute the floating-point instruction set that is 100% binary compatible to the 387™ DX math coprocessor

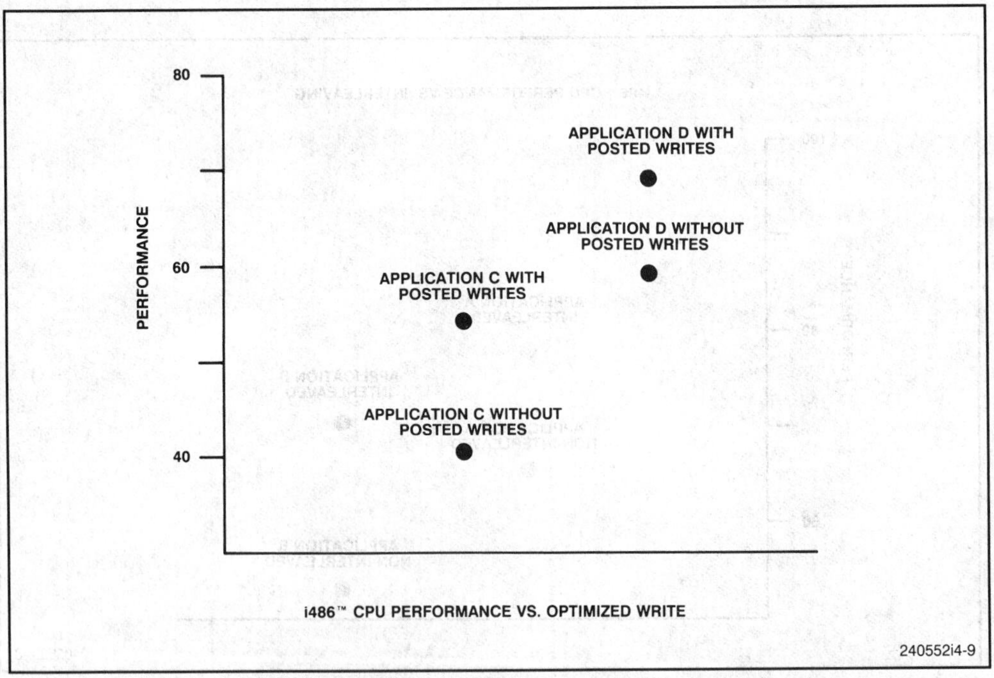

Figure 4-9. Performance in Systems with and without Posted Writes

(387 DX NPX). The floating-point unit operates in parallel with the arithmetic and logic unit, and provides arithmetic functions and transcendental functions. The enhanced floating-point unit provides three to four times the performance of the math coprocessor 387 DX NPX.

The on-chip floating-point unit has a multiplier that operates on eight bits per clock cycle, as opposed to two bits per clock cycle in the 387 DX NPX. An overlap of floating-point instruction execution and non-floating point instruction execution increases the overall throughput.

The floating-point unit can take advantage of pipelined instruction execution. Within the i486 processor, the floating-point instructions share the microcode ROM with integer instructions. However, floating-point operations do not utilize the microcode ROM after the operation has been prepared for execution. For example, only the first three clocks of the floating-point add, multiply and divide instructions use the microcode ROM. After the third clock, the floating-point unit completes the operations independently, and the microcode ROM can be utilized by non-floating point instructions.

Another feature that enhances performance is an efficient on-chip interface. The 386 DX CPU and the 387 DX NPX communicate asynchronously. The i486 CPU communicates with its on-chip floating-point unit synchronously allowing higher performance.

The i486 CPU's on-chip cache dramatically speeds floating-point loads and stores. For the 386/387 CPU, instructions such as FLD (floating-point load) will take 14-20 clock cycles if any external memory addressing is required. Once operands are on the internal stack, it takes 23 to 31 cycles to execute the floating-point add instruction, depending on the value of the operands. Finally an external memory store can take up to 11-44 cycles.

Because the floating-point unit of the i486 processor is integrated, the entire operation executes in fewer cycles. Data from the external memory can be cached. After that it can be accessed by the floating-point unit, and loaded into the stack in three cycles on a cache hit. The floating-point add instruction takes between 8 to 20 cycles depending on the value of the operands. Finally the store instruction takes 7 clocks.

Because the i486 processor provides a higher performance not only for floating point loads and stores, but also for floating-point compute operations, a 3x to 4x performance boost is realized for numerics-intensive routines. A large portion of the performance improvement is attributed to the fact that synchronous floating-point transfers occur on-chip.

4.8.2 Performance of the Floating-Point Unit

To achieve three to four times the floating-point performance of the 387 DX NPX, the i486 processor's floating-point circuitry has been enhanced to reduce the number of clock counts needed to execute frequently used instructions. Also, the interface to the processor's registers and buses is much more efficient since all of the interacting units are on the same chip.

Table 4-3 compares the number of clock counts per instruction on the 387 DX math coprocessor with the floating-point unit of the i486 processor.

The Whetstone benchmark measures the performance of processors executing floating-point multiplication, addition, subtraction, division, exponential and trigonometric instructions. Both single-precision and double-precision operations are exercised. The Whetstone benchmark also measures overall floating-point and integer performance by duplicating the type and frequency of floating-point and integer operations used in more than 100 scientific programs.

Figure 4-10 shows the results of Whetstones performance simulations on the 386 DX processor and the i486 processor. As seen here, a 25-MHz i486 processor significantly outperforms a 33-MHz 386/387 processor in floating-point operations.

Table 4-3. Floating-Point Instruction Execution Comparison

Instruction	Clock Counts 387™ DX Coprocessor	Clock Counts i486™ CPU
FLD-Load	14	3
FST-Store	11	3
FADD/FSUB Floating ADD/SUB	23-31	8-20
FMUL Floating multiply	29-57	16
FDIV Floating divide	88	73

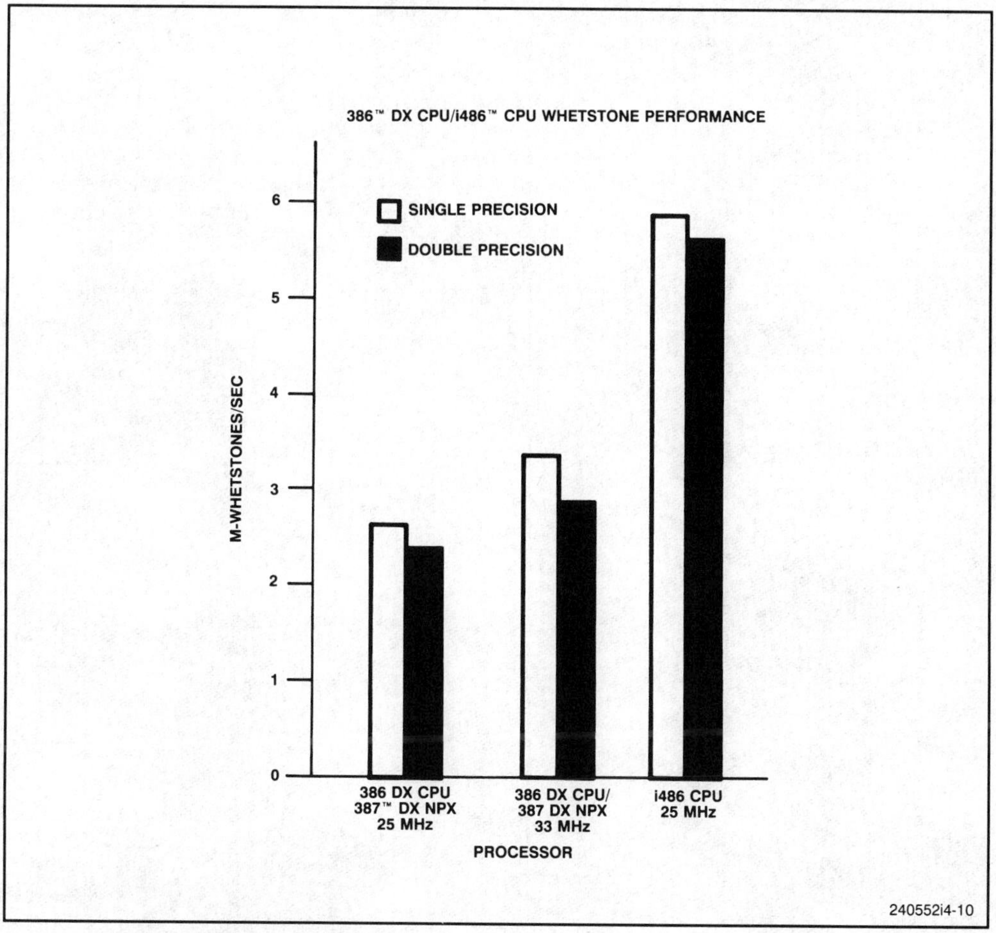

Figure 4-10. Whetstone Performance of the 386™ CPU and the i486™ CPU

Memory Subsystem Design 5

CHAPTER 5
MEMORY SUBSYSTEM DESIGN

5.1 INTRODUCTION

The i486™ CPU contains several improvements over its predecessor, the highly successful 386™ CPU. One of the most important of these is the processor's data access rate. The i486 CPU can access instructions and data from its on-chip cache in the same clock cycle. To support the processor's redesigned internal data path, the external bus has also been optimized and can access external memory at twice the rate of the 386 CPU. The internal cache requires rapid access to entire cache lines. Invalidation cycles must be supported to maintain consistency with external memory. All of these functions must be supported by the external memory system. Without them, the full performance potential of the CPU cannot be attained.

The requirements of todays multitasking and multiprocessor operating systems also put increased demand on the external memory system. OS support functions such as paging and context switching can degrade reference locality. Without efficient access to external memory, the performance of these functions is degraded.

Second-level caching is a technique used to improve the memory interface. Some applications, such as multiuser office computers, require this feature to meet performance goals. Single-user systems, on the other hand, may not warrant the extra cost. Given the variety of applications incorporating the i486 CPU, memory system architecture will be very diverse.

In this chapter, we will work with an example to discuss the details of memory system design. In the example, we have supported as many functions of the CPU as possible. An optional second-level cache is included. A write buffer is also implemented to reduce write latency. The cache supports zero wait state read cycles. The DRAM controller supports the following devices with the wait states shown in Table 5-2. The DRAM speed given in Table 5-1 is the RAS access time (tRAC). Table 5-2 summarizes the bus clocks required for each function.

Many of the functions and optimizations included here will not be required in every application. The example provides guidelines for the hardware designer but will not necessarily provide the optimal cost/performance solution for many applications. For example, 11 PLDs are required to implement the memory control logic partially due to the implementation of a back-off capability. An address register must also be used to

Table 5-1. DRAM Device Requirements

CPU Clock Frequency	DRAM Speed
25 MHz	100 ns
33 MHz	70 ns

Table 5-2. Clock Latencies for DRAM Functions

DRAM Function	First Access Burst	Subsequent Burst Accesses	Write Cycles
Page hit	3	1	2
Page miss	7	1	5*

*Latency only incurred for back-to-back cycles.

implement this function. If this function is not used, the control logic can be substantially reduced. These and other optimizations will be discussed in the summary of this chapter. The design has been tested as a prototype, however, it may be used as shown in Appendix B.

The discussion assumes a working knowledge of computer system design. Items discussed but not explained include DRAM operation, PLD programming and operation, worst-case timing analysis and i486 CPU bus operation. The complete schematics and PLD equations are included in Appendix B.

5.2 PROCESSOR AND CACHE FEATURE REVIEW

The improvements made to the CPU bus interface obviously impact the memory subsystem design. It is important to understand the impact of these features before attempting to define the system. This section is a review of the bus features which affect the memory interface. The features and their impact on memory system design is discussed.

5.2.1 The Burst Cycle

The i486 CPU's burst bus cycle feature has more impact on the memory logic than any other feature. It is the most significant departure from previous bus architectures. A large portion of the control logic is dedicated to supporting this feature. The second level cache control is also primarily dedicated to supporting burst cycles.

To understand why the logic is designed this way, we must first understand the function of the burst cycle. Burst cycles are generated by the CPU if, and only if, two events occur. First, the CPU must request a cycle which is longer in bytes than the data bus can accommodate. Second, the BRDY# signal must be activated to terminate the cycle. When these two events occur a burst cycle will take place. Note that this cycle will occur regardless of the state of the KEN# input. The KEN# input's function is discussed in the next section.

With this definition we see that several cases are included as "burstable." Some examples of burstable cycles are listed in Table 5-3. These cycle's length is shown in bytes to clarify the case listed.

Table 5-3. Access Length of Typical CPU Functions

Bus Cycle	Size (Bytes)
All code fetches	16
Descriptor loads	8
Cacheable reads	16
Floating-point operand loads	8
Bus size 8 (16) writes	4 (Max.)

The last two cases show that write cycles are burstable. In the last case a write cycle is transferred on an 8- or 16-bit bus. If BRDY# is returned to terminate this cycle the CPU will generate another without activating ADS#.

Using the burst write feature has debatable performance benefit. Some systems may implement special functions which benefit from the use of burst writes. However, the i486 CPU does not write cache lines. Therefore, all write cycles are 4 bytes long. Also, most of the devices which use dynamic bus sizing are read only. This fact further reduces the utility of burst writes.

Due to these facts, the design example used here does not implement burst write cycles. In fact, the BRDY# input is only asserted during main memory read cycles. RDY# is used to terminate all memory write cycles. RDY# is also used for all cycles which are not in the memory subsystem or are not capable of supporting burst cycles. The RDY# input is used, for example, to terminate an EPROM or I/O cycle.

5.2.2 The KEN# Input

The primary purpose of the KEN# input is to determine whether a cycle is to be cached. Only read data and code cycles can be cached. Therefore, these cycles are the only cycles affected by the KEN# input.

Figure 5-1 shows a typical burst cycle. In this sequence the value of KEN# is important in two different places. First, to begin a cacheable cycle KEN# must be active the clock before BRDY# is returned. Second, KEN# is sampled the clock before BLAST# is active. At this time the CPU determines whether this line will be written to the cache.

The state of KEN# also determines when read cycles can be bursted. Most read cycles are initiated as 4 byte long from the CPU's cache unit. When KEN# is sampled active the clock before BRDY# or RDY# is returned, the cycle is converted to a 16-byte cache line fill by the bus unit. This way, a cycle which would not have been bursted can now be bursted by activating BRDY#.

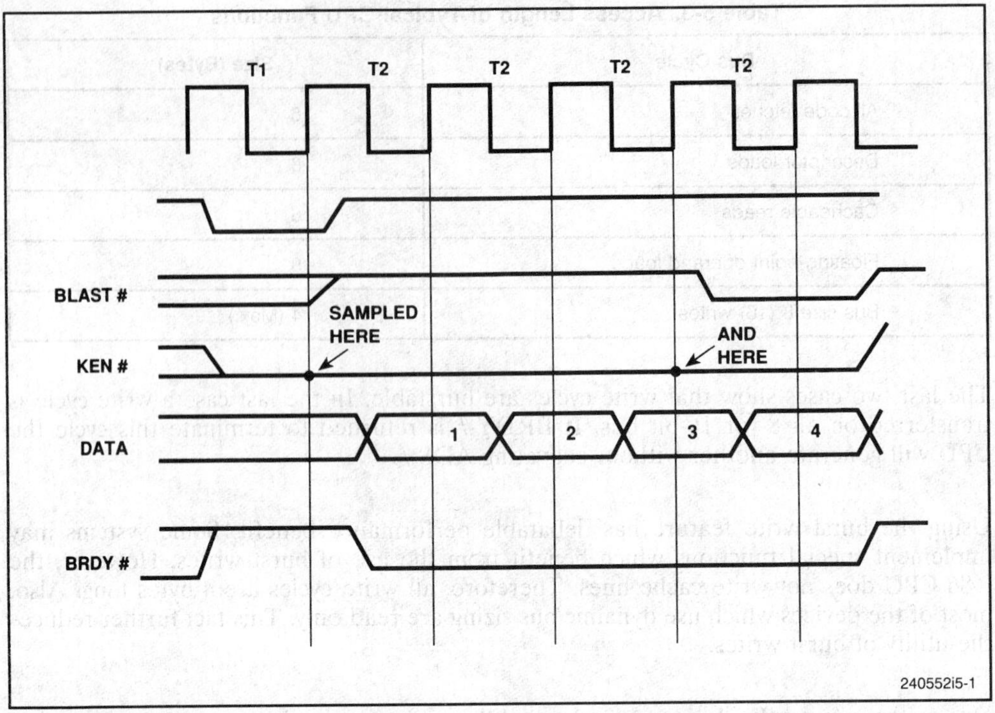

Figure 5-1. Typical Burst Cycle

Some read cycles can be bursted without activating KEN#. The most prevalent example of this type of read cycle is code fetches. All code fetches are generated as 16-byte cycles from the CPU's cache unit. So, regardless of the state of KEN#, code fetches are always burstable. In addition, several types of data read cycles are generated as 8-byte cycles. These cycles, mentioned previously, are descriptor loads and floating-point operand loads. These cycles can also be bursted at any time.

It's obvious that the use of the KEN# input affects performance. The design example used in Figure 5-1 illustrates one way to use this signal effectively.

The primary concern when using KEN# is generating it in time for zero wait state read cycles. Most main memory cycles will be zero wait state if a second level cache is implemented. In this example, the main memory is one wait state during most read cycles. Any cache access will take place with zero wait states. KEN# must, therefore, be valid during the first T2 of any read cycle.

Once this requirement is established, a problem arises. Decode functions are inherently asynchronous. Therefore, the decoded output which generates KEN# must be synchronized. If not, the setup and hold times of the CPU will be violated and internal metastability will result. With synchronization, the delay required to generate KEN# will beat least three clocks. In this example 4 clocks are required. In either case the KEN# signal will not be valid before BRDY# is returned for zero or one wait state cycles.

This problem is resolved if KEN# is made normally active. Figure 5-2 illustrates this function. In this diagram KEN# is active during the first two clocks of the burst cycle. If this is a data read cycle, KEN# being active at this time causes it to be converted to a 16-byte length. The decode and synchronization of KEN# takes place during the first two T2 states of the cycle. If the cycle turns out to be non-cacheable, KEN# will be deactivated in the third T2. Otherwise KEN# will be left active and the data retrieved will be written to the cache.

Some memory devices may be slow enough that 16-byte cycles are undesireable. In this case more than three wait states will exist. The KEN# signal can be deactivated prior to returning RDY# or BRDY# if three or more wait states are present. As a result these slow cycles will would not be converted to 16-byte cache line fills.

5.2.3 Bus Characteristics

The internal cache causes other effects which impact the memory subsystem design. Perhaps the most obvious of these is the effect on bus traffic. The fact that the internal cache uses the write-through policy dramatically increases the number of write bus cycles. Figure 5-3 illustrates this effect. The chart on the left shows the bus cycle mix for

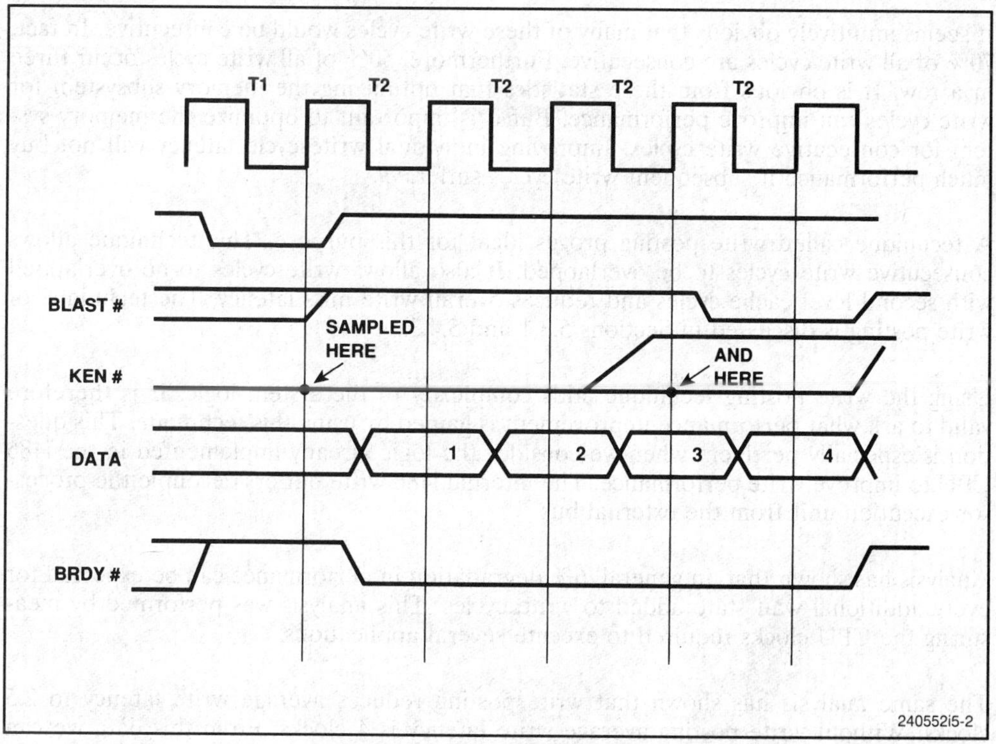

Figure 5-2. Burst Cycle: KEN# Normally Active

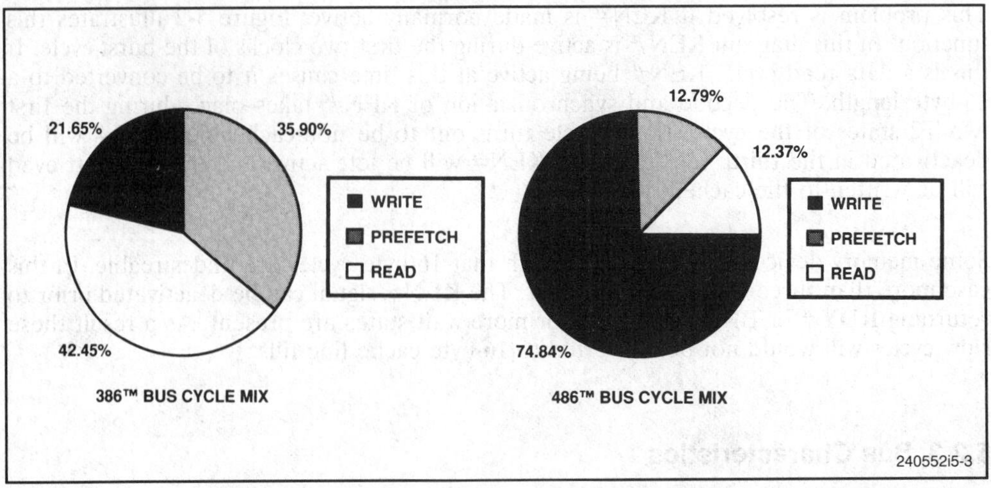

Figure 5-3. 386™ Bus Cycle Mix/486™ Bus Cycle Mix

an application executed with the 386 DX CPU. The chart on the right shows the same application executed with the i486 CPU. The percentage of write bus cycles jumps to 70% from 30% when this application is executed with the i486 CPU.

It seems intuitively obvious that many of these write cycles would be consecutive. In fact, 70% of all write cycles are consecutive. Furthermore, 50% of all write cycles occur three in a row. It is obvious from these statistics that optimizing the memory subsystem for write cycles can improve performance. But it is important to optimize the memory system for consecutive write cycles. Improving individual write cycle latency will not buy much performance if subsequent write cycles suffer.

A technique called write posting proves ideal for this purpose. This technique allows consecutive write cycles to be overlapped. It also allows write cycles to be overlapped with second level cache cycles and reduces overall write miss latency. The technique of write posting is discussed in Sections 5.3.1 and 5.4.3.

Using the write posting technique adds complexity to the system logic. It is therefore valid to ask what performance improvement is gained by using this technique. This question is especially pertinent when we consider the logic already implemented in the i486 CPU to improve write performance. The internal i486 write buffers decouple the processor execution unit from the external bus.

Analysis has shown that, in general, 6% degradation in performance can be expected for every additional wait state added to write cycles. This analysis was performed by measuring the CPU clocks required to execute several applications.

The same analysis has shown that write posting reduces average write latency to 2.5 clocks. Without write posting average write latency is 4 clocks. From this data we can conclude that approximately 9% performance improvement can be obtained by using write posting. This improvement may increase due to other affects. These affects, such as overlapping write cycles with cache reads, are discussed in subsequent sections of this chapter.

5.2.4 Second-Level Cache

Several different types of second-level cache architectures are possible candidates for use with the i486 CPU. For single CPU systems the different architectures offer similar performance benefits in most cases. The reason they are so similar is the mechanism which improves performance. The primary benefit of the second level cache is bus cycle latency reduction.

In most systems which incorporate a single i486 CPU, bus traffic from other bus masters is minimal. With any reasonable memory system the CPU uses at most 50% to 70% of the bus. Therefore reduction of bus cycle latency is the only performance benefit external logic can offer.

The second-level cache used in this example is an economical method of reducing read cycle latency. The 485Turbocache Module contains the control circuits, data and tag ram required to implement a 128K byte cache. It is organized as a two way set associative cache. Modules can be cascaded to provide up to 512K bytes of cache memory. This device is described completely in Chapter 6.

One of the most interesting aspects of this device is it can be a system option. To provide this capability the device is configured as a look-aside cache. It monitors the CPU address and control signals. When a cycle occurs in which the cache can supply data, it intervenes. The cache module then supplies an entire 16-byte line with no wait states.

The performance improvement offered by this cache is substantial in some environments. This performance improvement is particularly obvious when executing multitasking, multiuser operating systems such as UNIX and OS/2. Some users, however, may not require the performance improvement offered by the cache. In these cases the cache as an option is attractive.

By designing the cache subsystem as an option both users requirements can be met. A single system design can be manufactured for both customers. The UNIX or OS/2 user can add the cache module. Other users may or may not require the module. They can choose the system configuration which meets their price-performance needs.

A few functions must be considered when using the 485Turbocache Module as an option. First, the DRAM logic must be capable of handling cache intervene cycles. To perform this function it must monitor one of two signals. The activation of the BRDYO# or START signals indicates the cache's intention to intervene. When these signals are active, the DRAM control logic must ignore the current read cycle.

Second, several cache signals must be combined with CPU signals for proper operation. The cacheability indicator signals, SKEN# and CKEN#, are two of these. These signals can be combined with the CPU's KEN # signals in two ways. If SKEN# is connected to a separate decode signal, some memory can be made non-cacheable in the CPU's cache while it is cacheable in the 485Turbocache Module. Alternatively, the SKEN# and KEN# inputs may be connected together. In this configuration, all cacheable memory can be contained in either cache. Figure 5-4 shows the proper connection of these signals for both configurations.

The last function required is the combination of the BRDYO# signal. BRDYO# must be combined with other system burst ready signals to create the CPU BRDY# input. These three logic functions are all that is required for proper operation of one module. Additional functions are required for use of more than one module. Other configurations also require additional logic. All configurations will require the three functions listed above. These are the only functions which have been tested in this example. Further discussion on 485Turbocache Module system configurations are discussed in Chapter 6.

5.3 DRAM INTERFACE OVERVIEW

The i486 CPU bus interface unit integrates several functions which improve the memory access rate. These features must be supported by the memory subsystem to provide the

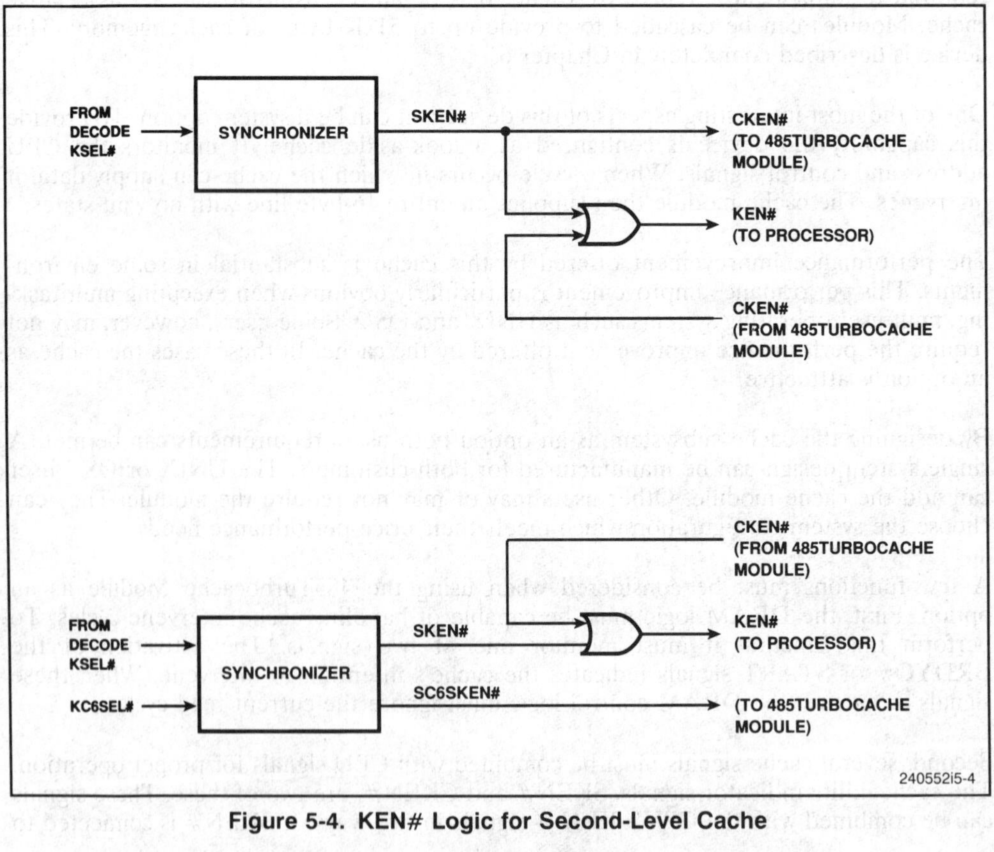

Figure 5-4. KEN# Logic for Second-Level Cache

intended performance benefit. They are supported by the memory subsystem example described in this chapter. The example also includes logic support for a second-level cache. An overview of the subsystem is presented in this section. Details of the function and logic design of this subsystem are presented in later sections.

This subsystem follows a moduler design. Only minor changes to particular logic sections are needed to implement variations. For instance, the PLD which generates the CAS# signal needs only minor changes to support Static Column mode DRAMs. It is also simple to implement a non-interleaved DRAM controller based on this design.

Other possible optimizations will be pointed out throughout the chapter. This first section summarizes only the features and functions present in the design example presented in this section.

5.3.1 Functional Blocks

Two common design techniques are employed in interfacing the i486 CPU to DRAMs. The first, interleaving, is used to support the burst bus feature. The second, write posting, is used to reduce write cycle latency. Both techniques improve performance, and without them, performance is degraded by the access requirements of currently available DRAMs.

Interleaving can be implemented in several ways. Here, alternate 32-bit DRAM banks are accessed. The bank accessed is determined by the value of A2. In this way, even DWORDs (A2=0) are stored in one bank while odd DWORDs (A2=1) are stored in the other. When data is retrieved from memory during a cache line fill, cycles are overlapped to allow single clock DWORD accesses.Timing of this operation is detailed in the next section.

A multiplexor alternates data flow between the DRAM banks and the appropriate data path is selected according to the value of A2. The multiplexor prevents bus contention.

Write posting, bus cycles are again overlapped to reduce latency. Figure 5-5 illustrates how this technique is applied within the write cycle. The RDY# signal terminates the cycle in the clock after ADS# becomes active. This creates a zero wait state write cycle, the fastest possible.

When the cycle terminates, however, data must still be written to memory. A delay allows additional DRAM access time. Figure 5-5 shows that data is actually written to memory two clocks after RDY# is returned to the CPU. The CAS# signal completes the write cycle four clocks after it is started by the CPU.

Write data and address registers support the posted write function by holding write data and address after RDY# is returned to the CPU. These registers are required to allow the CPU to start another cycle immediately following the first (see Figure 5-5). ADS# is activated in the clock after RDY# is returned to the CPU. This cycle starts before the first is complete, and the cycles overlap by two clocks.

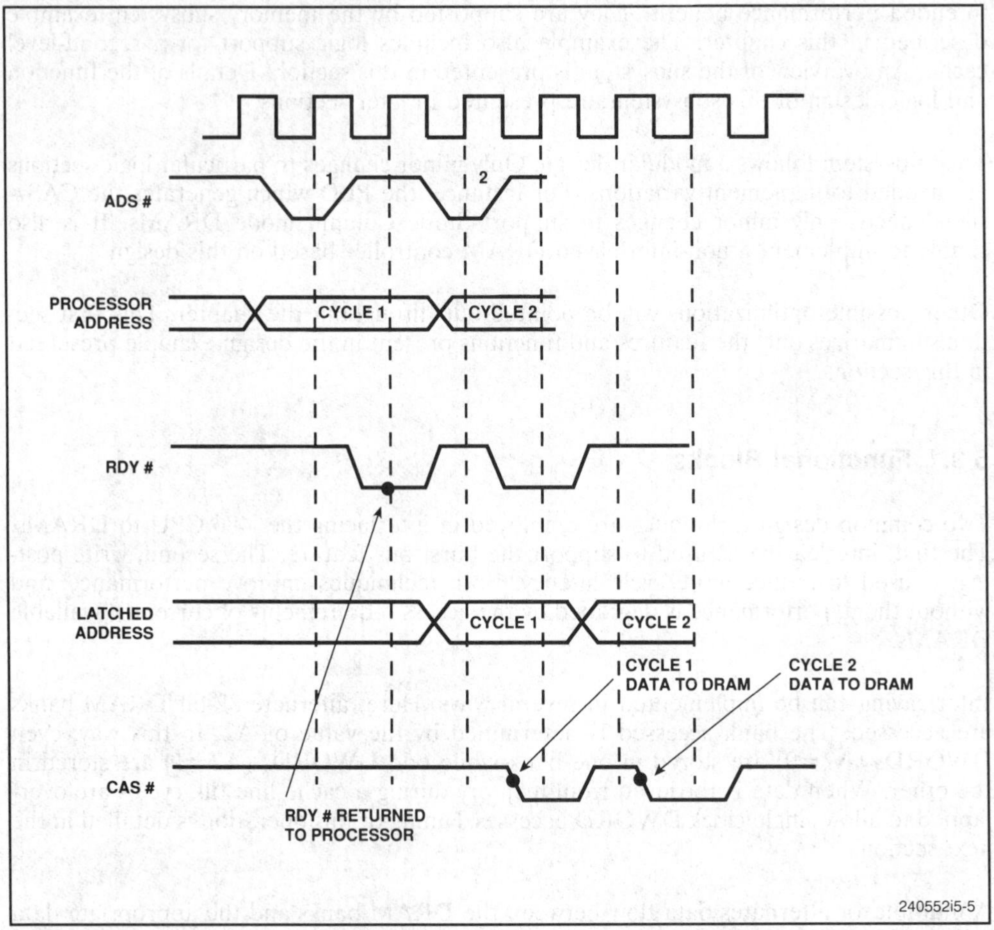

Figure 5-5. Write "Posting"

In effect the write cycle completes in two clocks. Write cycles can be overlapped in this manner indefinitely. The timing and logic required to support this function is described in Section 5.4.3.

Address registers also support invalidation with the AHOLD signal. They are required if AHOLD is activated when bus are cycles in progress to hold the current address while the bus cycle completes.

The efficient CPU interface and invalidation support make this DRAM subsystem well-suited for use with an optional cache. The memory system includes specific functions designed to support the optional 485Turbocache Module (see Chapter 6). The subsystem supports 256K × 4 and 1 Mbyte × 1 DRAM configurations. The minimum memory configuration is 2 Mbytes with 256K × 4 devices; the maximum is 16 Mbytes with 1 Mbyte × 1 devices. Additional banks can be added to increase the memory capacity.

The control logic for this example is implemented with EPLDs. The modular approach allows quick modification so that the example can be tailored for specific implementation requirements.

The control state machine is distributed among the various EPLDs, and each functional block receives control input from other blocks. In addition most of the functional blocks are implemented as state machines.

Figure 5-5 is a top level block diagram of the memory system. This diagram depicts the sections of logic that will be described subsequently. We will first discuss the address path logic.

5.3.2 Address Path Logic

Unlike processors without on-chip caches, the address bus of the i486 processor is bidirectional. The address pins serve as inputs whenever external memory is changed by DMA or another CPU. The address is driven into the CPU to invalidate the corresponding cache entry if present.

Invalidation of the i486 CPU's internal cache can be performed in several different ways. This example supports invalidation cycles during a memory access.

As described in the previous section, AHOLD is used to perform the invalidation function. AHOLD tristates the 486 address bus. Address registers must be used to hold the address to allow the current bus cycle to be completed. These registers hold the current address when AHOLD is activated.

The registers shown in Figure 5-6 hold the entire row and column address, as well as the current byte enables and control definition. These signals are latched at the rising clock edge of the first T2 of a bus cycle. They must be held from this edge to allow zero wait state write cycles. See Section 5.4 for a more detailed discussion of the individual cycles.

Registers with enable inputs are needed. The enable input can select the CLK edge appropriate for latching the address and control state. The control logic generates the enable signal ALD which disables the CLK input of the registers during a bus cycle. When ALD is active (High) the current row and column addresses are held in the registers. 74AS823 registers have enable inputs and are used in this example.

An additional address register is required for posted write cycles. This register holds the write column address. The address is latched only on write cycles and is held until the write cycle completes at the DRAM.

Separate write and read address paths are implemented with a 3 to 1 address multiplexor. The read address path is required to meet the timing of a three CLKs read cycle. In this case the read address must propagate through the address mux one CLK sooner than the write address. If the initial read access is 4 CLKs long the read and write address paths can be combined. See Section 5.4.1 for a complete description of read cycle timing. The third address path is for the row address.

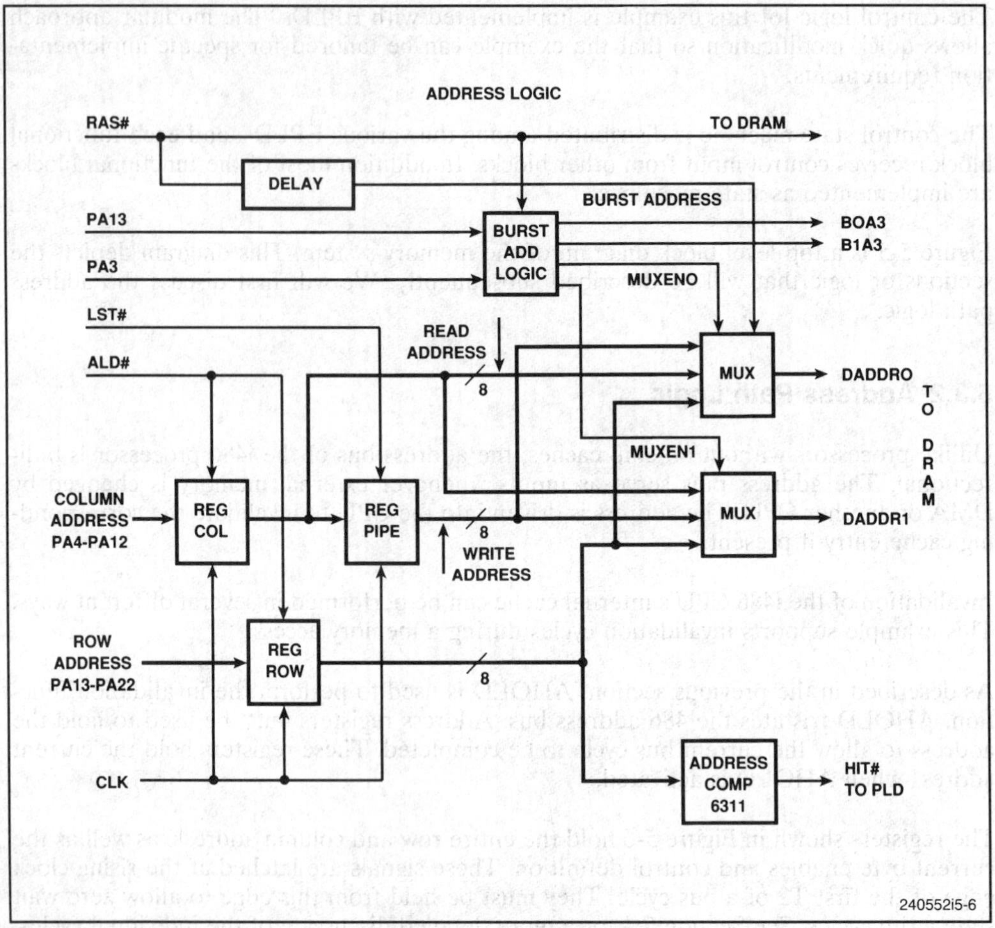

Figure 5-6. Address Logic

A delay line is used to meet the row address DRAM hold time requirement (tRAH). The RAS# signal is delayed 20 ns to create the DRAS# signal. This signal is used as the multiplexor path select input. When DRAS# is inactive (high) the multiplexor always selects the row address path. When DRAS# is active (low) the mux enable signal (MEN0# or MEN1#) controls whether the read path or the write path is selected.

The comparator and register combination is connected to the row address path to generate the HIT# signal. This signal indicates that the current cycles address is in the same DRAM row as that of the previous cycle and also determines whether RAS# will be deactivated.

In this example a standard component designed specifically for this purpose isused. This component contains a register and a comparator. The register in this component holds the previous row address. When a bus cycle occurs to a new DRAM row, the new row address is latched. The RALE signal enables the row address latch.

The timing of this component meets the requirements of a 33-MHz CPU clock. Discrete registers and comparators can be used to improve the timing of the HIT# signal, if desired.

The last important address logic component is the burst address generator. This state machine generate A3 and A2 during burst accesses and is needed to achieve zero wait state performance during burst cycles. It predicts the value of A2 and A3. Section 5.4.2 contains a complete description of the burst cycle timing.

Note that because interleaving is used, A3 is the lowest order DRAM address. Two A3 equivalent signals are generated. One for Bank 0 (B0A0) and one for Bank (B1A0). These signals are connected directly to the DRAM devices to meet critical timing requirements. The signals must also reflect the lowest order row address during miss cycles. As a result A13 is, therefore, an input to this logic. It is the lowest order row address when 1 MB × 1 DRAMs are used.

5.3.3 Data Path

A2 must also be predicted during burst read accesses. For this purpose, the burst address logic creates the DATASEL signal. DATASEL reflects the value of A2 for each access of a burst cycle and is used to control the data multiplexor as shown in Figure 5-7.

During burst cycles, the data multiplexor alternates between the bank 0 and bank 1 data paths. A2 must alternate states each clock for interleaving to function properly. The i486 CPU's burst address sequence is defined such that A2 changes state on every access (see Chapter 3).

A2 also selects the bank to which data is written. Data path logic is not involved in steering data during writes. Figure 5-7 shows separate data registers for each bank. Separate registers are only required to keep the data paths separate. These registers hold the same write data on every write cycle. The CAS# and WE# (write enable) signals control doubleword and byte steering.

Because of write data timing, the data registers must have the enable function (see Section 5.2.2). This function, can be used to select the clock upon which data is latched. The processor clock can be used as the register clock input to guarantee proper data setup and hold times.

As Figure 5-7 indicates, the MRDY# signal enables the write data registers and terminates memory write cycles. Data is therefore latched during the last clock of any write cycle.

MRDY# is restricted to write cycles while the MBRDY# signal is used for read cycles. The need for these signals illustrates the convenience of the CPU's dual-ready inputs. The MBRDY# signal enables the output of the data path multiplexor to prevent bus contention.

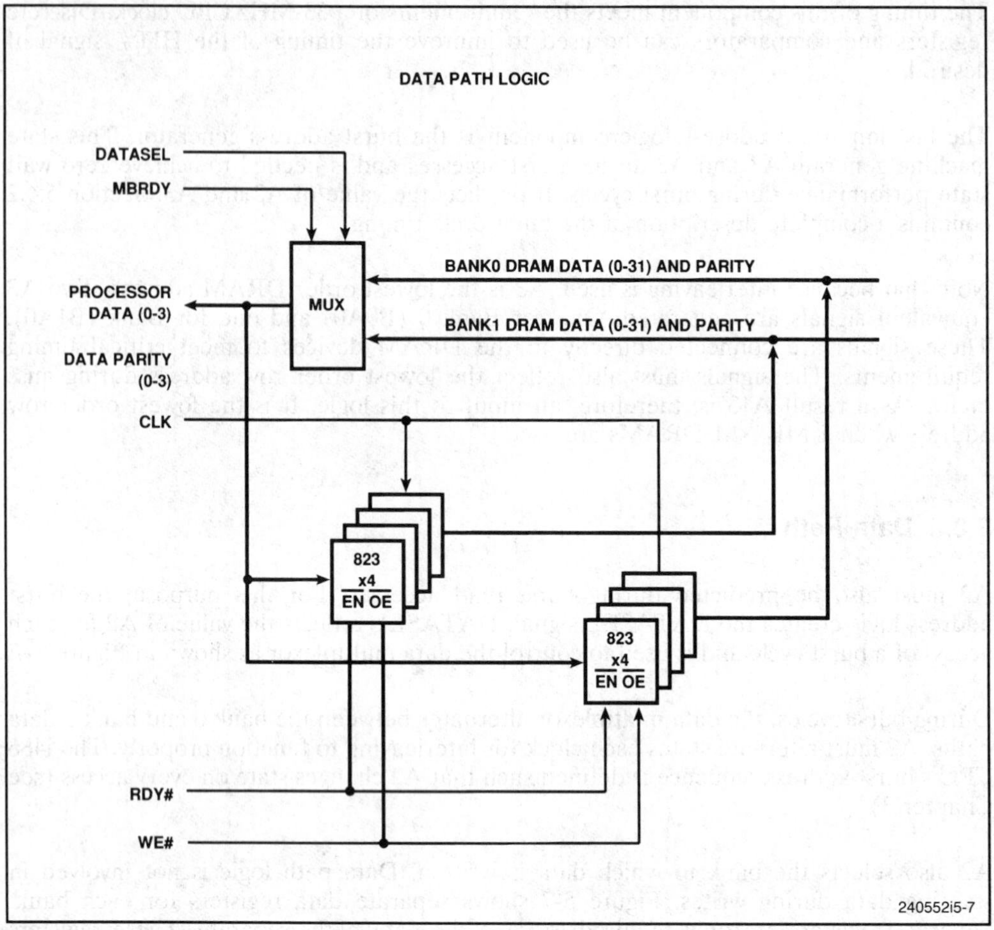

Figure 5-7. Data Path Logic

These ready signals are combined with similar system logic signals to form the processor RDY# and BRDY# inputs. I/O, peripheral and other non-burst devices can use the RDY# input. Burst devices, such as a second level cache controller must also use the BRDY# input. The MBRDY# and MRDY# signals are, therefore, used only with the DRAM control logic. They are isolated from the rest of the system by combinatorial logic.

5.3.4 Second-Level Cache Support

Second level cache strategies for the i486 CPU are diverse and application dependent. Chapter 6 discusses the requirements and tradeoffs of different cache strategies. The example described in this chapter illustrates a second-level cache strategy that is ideal for single CPU systems.

The 485Turbocache Module second-level cache used in this example is optional and is used to complement the i486 internal cache to improve the performance when running complex applications and operating systems. Some users will not require the extra performance. Since the cache is optional, O.E.M.'s or end-users can decide whether it should be included. System board design and manufacturing costs are thus eased since one system board supports multiple performance requirements.

The 485Turbocache Module is a completely self contained cache module. Optionality is accomplished by including control logic, tag RAM and data RAM in one package. A socket is added to the system board in much the same manner as a math coprocessor socket. In systems which, for example, run UNIX, the cache module is simply plugged in. The 485Turbocache Module is described in Chapter 6.

This option must, of course, be supported by the system logic. Specifically, the memory control logic is directly interfaced to the cache module. The DRAM controller example described here is particularly well-suited for this cache strategy.

The support included in the 485Turbocache Module's memory control logic for the 485Turbocache Module is illustrated in Figure 5-8. Since the 485Turbocache Module is a write-through cache, provision must be made for read cycles. When read data is found in the second-level cache, the cycle is called a cache hit. At the time this cycle is determined to be a cache hit, it has already been started in the DRAM controller. This cycle must be aborted by the DRAM controller.

The BRDYO# signal from the 485Turbocache Module provides a convenient cache hit indication. This signal is included in the decoder function. When a cache hit occurs, the DRAM controller aborts the cycle. The memory chip select signal is not activated and the first level control logic is reset aborting the cycle. The control logic then waits for another cycle to start. This function is very similar to the back-off function.

Like the i486 internal cache, the 485Turbocache Module supports non-cacheable memory by decoding. The SKEN# input is analogous to the i486 CPU's KEN# input. This function is also supported by the decode logic. Note that, as with the KEN# signal, SKEN# must be synchronized to the CPU clock.

Separate cache enable inputs also allow areas of memory to be noncacheable in the i486 CPU internal cache yet cachable in the second level cache. This feature is convenient for BIOS.

5.3.5 Control Logic

Memory control logic generates the signals that control the memory devices, multiplexors, and registers described earlier. These control signals can be generated in a variety of ways and this example employs a distributed state machine.

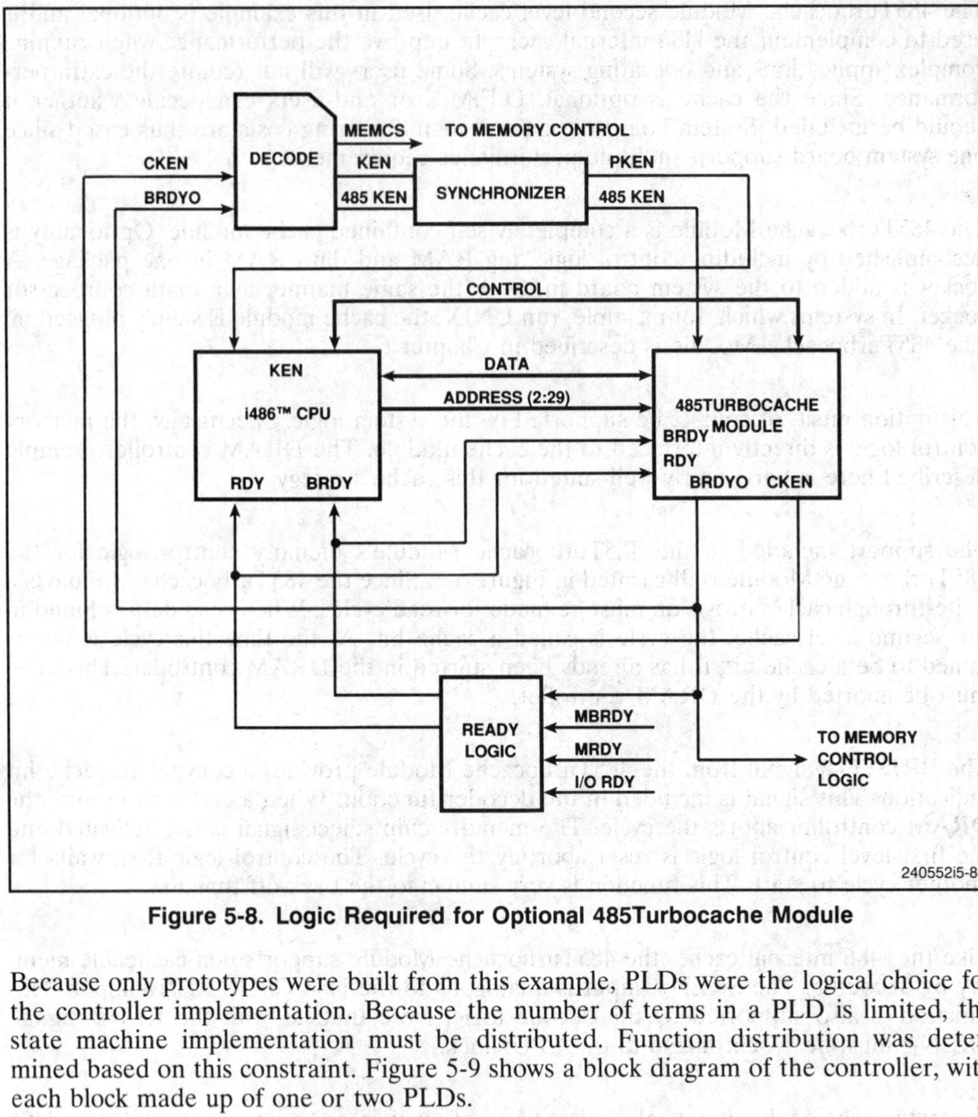

Figure 5-8. Logic Required for Optional 485Turbocache Module

Because only prototypes were built from this example, PLDs were the logical choice for the controller implementation. Because the number of terms in a PLD is limited, the state machine implementation must be distributed. Function distribution was determined based on this constraint. Figure 5-9 shows a block diagram of the controller, with each block made up of one or two PLDs.

There are two levels of logic in the controller shown in Figure 5-9. The first is made up of two PLDs, one which tracks bus cycles and another which generates the MRDY# signal. The first level signals to PLDs in the second level that a cycle has started. The second level is made up of several PLDs which generate the actual control signals such as RAS# and CAS#.

Implementing the controller in this manner has two important advantages. First, more decode time is allowed. The cycle start signal, CIP#, is used by the second-level logic to sample the decode output. CIP# is valid in the first T2 of any bus cycle. As a result,

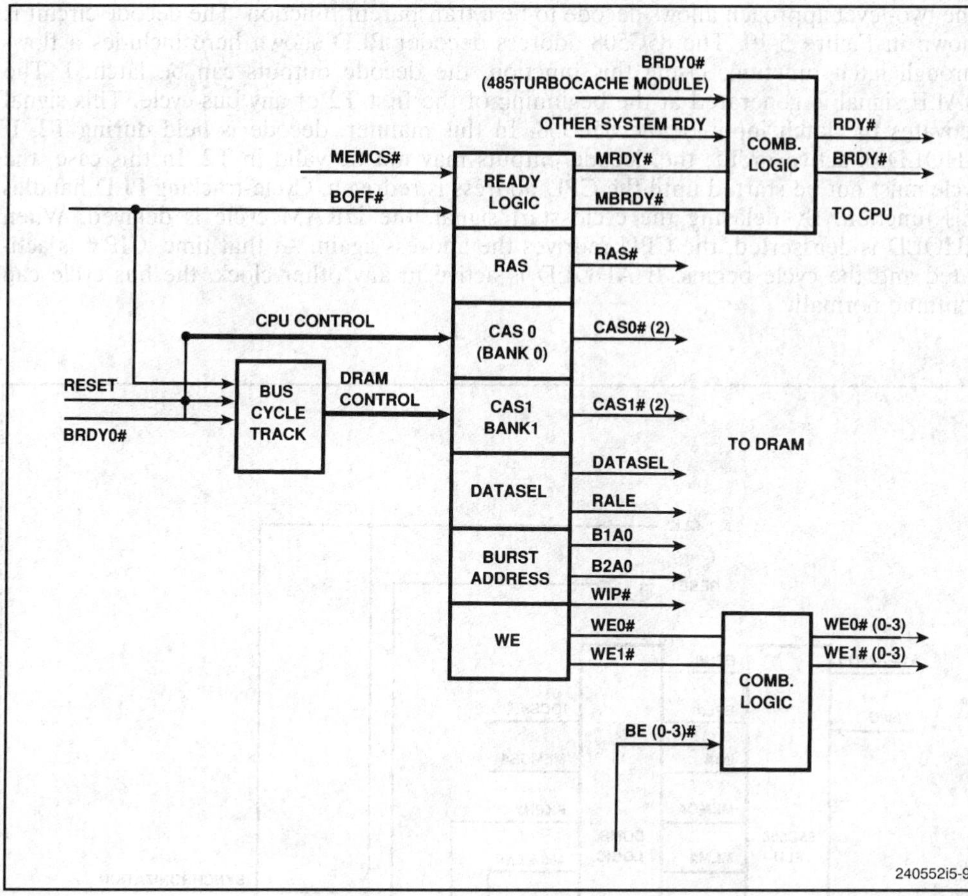

Figure 5-9. Control Logic Overview

decode does not need to be valid until the end of this T2 bus state. Without this function, the decode output must be valid at the end of every T1 bus state. The time allowed for decode at 33 MHz is very short. With 7-ns PLDs, the time allowed for decode would be 7 ns. With 5-ns PLDs, this time is still only 9 ns. The advantage of the extra clock period is clear.

The second advantage of the two-level approach is similarly clear. The AQ0 signal indicates the start of a bus cycle to all second-level PLDs. Without this signal ADS# would have to be connected to these devices, and the resulting load on ADS# would be prohibitive.

Invalidation within bus cycles is another case that makes decode design difficult. The AHOLD signal must be used to implement this function. As its name implies, AHOLD can be active in any clock. If AHOLD is active in the first clock (T1) of a bus cycle, the CPU address lines are tristated in T2. Unless decode is latched at the beginning of T2, it will not be valid for the DRAM cycle. This case is explored in detail in Section 5.5.1.

The two-level approach allows decode to be a transparent function. The decode circuit is shown in Figure 5-10. The 85C508 address decoder PLD shown here includes a flow-through latch function. Using this function, the decode outputs can be latched. The DALE signal is generated at the beginning of the first T2 of any bus cycle. This signal activates the latch input of the 85C508. In this manner, decode is held during T2. If AHOLD is active in T1, the decode outputs may not be valid in T2. In this case, the cycle must not be started until the CPU address is redriven. Cycle-tracking PLD handles this function. By delaying the cycle start signal, the DRAM cycle is delayed. When AHOLD is deasserted, the CPU redrives the address again. At that time, CIP# is activated and the cycle begins. If AHOLD is active in any other clock, the bus cycle can continue normally.

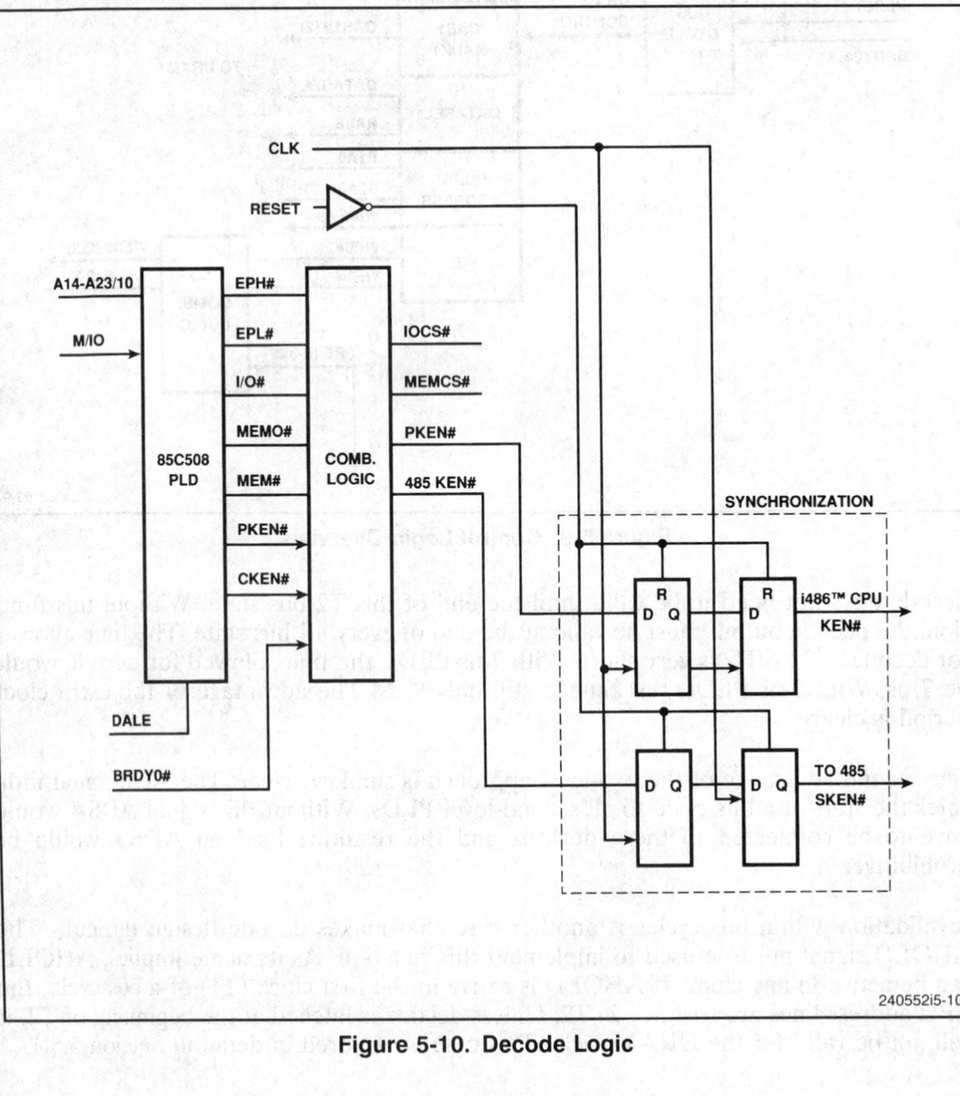

Figure 5-10. Decode Logic

The first level of interface with the memory subsystem, the cycle tracking PLD handles many other functions, most of which relate to synchronization. Refresh synchronization is one example, as is determining the RAS# precharge duration. AQ0# is not the only signal which supports the AHOLD function. Address registers, controlled by the PLD, generate the ALD signal to disable the registers during bus cycles. These and other functions of the control logic are described completely in Section 5.5.

The PLDs in the next level of logic perform more specific functions. RAS# and CAS# are generated at this level, and the PLDs that generate these signals are devoted solely to this function. The RAS# PLD generates four RAS# signals, RAS0#-RAS3#. These signals are identical but drive different DRAM modules to reduce the load on the RAS# signal.

The RAS# function is designed to support page or static column mode memory devices. To support these devices, RAS# must be left active between accesses to the same row. The RAS# state machine is designed so that RAS is deactivated only for are fresh or page miss cycle. This module generates RAS# for both DRAM banks.

For the CAS# function, the PLD's are responsible for implementing burst accesses. During write cycles, the CAS# signals determine which DRAM bank is written to. All even doublewords (A2 = 0) are stored in bank 0 while odd doublewords (A2 = 1) are stored in bank 1. When data is retrieved from memory, cycles can be overlapped to allows zero wait state burst accesses.

Address generation is another important consideration in burst accesses. The address for the last three access of a burst must be generated by logic because the CPU cannot generate these addresses in time to allow zero wait state accesses. The burst address logic shown in Figure 5-9 is actually two PLDs which generate the burst address for bank 0 and bank 1, respectively. The burst address consists of two signals—the lowest order DRAM addresses from each PLD.

Because of timing constraints, these signals are connected directly to the DRAM devices. The burst address PLD must generate the burst address, provide the multiplexor function for row and column addresses and generate the write address. The burst address signals must, therefore, reflect the value of A13 during miss cycles. These reflect during burst read and write cycles. These signals reflect A3.

B00MA0 and B01MA0 are the burst address signals for bank 0. Two identical signals are used to divide loading. B10MA0 and B11MA0 are the burst address signals for bank 1. A detailed description of the burst address function is given in Sections 5.4.2 and 5.5.5.

The DSEL PLD functions this signal to generate the data select signal. As described above, this signal is used during burst to switch the data path multiplexer. It reflects the value of A2 during burst read cycles only and is one component of the burst address. The DSEL PLD also generates the RALE signal to control the row address register described above.

BRDY# terminates all read cycles. MBRDY# is generated by the MRDY PLD and is separated from the RDY# signal to facilitate posted writes by preventing data bus contention. When a write cycle is immediately followed by a read, the read cycle must be delayed. This delay is implemented by delaying MBRDY# signal until the previous write cycle is complete. MBRDY# is combined with other burst ready inputs using combinatorial logic.

WIP# (write in progress) indicates to the MRDY PLD that a write is taking place, and MBRDY# is not generated unless this signal is inactive. WIP# tracks the state of the CAS# state machines.

The WE PLD generates WIP# and other signals associated with the write function. The MUXEN# signals control the address multiplexors and activate the write address path during write cycles. The WE# signals are used to create the DRAM W inputs and to implement byte steering. They are combined with latched CPU byte enables using combinatorial logic in this way, DRAM W inputs are not active for unselected bytes. Data bus contention on unselected bytes is prevented by controlling the write data register output enables.

By implementing byte steering in this way the CAS# logic is simplified. The CAS# timing path is critical during burst read cycles, and by placing the byte steering logic in the write enable path, CAS# timing restrictions are eased.

The MRDY# signal terminates all write cycles. The logic used to generate this signal is unusual because it uses the ADS# input and is therefore at the first level. This configuration is needed to implement zero wait-state write cycles.

MRDY# must be active by the end of the first T2 to terminate a write cycle and maintain zero wait-state performance. To meet this restriction, it must be active during any write cycle, or before decode is available because the CPU RDY# signal must not be activated during non-memory write cycles, MRDY# is inhibited by the decode output, MEMCS#, in combinatorial logic.

5.4 MEMORY SUBSYSTEM FUNCTION

In this section we will explore the function of the memory subsystem in detail. Each of the signals will be described, and bus cycles will be illustrated to show the memory logic function.

The bus cycle description in this section is specific to this example. Signals such as KEN# and RDY#, for example, are shown as they are driven by this particular control logic. The signals are not restricted to the timing shown here.

A list of the memory control signals follows.

5.4.1 Memory Interface Signals

5.4.1.1 CPU INTERFACE SIGNALS

KEN#	KEN# is an input to the processor, indicating whether the next bus cycle is cacheable or not. This signal is a logical AND of SKEN# and CKEN# signals.
PBRDY#	PBRDY# is the burst ready input to the processor. This is a logical AND of the BRDY# signal from the system and the BRDYO# from the second-level cache.

5.4.1.2 DATA PATH CONTROL

DATASEL	DATASEL reflects the value of A2 during burst accesses. It is used to control the data multiplexor for bank 0 and bank 1 data paths.
MRDY#	MRDY# enables the write data registers that are used to support write posting and terminates memory write cycles.
MBRDY#	MBRDY# is used for read cycles and enables the output of the data path multiplexor.
WE0#/WE1#	WE0# and WE1# signals enable the outputs of data write registers used for write posting. Both the signals are active during a write and CAS# determines the correct bank to which the data is written.
WBE00#-WBE03#	WBE00#-WBE03# are a combination of write enable and byte enable signals. They control which byte is written into bank 0 during a write cycle.
WBE10#-WBE13#	WBE10-WBE13# control which byte is written into bank 1 during write cycles.

5.4.1.3 ADDRESS PATH CONTROL

ALD	ALD disables the clock input to the registers that hold the row and column addresses corresponding to the current bus cycle.
MUXEN0#,1#	MUXEN0#, MUXEN1# control signals are inputs to the address multiplexors and are used in selecting the read or write paths to the respective banks.

RALE#	RALE# enables the row address latch, allowing a new row address to be latched for successive bus cycles.
DALE#	DALE# activates the latch inputs of the decode logic in the first T2 of a bus cycle and holds the decode during the bus cycle.
B00MA0/B01MA0	B00MA0 and B01MA0 are the burst address signals for bank 0. They correspond to the value of A3 during burst read cycles.
B10MA0/B11MA0	B10MA0 and B11MA0 are the burst address signals for bank 1. They correspond to the value of A3 during burst read cycles.

5.4.1.4 DRAM INTERFACE

HIT#	HIT# is active if the row address for the current memory cycle is the same as the previous memory cycle.
WIP#	WIP# indicates that a write cycle is in progress and a read to the DRAM needs to be delayed till WIP# becomes inactive.
CIP#	CIP# indicates a memory cycle is in progress. If the current cycle is not to DRAM, CIP# is deactivated else it remains active till the end of the bus cycle.
RAS0-3#	RAS0-3# go active for a valid row address. It remains active between accesses to the same row and is deactivated only for page miss and refresh cycles.
DRAS#	DRAS# is the delayed RAS# signal to accommodate the RAS# hold-time requirements.
RFRQ	RFRQ indicates that a refresh of the DRAM is required. This signal is activated every 15.6 us.
RFACK	RFACK is asserted as a response to RFRQ and indicates that the DRAM controller is ready to perform the refresh cycle. It is active during idle cycles or after the current cycle is complete.
PCHG	PCHG determines the timing of refresh cycles and RAS# pre-charge count.
CAS0#/CAS1#	CAS0# and CAS1# signals are active when a valid column address is present on the bus and control the bank to which the data is written into.
MEMCS#	MEMCS# is active when a read or a write is performed to the DRAM. It is the synchronized output of the address decoder.

5.4.1.5 CONTROLLER SIGNALS

CT	CT indicates that a new cycle had started while a cycle was in progress or the refresh cycle was taking place. It is deactivated when the pending cycle is recognized.
SKEN#	SKEN# indicates if any of the caches is enabled. It is an input to the second-level cache and is similar to the KEN# signal input to the processor.
CKEN#	CKEN# is the output of the second-level cache. It is activated twice for a valid line fill first to enable a 485Turbocache Module line fill and the second time to validate it.
LA2, LA313	LA2 and LA313 are latched versions of address lines A2 and A13. LA313 is the lowest order DRAM address line. The multiplexor output reflects A3 when RAS# is low and A13 when RAS# is high.
M#	M# indicates the occurrence of a write miss.
BRDYO#	BRDYO# is a burst ready signal driven by the second-level cache. It is activated when a read hit occurs in this cache.

5.4.2 Read Cycles

Figure 5-11 shows a burst read cycle. At the start of the bus cycle, RAS# is inactive. This case is a rare occurrence because RAS# is normally active. Unless a cycle is the first bus cycle after a reset or refresh cycle, RAS# will be active in T1.

It is useful to examine this case because it demonstrates a complete DRAM cycle. The basic function of most of the control logic is illustrated.

The cycle begins with the activation of ADS#. The controller samples this signal and activates both ALD and CIP#. The CPU address registers are disabled by ALD. Therefore, the previously latched address is held throughout the bus cycle. The latched address is valid in the first T2 of the bus cycle.

The row address comparison is made with this address. As a result, the HIT# signal is not valid until the rising edge of the second T2. At this rising clock edge, the CIP#, MEMCS# and HIT# signals are sampled. If MEMCS# is sampled active, the RAS# signal is activated.

The delay line holds the DRAS# signal high for 20 ns after RAS# is activated. In this way the row address is maintained to meet tRAH, the row address hold time. When DRAS# is activated, the address multiplexers switch to the column address path. The MUXEN# signals are not active, and the read path is selected.

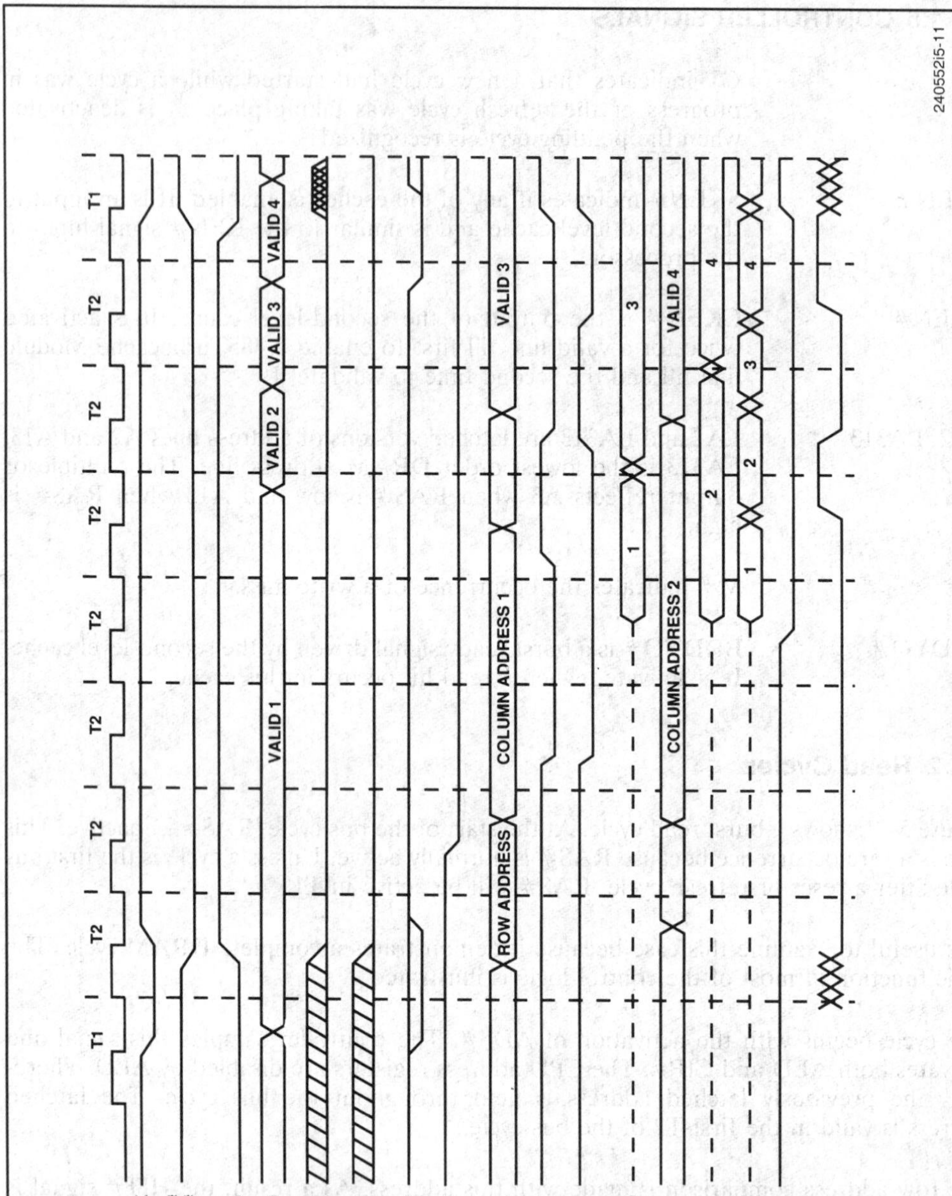

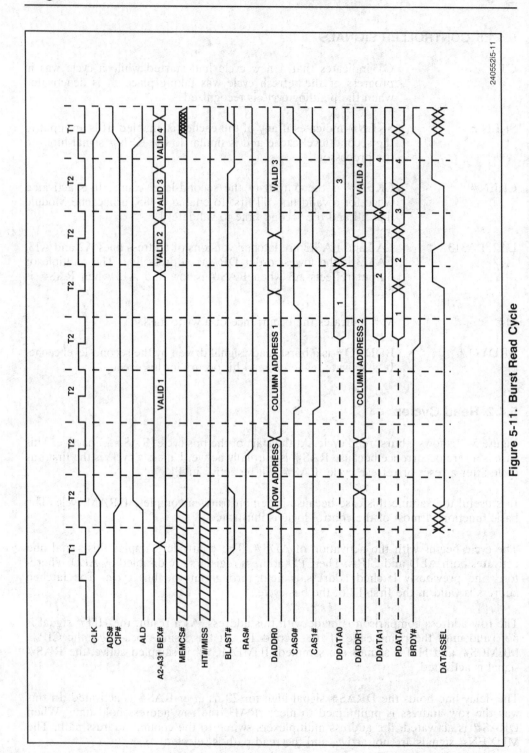

Figure 5-11. Burst Read Cycle

In the third T2 of the bus cycle CAS# is asserted. This cycle begins with A2 low and the first access is to bank 0. Due to the access time of the DRAM two clocks are required to retrieve data from memory. MBRDY# is asserted in the fourth T2 of the bus cycle, and this action completes the first access of the burst read. The access is completed in five clocks. The minimum time for this access is two clocks indicating that three wait states were added to the first cycle.

The timing diagram reveals two important points about burst cycle implementation. First DRAM access requires two clocks. Second, the burst address from the CPU is not available until the clock after MBRDY# is sampled active. These circumstances make zero wait-state burst cycles. The DRAM bank interleaving alleviates this difficulty.

The first advantage of interleaving is revealed in the second and third T2 states. Access to both the first and second memory doublewords can be made simultaneously. This function requires that the burst address be predicted. As mentioned above, the burst address from the CPU is not available until several clocks later. The burst address for both the first and second accesses is generated in the second T2. Therefore, CAS# for both banks can be asserted in the next T2 state.

The second advantage of interleaving is seen in fifth T2 of the burst cycles in which DATASEL switches the data multiplexer. The second doubleword is driven on the CPU data bus. In this CLK, the burst address for the third access of the cycle is generated. CAS00# and CAS01# are also deasserted to begin the third access. Note that this access is started before the second access is completed. The cycle overlap shown allows new data to be driven on the CPU data bus every clock. This way zero wait-state accessis achieved.

Timing is even more critical during page hit cycles. Figure 5-12 shows the timing of this cycle. Because of the function of RAS#, this cycle is more common than the cycle discussed above. The row address is the same as in the previous cycle. Therefore, the RAS# signal is left active.

When a burst read starts with RAS# active, fewer clock, are required to complete the first access. This reduction improves performance. As a result, however, some timings become more critical. One of these is the time allowed to generate the burst address.

The CAS# signals are asserted in the second T2 of the bus cycle. MBRDY# is also asserted at this time. To meet the address access time of the DRAMS, the burst address must be generated in the second T2. The rest of the read column address must also be available at this time. Two logic functions are needed to meet this timing requirement. First, read and write address paths must be separate to allow the read address to be available in the first T2. Second, the burst address path logic must latch the CPU A3 signal directly. In this way, the logic can generate the necessary address in time. The burst address state machine must track the state of A3 at the beginning of every cycle. The state machine function is described in Section 5.5.

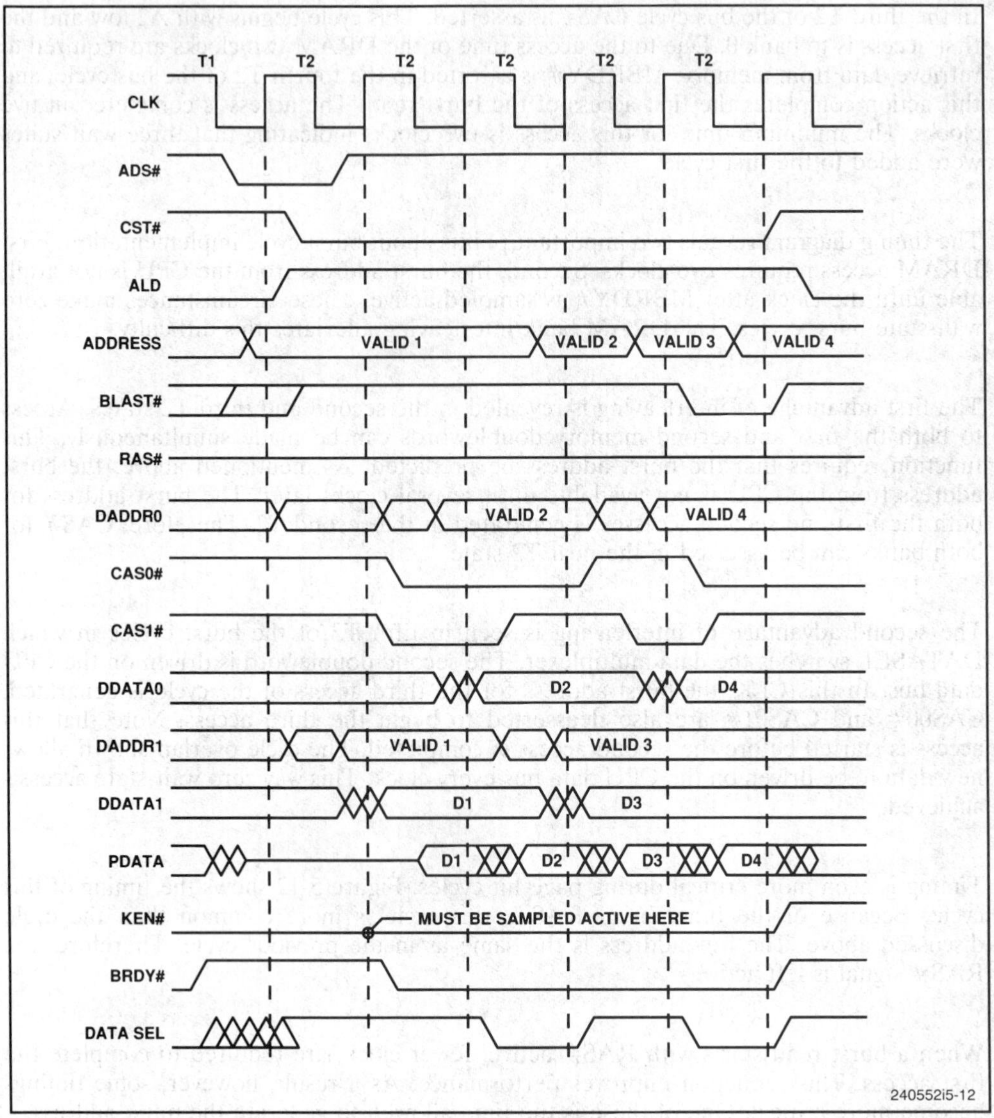

Figure 5-12. Burst Read DRAM Page, Hit

The timing of KEN# must also be considered in this example. KEN# must be valid at the beginning of the second T2 of the cycle. If it is not, the cycle will not be cached, and a 16-byte access cannot be generated. If KEN# is active, a 16-byte burst access will be generated, and the cycle will be cached as long as KEN# is active in the second to last T2.

At first glance this timing may not appear critical. KEN# is a decode function, and decode is valid at the clock edge called for. The KEN# input to the CPU must be synchronized to clock, however. Since decode is not synchronous, a two-clock synchronizer delay is required, and this delay is the reason that KEN# is normally active in this example.

From the time CAS# is activated, this cycle is exactly the same as in the previously described burst cycle. It is terminated when BLAST# is asserted, and MBRDY# is deasserted when BLAST# is sampled active.

5.4.3 Write Cycles

As described in Section 5.3.1, a posted or delayed write function is employed in this example to reduce write cycle latency. Latency is reduced since write cyles with are overlapped with other cycles including other write cycles or reads from the second-level cache. Write cycles normally make up 70 percent of all cycles, and overlapping can increase performance accordingly.

Figure 5-13 illustrates the posted write implementation. In this example cycles begin when RAS# is inactive. As with read cycles, this case is rare in practice.

The cycle begins like a read. The CPU drives ADS# active, and the decode is sampled. RAS# is activated if the cycle is in DRAM space. In the second T2 of the cycle, however, the latched version of W/R# (LW/R#) is sampled active at the rising edge of the second T2. In response, the control logic begins several write cycle functions at this clock edge.

The CAS# state machine for the appropriate bank enters the write sequence. The MUXEN# and WE# signals are asserted. MRDY# is also asserted, terminating the cycle at the CPU. The MUXEN# signals activate the write address path. This address is not present at the multiplexor outputs, however, until the next clock at which the write pipeline register latches the write address.

The write data is latched at the same clock edge. The write data registers are enabled by MRDY# which simultaneously terminates the CPU cycle. Note that data is latched in both the bank 0 and bank 1 registers.

The WE0# and WE1# signals are also both active. The CAS# signals determine which bank is written to. These signals are asserted within two clocks after MRDY#. This action completes the write cycle. Note that, while five clocks are required to complete the cycle, the CPU cycle is terminated in three CLKs. The wait state is only required if RAS# is inactive at the start of the cycle.

In Figure 5-13 the next bus cycle starts immediately after RDY# is sampled. In this case, CAS# is activated during the second clock of the next bus cycle. This overlap of cycles is similar to the pipelining feature used by many processors except that the i486 processor bus is not involved in the posting function. All logic for this function is implemented in the memory controller.

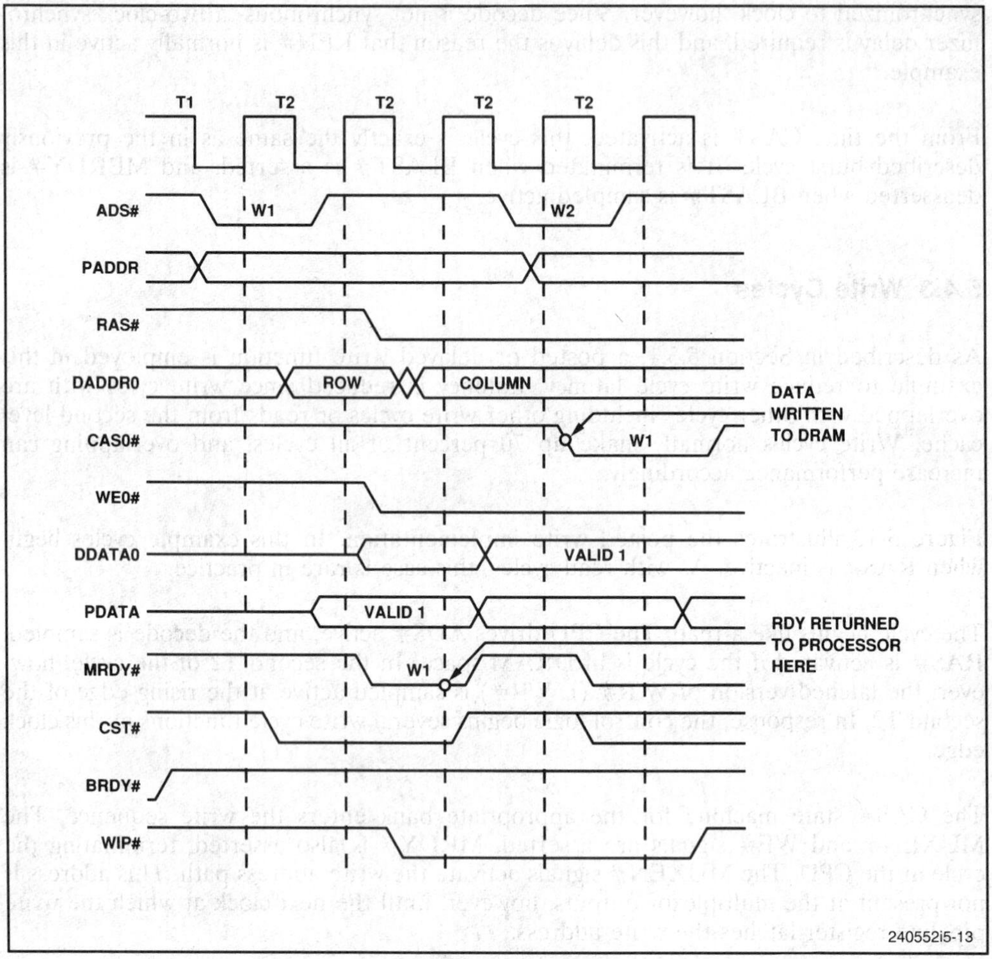

Figure 5-13. Basic Write Cycle

Figure 5-14 is a more typical i486 processor bus sequence which more clearly illustrates the advantages of the posting technique. Four write cycles have occurred together without idle bus clocks occurring between cycles. Since all writes access the same DRAM row, RAS# is active throughout the sequence.

Without the extra clock to activate RAS#, MRDY# can be asserted in the clock after ADS# is asserted. These cycles, therefore, have no wait states. As before, the write cycle is not complete when MRDY# is asserted but instead when CAS# is asserted two clocks after MRDY# to terminate the CPU bus cycle.

At zero wait states, each write cycle still requires four clock cycles. The last two clocks of each write cycle overlap with the next cycle. The net effect on the CPU bus is the same as a string of two-clock write cycles, as illustrated in Figure 5-14.

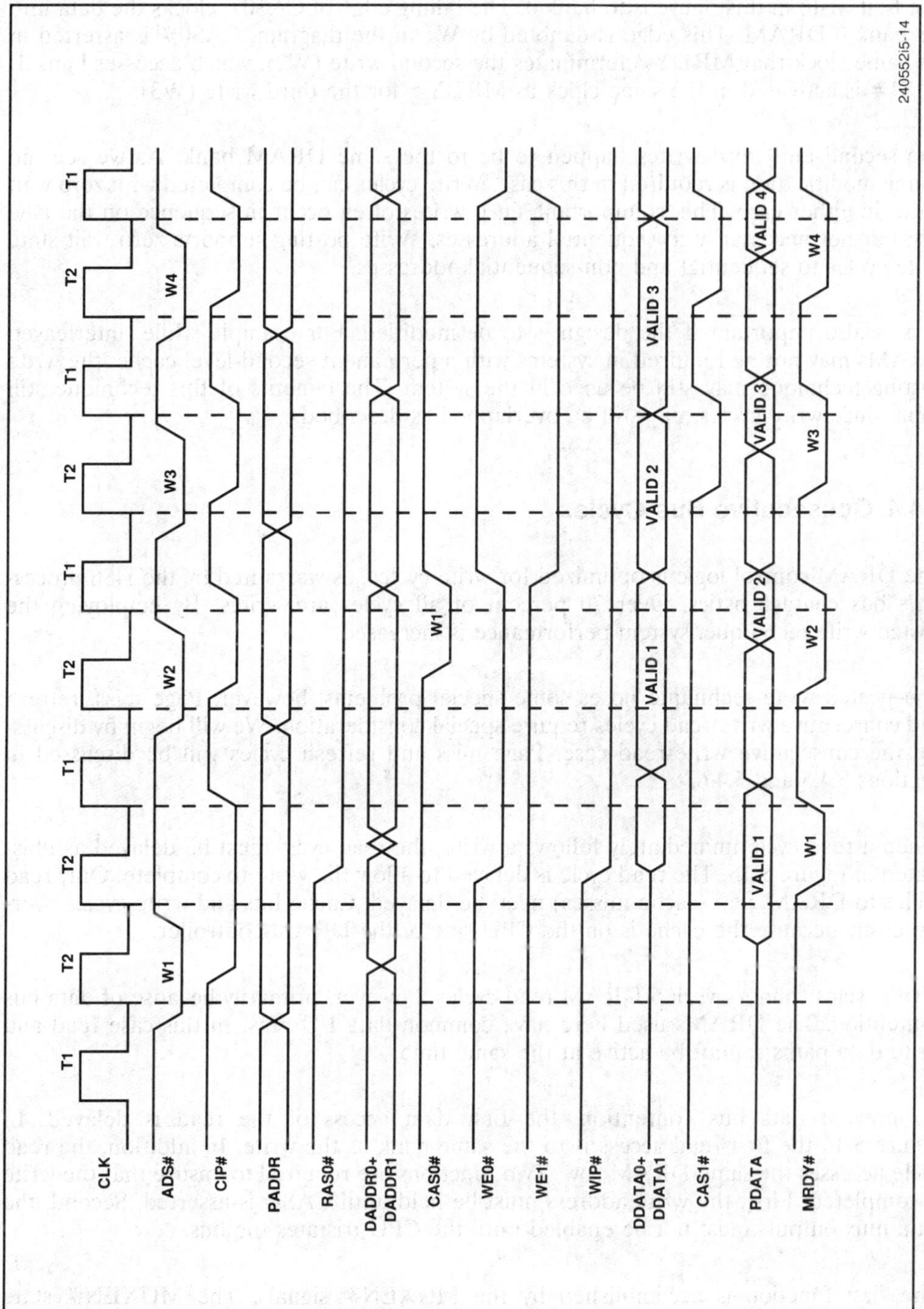

Figure 5-14. Back-to-Back Write Cycles

The first write in this figure is to bank 0. The falling edge of CAS0# clocks the data into the bank 0 DRAM. This edge is denoted by W1 in the diagram. CAS0# is asserted in the same clock that MRDY# terminates the second write (W2), which accesses bank 1. CAS1# is activated in the same clock as MRDY# for the third write (W3).

The second and third writes happen to be to the same DRAM bank. As we see, no timing modification is required in this case. Write cycles can be completed with zero wait states in either case. This is important since writes often occur in sequence on the i486 bus, but not necessarily to sequential addresses. Write posting supports zero wait-state write cycles to sequential and non-sequential addresses.

This is also important if the design is to be modified. For example while, interleaved DRAMs may not be required in systems with a permanent second-level cache, the write posting technique may still be used in the system. The benefits of this technique still apply since write cycles may still be overlapped as described.

5.4.4 Consecutive Bus Cycles

The DRAM control logic is optimized for write cycles, as warranted by the i486 processor's bus characteristics. Over 70 percent of all cycles are writes. By employing the posted write technique, system performance is increased.

The posted write technique poses some special problems, however. Page miss, refresh and consecutive write-read cycles require special consideration. We will begin by discussing the consecutive write-read case. Page miss and refresh cycles will be discussed in Sections 5.4.5 and 5.4.6.

When a read cycle immediately follows a write, the read cycle must be delayed as illustrated in Figure 5-15. The read cycle is delayed to allow the write to complete. Only read cycles to DRAM, i.e., (cache misses) need be delayed. Cache hits and write cycles overlap easily because the cache is on the CPU side of the DRAM controller.

Write cycles cannot overlap DRAM read cycles, however, primarily because of data bus contention. The DRAMs used here have common data I/O pins. In this case read and write data paths cannot be active at the same time.

To prevent data bus contention, the first data access of the read is delayed. In Figure 5-15 the first read access is to the same bank as the write. In addition, the read cycle accesses the same DRAM row. Two functions are required to ensure that the write is completed. First, the write address must be held until CAS# is asserted. Second, the data mux outputs must not be enabled until the CPU tristates the bus.

The first function is accomplished by the MUXEN# signals. The MUXEN# state machine tracks the CAS# function for the appropriate bank. When the write for that bank is complete, MUXEN# is deactivated. In this way, the read address path is not

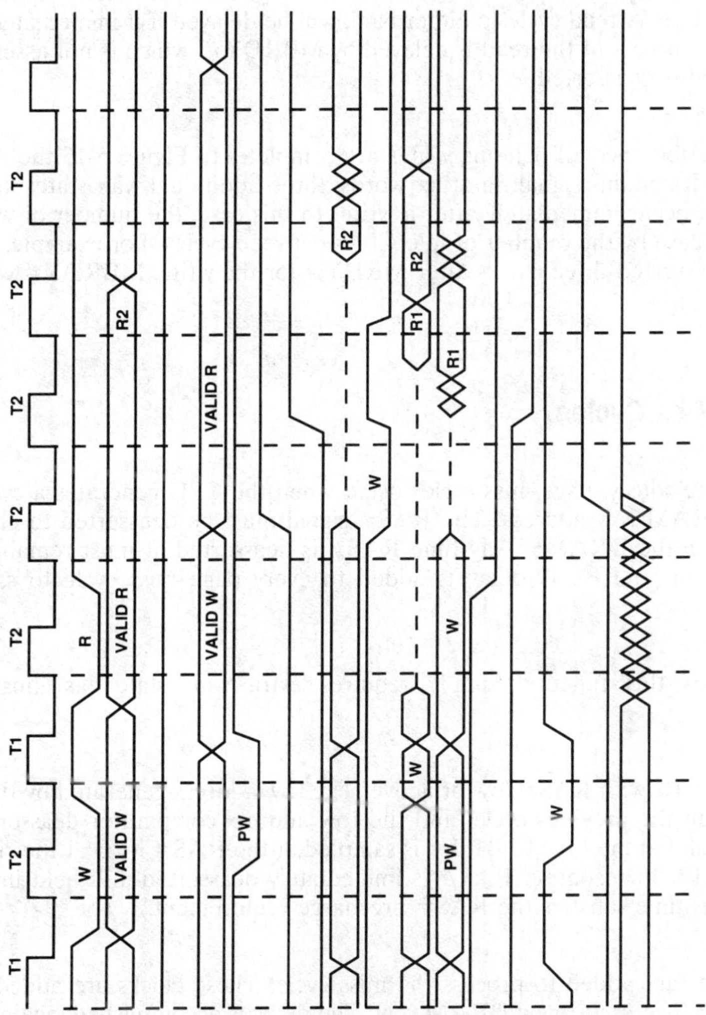

240552i5-15

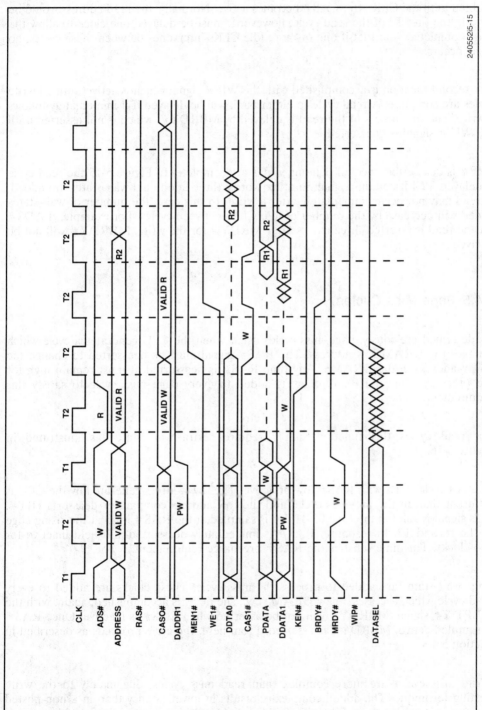

Figure 5-15. Consecutive Write-Read Cycle

enabled until the CLK after CAS# becomes active. Normally, the read address would be valid in the first T2 of the read cycle; however it must be delayed one clock to allow the write complete. Note that if one or more idle CLKs intervenes between these cycles, no delay occurs.

The second function is accomplished with the WIP# signal which is active until all write cycles are complete. A read cycle to either bank will be delayed if it immediately follows a write. The first access of the read is delayed by MBRDY#, which is not asserted until the WIP# signal is deasserted.

WIP# is deasserted once all pending writes are complete. In Figure 5-15 the read cycle is delayed 3 CLKs by this signal; in other words, three additional wait states are added. A read may not occur immediately after a write. In this case, the number of wait-states added will decrease by the number of idle CLKs between cycles. For example, if ADS# for the read is asserted three clocks after MRDY# for the write, MBRDY# will not be delayed.

5.4.5 Page Miss Cycles

As described previously, page miss cycles occur when the CPU generates a cycle which changes the DRAM row address. The RAS# signal must be deasserted to change the ROW address in the DRAMS. Any time RAS# is deasserted, it must remain high for the precharge time (tRP). A delay is added to every page miss cycle to satisfy this requirement.

For read cycles this function simply requires extra wait states as illustrated in Figure 5-16.

The bus cycle starts with RAS# low or active. The row address generated by the CPU is different than in the previous cycle, and the row address comparator deasserts HIT#. This signal is valid in the first T2. HIT# is sampled at the RAS# PLD at the rising edge of the second T2. In response, RAS# is immediately deasserted and held inactive for two clocks. This time satisfies the RAS# precharge requirement.

Four wait states are added to process the miss cycle. These clocks are added to every read cycle which accesses a new DRAM row. The delay is accomplished, again, with the MBRDY# signal. MBRDY# will not be asserted when RAS# is inactive. Once RAS# is sampled active, MBRDY# is asserted. From here, the cycle proceeds as described in Section 5.4.3.

Write miss cycles are more complex than read miss cycles, due mainly to the write posting technique. The added complexity results in lower latency than in a non-posted memory system, however. Figure 5-17 illustrates how this improvement is achieved.

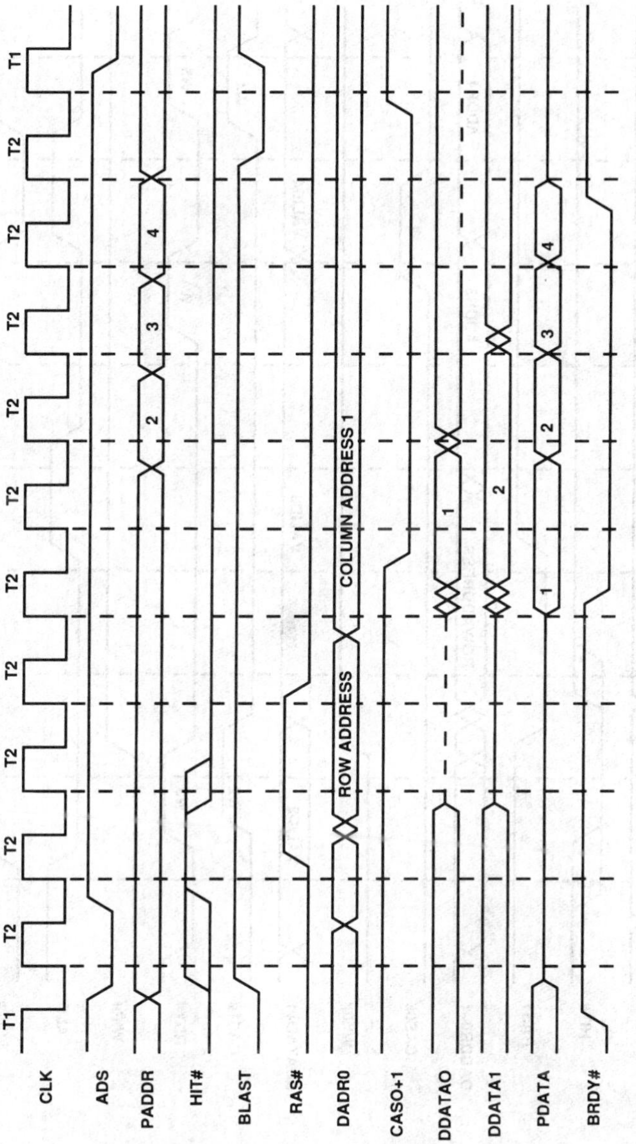

240552i5-16

Figure 5-16. DRAM Page Miss-Read Cycle

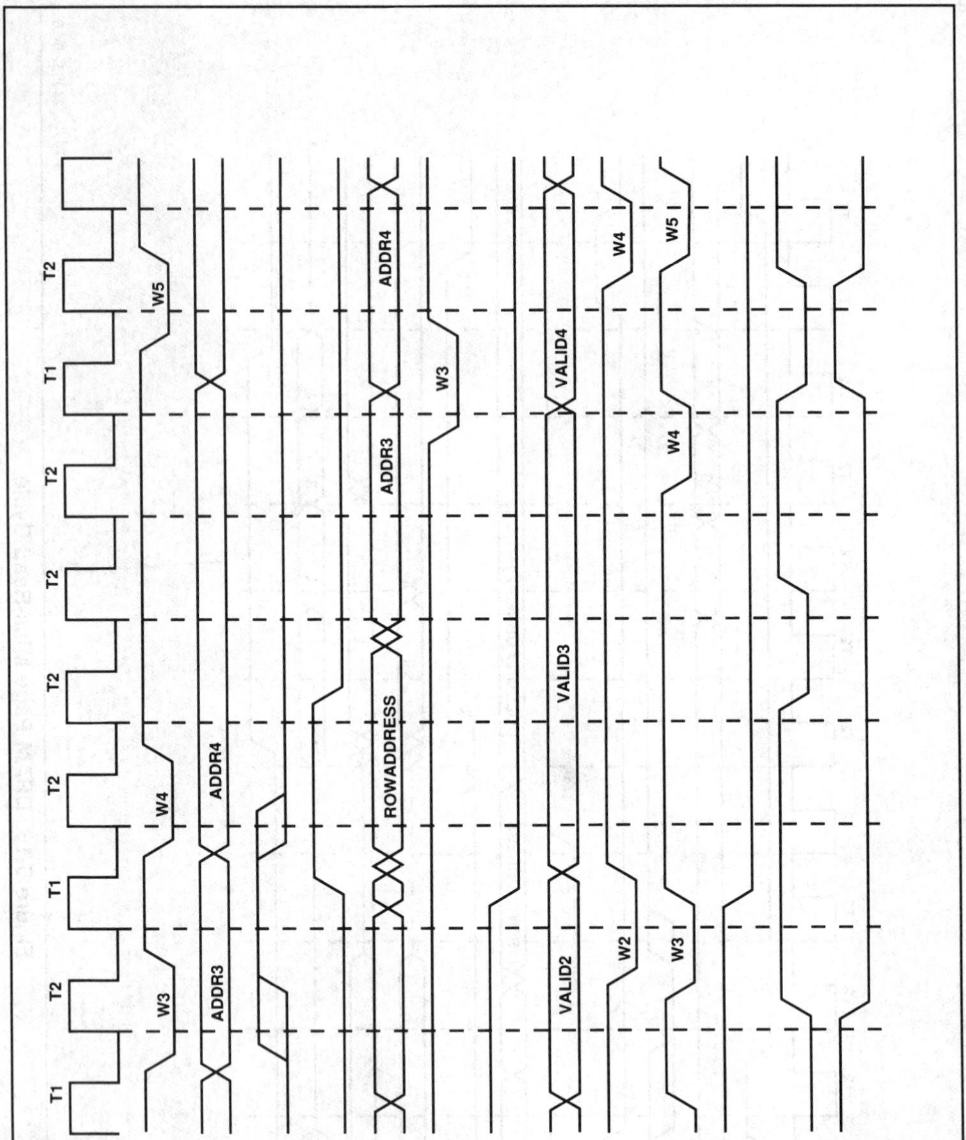

Figure 5-17. DRAM Page Miss-Write Cycle

The write cycle in Figure 5-17 also begins with RAS# active. The HIT# signal is deasserted in the first T2 at the same time that MRDY# is asserted. MRDY# could be inhibited at this point to prevent write cycle termination. The wait states added to meet RAS# precharge time would then be added to this cycle. Five wait states are required to meet the precharge time.

The average number of write cycle clocks can be reduced, however, if another method is used. MRDY# can be allowed to terminate the cycle. In this case, any necessary wait states will be added to the next cycle.

This method improves the average in two ways. First, some write miss cycles will not require wait-states. This is the case when the next cycle occurs four or more clocks after a write miss. In addition, wait states will be reduced when the next cycle occurs in two or three clocks. Second, three wait-states are required to complete the next cycle when it follows immediately as illustrated in Figure 5-17.

The first cycle in this figure is a page miss. It is terminated at the CPU without wait-states. Because HIT# is not active in the first T2, RAS# is deasserted. At this point, additional clocks are added to perform the miss function. Part of the time required for RAS# precharge is overlapped with the next cycle. The two clock overlap reduces the number of wait states required in the next cycle. Therefore, the average write cycle latency is reduced.

5.4.6 Refresh Cycles

The CAS# before RAS# refresh function is used in this example. This function uses internal counters in the DRAM devices to generate the refresh address. When the CAS# input is activated prior to RAS#, the internal counter is incremented. The output of the counter is then used as the address of the row to be refreshed.

Each refresh cycle refreshes one row of the DRAM array. The refresh cycles are distributed such that one occurs every 15.6 uS, with every row being refreshed in 8 uS. Refresh cycles are initiated by the RFRQ signal. This signal is activated every 15.6 uS by a counter. The counter circuit is shown in Appendix B.

RFACK is asserted in response to RFRQ. This signal indicates that the DRAM controller is ready to perform the refresh cycle. It also signals the counter circuit that RFRQ can be deasserted.

The function of RFRQ and RFACK is very similar to that of the CPU's HOLD and HLDA signals. RFRQ is sampled at the end of each cycle and during idle cycles. RFACK is activated in the clock after RFRQ is sampled, except immediately after write cycles.

Again, the posted write function must complete before the refresh cycle begins. If WIP# is active when RFRQ is sampled, RFACK will not be immediately asserted. RFACK will be asserted after WIP# is deactivated as illustrated in Figure 5-18.

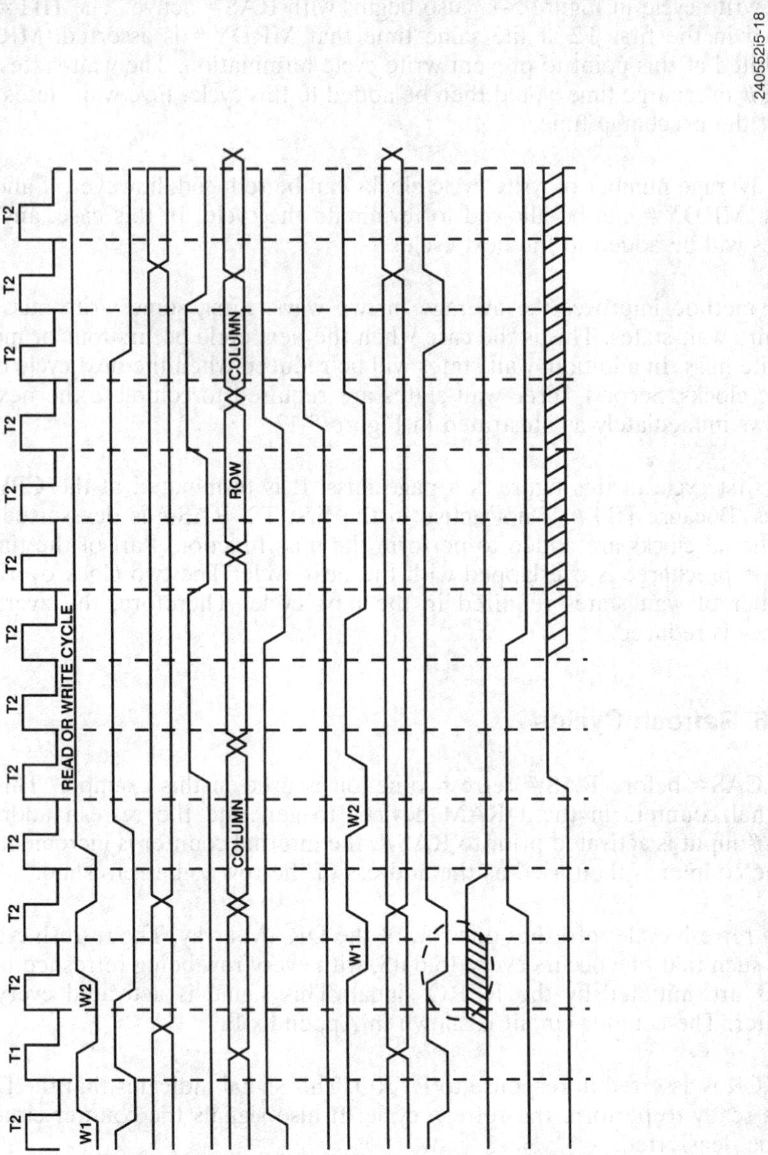

Figure 5-18. Refresh Timing Concurrent with Write

Another cycle can start between RFRQ and RFACK. The cycle start PLD tracks this case. CIP# will not be asserted for any cycle that starts during this interval. Once the refresh cycle is complete, this cycle can be started.

5.5 CONTROLLER IMPLEMENTATION

The functions described in the previous section are generated by the control logic. The controller, as outlined in Section 5.3, is made up of several PLDs. These devices generate the control signals described in Section 5.4. The function of the logic is determined by the state machine definition. These state machines are distributed in the different PLDs of the controller.

In this section, we will explore the implementation of the control logic. The discussion will focus on the state machine definition. Certain conventions are followed throughout the discussion. These conventions are based on the state machine compiler used to generate the PLD equations. This compiler uses the exclamation point (!) to indicate the low or "0" condition of a signal. It uses the number sysmbols (#) to indicate that the signal is active. For example, !ADS# indicates that the ADS signal is both and active. The # symbol indicates that asignal is active when low. So symbol !ALD means that the ALD signal is not active.

These symbols are used to indicate state transitions as shown in Figure 5-19. The state transition in 5-19 depends on three signals: ADS#, ALD, and RAS#. The equation indicates that if both ADS# and ALD are active or if RAS# is not active at the next clock edge. The transition from S0 to S1 takes place. In the transition between S0 and S1, the Y# signal is activated. The definition of states indicates which outputs are changed in the transition. These conventions are used to describe the control state machines in the next section.

5.5.1 Cycle Tracking Logic

The cycle tracking logic is contained in one PLD. The five state machines implemented in this PLD start and end DRAM cycles, control refresh timing and control the address registers. These state machines, along with the MRDY# state machine, comprise the first level of control logic. All other control state machines depend on this first level to generate signals at the proper time.

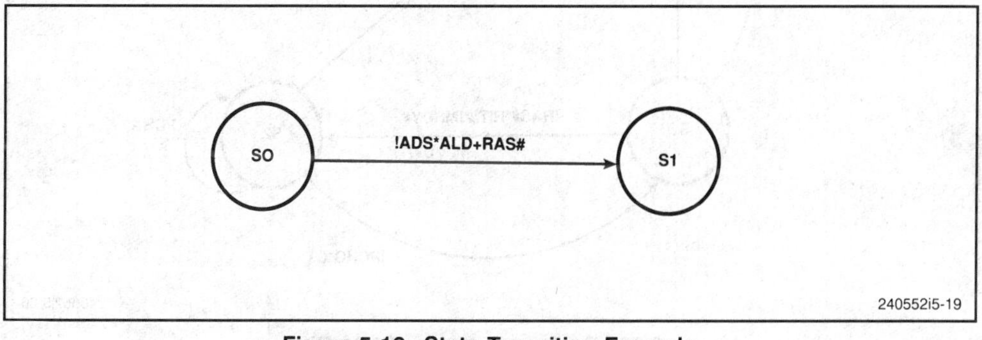

Figure 5-19. State Transition Example

The signals generated by this PLD are the following:

CIP# – Cycle in Progress
ALD – Address Latch Disable
CT – Cycle Track
RFACK – Refresh Acknowledge
PCHG – RAS Precharge Count

The primary cycle tracking state machine is shown in Figure 5-20. This state machine generates the CIP# and M# signals. CIP# indicates that the CPU has started a cycle. When it is active, the rest of the logic samples the CPU control and MEMCS# signals. If the current cycle is not to DRAM, it will be ignored and CIP# will be deactivated.

This function is defined by the S0 and S1 states in Figure 5-20. As shown, CIP# is activated when either ADS# or CT are sampled active. If the cycle is not to a DRAM address, the MEMCS# signal will not be active in the next clock. In this case, CIP# is deactivated o wait for the next ADS#. If the cycle is to DRAM, CIP# stays active until the end of the bus cycle. The bus cycle is terminated by one of three circumstances. All write cycles are terminated with the MRDY# signal. Read cycles are terminated by BRDY# and by BLAST#. The cycle can be aborted by BOFF#. Any of these three events causes CIP# to be deactivated (S1 to S0).

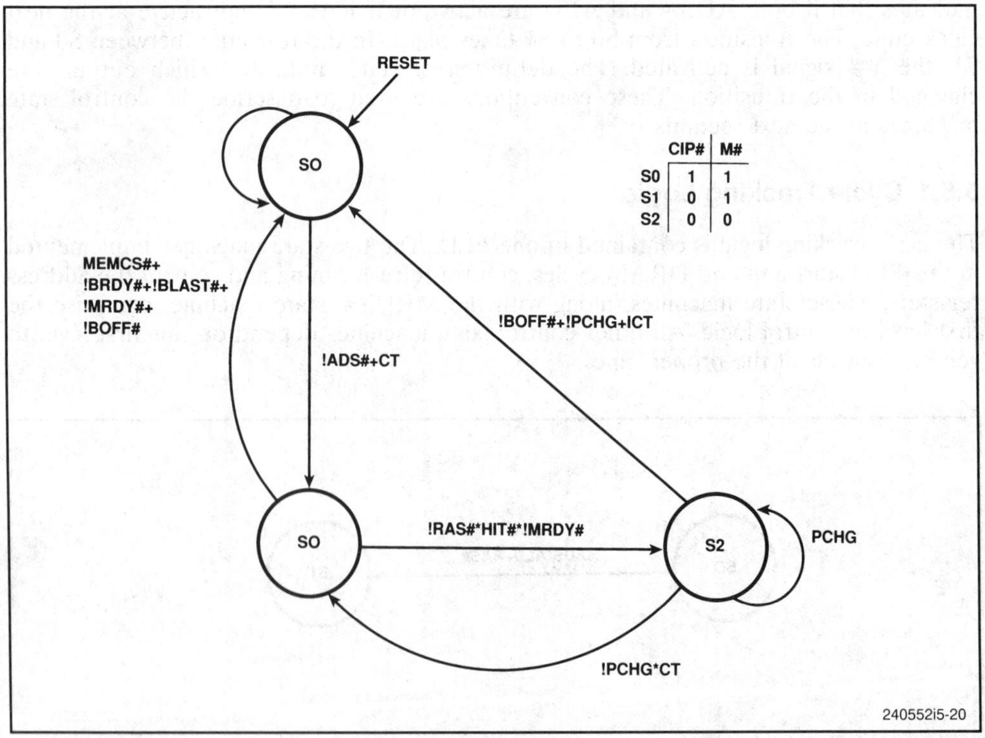

	CIP#	M#
S0	1	1
S1	0	1
S2	0	0

Figure 5-20. Cycle in Progress State Diagram

Two special cases are also handled by this state machine. When AHOLD is active in the same clock as ADS#, MEMCS# is not valid. In this case, the CIP# signal is not activated until AHOLD is deasserted. The state machine remains in S0 when AHOLD is active.

The second case is a write miss cycle. During a write miss, CIP# must be active for the cycle to complete. CIP# is active in this case after MRDY# is returned to the CPU. Cycles that start during the time CIP# is active must be tracked by the CT state machine. The M# signal indicates to the CT state machine that the cycles must be tracked.

The state in which M# and CIP# are both active is S2. This state is entered when MRDY# and RAS# are active and HIT# is inactive. By using MRDY# to qualify this transition, S2 is entered only during write cycles. Therefore, M# is only activated during write miss cycles. Note that any cycle will be recognized by the CT state machine when M# is active.

The CT state machine is shown in Figure 5-21. This state machine tracks cycles that start while the CIP# state machine is busy. It tracks CPU cycles that start during refresh cycles as well as to the two cases mentioned above.

This state machine tracks one cycle. Any cycle that starts while CIP# is busy is not terminated immediately. The MRDY# and MBRDY# signals are delayed until the previous cycle is finished. Therefore, anytime CT is active, there is only one cycle pending.

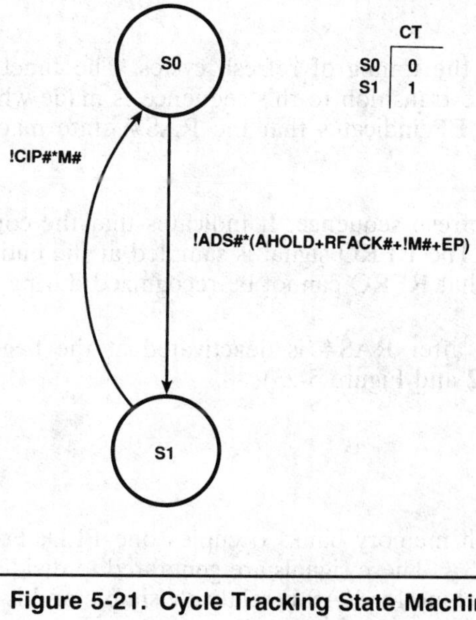

Figure 5-21. Cycle Tracking State Machine

CT is deactivated when the pending cycle is recognized by the CIP# state machine. This event is indicated by CIP# active and M# inactive. When this event occurs, the CT state machine transitions to S0 deactivating CT.

The ALD signal is also active only during DRAM cycles. Therefore, its state machine is very similar to that of CIP#. As with CIP#, ALD is asserted when ADS# is sampled active. If the cycle is not to a DRAM address, ALD is deasserted. When a DRAM cycle is terminated, ALD is also deasserted. The S0-to-S1 transition is quite similar to that of CIP#.

The difference between the two state machines is revealed during write miss cycles. The S1-to-S2 transition is made if a write miss occurs. ALD must be held active during a write miss until RAS# is active. In this way the row address is held even if another cycle occurs. The combination of CIP# being active while PCHG is inactive indicates that RAS# will be active in this clock. ALD must be deactivated in this clock to allow the next address to be latched. ALD is re-activated if another cycle has started during the write miss process. CIP# and MEMCS# are sampled during S0 for this purpose.

The PCHG state machine provides two functions. It determines the time RAS# is inactive during a miss or refresh cycle, and it determines the timing of refresh cycles. Figure 5-22 shows the state transitions of the PCHG state machine. Because the timing of this signal is not obvious, Figure 5-23 has been included. It shows a refresh cycle which occurs following a write cycle.

After RAS# is active the PCHG signal is activated. State S1 is maintained then until RAS# is deactivated. RAS# is only deactivated during a miss or refresh cycle or, of course, if RESET is asserted. During a miss cycle the transition to S0 is made deactivating PCHG. RAS# is then activated, resulting in two CPU clocks of RAS# precharge time.

States S2 and S3 define the timing of refresh cycles. The function of these states is shown in Figure 5-23. The transition to this sequence is made when RAS# is sampled inactive while EP active. EP indicates that the RAS# state machine has entered the refresh sequence.

RFACK# initiates the refresh sequence. It indicates that the control logic is ready to accept a refresh request. The RFRQ signal is sampled at the end of a DRAM cycle or during idle clocks. Note that RFRQ cannot be recognized during a write miss.

RFACK# is deactivated after RAS# is deactivated at the beginning of the refresh sequence (see Figure 5-22 and Figure 5-23).

5.5.2 RAS# Logic

The RAS# logic for both memory banks occupies one PLD. Four RAS# signals are generated: RAS0#- RAS3#. These signals are generated to divide loading. Their timing is identical. The state machine for RAS is relatively simple and is shown in Figure 5-24.

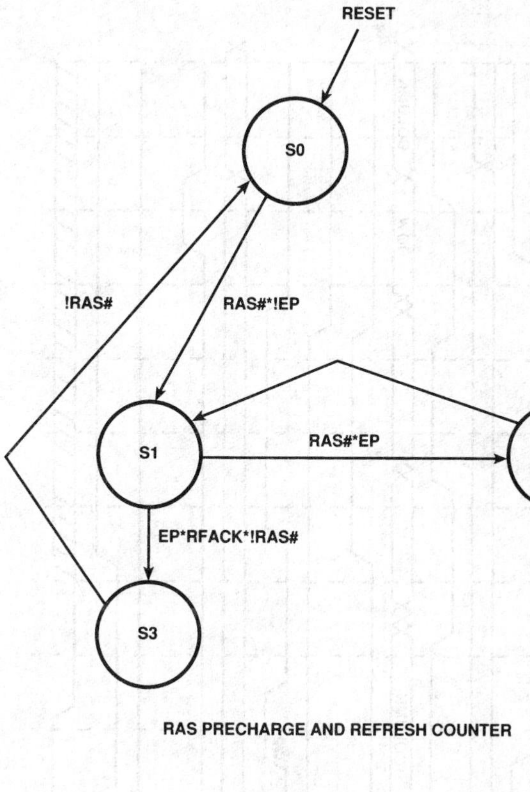

Figure 5-22. Precharge State Machine

States S0 and S1 are used to implement RAS# function for normal cycles. After RESET, the state machine waits for the first bus cycle. The first bus cycle is signaled by the CIP# signal. When CIP#, MEMCS# and PCHG are sampled active, RAS# is asserted. RAS# stays active until a miss or refresh cycle occurs.

A miss cycle is indicated when the HIT# signal is driven inactive. It is qualified by CIP# and MEMCS# being active. In this way, RAS# is only deactivated during DRAM cycles.

Once RAS# is deasserted during a miss cycle, it stays high until PCHG is sampled active. This function implements the RAS# precharge time. CIP# and MEMCS# will still be active during read miss cycles. Therefore, RAS# will be asserted in the next clock. For write miss cycles the WIP# signal must be used to restart RAS#. With a write miss, an on-DRAM cycle can occur before RAS# is asserted. WIP# is the only valid indication that a DRAM cycle has occurred in this case. WIP# is combined with MEMCS# to create the CSWIP# term which indicates a valid RAS# cycle.

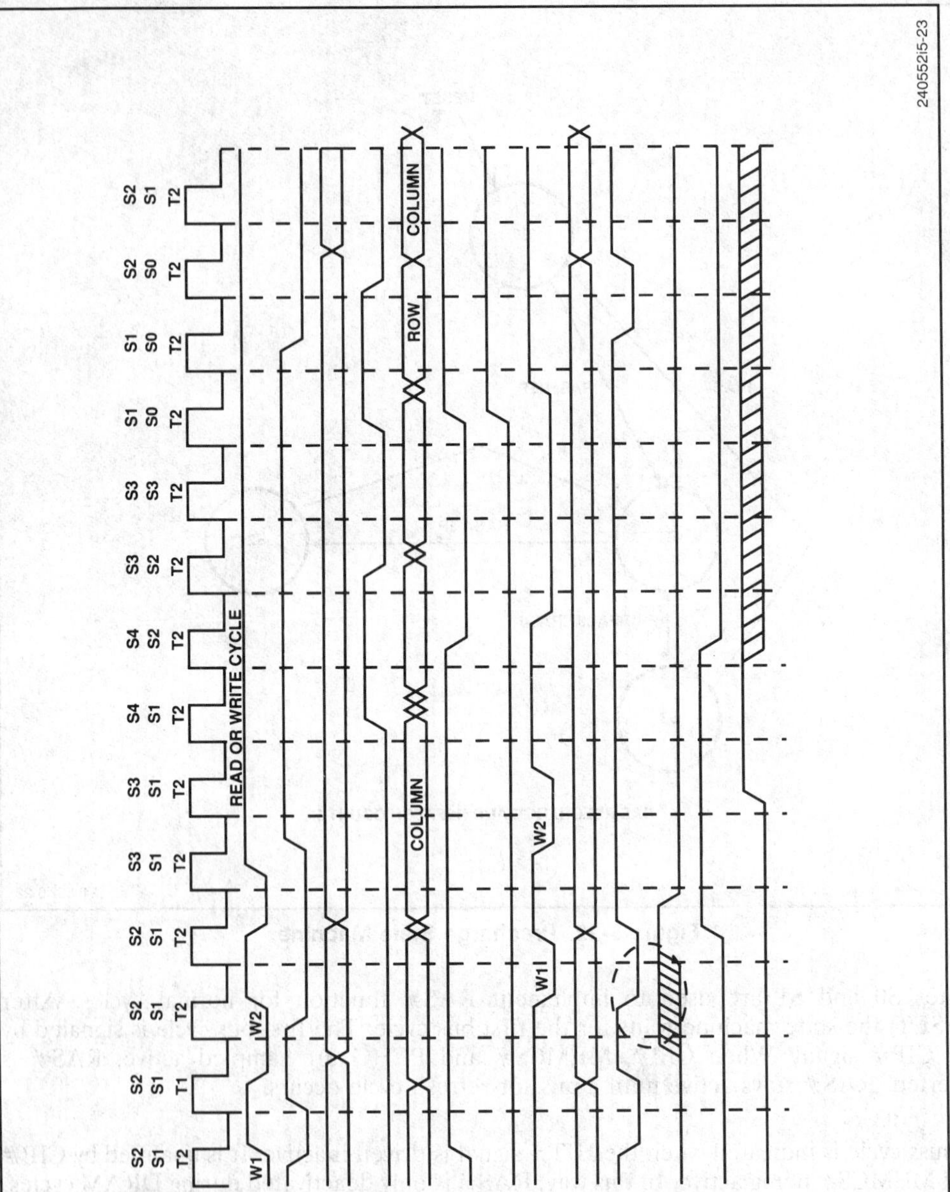

Figure 5-23. Refresh State – Timing Example

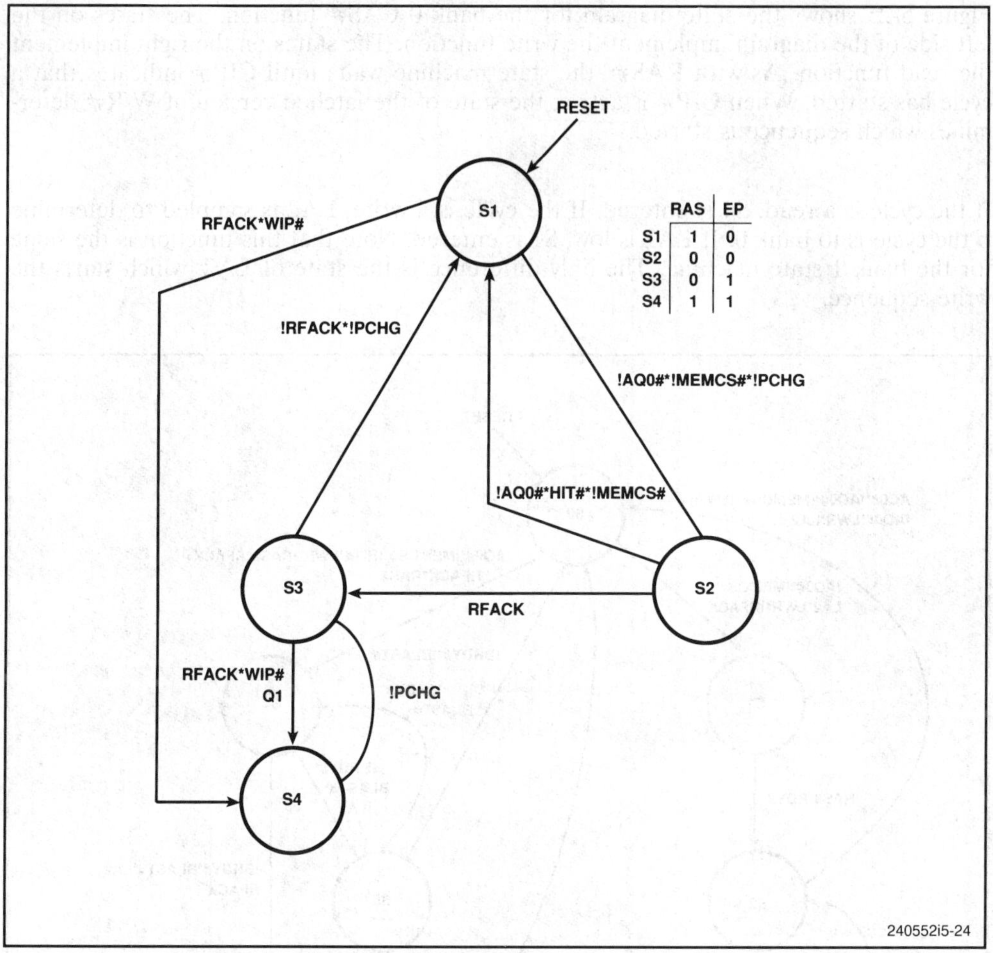

Figure 5-24. RAS State Machine

When a refresh cycle occurs, the RAS# state machine transitions to S2. S2 and S3 are devoted to the refresh function. When RFACK is sampled active, the transition occurs. The refresh sequence shown in Figure 5-23 illustrates the function of these two states. Note that after a refresh cycle, RAS# is left inactive. The transition from S0 to S4 allows for refresh cycles that start when RAS# is inactive.

5.5.3 CAS# Logic

Two separate PLDs implement the CAS# function. These PLDs generate the CAS# signals for bank 0 and bank 1, respectively. The state machines which generate these signals are separate and independent. Each generates two CAS# signals. CAS00# and CAS01# for bank 0, and CAS10# and CAS11# for bank 1. These signals drive separate DRAM modules due to drive requirements.

Figure 5-25 shows the state diagram for the bank 0 CAS# function. The states on the left side of the diagram implement the write function. The states on the right implement the read function. As with RAS#, the state machine waits until CIP# indicates that a cycle has started. When CIP# is active, the state of the latched version of W/R# determines which sequence is started.

If the cycle is a read, S4 is entered. If the cycle is a write, LA2 is sampled to determine if the cycle is to bank 0. If LA2 is low, S1 is entered. Note that this function is the same for the bank 1 state machine. The only difference is the state of LA2, which starts the write sequence.

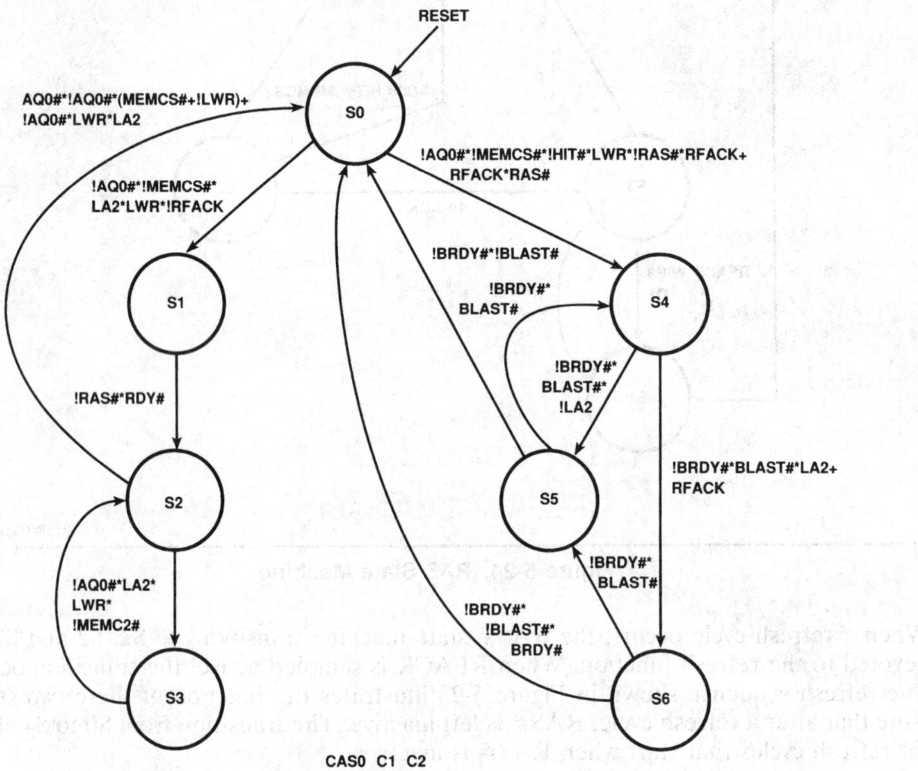

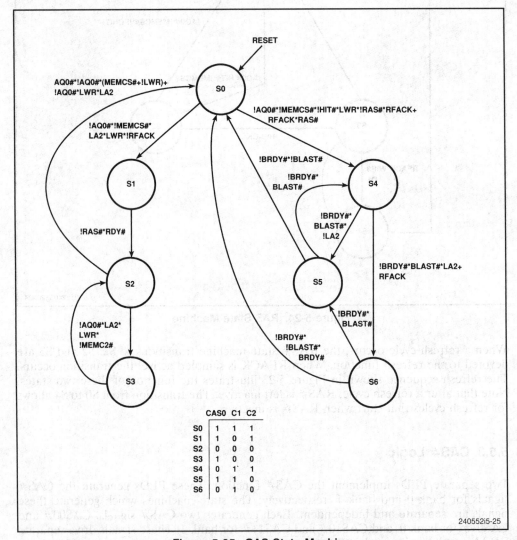

	CAS0	C1	C2
S0	1	1	1
S1	1	0	1
S2	0	0	0
S3	1	0	0
S4	0	1`	1
S5	1	1	0
S6	0	1	0

240552i5-25

Figure 5-25. CAS State Machine

During a write cycle, CAS# is held inactive until the clock after RDY# is asserted. The state machine also waits in S1 during a write miss cycle. CAS# is asserted during S2. In this state, several events can occur. First, the CPU may not start another bus cycle. Second, it may start a bus cycle other than a DRAM cycle. Third, it may initiate a read cycle, and fourth, it may begin a write cycle to bank 1. If any of these events occur, S1 is entered. If another write cycle starts to the same bank, however, S3 is entered.

The case of sequential writes to the same bank involves S2 and S3 only. An unlimited number of write cycles can occur in the same bank. If the DRAM row is same, they will occur without wait states. If a write miss occurs, RAS# will be deasserted, and the transition from S3 to S1 takes place.

During read cycles, the CAS# signals for bank 0 and bank 1 are activated at the same time. Therefore, the state machines enter S4 at the same clock. At this point, however, the state of LA2 determines which state machine enters S5. In S5, CAS# is deasserted to prepare that bank for the next access. If S6 is entered, the DATA from that bank has not yet been accessed. CAS# must be held active, in this case, until the data is sampled by the CPU. From S6, the next transition will be to S5 to continue the cycle, or S0 to terminate the cycle. If this bank was accessed first, the cycle will terminate from this state.

The read sequence is much simpler if static column mode DRAMs are used. The state sequence for static column mode is shown in Figure 5-26. The write sequence in this diagram is exactly the same as for the page mode CAS# control logic. The read function, however, requires only two states. From S0, the transition is made to S5 any time that a DRAM read cycle starts. Note that LA2 is not used to qualify this transition. Therefore, the CAS# signals for bank 0 and bank 1 are active at the same time.

5.5.4 Write Control Logic

The posted write implementation requires logic support for a few key functions. These functions are required mainly to support posting with interleaved memory. Three types of signals are generated to implement these functions:

- Multiplexer Select – These signals control the address multiplexers when RAS# is active. During write cycles, they must be active to select the write address path. These signals stay active during read cycles which are immediately preceded by a write. They are deactivated, when the write cycle is complete. Once they are deactivated the read cycle may proceed as the read path is selected.

- Write Enable – These signals are combined with the byte enable CPU outputs (BE0#-BE3#) to create the WBE# signals. The WBE00#-WBE03# signals control which byte is written in bank 0 during a write cycle. The WBE10#-WBE13# signals perform the same function for bank 1.

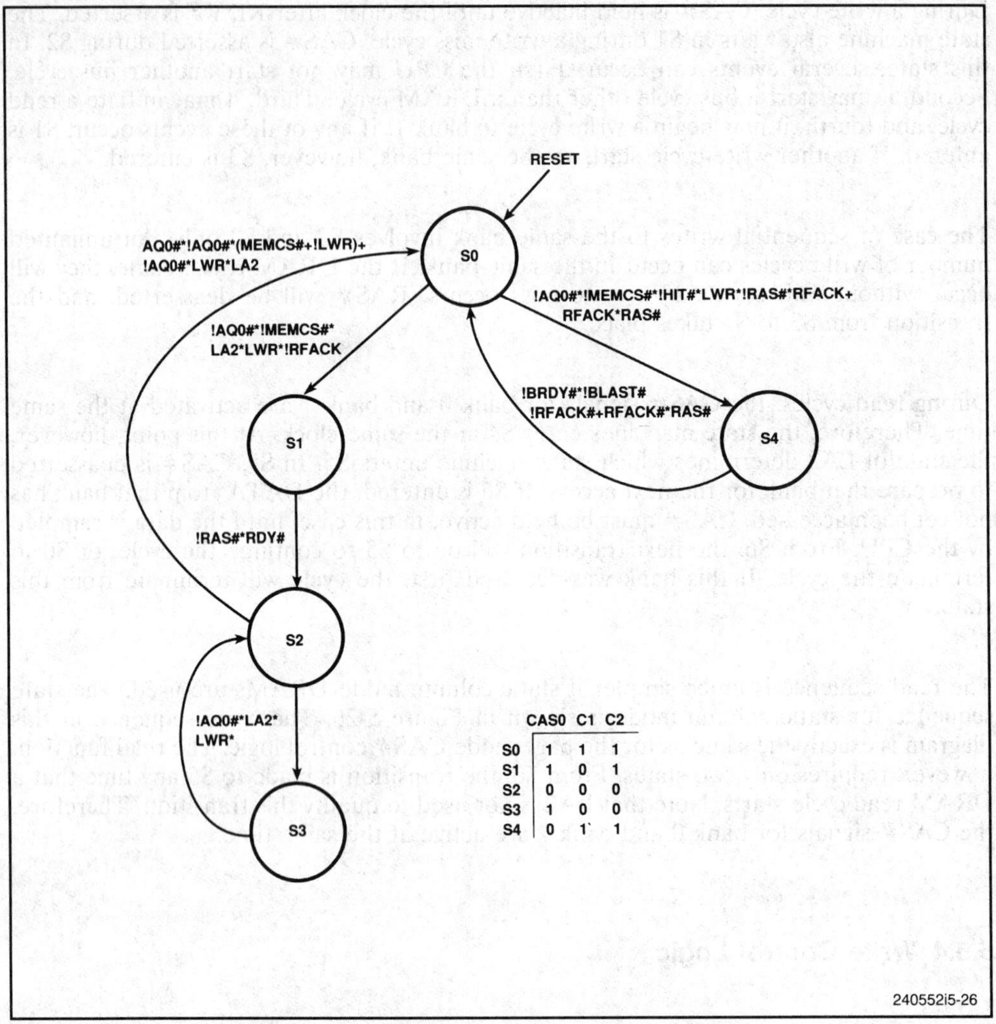

Figure 5-26. Static Column CAS State Machine

- Write In Progress – This signal is active when a write cycle has been started by either DRAM bank. It is active when either C01# or C11# is active. C01# and C11# are state outputs from the CAS# state machine which indicates that a write cycle is being performed. C01# is generated for bank 0 and C11# for bank 1. WIP# is only required for interleaved memory systems. The C01# (or C11#) output would be sufficient for a non-interleaved (single bank) system.

The state machines which generate these signals are shown in Figure 5-27. The state diagram for the MEN0# signal is shown. This signal enables the address multiplexer for bank 0. MEN0# is activated whenever a write cycle occurs to an address with A2 low (0). The MEN1# function is the same except that it is activated when A2 is high (1). The AQ0#, MEMCS# and LW/R# signals are used to indicate a valid write cycle.

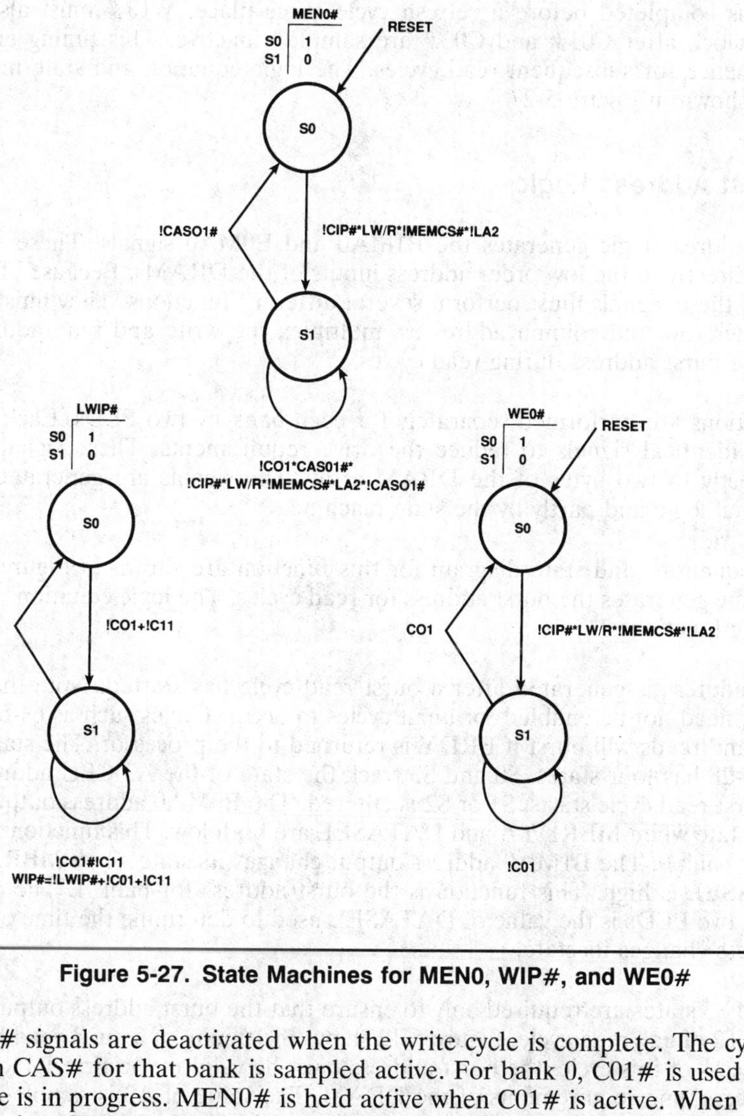

Figure 5-27. State Machines for MEN0, WIP#, and WE0#

The MEN# signals are deactivated when the write cycle is complete. The cycle is complete when CAS# for that bank is sampled active. For bank 0, C01# is used to indicate that a write is in progress. MEN0# is held active when C01# is active. When CAS00# is sampled active, CIP# is checked to determine if another valid write to the same bank has occurred. If so, MEN0# stays active until CAS00# is sampled active. This function keeps the write address path open during consecutive writes to the same bank.

The WE# state machine is very similar to that of the MEN# state machine. When a write cycle starts, WE0# is activated in the same manner as MEN0#. The write enable signals, however, must stay active one clock longer than the MEN# signals. Therefore, the WE# signal is not deactivated until C01# is sampled inactive.

WIP# is generated in part by combinatorial logic so that it can be active in the same clock as the C01# and C11# signals. WIP# must be active in this clock to ensure that a write miss is completed before a refresh cycle takes place. WIP# must also be held active one clock after C01# and C02# are sampled inactive. This timing ensures the proper sequence for subsequent read cycles. The logic equation and state machine for WIP# are shown in Figure 5-27.

5.5.5 Burst Address Logic

The burst address logic generates the B1MA0 and B0MA0 signals. These signals are connected directly to the low order address inputs of the DRAMs. Because of the direct connection, these signals must perform several different functions. They must multiplex the low order row and column addresses, multiplex the write and read addresses and generate the burst address during read cycles.

These functions are performed separately for each bank by two PLDs. Each PLD generates two identical signals to reduce the drive requirements. These signals are connected directly to two bytes of the DRAM array. The signals are generated partly by combinatorial logic and partly by the state machine.

The logic equations and state diagram for this function are shown in Figure 5-28. The state machine generates the burst address for read cycles. The logic equations handle the multiplexing functions.

The burst address is generated after a burst read cycle has started. Note that the i486 CPU cache need not be enabled for burst cycles to occur. Cycles such as 64-bit floating-point operand reads will burst if BRDY is returned to the processor. The state machine in Figure 5-28 has four states. S0 and S3 track the state of the A3 CPU address output. When a burst read cycle starts, S1 or S2 is entered. The B0MA0 address output will then change its state when MBRDY# and DATASEL are both low. This function is the burst address for bank 0. The B1MA0 address output changes its state when MBRDY#is low and DATASEL is high. This function is the burst address for bank 1. The only difference in the two PLDs is the value of DATASEL used to determine the time of which the burst address changes its state.

The S0 and S3 states are required only to ensure that the burst address outputs are valid during the T2 of any read cycle. Figure 5-12 shows the timing of a burst read hit cycle. In the first access of this cycle, the burst address must be valid in the first T2 to satisfy the address access time requirements of the DRAM. The value of A3 is sampled with ALD to statisfy this requirement. In this way, the burst address state machine always starts from the correct value of A3. If another wait state is added to this access, this function is not required.

The logic equations which provide the multiplexor function are very simple. The first term of the equations shown in Figure 5-28 enables the write path. The write enable signals are used to enable this path. When WE0 is active, for example, the value of the multiplexor output is passed through to the DRAM. The second term allows the row address A13 to be passed to the DRAM during a read page miss. This term is also

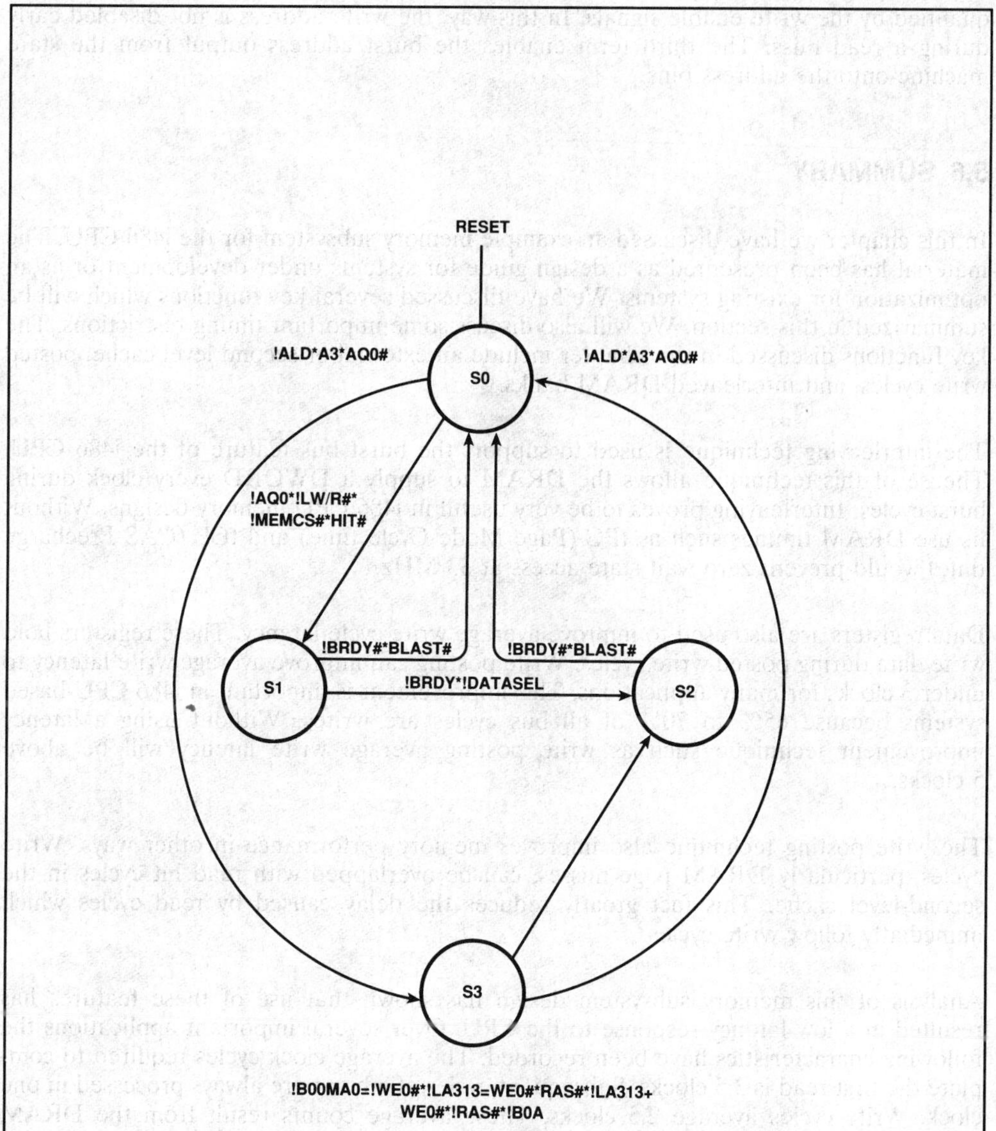

Figure 5-28. Burst Address Generation

qualified by the write enable signals. In this way, the write address is not disabled early during a read miss. The third term enables the burst address output from the state machine onto the address pins.

5.6 SUMMARY

In this chapter we have discussed an example memory subsystem for the i486 CPU. The material has been presented as a design guide for systems under development or as an optimization for existing systems. We have discussed several key functions which will be summarized in this section. We will also discuss some important timing restrictions. The key functions discussed in this chapter include an external or second level cache, posted write cycles, and interleaved DRAM banks.

The interleaving technique is used to support the burst bus feature of the i486 CPU. Theuse of this technique allows the DRAM to supply a DWORD every clock during burst cycles. Interleaving proves to be very useful in i486 CPU memory designs. Without its use DRAM timings such as tPC (Page Mode Cycle time) and tCP (CAS Precharge time) would prevent zero wait state access at 33 MHz.

Data registers are also used to improve average write cycle latency. These registers hold write data during posted write cycles. Write posting can improve average write latency to under 3 clocks for many applications. This improvement is important in i486 CPU-based systems because 65% to 70% of all bus cycles are writes. Without using a latency improvement technique such as write posting average write latency will be above 5 clocks.

The write posting technique also improves memory performance in other ways. Write cycles, particularly DRAM page misses, can be overlapped with read hit cycles in the second-level cache. This fact greatly reduces the delay caused by read cycles which immediatly follow write cycles.

Analysis of this memory subsystem design has shown that use of these features has resulted in a low latency response to the CPU. Over several important applications the following characteristics have been recorded. The average clock cycles required to complete the first read is 3.5 clocks. Subsequent cycles of a burst are always processed in one clock. Write cycles average 2.5 clocks. These average counts result from the DRAM access rates in Table 5-4. Read accesses from the cache always occur in zero wait states.

Table 5-4. Clock Latencies for DRAM Functions

DRAM Function	First Access Burst	Subsequent Burst Accesses	Write Cycles
Page hit	3	1	2
Page miss	7	1	5*

*Latency only incurred for back-to-back cycles.

5.7 TIMING RESTRICTIONS

A few DRAM timing restrictions must be mentioned. These timings become critical at 33 MHz. These timings are critical due primarily to the latency of the first cycle of a read page hit. Since three clocks are used the following timing restrictions exist:

tRAC = Data access time from RAS# active
tCAA = Data access time from column address valid
tCAC = Data access time from CAS# active
tRP = RAS# precharge time

At 33 MHz:

tRAC = 71.5 ns
tCAA = 37.5 ns
tCAC = 34 ns
tRP = 60.6 ns

At 25 MHz:

tRAC = 101.5 ns
tCAA = 51 ns
tCAC = 61.5 ns
tRP = 80 ns

Cache Subsystem 6

CHAPTER 6
CACHE SUBSYSTEM

6.1 INTRODUCTION

Caches are an important means of improving system performance. The i486™ DX microprocessor has an on-chip, unified code and data cache. The on-chip cache is used for both instruction and data accesses and operates on physical addresses. The i486 CPU has an 8-Kbyte cache which is organized in a 4-way set associative manner. To understand cache philosophy and the system advantages of a cache, many issues must be considered.

This chapter discusses the following related cache issues:

- Cache theory and the impact of caches on performance.
- The relationship between cache size and hit rates when using a single-level cache.
- Issues in mapping (or associativity) that arise when main memory is cached. Different cache configurations including direct-mapped, set associative, and fully associative. They are discussed along with the performance tradeoffs inherent to each configuration.
- The impact of cache line sizes and cache re-filling algorithms on performance.
- Write-back and write-through methods for updating main memory. How they maintain cache consistency and their impact on external bus utilization.
- Cache consistency issues that arise when a DMA occurs while the i486 CPU's cache is enabled. Methods that ensure cache and main memory consistency during cache accesses.
- Caches used in single versus multiple CPU systems.

6.2 CACHE MEMORY

Cache memories are high-speed memories that are placed between microprocessors and main memories. They keep copies of main memory that are currently in use to speed microprocessor access to requested data and instructions. When properly implemented, their access time can be three to eight times faster than that of main memory, and thus can reduce the overall access time. Caches also reduce the number of accesses to main memory DRAM which is important to systems with multiple CPU's which all access that same memory. This section introduces the cache concept and memory performance benefits provided by a cache.

6.2.1 What is a Cache?

A cache memory is a smaller high-speed memory that fits between a CPU and a slower main memory. Cache memories are important in increasing computer performance by reducing total memory latency. A cache memory consists of a directory (or tag), and a data memory. Whenever the CPU is required to read or write data it first accesses the tag memory and determines if a cache hit occurred, implying that the requested word is present in the cache. If the tags do not match, the data word is not present in the cache. This is called a cache miss. On a cache hit, the cache data memory allows a read operation to be completed more quickly from its faster memory than from a slower main memory access. The hit rate is the percentage of the accesses that are hits, and is affected by the size and organization of the cache, the cache algorithm used, and the program running. An effective cache system should maintain data in a way that increases the hit rate. Different cache organizations will be discussed later in this chapter. The main advantage of caches is that a larger main memory appears to have the high speed of a cache. For example, a zero-waitstate cache that has a hit rate of 90 percent will make main memory appear to be zero-waitstate memory for 9 out of 10 accesses.

Programs usually address memory in the neighborhood of recently accessed locations. This is called program locality or locality of reference and it is locality that makes cache systems possible. Code, data character strings, and vectors tend to be sequentially scanned items or items accessed repeatedly, and caches will help the performance in these cases. In some cases the program locality principle does not apply. Jumps in code sequences and context switching are some examples.

6.2.2 Why Add a Cache?

A cache can increase system performance at a reduced cost. Caches make main memory act as though it is performing at near-SRAM speed at a cost much less than a complete SRAM memory system. Caches are commonly used in high-speed 386™ CPU systems. A 386 DX CPU system with a 32-Kbyte cache and a main memory of 16 Mbytes is shown in Figure 6-1. A 32-Kbyte, direct-mapped cache using an 82385 cache controller has an 86 percent hit rate; it responds to the CPU in 0 waitstates (SRAM speeds) 86 percent of the time. This makes the 16 Mbytes of slower main memory appear to be 16 Mbytes of SRAM in 86 percent of its reads.

The 386 DX performance benefits from an 82385 cache about 25-35% compared to DRAM alone. The i486 CPU, however, has an 8K internal cache. An external cache for the i486 CPU, called a second-level cache, will offer anywhere from no to moderate performance increases. The on-chip, 8K cache is sufficient for most applications, but thrashes during larger, memory-intensive or multi-process applications. A large, second-level cache can capture the data that misses the internal cache and provide near-SRAM speed response. The effectiveness of the second-level cache widely varies and depends on the application being executed and the main memory speed.

6.3 CACHE TRADEOFFS

Cache efficiency is the cache's ability to keep the most frequently used code and data used by the microprocessor, and it is measured in terms of the hit rate. Another indication of cache efficiency is system performance; this is the speed in which the microprocessor can perform a certain task and is measured in effective bus cycles. An efficient cache reduces external bus cycles and enhances overall system performance. Hit rates are discussed in the next section.

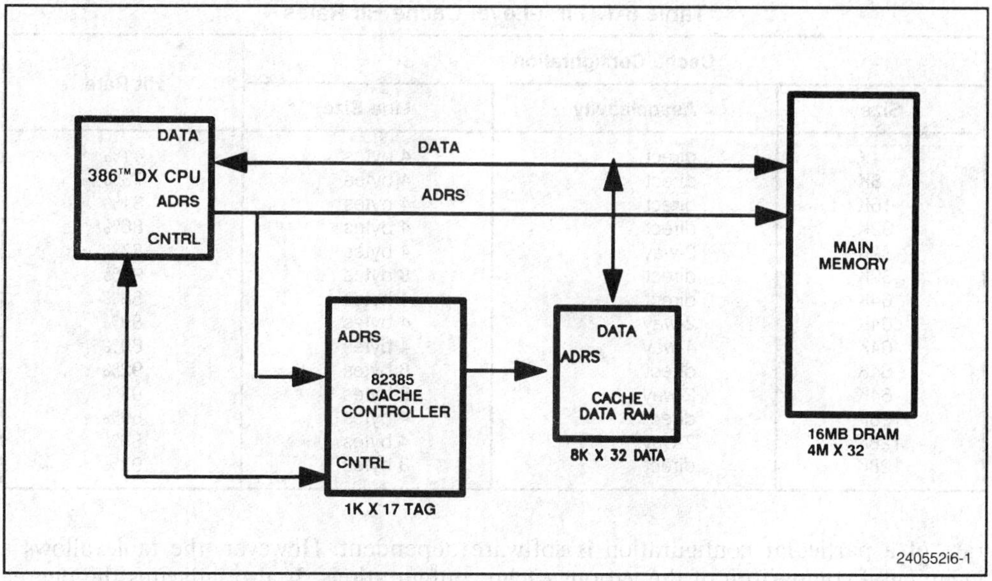

Figure 6-1. A Typical 386™ DX CPU System with an 82385 Cache Memory

Factors that can affect a cache's performance are:

- Size: Increasing the cache size allows more items to be contained in the cache. Cost is increased, however, and a larger cache cannot operate as quickly as a smaller one.
- Associativity (discussed in Section 6.2.2): Increased associativity increases the cache's hit rate but also increases its complexity and reduces its speed.
- Line Size: The amount of data the cache must fetch during each cache line replacement (every miss) affects performance. More data takes more time to fill a cache line, but then more data is available and the hit rate increases.
- Write-Back and Write Posting: The ability to write quickly to the cache and have the cache then write to the slower memory increases performance. Implementing these types of caches can be very complex, however.
- Features: Adding features such as write-protection (to be able to cache ROM memory), bus watching, and multiprocessing protocols can speed a cache but increases cost and complexity.
- Speed: Not all caches return data to the CPU as quickly as possible. It is less expensive and complex to use slower cache memories and cache logic. Intel's 82385 and 485Turbocache Module are, however, the fastest possible solutions for the 386 DX and i486 microprocessor.

6.3.1 Cache Size and Performance

Hit rates for various first-level cache configurations are shown in Table 6-1. These statistics are conservative because they illustrate the lowest hit rates generated by analyzing several mainframe traces. The hit rates are not absolute quantities, and the hit

Table 6-1. First-Level Cache Hit Rates

Cache Configuration			Hit Rate
Size	**Associativity**	**Line Size**	
1K	direct	4 bytes	41%
8K	direct	4 bytes	73%
16K	direct	4 bytes	81%
32K	direct	4 bytes	86%
32K	2-way	4 bytes	87%
32K	direct	8 bytes	91%
64K	direct	4 bytes	88%
64K	2-way	4 bytes	89%
64K	4-way	4 bytes	89%
64K	direct	8 bytes	92%
64K	2-way	8 bytes	93%
128K	direct	4 bytes	89%
128K	2-way	4 bytes	89%
128K	direct	8 bytes	93%

rate of a particular configuration is software dependent. However, the table allows a meaningful comparison of the various cache configurations. It also indicates the degree of hardware complexity needed to arrive at a particular cache efficiency. Table 6-1 presents direct-mapped, 2-way, and 4-way set associative caches which are all discussed in the next section.

Program behavior is another important factor in determining cache efficiency. If a program uses a piece of data only once, then the cache may spend all its time thrashing or replacing itself with new data from memory. This is common in vector processing. The processor receives no added efficiency from the cache as main memory is being requested frequently. In such instances, the user can consider mapping the data entries as noncacheable.

Cache system performance can be calculated based on the main memory access time, the cache access time, the miss rate, and the write cycle time.

Cs is defined as the ratio of the cache system access time to the main memory access time. Cs is a dimensionless number but provides a useful measure of the cache performance.

$$Ca = (1-M)Tc + MTm$$
$$Cs = Ca/Tm = (1-M)(Tc/Tm) + M = (1-M)Cm + M$$

where:

Ca = average cache system cycle time averaged over reads and writes
Tc = cache cycle time
Tm = main memory cycle time
M = miss rate = 1-hit rate
Cs = cache system access time as a fraction of main memory access time
Cm = cache memory access time as compared to main memory cycle time

If the cache always misses then M = 1 and Cm = 1, and the main memory access is equal to the effective access time of the cache. If the cache is infinitely fast, then Cm is equal to the miss rate. Because the cache access time is finite, the cache system access time approaches the cache access time as the miss rate approaches zero.

While the above discussion applies to read operations it can be easily extended to write operations, which also affect system performance. When memory has to be written to, the CPU has to wait for the completion of the write cycle before proceeding to the next instruction. In a buffered memory system, where posted writes occur, data can be loaded in a register, and the memory can be updated later. This allows the CPU to begin the next cycle without being delayed by the main memory write access time. Both these memory updating techniques are discussed later in this chapter.

6.3.2 Associativity and Performance Issues

Data and instructions are written into the cache by a function that maps the main memory address into a cache location. The placement policy determines the mapping function from the main memory address to the cache location. There are four policies to consider: fully associative, direct-mapped, set associative, and sector buffering.

Fully Associative: A fully associative cache system provides maximum flexibility in determining which blocks are stored in the cache at any time. Ideally the blocks of words in the cache would contain the main memory locations needed most by the processor regardless of the distance between the words in main memory. The size of a block in the cache is also known as the line size, and corresponds to the width of a cache word. For example, a block can be eight bytes for a 32-bit processor, in which case two doublewords are accessed each time the cache line is filled. In the example shown in Figure 6-2, the block size is one doubleword.

Because there is no single relationship between all of the addresses in the 64 blocks, the cache would have to store the entire address of each block. When the processor requests data, the cache controller would have to compare the address with each of the 64 addresses in the cache for a match condition. This organization, shown in Figure 6-2 is called fully associative.

Direct Mapped: In a direct mapped cache, the simplest of the three policies, only one address comparison is required to determine if the requested word is in the cache. This is because each block in the cache maps to only one location in the cache. A direct mapped cache address has two parts: a cache index field, which specifies the block's location in the cache, and a tag field that distinguishes blocks within a particular cache location.

For example, consider a 64-Kbyte direct mapped cache that contains 16K 32-bit locations and caches 16 Mbytes of memory. The cache index field must include 14 bits to select one of the 16-Kbyte blocks in cache plus two bits to decode one of the four byte enables. The tag field must be eight bits wide to identify one of the 256 blocks that can

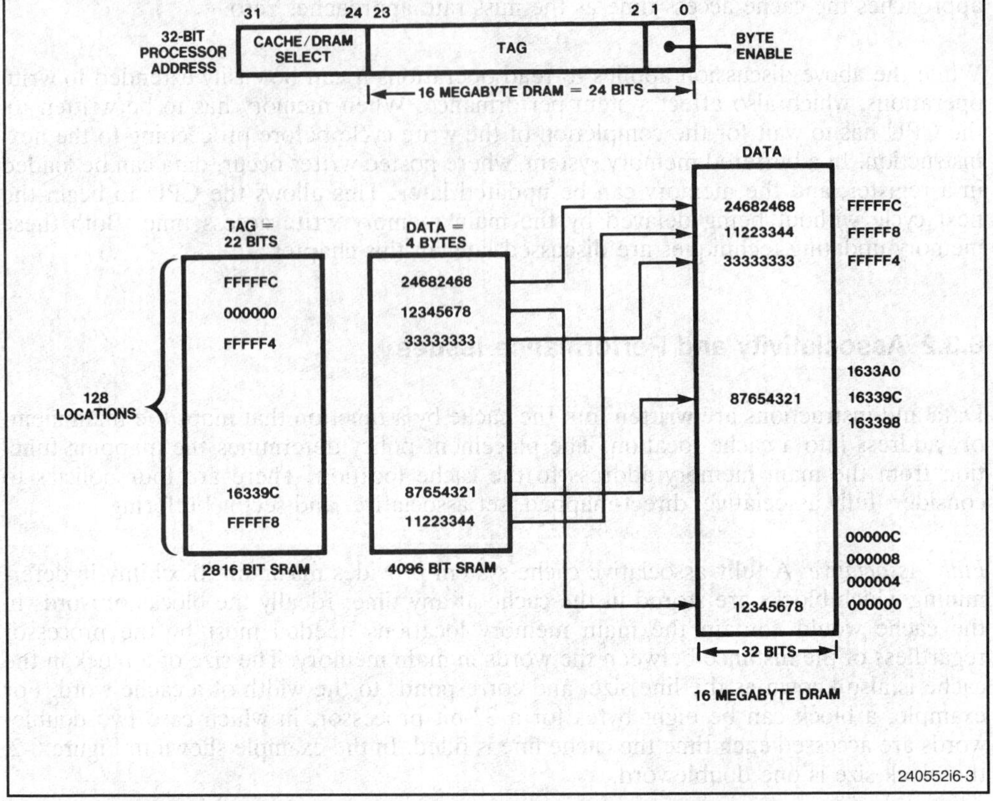

Figure 6-2. A Fully Associative Cache Organization

occupy the selected cache location. The most significant eight bits of the address are decoded to select the cache subsystem from other memories in the memory space. The direct-mapped cache organization is shown in Figure 6-3.

If the processor requests data at FFFFF8, then the first step is to send the most significant 14 bits of FFF8 to the cache tag RAM. If the tag field stored at FFF8 is FF (as shown in the diagram), then a hit has occurred and the data word "B" is sent to the CPU. If the requested word has 020004, then the tags would not match. In this case the tag RAM would be updated with the value 02 corresponding to the index 0004, and the data "D" would be replaced by the word at location 020004.

If the processor accesses locations that have the same index bits, then the cache would have to be updated constantly. This type of program behavior is infrequent, however, so a direct mapped cache may provide acceptable performance at a lower cost when compared to a fully associative cache memory.

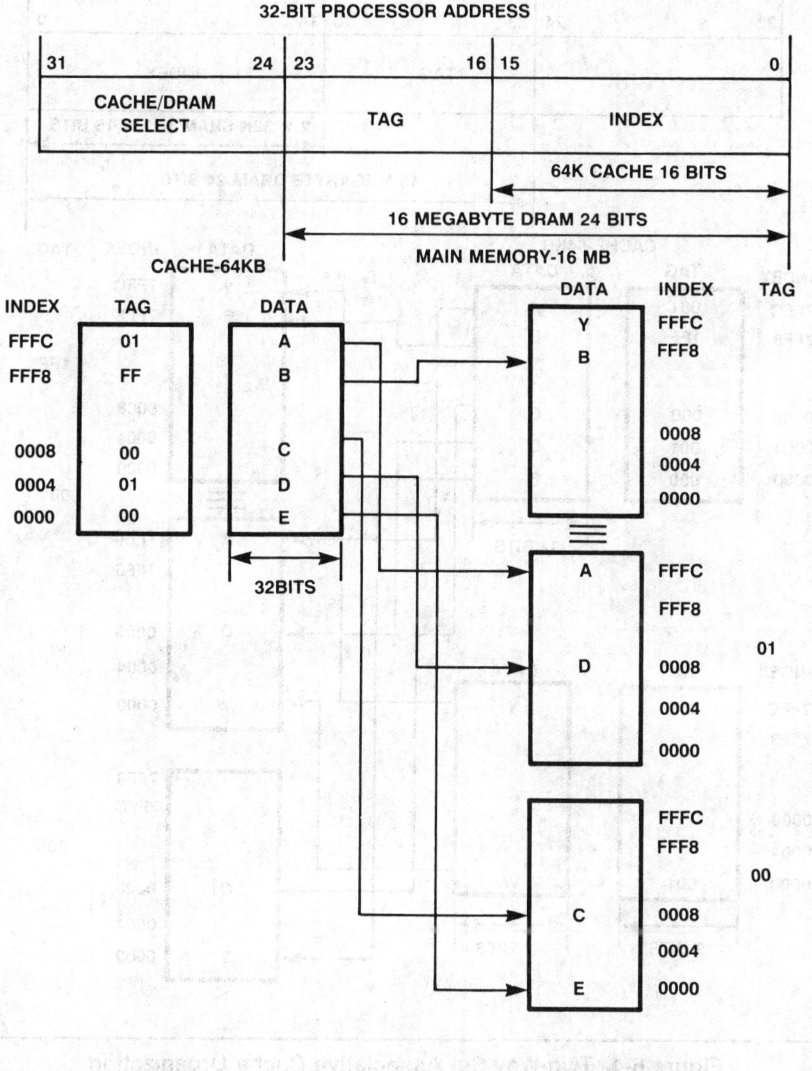

240552i6-4

Figure 6-3. Direct Mapped Cache Organization

Set Associative: The set-associative cache is a compromise between the fully associative and direct-mapped caches. The set-associative cache has more than one set and it is equivalent to several direct mapped caches operating in parallel. For each cache index there are several block locations allowed, and the block can be placed in any set or retrieved from any set. Figure 6-4 shows a two-way set associative cache memory.

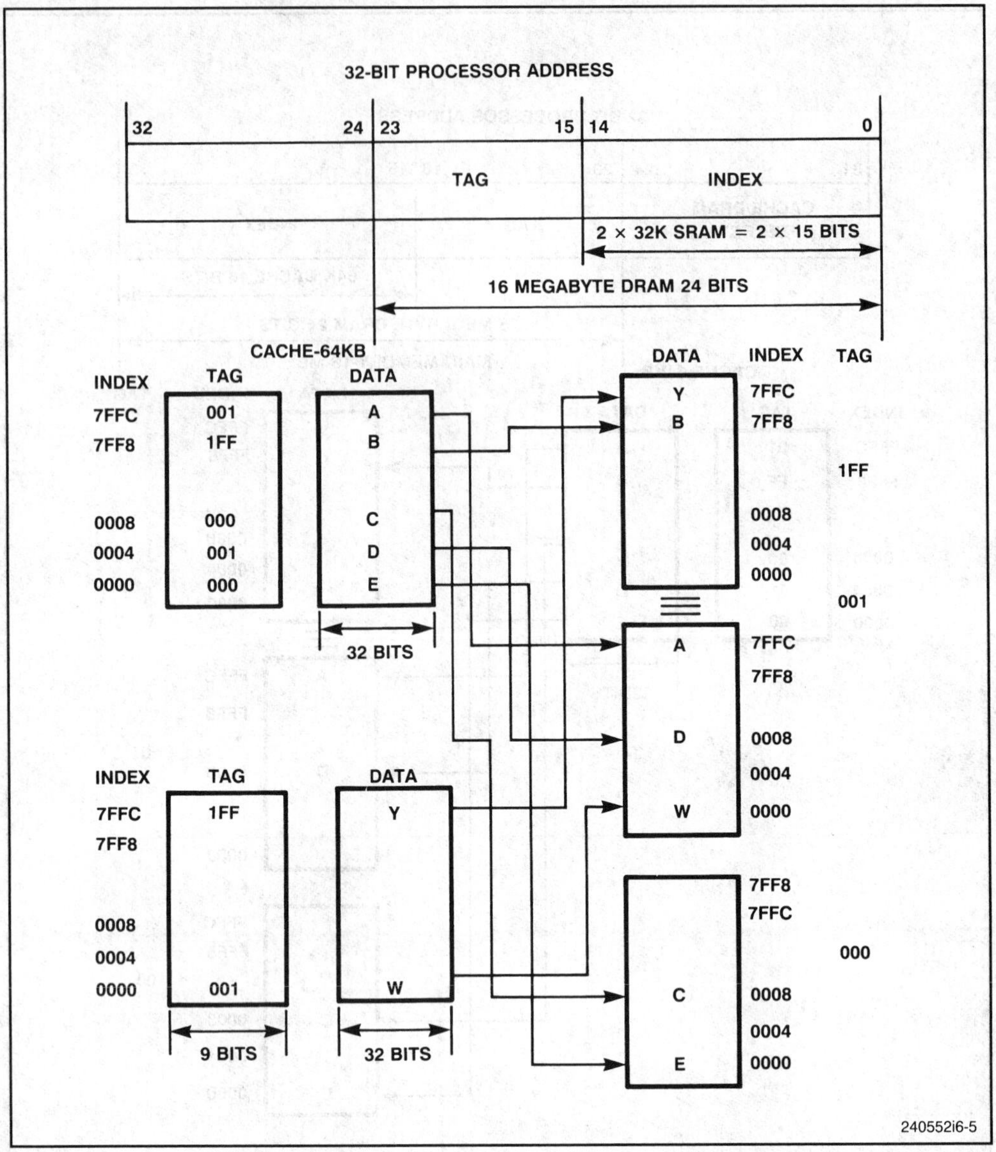

Figure 6-4. Two-Way Set Associative Cache Organization

Given an equal amount of cache memory as in the direct mapped example, the set associative cache has half as many locations, and the extra address bit becomes part of the tag field. Because the set-associative cache has several places for a block with the same cache index, the hit rate is increased. The set associative cache performs more efficiently than a direct mapped cache, but it needs a wider tag field and additional logic to determine which set should receive the data. This function is determined by the replacement policy, which is covered later in this section.

Sector Buffering: Another cache configuration uses a sector buffer and is sometimes called a sub-block cache. The cache is a number of sectors, and the sectors in turn are a number of blocks. Each block can have its own valid bit, but only one tag address exists per sector. When a word is accessed whose sector is in the cache but the block is not, then the block is fetched from the main memory. Sector buffering has its own tradeoffs associated with miss ratios and bus utilization. Having smaller blocks increases the miss ratio, but reduces the number of external bus accesses. Conversely, having a large number of blocks increases the hit ratio but also increases the external bus utilization. Figure 6-5 shows the cache organization in sector buffering.

The i486 CPU's on-board cache is organized 4-way set associative with a line size of 16 bytes. The 8-Kbyte cache is organized as four 2-Kbyte sets. Each 2-Kbyte set is comprised of one hundred and twenty-eight 16 byte-lines. Figure 6-6 shows the cache organization. Because the cache is on-chip, the user can achieve an extremely high hit rate with the 4-way associativity. The cache is transparent so that the i486 CPU remains software compatible with its non-cache predecessors.

6.3.3 Block/Line Size

As mentioned earlier, block size is an important consideration in cache memory design. Block size is also referred to as the line size or the width of the cache data word. The block size may be larger than the word, and this can impact the performance as the cache may be fetching and storing more information than the CPU needs.

As the block size increases, the number of blocks that fit in the cache are reduced. Because each block fetch overwrites the older cache contents, some blocks are overwritten shortly after being fetched. In addition, as block size increases, additional words are fetched with the requested word. Because of program locality the additional words are less likely to be needed by the processor.

TAG 1	BLOCK 1.1	BLOCK 1.2	BLOCK 1.3	. . .	BLOCK 1.N
TAG 2	BLOCK 2.1	BLOCK 2.2	BLOCK 2.3	. . .	BLOCK 2.N
. . .	. . .	. . .	. . .	. . .	. . .
TAG M	BLOCK M.1	BLOCK M.2	BLOCK M.3	. . .	. . .

TAG PER SECTOR　　BLOCKS PER SECTOR

Figure 6-5. Sector Buffer Cache Organization

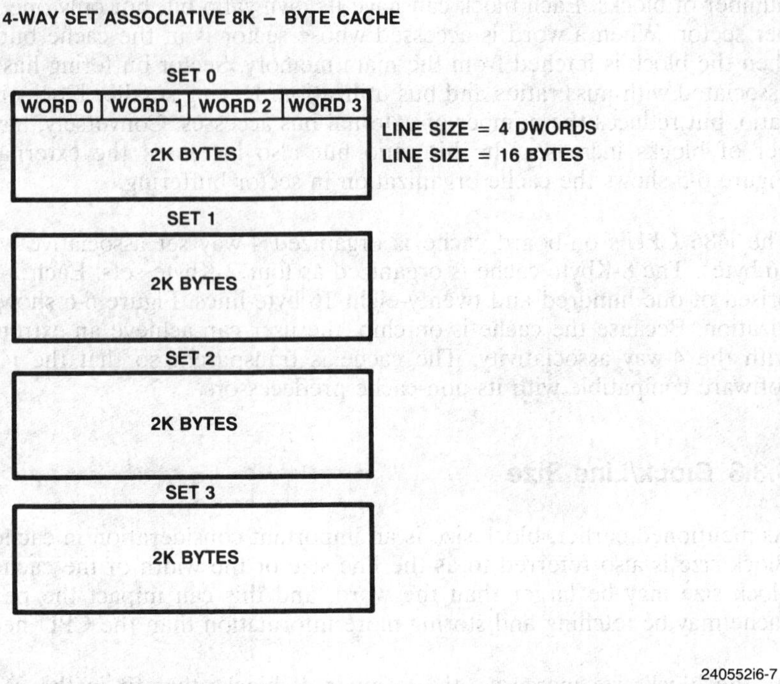

Figure 6-6. The Cache Data Organization for the On-Chip i486™ CPU's Cache

If a cache is refilled with 4 or 8 CPU words on a miss then the performance improves dramatically over a cache size that employs single word refills. Those extra words that were read into the cache, because they are subsequent words and by the sequential nature of programs, will most likely be hits in subsequent cache accesses. As well, the cache refill algorithm is a significant performance factor in systems where the delay in transferring the first word from the main memory is long but in which several subsequent words can be transferred in a shorter time. This situation applies when using page mode accesses in dynamic RAMs, and the initial word is read after the normal access time, while subsequent words can be quickly accessed by changing only the column addresses. Taking advantage of this situation while selecting the optimum line size can greatly increase cache performance.

6.3.4 Replacement Policy

In a set-associative cache configuration, a replacement policy is needed to determine which set should receive new data when the cache is updated. There are three common approaches for choosing which block (or single word) within a set will be overwritten. These are the least recently used (LRU) method, the first-in first-out (FIFO) method, and the random method.

In the LRU method, the set that was least recently accessed is overwritten. The control logic must maintain least recently used bits and must examine the bits before an update occurs. In the FIFO method, the cache overwrites the block that is resident for the longest time. In the random method, the cache arbitrarily replaces a block. The performance of the algorithms depends on the program behavior. The LRU method is preferred because it provides the best hit rate.

6.4 UPDATING MAIN MEMORY

When the processor executes instructions that modify the contents of the cache, changes have to be made in the main memory as well, otherwise, the cache is only a temporary buffer and it is possible for data inconsistencies to arise between the main memory and the cache. If only one of the two, the cache or the main memory, is altered and the other is not, two different sets of data become associated with the same address. A potential situation of incorrect or stale data is shown in Figure 6-7. There are two general approaches to updating the main memory. The first is the write-through method, and the second is the write-back, also known as copy-back method. Memory traffic issues are discussed for both the methods.

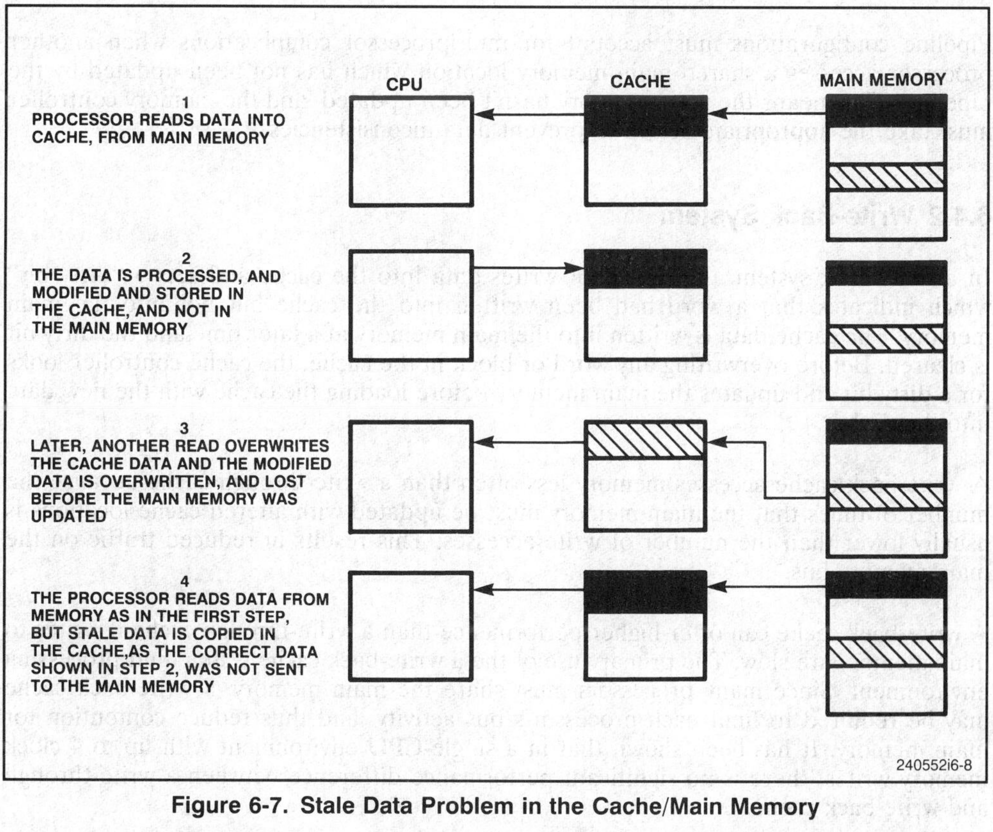

Figure 6-7. Stale Data Problem in the Cache/Main Memory

6.4.1 Write-Through and Buffered Write-Through Systems

In a write-through system, data is written to the main memory immediately after or while it is written into the cache. As a result, the main memory always contains valid data. The advantage to this approach is that any block in the cache can be overwritten without data loss, while the hardware implementation remains fairly straightforward. There is a memory traffic tradeoff, however, because every write cycle increases the bus traffic on a slower memory bus. This can create contention by multiple bus masters for use of the memory bus. Even in a buffered write-through scheme, each write will eventually go to memory. Thus, bus utilization for write cycles is not reduced by using a write-through or buffered write-through cache.

Users sometimes adopt a buffered write-through approach in which the write accesses to the main memory can be buffered with a N-deep pipeline. A number of words are stored in pipelined registers, and will subsequently be written to the main memory. The processor can begin a new operation before the write operation to main memory is completed. If a read access follows a write access, and a cache hit occurs, then data can be accessed from the cache memory while the main memory is updated. If the N-deep pipeline is full the processor must wait if another write access occurs and the main memory has not been as yet been updated. A write access followed by a read miss also requires the processor to wait as the main memory has to be updated before the next read access.

Pipeline configurations must account for multiprocessor complications when another processor accesses a shared main memory location which has not been updated by the pipeline. This means the main memory hasn't been updated, and the memory controller must take the appropriate action to prevent data inconsistencies.

6.4.2 Write-Back System

In a write-back system, the processor writes data into the cache and sets a "dirty bit" which indicates that a word had been written into the cache but not into the main memory. The cache data is written into the main memory at a later time and the dirty bit is cleared. Before overwriting any word or block in the cache, the cache controller looks for a dirty bit and updates the main memory before loading the cache with the new data into the cache.

A write-back cache accesses memory less often than a write-through cache because the number of times that the main memory must be updated with altered cache locations is usually lower than the number of write accesses. This results in reduced traffic on the main memory bus.

A write-back cache can offer higher performance than a write-through cache if writes to main memory are slow. The primary use of the a write-back cache is in a multiprocessing environment. Since many processors must share the main memory, a write-back cache may be required to limit each processor's bus activity, and thus reduce contention for main memory. It has been shown that in a single-CPU environment with up to 4 clock memory writes, there is no significant performance difference between a write-through and write-back cache.

There are some disadvantages to a write-back system. The cache control logic is more complex because addresses have to be reconstructed from the tag RAM and the main memory has to be updated along with the pending request. For DMA and multiprocessor operations, all locations with an asserted dirty bit must be written to the main memory before another device can access the corresponding main memory locations.

6.4.3 Cache Consistency

Write-through and write-back systems require mechanisms to eliminate the problem of stale main memory in a multiprocessing system or in a system with a DMA controller. If the main memory is updated by one processor then the cache data maintained by another processor can contain stale data. A system that prevents the stale data problem is said to maintain cache consistency. There are four methods commonly used to maintain cache consistency: snooping (or bus watching), broadcasting (or hardware transparency), non-cacheable memory designation, and cache flushing.

In snooping, cache controllers monitor the bus lines and invalidate any shared locations that are written by another processor. The common cache location is invalidated and cache consistency is maintained. This method is shown in Figure 6-8.

In broadcasting/hardware transparency, the addresses of all stores are transmitted to all the other caches so that all copies are updated. This is accomplished by routing the accesses of all devices to main memory through the same cache. Another method is by copying all cache writes to main memory and to all of the caches that share main memory. A hardware transparent system is shown in Figure 6-9.

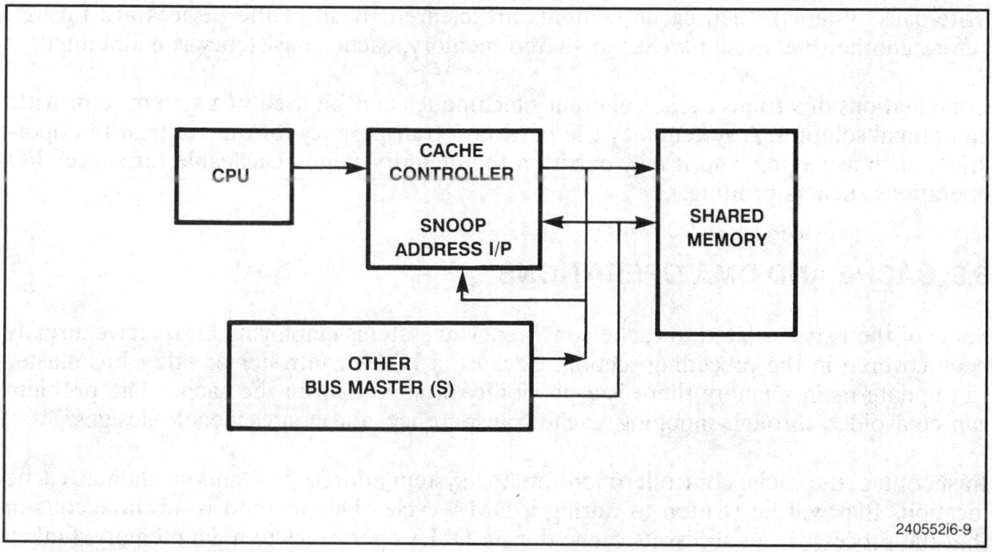

Figure 6-8. Bus Watching/Snooping for Shared Memory Systems

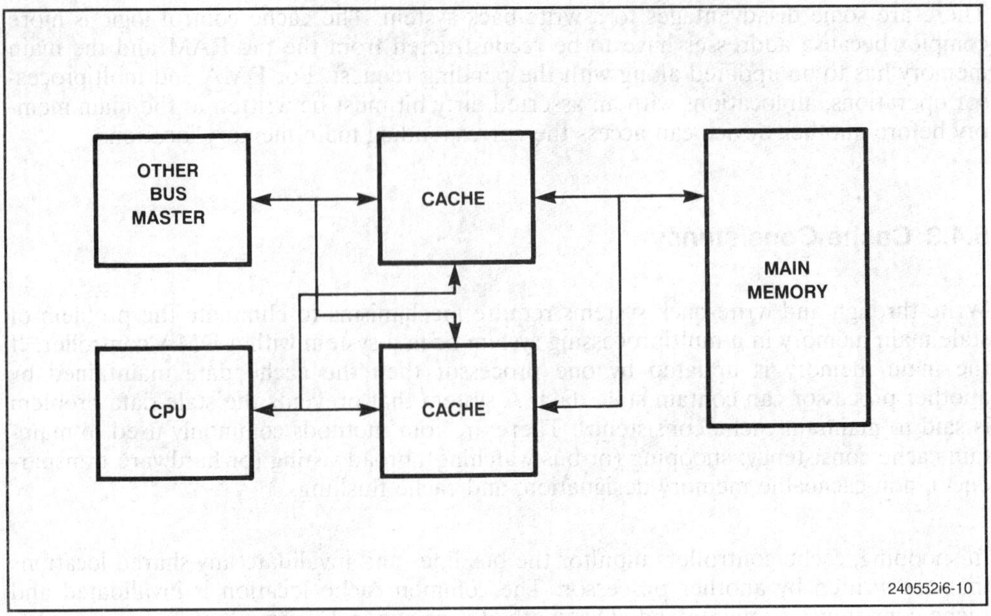

Figure 6-9. Hardware Transparency

In non-cacheable memory systems, all shared memory locations are considered non-cacheable. In such systems, access to the shared memory is never copied in the cache, and the cache never receives stale data. This can be implemented with chip select logic or with the high order address bits. Figure 6-10 shows non-cacheable memory.

In cache flushing, all cache locations with set dirty bits are written to main memory (for write-back systems), then cache contents are cleared. If all of the devices are flushed before another bus master writes to shared memory, cache consistency is maintained.

Combinations of various cache coherency techniques may be used in a system to provide an optimal solution. A system may use hardware transparency for time critical I/O operations such as paging, and it may partition the memory as non-cacheable for slower I/O operations such as printing.

6.5 CACHE AND DMA OPERATIONS

Some of the issues related to cache consistency in systems employing DMA have already been covered in the preceding section. Because a DMA controller or other bus master can update main memory there is a possibility of stale data in the cache. The problem can be avoided through snooping, cache transparency, and non-cacheable designs.

In snooping, the cache controller monitors the system address bus, and invalidates cache locations that will be written to during a DMA cycle. This method is advantageous in that the processor can access its cache during DMA operations to main memory. Only a "snoop hit" causes an invalidation cycle (or update cycle) to occur.

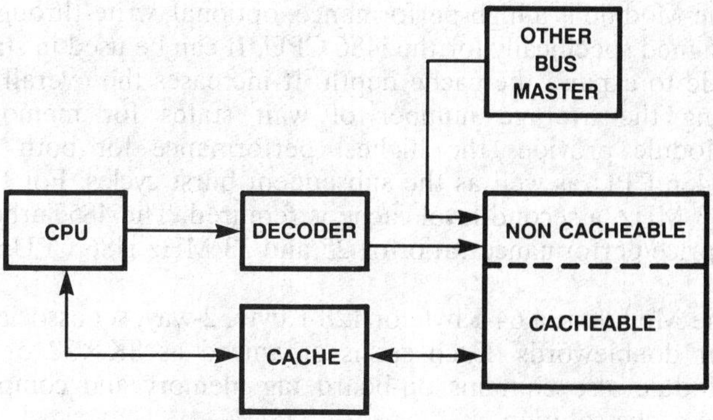

Figure 6-10. Non-Cacheable Shared Memory

In cache transparency, memory accesses through the CPU and the DMA controller are directed through the cache, requiring minimal hardware. However, the main disadvantage is that while a DMA operation is in progress the CPU bus is placed in HOLD. The concurrency of CPU/cache and DMA controller/main memory operations is cannot supported.

In non-cacheable designs, a separate dual-ported memory can be used as the non-cacheable portion of the memory, and the DMA device is tightly coupled to this memory. In this way the problem of stale data cannot occur.

In all of the approaches, the cache should be made software transparent so that DMA cycles do not require special software programming to ensure cache coherency.

6.6 CACHES FOR SINGLE VERSUS MULTIPLE CPU SYSTEMS

In single CPU systems, a write-through cache is an ideal cache solution. Write-through caches solve consistency issues, may be designed to be a plug-in option, and are less-expensive. For example, the 485Turbocache Module is a write-through, optional, expandable, second-level cache designed for the i486 CPU. The main drawback of a write-through cache is its inability to reduce main memory utilization for write cycles. However, this is not as critical a consideration to single CPU designs.

Memory bus utilization in multiple CPU systems is, perhaps, the most important performance consideration. In this type of system, a cache should have a very high hit rate for both reads and writes. Accesses to main, shared memory must be minimized. Write-back caches are best-suited for these multiprocessor environments. A write-back cache will, however, be more complex in its architecture and coherency mechanisms.

6.7 INTRODUCTION TO THE 485TURBOCACHE MODULE EXTERNAL CACHE AND THE MEMORY HIERARCHY

The 485Turbocache Module is a high-performance, optional, write-through, second-level cache that was designed specifically for the i486 CPU. It can be used in standalone mode or a cascaded mode to expand the cache depth. It increases the overall system performance by reducing the average number of wait states for memory reads. The 485Turbocache Module provides the highest performance for both the first word requested by the i486 CPU as well as the subsequent burst cycles. For the best performance at 25 and 33 MHz, a second-level cache is required. The 485Turbocache Module provides the best price/performance ratio for 25 and 33 MHz i486 CPU system designs.

The 485Turbocache Module is a 64-Kbyte or 128-Kbyte, 2-way, set associative cache with a line size of four doublewords. Each set is organized as 8K × 32 or 16K × 32. The 485Turbocache Module also contains on-board tag memory and comparator logic to provide a complete cache solution.

With a good memory design, the on-chip cache of the i486 CPU limits the performance increase that a second-level cache will offer. Additionally, some applications, such as Lotus 1-2-3, benefit less than 5 percent from an external cache, while others, such as Excel, benefit greater than 30 percent. Performance is extremely application sensitive as an application may or may not operate effectively within the confines of the on-chip 8K cache.

6.7.1 An i486 Processor System

A typical i486 microprocessor system is shown in Figure 6-11. The i486 processor has a local bus that consists of address, data and control buses. These buses are either buffered, registered or latched to comprise the system bus.

The memory subsystem is made up of DRAMs, SRAMs, and EPROMs. Main memory accesses are usually addressed to a DRAM subsystem, however the I/O subsystem can communicate with the i486 CPU, and it can also communicate with the memory subsystem during DMA operations.

Cache consistency must be maintained whenever main memory accesses occur during DMA operations. Bus snooping and validation logic can monitor the bus to detect memory writes that may be initiated by other bus masters. If such writes are detected, portions of the processor and the 485Turbocache Module second-level cache may have to be invalidated. Both the i486 CPU and the 485Turbocache Module have mechanisms that can invalidate cache entries.

The 485Turbocache Module is closely coupled to the i486 processor. The address, data, and control signals are connected to the processor's local bus, and 485Turbocache Module control signals interface to the system bus as well. The system bus control signals interface to the processor and the 485Turbocache Module in a similar manner. This allows the second-level 485Turbocache Module cache to be implemented into an i486 processor system with ease.

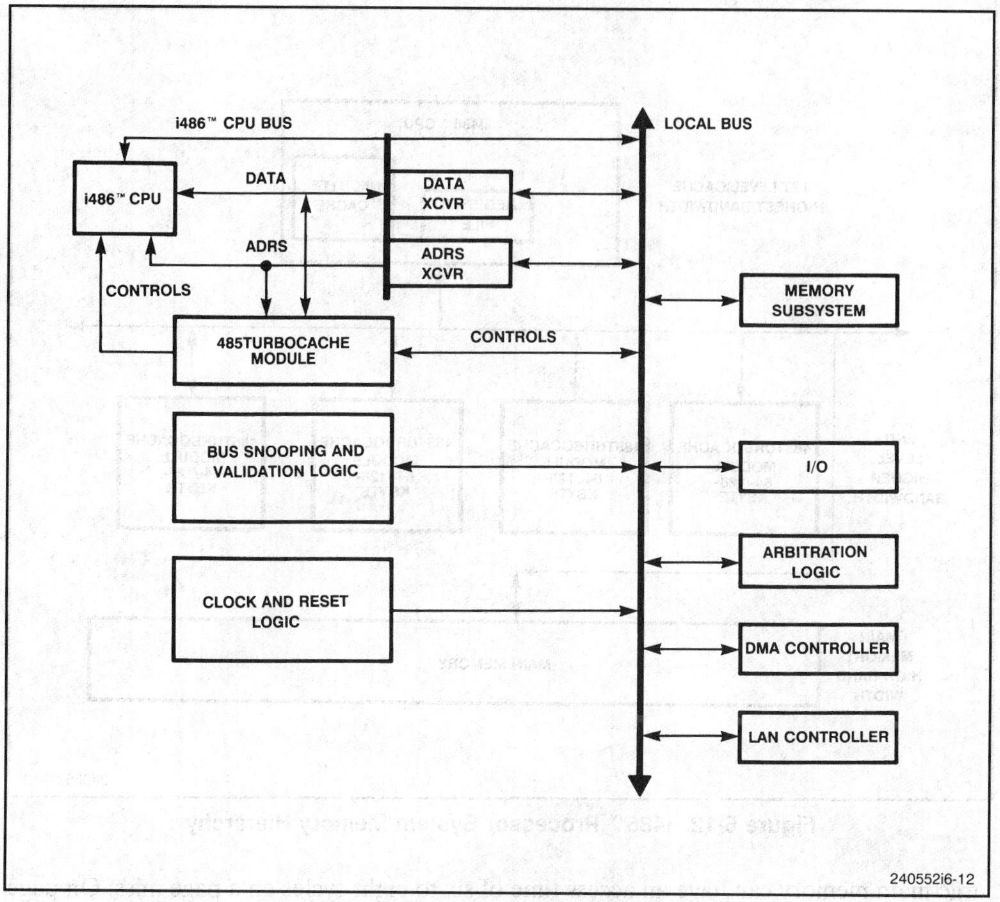

Figure 6-11. A Typical i486™ CPU System

6.7.2 The Memory Hierarchy and Advantages of a Secondary Cache

The i486 CPU has a high-speed register set and on-chip cache and these are accorded the first level of memory hierarchy. Instructions can be executed in a single clock, and at an average cycles per instruction rate of 1.8 (CPI). The next level of hierarchy is accorded to the secondary cache, which can consist of one or more 485Turbocache Modules. These sustain a high level of performance by supporting the fastest possible memory accesses, requiring only two clock cycles for the first read and one clock cycle for each of the subsequent three reads in a burst cycle. System performance degrades if main memory accesses are required. However, with the on-chip first-level cache and the external second-level cache, the number of main memory read accesses is reduced considerably. Figure 6-12 shows the memory hierarchy in a typical i486 processor system.

Because the i486 microprocessor internal cache is so efficient, most external CPU bus cycles are DRAM page misses. A second-level cache improves the bus latency problem, as data is available a large percentage of the time from the cache for read operations. A

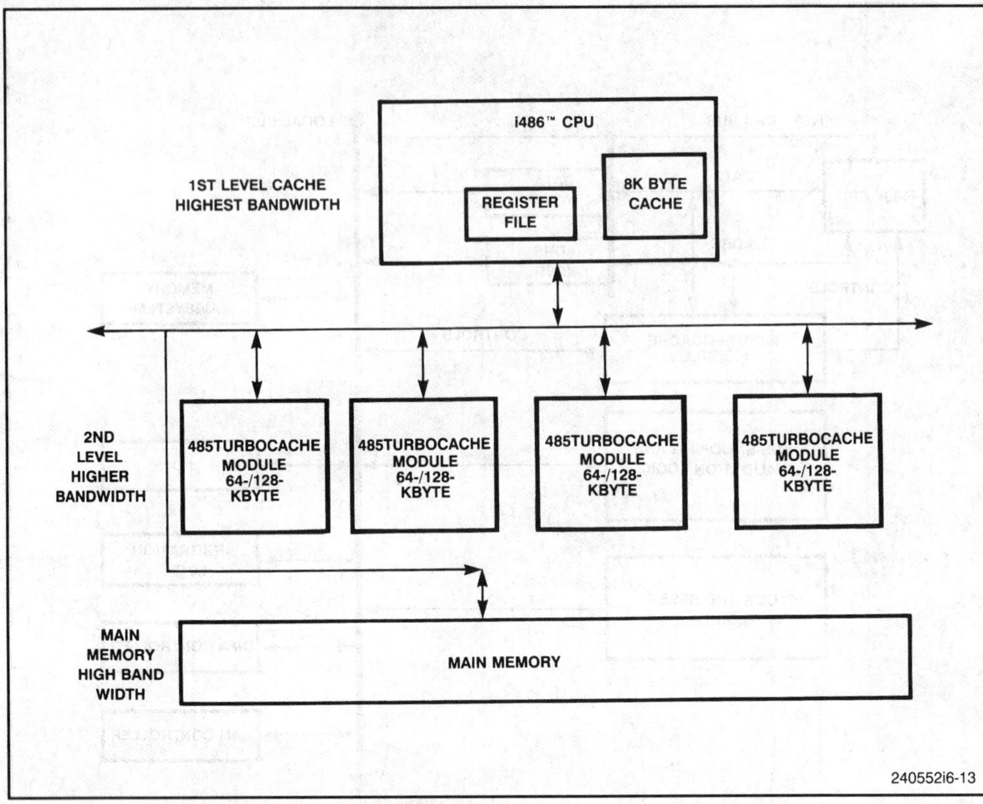

Figure 6-12. i486™ Processor System Memory Hierarchy

large main memory can have an access time of six to eight cycles on a page miss. On page hits data can be provided in three or four cycles.

The 485Turbocache Module has a write protection feature that allows the cacheing of BIOS which greatly improves BIOS function performance. The i486 CPU can write-protect code on a page basis, but not in real mode. Common BIOS functions which can be accelerated by cacheing are extended memory accesses, video accesses, disk copies, and LAN card code. The 485Turbocache Module also can support 1-clock bursts, and supply the i486 CPU data at the fastest possible rate. Its 2-way set-associative configuration allows a main memory location to have the possibility of being present in one of two sets improving its hit rate. See Section 6.5.5 for 485Turbocache Module performance measurements.

6.7.3 485Turbocache Module Architecture

Figure 6-13 is an architectural block diagram of the 485Turbocache Module. The 485Turbocache Module has control signals that interface with the i486 processor, a main memory controller, and a bus controller.

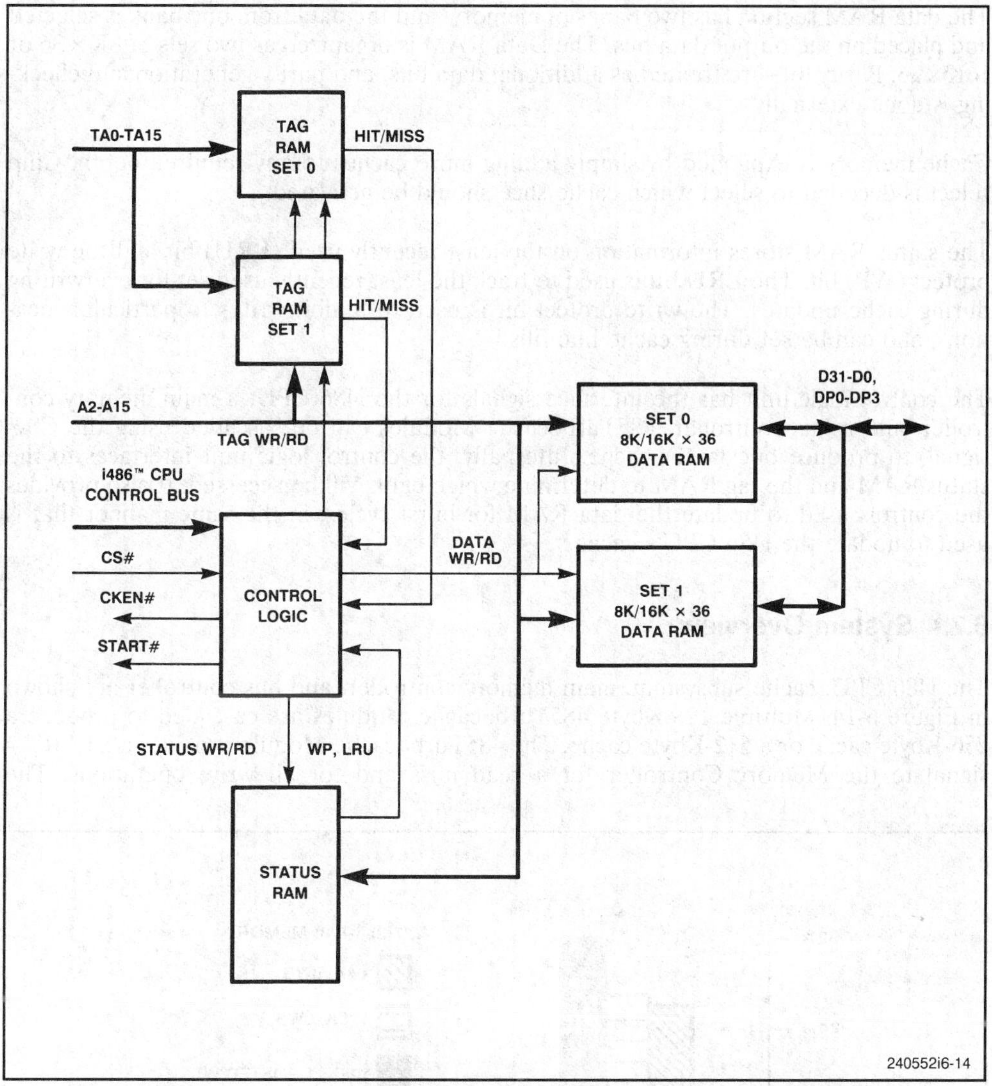

Figure 6-13. Internal Block Diagram of the 485Turbocache Module

The 485Turbocache Module is organized as two sets of 8K or 16K doublewords. When the cache is updated, four doublewords are accessed, making one of the sets is equivalent to 2K or 4K locations containing four doublewords. During a cache read operation, bits A2-A15 address both tag RAM sets. Tag addresses, TA0-TA15 are compared to the previously stored tags. If there is a hit condition, when the tags match, then data from the appropriate set is placed on the data bus. If there is a miss, then the START# signal is asserted to initiate a main memory access. On a cache read miss, four doublewords are read to the cache. Write operations update the tag RAMs and data RAMs only if a cache hit occurs.

The data RAM section has two banks of memory, and the data from one bank is selected and placed on the output data bus. The Data RAM is organized as two sets of 8K × 36 or 16K × 36. Parity bits are treated as additional data bits, and parity generation and checking is done externally.

Cache memory is expanded by simply adding more caches to any required depth. Chip select is decoded to select which cache slice should be activated.

The status RAM stores information on the least recently used (LRU) bit and the write protect (WP) bit. The LRU bit is used to track the least recently used set for overwriting during cache updates. The write protect bit is used to inhibit writes to particular locations, and can be set during cache line fills.

The control logic unit has the interface signals for the i486 CPU, a main memory controller, and a bus controller. 485Turbocache Modules can be cascaded using the CS# signal, to produce one larger cache. Internally, the control logic unit interfaces to the status RAM and the tag RAM to determine which bank will be accessed. It also provides the controls used to update the data RAM for burst cycles, in the same manner that is used to update the i486 CPU's cache.

6.7.4 System Overview

The i486 CPU, cache subsystem, main memory controller, and bus controller are shown in Figure 6-14. Multiple 128-Kbyte 485Turbocache Modules are cascaded to produce a 256-Kbyte cache or a 512-Kbyte cache. The 485Turbocache Module provides a START# signal to the Memory Controller for a read miss and for all write operations. The

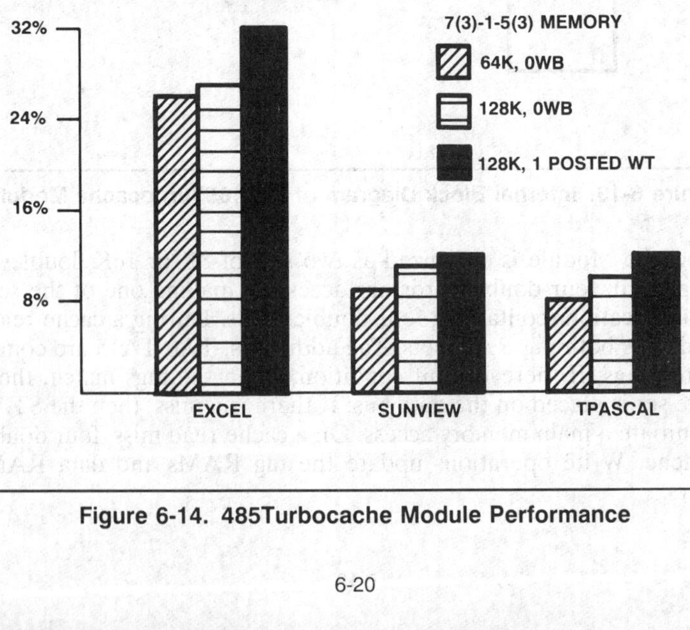

Figure 6-14. 485Turbocache Module Performance

START# signal is not asserted for I/O cycles. The memory controller provides an SKEN# signal, just like the i486 CPU's KEN# signal, to indicate whether an accessed word is cacheable.

The 485Turbocache Module has all of the required control signals needed to interface with the i486 CPU, and can be connected to a main memory controller or a bus controller with ease.

6.7.5 Performance

Figure 6-14 shows the performance boost that the 485Turbocache Module gives to various applications. Also included is the gain a single write buffer (posted write) will offer. The graphs were obtained by simulation of the i486 CPU with actual traces of each application. The simulator modeled a 128K 485Turbocache Module acting with a 7(3)-1-5(3) (reads take 7 clocks page miss, 3 clocks page hit, and 1 clock bursting. Write takes 5 clocks on a page miss, 3 clocks page hit.).

The performance boost a 485Turbocache Module will offer is 3 to 30 percent and is application sensitive.

6.8 485TURBOCACHE MODULE HARDWARE INTERFACE

The 485Turbocache Module has all of the control signals needed to interact with the i486 CPU. It decodes all bus cycles directly, and has the same timing and functionality for all i486 CPU pins. It is designed to operate without adding wait states during cache read hits and during transfers to the i486 CPU. The 485Turbocache Module has a bidirectional data bus for read and write accesses. The tag address bus contains the tag that is used for comparison with the previously stored tags.

The 485Turbocache Module supports burst operations similar to the processor's, transferring four doublewords to fill a line in the cache. As in the i486 processor, the 485Turbocache Module performs cache invalidation via a snoop address that resides on the address bus.

All signals and functions have been defined to allow the 485Turbocache Module to be designed as an optional add-in solution. A system can be designed with one or more sockets for one or more 485Turbocache Modules so the user may improve system performance as necessary by installing additional modules. The hardware can be designed so that it will automatically reconfigure the system when a 485Turbocache Module is added.

6.8.1 Pin Description

This section provides a summary of the signals and pins used in 485Turbocache Module. It is not a complete description, but provides an overview of function. See 485Turbocache Module data sheet, Order Number 240722 for a complete description. Note that pins using the same name as the i486 CPU are directly connected to the same i486 CPU pin.

6.8.2 Control Signals

Pin Name	Type	Description
ADS#	I	**ADDRESS STROBE** generated by the i486™ microprocessor. It is used to determine that a new cycle has been started.
M/IO#	I	**MEMORY/IO** cycle definition signal which used to indicate a Memory or IO access.
W/R#	I	**WRITE/READ** cycle definition signal which used to indicate a Write or Read access.
START#	O	**MEMORY START** is normally activated in the first T2 and indicates that a cache read miss or a write has occurred and that the current access must be serviced by the memory system. START# is not activated for IO cycles, and is not asserted if CS# is inactive. START# is always valid and must be logically ORed with other START# signals from additional modules.
BRDYO#	O	**BURST READY OUT** is a burst ready signal driven by the 485Turbocache Module to the i486 CPU. It is activated when a read hit occurs to the 485Turbocache Module.
CBRDY#	I	**CACHE BURST READY IN** is the burst ready input from the memory system. It is applied to both the 485Turbocache Module and the CPU in parallel. CBRDY# is ignored during T1 and idle cycles. BLAST# determines the length of the transfer. All cacheable read cycles are 4 dword transfers.
CRDY#	I	**CACHE READY IN** is the non-burst ready input from the system. Like CBRDY#, it applied to both the cache and CPU in parallel. CRDY# is ignored during T1 and idle cycles.
BLAST#	I	**BURST LAST** is output by the CPU and is sampled by the 485Turbocache Module to determine when the end of a burst transfer will occur.
BOFF#	I	**BACKOFF** is an input sampled by the i486CM to indicate that a cycle be immediately terminated. If BOFF# is sampled active, the 485Turbocache Module will float the data bus if it is currently active. The 485Turbocache Module will ignore all cycles, except invalidation cycles, until BOFF# is deactivated.

Pin Name	Type	Description
PRSN#	O	**PRESENCE** may be used as a 485Turbocache Module presence indicator. It should be connected via a 10K pullup resistor.
CLK	I	**CLOCK** is the timing reference from which the 485Turbocache Module monitors and generates events. CLK must be the same as the i486 CLK.
RESET	I	**RESET CACHE** forces the 485Turbocache Module to begin execution in a known state. It also causes all cache lines to be invalidated.

6.8.2.1 ADDRESS SIGNALS

Pin Name	Type	Description
A2-A31	I	**PROCESSOR ADDRESS LINES A2-A31** are the address lines used by the 485Turbocache Module. Address lines A2 and A3 are used as burst address bits. For 64K modules, A4-A14 comprise the set address inputs to the 485Turbocache Module and A15-A31 are used as the tag address. In 128K modules, A4 becomes a line select input, A5-A15 is the set address input and A16-A31 is used as the tag address.
BE0-BE3	I	**BYTE ENABLE** inputs are connected to the CPU byte enable outputs. They are specifically used for completing partial writes to the 485Turbocache Module in write hit cycles. They cause the cache to ignore read cycles.
CS#	I	**CHIP SELECT** is used to cascade 485Turbocache Modules. Address bits may be decoded in order to cascade multiple devices or be decoded to selectively cache portions of memory.

6.8.2.2 DATA SIGNALS

Pin Name	Type	Description
D0-D31	I/O	**PROCESSOR DATA LINES D0-D31** are connected to the system data bus. D0-D7 define the least significant byte while D24-D31 define the most significant byte.
DP0-DP3	I/O	**DATA PARITY** are the bits associated with the data on the data bus. Parity is treated by the 485Turbocache Module as additional data bits to be stored. Parity is important as commonly used 4-transistor SRAM cells are susceptible to soft errors.

6.8.2.3 CACHEABILITY SIGNALS

Pin Name	Type	Description
CKEN#	O	**CACHE ENABLE TO CPU** is the KEN# term generated by the 485Turbocache Module to the i486 microprocessor. CKEN# is activated twice; first during T1 to enable a cache line fill, and second before the last BRDY# to validate the line fill. CKEN# is ALWAYS active in T1, but will not validate a line fill if the line fill is a write protected line and WPSTRP# is low, or if the cycle is a read miss.
SKEN#	I	**SYSTEM CACHE ENABLE** is an input from the main memory system to indicate whether the current line fill is cacheable in the 485Turbocache Module.
FLUSH#	I	**FLUSH CACHE** causes the 485Turbocache Module to invalidate its entire cache contents regardless of CS#. Any line fill in progress will continue, but will be invalidated immediately. The i486 CPU flush instruction does not affect the 485Turbocache Module.
WP	I	**WRITE PROTECT** defines a line as write protected. WP is maintained internally as a state bit. Any subsequent writes to a write protected line will have no effect. In 128K configurations where the 485Turbocache Module is configured as 2 lines per sector, write protection is defined on a sector, not line, basis.
WPSTRP#	I	**WRITE PROTECT STRAPPING OPTION** changes the behavior of CKEN#. CKEN# is always asserted in T1 to indicate a cacheable line transfer. CKEN# is also asserted the clock before the last transfer of a line fill from 485Turbocache Module to i486 CPU. If WPSTRP# is strapped low, and a write protected line is being transferred, CKEN# is not activated before the last transfer.

6.8.2.4 SNOOP SIGNALS

Pin Name	Type	Description
EADS#	I	**VALID EXTERNAL ADDRESS STROBE** indicates that an invalidation address is present on the address bus. The 485Turbocache Module will invalidate this address, if present, but will only do so if CS# is active. The 485Turbocache Module is capable of accepting an EADS# every other clock.

6.8.3 System Configuration and Processor Interface

This section discusses the 485Turbocache Module operation in relation to two interfaces: the CPU-to-485Turbocache Module interface, and the main memory and bus controller-to-485Turbocache Module interface.

6.8.3.1 i486 CPU CONNECTIONS AND TAG MAPPING

When single or multiple 485Turbocache Module devices are connected to an i486 processor system, the processor's internal cache should map the entire address space including that of the 485Turbocache Module devices to provide the highest performance. This is the most efficient configuration. The i486 CPU can complete internal cache read hits in a single clock cycle, and the 485Turbocache Module provides the next fastest access in two clocks for the first doubleword and the remaining three doublewords in three clocks.

On reads, when the i486 processor cache has an internal cache hit, ADS# is not asserted, and the 485Turbocache Module does not begin a new cycle. Otherwise, ADS# is asserted and data is accessed from the 485Turbocache Module, from main memory, or from an I/O device.

No matter how many 128-Kbyte caches are cascaded, the set and tag addresses are connected to the same pins on the 485Turbocache Module. The processor's address bits A2–A31 are connected to A2-A31 on the 485Turbocache Module. Internally, address bits A4–A15 are sent to both sets, to select one of 4,096 locations. Because the cache is two-way set associative, each address points to information stored in two banks. On each read or write cycle, the value of A16–A31 is compared to the tags stored at the location addressed by A4–A15. If they are equal, and if the valid bit is set, then a hit occurs. If a read cycle is in progress, then the 485Turbocache Module returns data to the i486 CPU. If the hit cycle is a write cycle, then the new data is updated in the 485Turbocache Module.

When multiple 485Turbocache Modules are used the chip select starts by decoding A16 onwards. For example, with a 256-Kbyte cache A16 and A17 are decoded for generating the CS#. The set and tag addresses of a system with four 485Turbocache Modules used as shown in Figure 6-15.

The BRDYO# output and the CBRDY# input must be used in forming of the i486 CPU's BRDY# input. Similarly, the CRDY# input must be used in forming of the i486 CPU's RDY# input. Signals that are common to the i486 CPU and the 485Turbocache Module include BOFF#, BLAST#, EADS#, BE0#-BE3#, and DP0-DP3.

The memory system generates KEN# to the i486 CPU when read data needs to be cached. The 485Turbocache Module receives this signal as the SKEN# input and produces CKEN# when appropriate. The 485Turbocache Module's CKEN# output can be used in the formation of the KEN# input to the i486 CPU. CKEN# can be used in conjunction with other logic that can deassert KEN# to the CPU when the system wants the current line fill to be cached by the 485Turbocache Module and not cached in the i486 CPU. The CKEN# signal is always asserted in T1, but is then deasserted if CS# is inactive.

The 485Turbocache Module connects directly to the i486 CPU's address lines A2-A31. The designer may have to add external buffers to the address outputs, depending upon the loading. Other signals connected to the i486 CPU include the burst control signals, the bus cycle definition signals, the byte enables, the ADS# signal, and the data and

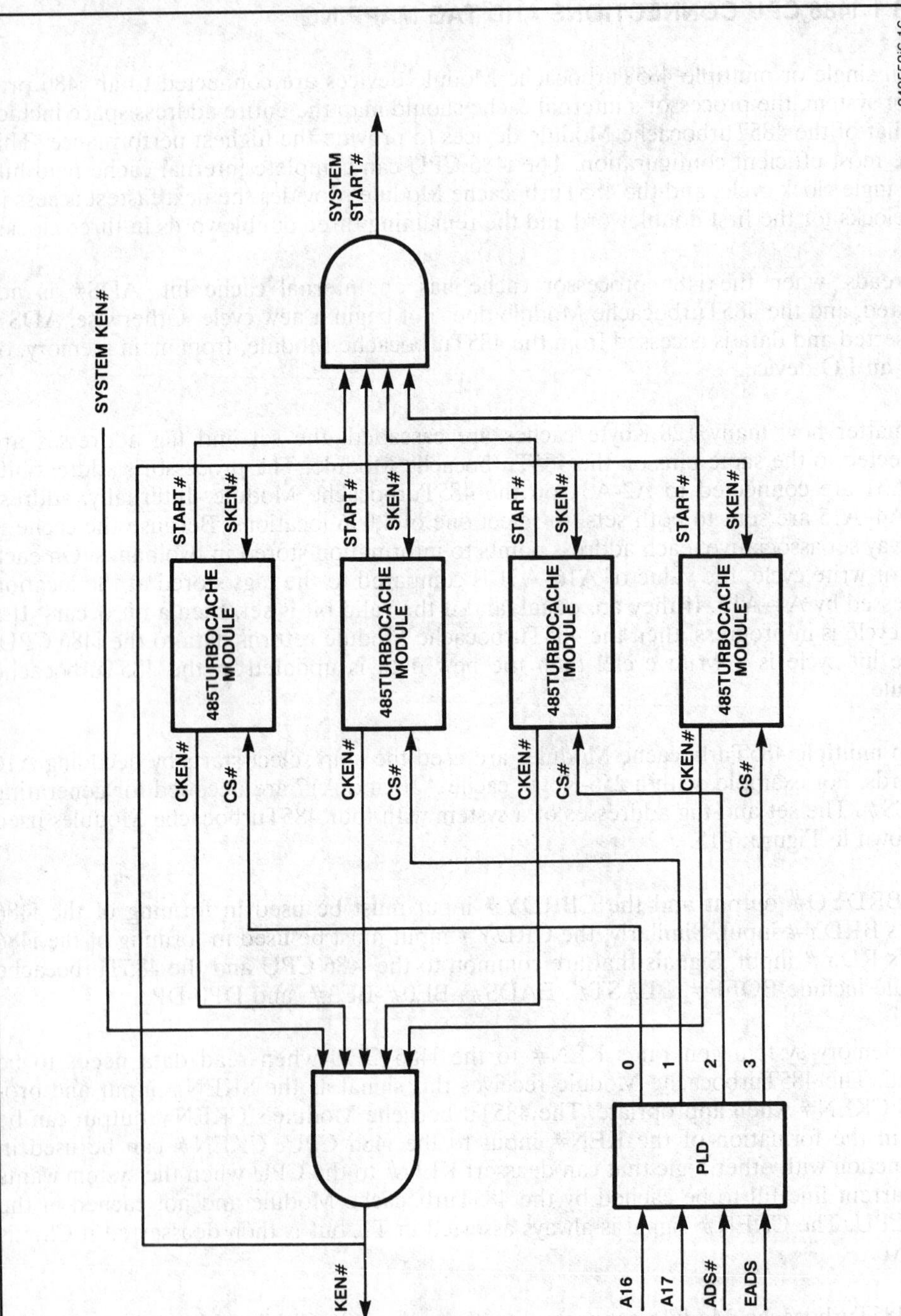

Figure 6-15. Multiple 485Turbocache Module Configuration

parity signals. The 485Turbocache Module and CPU connections are shown in Figure 6-16. The 485Turbocache Module, main memory controller, and bus controller interface are shown in Figure 6-17.

6.8.3.2 READ HIT CYCLES

A read hit cycle occurs when requested data is present in the 485Turbocache Module. The i486 CPU attempts to retrieve the entire line from the 485Turbocache Module without incurring wait states. This may be accomplished by activating the KEN# input at the end of T1 (the clock in which ADS# becomes active). There is very little time to decode the address, generate the KEN# signal to the i486 CPU, and complete a zero wait state read operation. Because KEN# is sampled twice, it is possible to always assert KEN# in T1 and to wait until the end of a line fill to decide whether the data is cacheable.

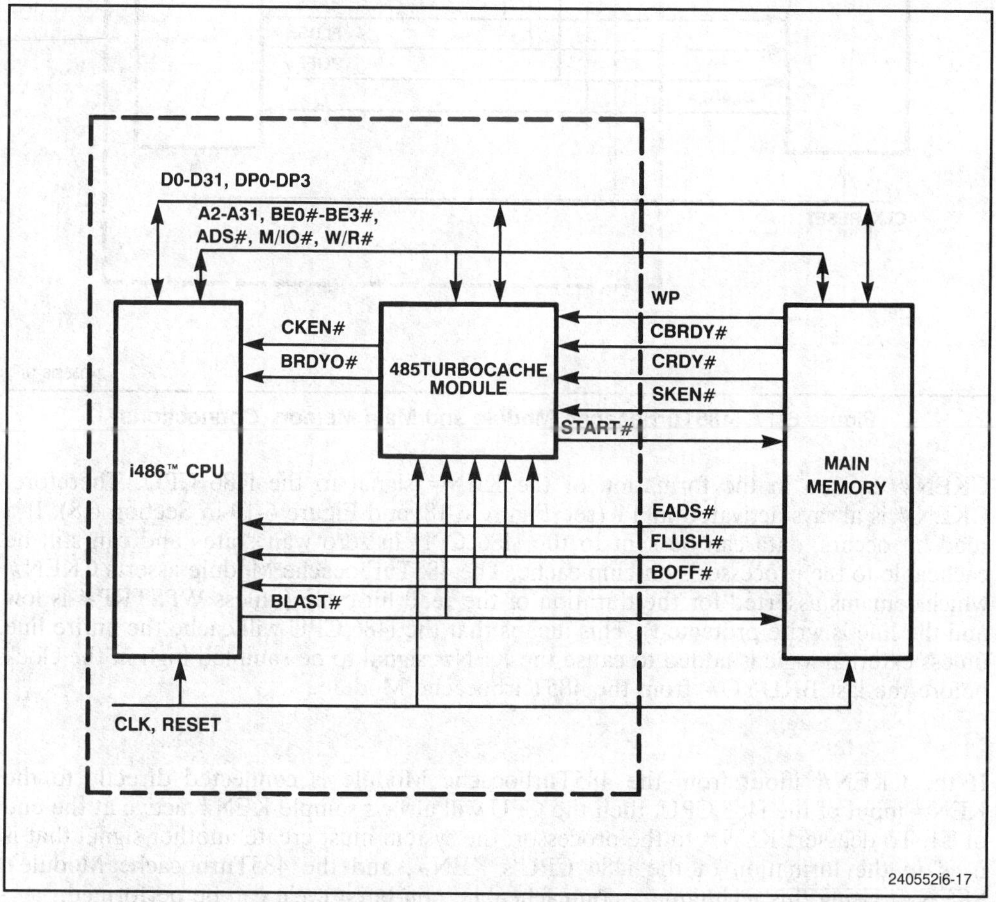

Figure 6-16. 485Turbocache Module and i486™ CPU Connections

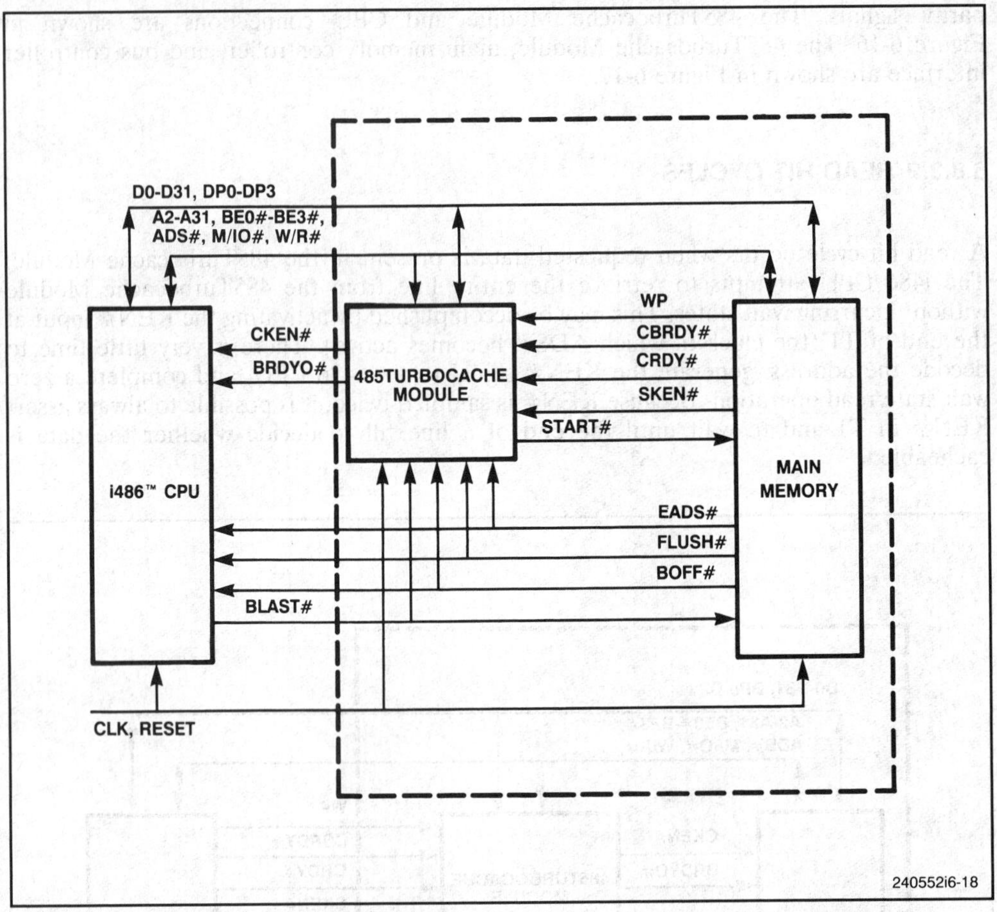

Figure 6-17. 485Turbocache Module and Main Memory Connections

CKEN# is used in the formation of the KEN# signal to the i486 CPU. Therefore, CKEN# is always activated in T1 (see Figure 6-18, and Figure 6-19 in Section 6.8). If a read hit occurs, data can be sent to the i486 CPU in zero wait states and can still be cacheable to the processor's on-chip cache. The 485Turbocache Module asserts CKEN# which remains asserted for the duration of the read hit cycle (unless WPSTRP# is low and the line is write protected). This means that the i486 CPU will cache the entire line unless external logic is added to cause the KEN# signal to be sampled high in the clock before the last BRDYO# from the 485Turbocache Module.

If the CKEN# input from the 485Turbocache Module is connected directly to the KEN# input of the i486 CPU, then the CPU will always sample KEN# active at the end of T1. To deassert KEN# to the processor, the system must create another signal that is used in the formation of the i486 CPU's KEN#, and the 485Turbocache Module's SKEN#. Using this technique a non-cacheable, non-burst cycle can be performed.

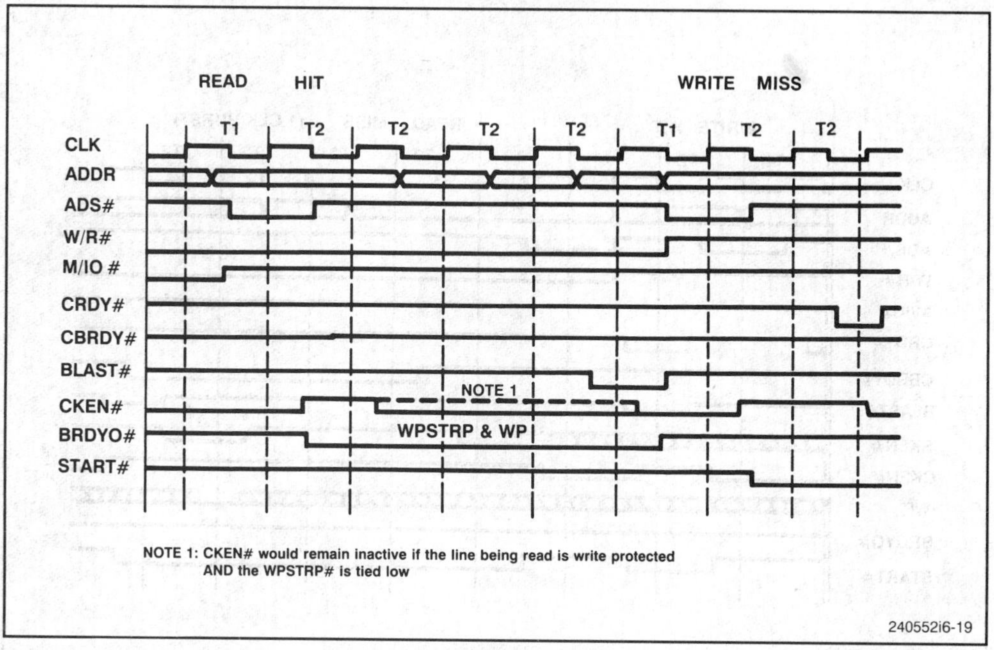

Figure 6-18. Read Hit—Write

The BRDY# signal to the i486 CPU can be generated from many sources. Therefore, the various signals should be logically "ORed" to generate the actual i486 BRDY# input.

On a cache read hit, the 485Turbocache Module generates a BRDYO# signal for each of the doublewords it transfers. The 485Turbocache Module asserts BRDYO# in the first T2 cycle, and BRDYO# remains asserted for the duration of the burst. If the i486 CPU either terminates a burst early or fails to generate a burst cycle as defined by BLAST#, the 485Turbocache Module will deassert BRDYO# after the i486 CPU has sampled the required data.

6.8.3.3 READ MISS CYCLES

On a cache read miss, the 485Turbocache Module initiates a system action, by asserting the START# signal. The system is responsible for generating a BRDY# or a RDY# signal to the i486 CPU. The 485Turbocache Module monitors the ready signals CRDY# and CBRDY# to determine when valid data appears on its data lines. If the system indicates that the cycle is cacheable, then the data is cached in the 485Turbocache Module. The system must transfer a complete line for the location to be cacheable. (See Figure 6-20 in Section 6.8.)

For read misses, CKEN# is asserted at the end of T1 but is deasserted during the first T2 of a read miss, and will remain inactive until the cycle is complete. The system may return a ready without ever activating the KEN# and SKEN# lines for a non-cacheable operation.

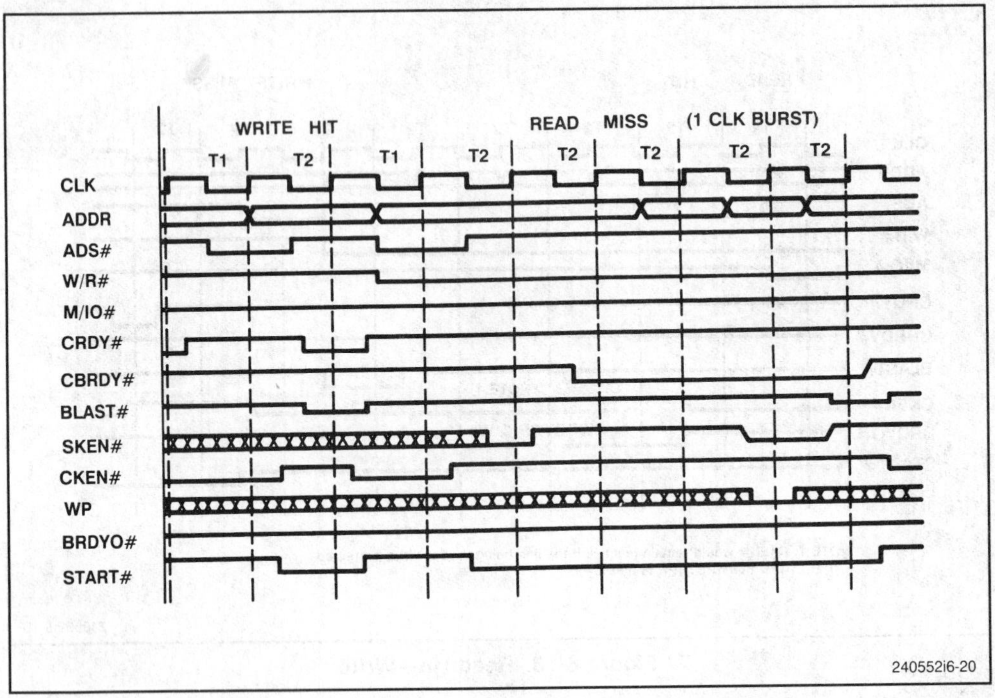

Figure 6-19. Write—Read Miss (Fastest Line Fill)

6.8.3.4 WRITE CYCLES AND I/O CYCLES

The 485Turbocache Module is a write-through cache, so main memory is updated with every write hit or miss. The 485Turbocache Module is not required to generate a ready signal to the i486 CPU for write cycles. However, it does perform a comparison and updates the cache memory when a write hit occurs (provided the location isn't write protected). The 485Turbocache Module is not updated on write misses. The timing diagrams for write operations are shown in Figure 6-18 and Figure 6-19 in Section 6.8.

The 485Turbocache Module ignores all I/O cycles. When an I/O cycle is executed by the i486 processor, the system responds and terminates the cycle. The 485Turbocache Module does not assert the START# signal for I/O accesses, and the system should monitor the M/IO# signal rather than wait for the assertion of the START# signal. The timings for an I/O read are shown in Figure 6-24 in Section 6.8.

6.8.4 System Interface

This section describes how general signals are used to control key actions of the 485Turbocache Module. The system design must generate or use these signals to efficiently use the 485Turbocache Module.

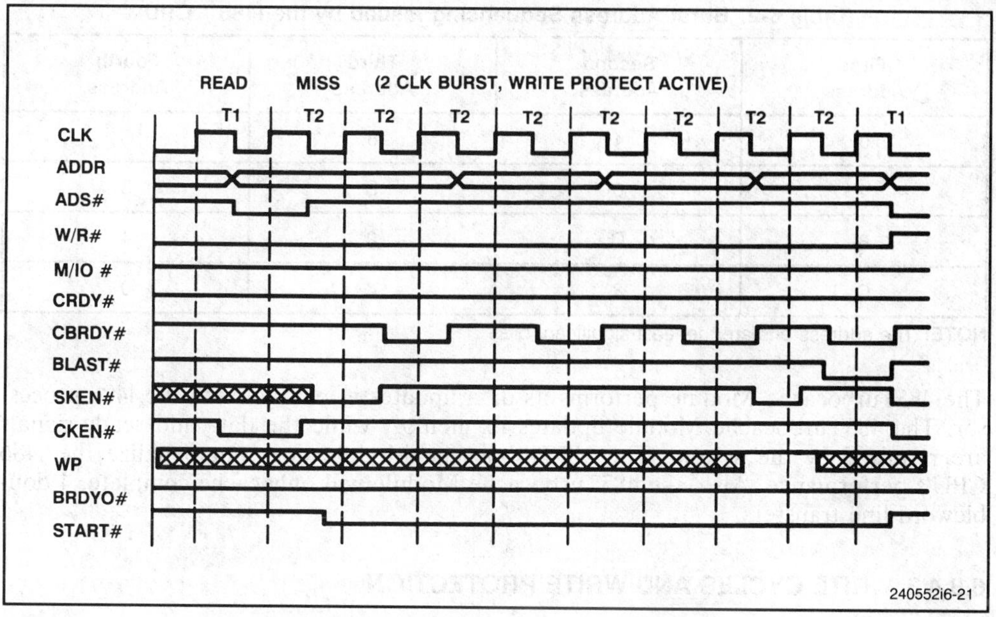

Figure 6-20. Read Miss—Two Clock Burst

6.8.4.1 READ MISS CYCLES

The system memory must return data to the processor for all cache read misses. The 485Turbocache Module asserts the START# signal on a read miss, and the START# signal indicates to main memory to begin a memory cycle. START# may be used to enable the data transceiver to route main memory data to the CPU.

6.8.4.2 LINE FILL

Because the 485Turbocache Module is a passive device, the i486 CPU must generate all of the control signals required in a line fill except for the START# signal. The CPU's KEN# input and the 485Turbocache Module's SKEN# input are asserted before the first ready is returned to the system. Once the line fill is initiated, the system can cache the line exclusively in the 485Turbocache Module by having SKEN# asserted and having the CPU's KEN# deasserted one clock prior to the ready of the last data word. The 485Turbocache Module will not cache data from a read miss when the first word of the access is returned in zero wait states. At least one wait state is required on the first doubleword transfer from the system to perform a cache update. The timings for a line fill are shown in Figure 6-19 in Section 6.8.

The order in which the doublewords are transferred is defined by the i486 CPU and is shown in Table 6-2. For example, if the first address was 104, then the next three addresses will be 100, 10C, and 108.

Table 6-2. Burst Address Sequencing Issued by the i486™ CPU

First Address	Second Address	Third Address	Fourth Address
0	4	8	C
4	0	C	8
8	C	0	4
C	8	4	0

NOTE: The address bits are the least significant bits.

The 485Turbocache Module performs its data updates in parallel with the i486 processor. The 485Turbocache Module updates its memory while the data and ready signals are returned by the system. The 485Turbocache Module does not penalize the i486 CPU's performance. Also, the 485Turbocache Module will only cache complete, 4 doubleword line transfers.

6.8.4.3 WRITE CYCLES AND WRITE PROTECTION

Because the 485Turbocache Module is a write-through cache, writes are immediately forwarded to the system. If a processor write occurs on a valid entry that is not write protected, the new data will be stored into the memory in zero wait states. The 485Turbocache Module will not generate a ready signal. It is the system's responsibility to update the system memory on all writes and to terminate all cycles with a ready signal. Even after the 485Turbocache Module has completed its internal write update, it remains idle until the system returns a ready to the processor.

A cache location can be write protected by asserting the WP input to the 485Turbocache Module. The WP signal must be valid during the third BRDY# or RDY# of a cache line fill cycle. It sets a state bit within a particular cache location and remains in effect until the bit is invalidated. Tieing WPSTRP# low will not allow the write protected entry to be cached by the i486 CPU in subsequent accesses. The entry can be invalidated by any of the following: a flush operation, a reset operation, an invalidation cycle, or an LRU replacement.

When an i486 CPU cycle produces a write hit to a write-protected 485Turbocache Module location, data in the cache is not modified. The 485Turbocache Module responds in the same way whether or not a write hit location is write protected by asserting the START# signal. It is the designer's responsibility to prevent inconsistencies between the 485Turbocache Module and main memory when using the WP signal.

6.8.4.4 SYSTEM CACHEABILITY INDICATION

The 485Turbocache Module uses the cache enable scheme of the i486 CPU. A cache update to the 485Turbocache Module requires activating the SKEN# signal. The signal is sampled twice, first with or after START# and before the first ready signal from

BRDY# or RDY#, and again on the rising clock edge before the last ready. If SKEN# was deasserted at either of the specified sample times, then the access is considered non-cacheable. SKEN# is ignored during write cycles.

Typically, the system will use the same logic to generate the i486 CPU's KEN# signal and the 485Turbocache Module's SKEN# signal. However, it is not necessary for both have to be asserted during an access. It is possible to use different cacheing maps for the CPU cache and the 485Turbocache Module cache because the i486 CPU and the 485Turbocache Module maintain their own cache contents via snooping.

6.8.4.5 INVALIDATE CYCLES

The 485Turbocache Module has the same snooping mechanism as the i486 CPU. Since the devices operate in parallel, they can snoop in parallel. Because both of the devices are write-through caches, it is only necessary for them to detect cache write cycles that are initiated by other bus masters.

EADS# indicates to the 485Turbocache Module that the address pins contain an address for invalidation. This address is normally generated by an external master but if AHOLD is inactive, then a snoop comparison is initiated on the address driven by the i486 CPU. EADS# is recognized regardless of the AHOLD and BOFF# signals. The fastest invalidation rate for the 485Turbocache Module is one invalidation on every clock cycle, whereas the i486 CPU can support snoop addresses on every clock cycle. CS# must be asserted for the 485Turbocache Module to recognize invalidation cycles.

6.9 DESIGN CONSIDERATIONS

This section deals with the main memory interface, cascadable caches, and multiple CPUs. Any design using the 485Turbocache Module must consider these issues to use it effectively.

6.9.1 DRAM Interface

In most applications, the 485Turbocache Module interfaces to a DRAM-based memory system which is the main memory. The START# signal can accomplish this interface. START# is asserted for all memory write cycles and read miss cycles and indicates that memory must process the current cycle.

The START# signal can be used to control the data transceivers from the memory system. During a read cycle, the memory controller determines that a page hit has occurred and initiates a memory access with a CAS cycle. If the 485Turbocache Module determines that the current cycle is a miss, then the START# signal is asserted, the data transceivers are enabled, and memory data is transmitted from memory to the i486 CPU. If the cycle was a read hit, then the data transceivers are disabled. During write operations the memory system ignores the START# signal.

The START# signal can also be used as an ADS# signal for the main memory. In this configuration, a memory cycle cannot begin until START# is sampled active. This provides maximum memory availability to DMA and other memory devices. Since the START# signal is not sampled until the end of T2, at least an extra wait state is added for main memory accesses.

Note that although START# normally appears in the first T2 of a memory cycle, it may not if the previous cycle contained an invalidation request.

If the 485Turbocache Module has been installed as a system option and is not present, the START# signal will never be asserted. A memory controller must take this into account and automatically begin a cycle if PRSN# (presence indicator) is sampled inactive.

6.9.2 Cascadable Cache

The 485Turbocache Module can be cascaded to configure a deeper cache memory for the processor. Up to four can be used to provide as much as 512 Kbyte of cache. This section discusses such designs.

6.9.2.1 SYSTEM CONTROL SIGNALS AND CASCADABLE CACHES

The START# signal used by memory is the logical OR for each individual 485Turbocache Module START# output. If any cache has information that is needed by the processor, then its START# signal is at a high level, and it inhibits the main memory START# signal (as there is no need to access the main memory). If needed data is not present in any of the 485Turbocache Modules, then the START# signals are low, and main memory data is accessed.

The KEN# input to the i486 processor should be a logical OR for each of the 485Turbocache Modules and for a memory controller output. The memory controller output can be asserted high to indicate that the information to the i486 CPU is non-cacheable.

The SKEN# signal is the cache input to the 485Turbocache Module. The memory controllers must assert SKEN# when a transfer to the 485Turbocache Module is cacheable. The SKEN# inputs for all of the 485Turbocache Modules must be tied together. The controller that has its CS# asserted determines which cache will receive the information.

The EADS# signal from the memory controller must be connected to the i486 CPU and to all of the 485Turbocache Modules. In this way, invalidation cycles are executed in all the 485Turbocache Module devices simultaneously.

This section reviews cascaded 485Turbocache Module configurations (see Section 6.6.2.1). The entire memory space is covered in a single cache or a cascaded cache configuration. When multiple 485Turbocache Modules are used, only one 485Turbocache Module is selected by asserting the CS# pin.

The tag address connections are shown earlier in Figure 6-15 for a 512-Kbyte cache. For example, TA0 through TA15 are always connected to A16 to A31. In the configuration with one 485Turbocache Module, the chip select is grounded. In the two 485Turbocache Module configuration, A16 is used to decode between the two caches. In the four 485Turbocache Module configuration, A16 and A17 are used to generate the CS# signals. These configurations are summarized in Table 6-3.

6.10 TIMING DIAGRAMS

This section shows the 485Turbocache Module interface signals for the standard execution cycles.

6.10.1 Read Hit Followed by a Write Miss

Figure 6-18 shows a read hit cycle followed by a write miss cycle. During the read hit, BRDYO# is asserted in the T2 cycle, and remains asserted until the entire line has been transferred to the i486 CPU. The CKEN# signal is asserted at the end of T1 to begin a line fill and is asserted throughout the transfer. CKEN# is deasserted in T2, and will remain deasserted only if a write-protected line is being transferred and WPSRTP# is low. START# is not asserted for a read hit but is asserted for the write cycle.

Write hits and write misses are indistinguishable to the system. On a write hit, the 485Turbocache Module is updated in zero wait states. The system is responsible for terminating all write cycles.

6.10.2 Write Hit Followed by a Read Miss

Figure 6-19 shows a write hit followed by a read miss. The read miss operation shown is the optimal line fill for the 485Turbocache Module. The START# signal is asserted for the write in the first T2. Once it is determined that the cycle is a read miss, START# is asserted again to request a main memory access. CKEN# is asserted in T1, but is deasserted once a miss has been determined. The system monitors SKEN# to determine whether the current access is cacheable. Because SKEN# is asserted by the system

Table 6-3. Tag Address and Address Connections

Cache Size in Bytes	Tag Address TA0-TA15	CS#
128K	A16-A31	Ground
256K	A16-A31	A16/$\overline{A16}$
512K	A16-A31	A16, A17 decoded

during both sample windows, the line is allowed to be stored in the 485Turbocache Module data RAM as a valid entry. Note that the first read of a 485Turbocache Module burst requires at least one wait state.

In this example, WP is sampled during the line fill. WP is low during the sample window, indicating that the line is not write protected.

6.10.3 Read Miss with a 2-Clock Burst Transfer and Write Protection

Figure 6-20 shows a read miss which has a 2-clock burst transfer rate. There are two cycles between each of the CBRDY# signals that are returned to the 485Turbocache Module. These indicate when data is valid for storage in the 485Turbocache Module. The line is cacheable because SKEN# is asserted at the appropriate sampling time.

In this example, set-up and hold times of the WP signal are timed to the clock edge before the last CRDY# or CBRDY#.

6.10.4 2-Clock Snoop

Figure 6-21 shows a 2-clock snoop to the 485Turbocache Module. The timings show that the optimal invalidation rate equals the rate at which EADS# can be received by the 485Turbocache Module. In this case, the maximum invalidation rate is one EADS# on every other clock cycle. Note that if the 485Turbocache Module is transferring data during the invalidation, the transfer will continue but that transferred line will also be invalidated.

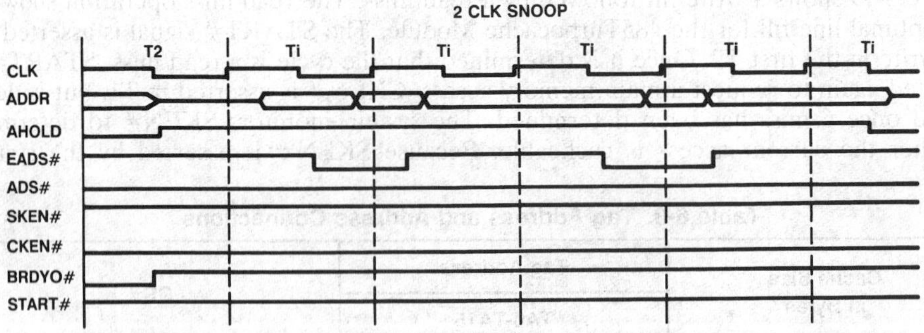

Figure 6-21. Snoop Cycle—Maximum Invalidation Rate

6.10.5 Snoop Cycle and Read Hits

Figure 6-22 shows a snoop cycle occurring in parallel with a 485Turbocache Module read hit. The 485Turbocache Module is able to continue data transfers to the i486 CPU while the snoop is being executed. The designer must observe the setup and hold time requirements for the snoop address. This line will be invalidated as well as the line at the invalidation address.

6.10.6 Backoff Cycles during a Read Hit

Figure 6-23 shows a read hit cycle in progress with a 485Turbocache Module. The system asserts the BOFF# signal. In response, the read cycle must be aborted and the address, control, and data buses have to be in high impedance for the next clock cycle. Only the data bus is active in the 485Turbocache Module. Figure 6-23 shows that in response to BOFF# the 485Turbocache Module will float the data bus during a read hit in the next clock cycle.

6.10.7 I/O Cycle Followed by a Read Miss

Figure 6-24 shows an I/O cycle followed by a read miss. The 485Turbocache Module does not assert START# for I/O cycles. It is the designer's responsibility to decode the cycle as an I/O cycle, and intiate an I/O cycle using external logic.

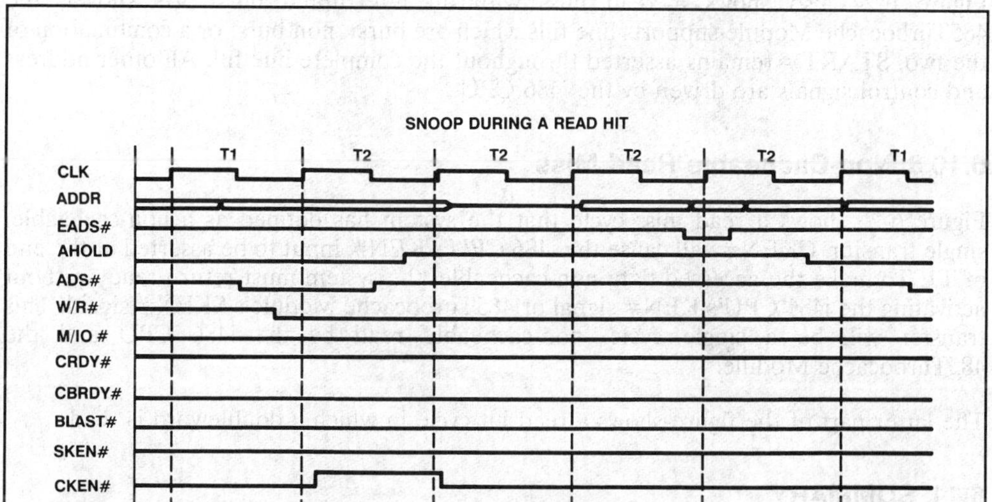

Figure 6-22. Snoop during Read Hit

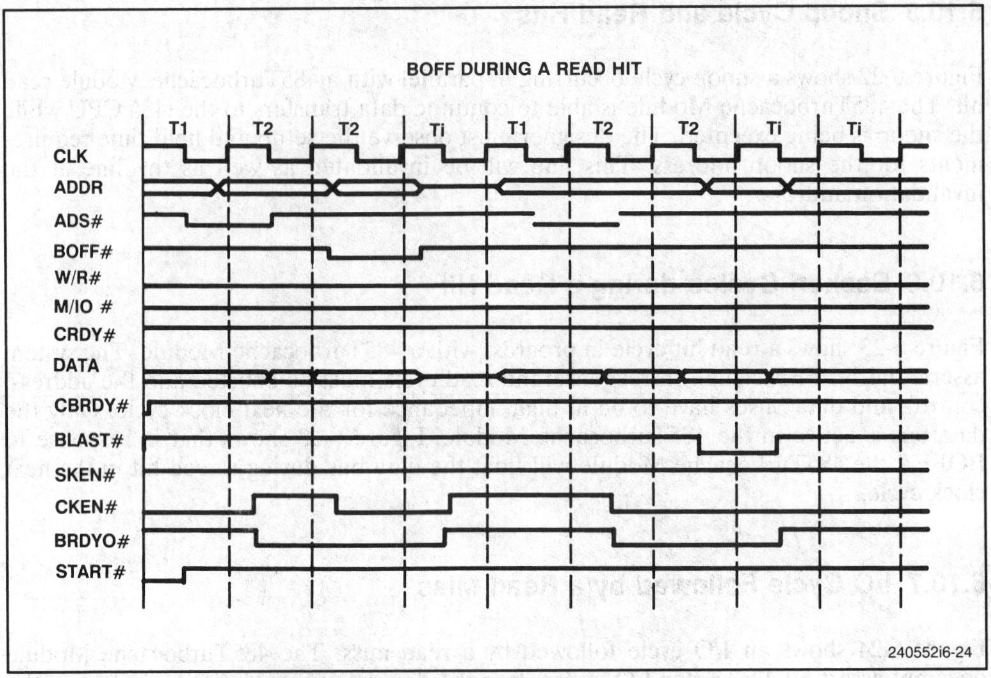

Figure 6-23. BOFF# during Read Hit

Figure 6-24 also shows a read miss with an interrupted burst. As shown, the 485Turbocache Module supports line fills which are burst, non-burst or a combination of the two. START# remains asserted throughout the complete line fill. All other address and control signals are driven by the i486 CPU.

6.10.8 Non-Cacheable Read Miss

Figure 6-25 shows a read miss cycle that the system has defined as a non-cacheable, single transfer. CKEN# will cause the i486 CPU's KEN# input to be asserted at the end of T1. To make the accessed data non-cacheable, the system must return ready without activating the i486 CPU's KEN# signal or 485Turbocache Module's SKEN# signal. This transfer will be a single cycle, non-cacheable read by the i486 CPU and the 485Turbocache Module.

The latter part of the figure shows a read hit cycle in which a doubleword is read.

6.11 SUMMARY

External caches can help i486 CPU performance or reduce main memory costs. For systems with multiple CPU's, they are required to reduce main memory traffic and avoid main memory contention. Single CPU systems, at 25 and 33 MHz, work best with an optional cache. The 485Turbocache Module is ideally suited as an option for systems with a good main memory design.

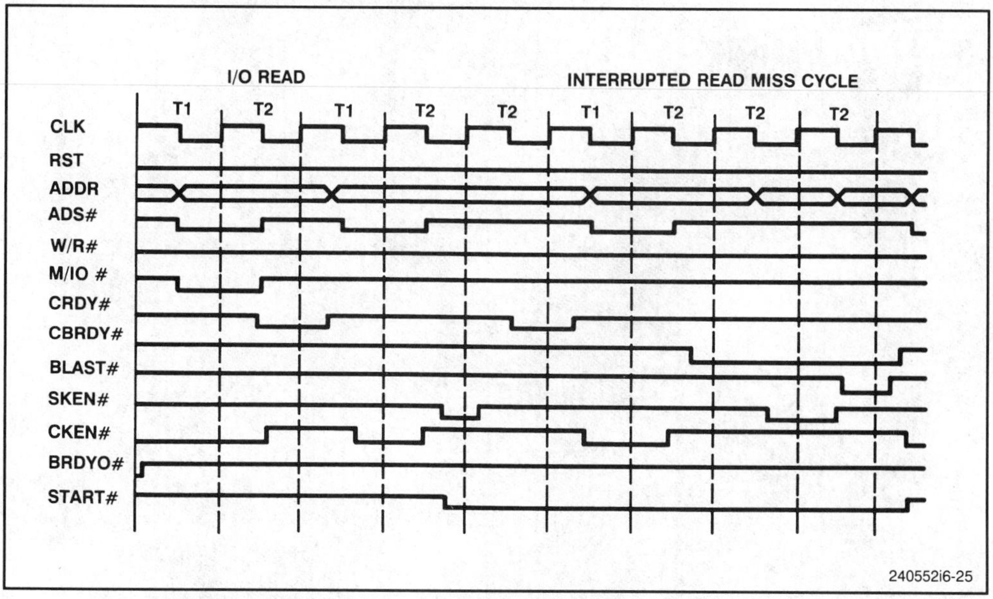

Figure 6-24. I/O Cycle – Interrupted Burst

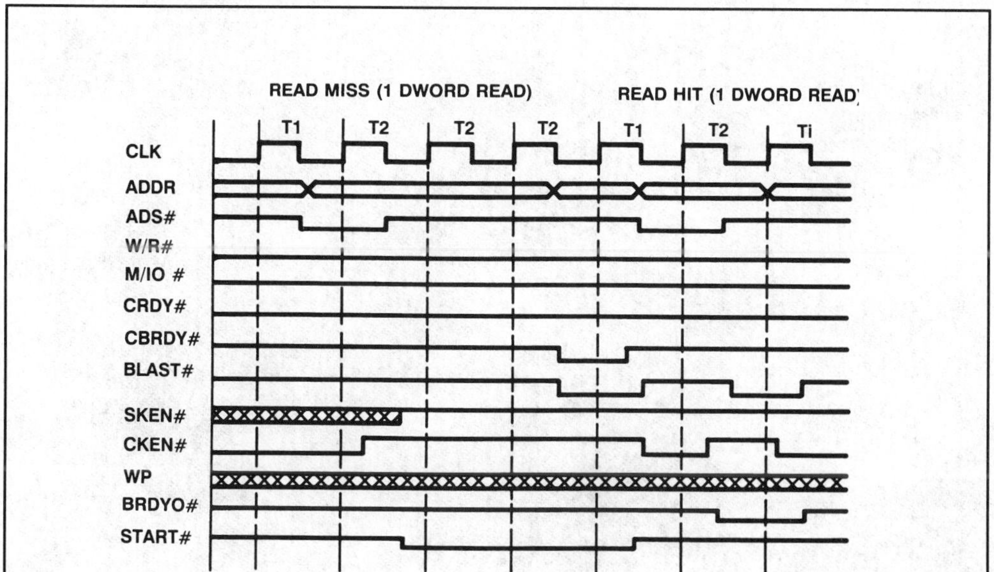

Figure 6-25. Single Cycle, Non-Cacheable Read

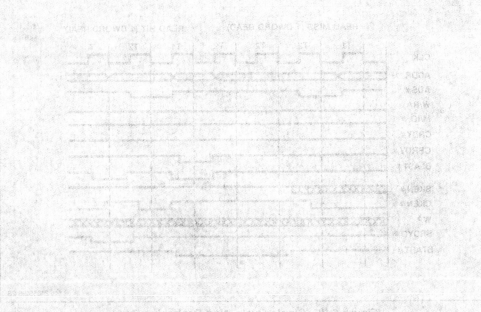

Peripheral Subsystem 7

CHAPTER 7
PERIPHERAL SUBSYSTEM

The peripheral (I/O) interface is an essential part of any microprocessor based system. It supports communications between the microprocessor and the peripherals. Given the variety of existing peripheral devices, a peripheral system must allow a variety of interfaces. Another important part of a microprocessor system are the buses which connect all major parts of the system. This chapter describes the connection of peripheral devices to the i486™ microprocessor bus. Design techniques are discussed for interfacing different devices including the i486 processor kit which includes LAN Controllers and EISA and MCA chip sets.

The peripheral subsystem must provide sufficiently high data bandwidth to suppport the i486 microprocessor. High speed devices like disks must be able to transfer data to memory with minimal CPU overhead or interaction. The on-chip cache of the i486 microprocessor requires further considerations to avoid stale data problems. These subjects are also covered in this chapter.

The i486 microprocessor supports 8-bit, 16-bit and 32-bit I/O devices which can be I/O mapped, memory mapped, or both. It has a 106 Mbyte/sec memory bandwidth at 33 MHz. Cache coherency is supported by cache line invalidation and cache flush cycles. I/O devices can be accessed by dedicated I/O instructions for I/O mapped devices, or by memory operand instructions for memory mapped devices. In addition, the i486 microprocessor always synchronizes I/O instruction execution with external bus activity. All previous instructions are completed before an I/O operation begins. In particular, all writes pending in the write buffers will be completed before an I/O read or write is performed. These functions are described in this chapter.

7.1 PERIPHERAL/PROCESSOR BUS INTERFACE

Because the i486 microprocessor supports both memory mapped and I/O mapped devices, this section includes brief discussion of the types of mapping, support of dynamic bus sizing, byte swap logic and critical timings. An example of a basic I/O controller implementation is also included. Additionally, some system-oriented interface considerations are discussed because they can have a significant influence on overall system performance.

7.1.1 Mapping Techniques

The system designer should have a thorough understanding of the system application and its use of peripherals in order to design the optional mapping scheme. Two techniques can be used to control the transmission of data between the computer and its peripherals. The most straight-forward approach is I/O mapping.

The i486 microprocessor allows 8-bit, 16-bit or 32-bit I/O devices which can be I/O mapped, memory mapped, or both. All I/O devices can be mapped into physical memory addresses ranging from 00000000H to FFFFFFFFH (four-gigabytes) or I/O addresses ranging from 00000000H to OOOOFFFFH (64 KBytes) for programmed I/O, as shown in Figure 7-1.

I/O mapping and memory-mapping differ in the following respects:

- The address decoding required to generate chip selects for the I/O mapped devices is much simpler than that required for memory mapped devices. I/O mapped devices reside within the I/O space of i486 microprocessor (64 Kbytes); memory-mapped devices reside in a much larger i486 microprocessor memory space (4-gigabytes) which requires more address lines to decode.
- The I/O space is 64 Kbytes in size and can be divided into 64K of 8-bit ports, 32K of 16-bit ports or 16K of 32-bit ports or any combinations of ports which add up to less than 64 Kbytes. The 64 Kbytes of I/O address space refers to physical memory since I/O instructions do not utilize the segmentation or paging hardware and are directly addressable using DX registers.
- Memory-mapped devices can be accessed using i486 microprocessor's instructions, so that I/O to memory, memory to I/O and I/O to I/O transfers as well as compare and test operations can be coded efficiently.

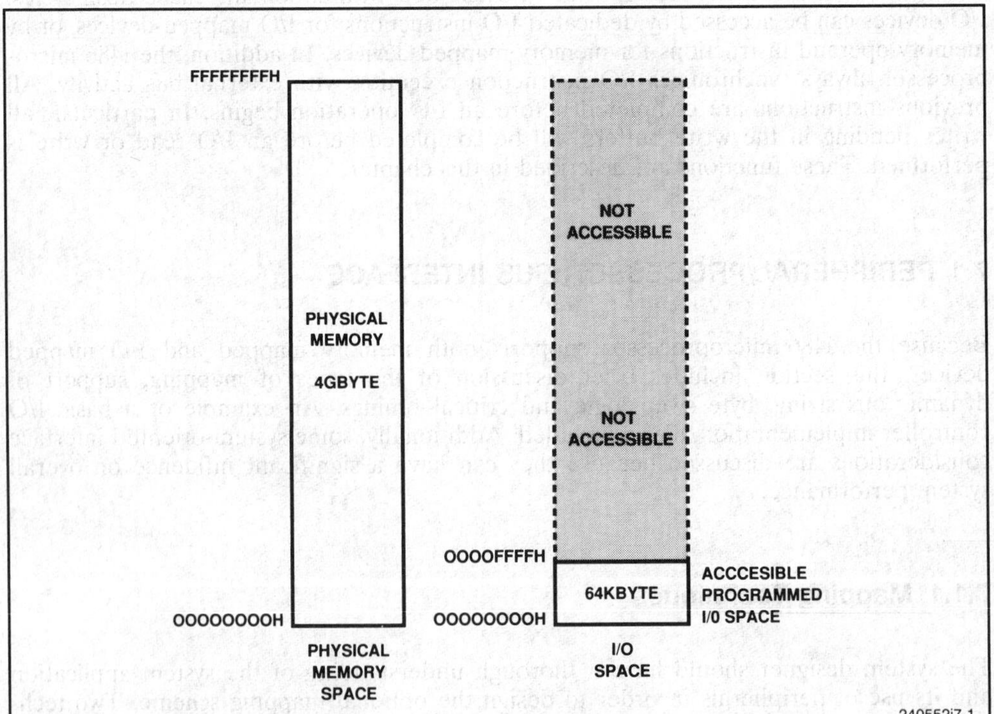

Figure 7-1. Mapping Scheme

- The I/O mapped device can be accessed only via IN, OUT, INS and OUTS instructions. I/O instruction execution is synchronized with external bus activity. All the I/O transfers are performed using the AL (8-bit), AX (16-bit), or EAX (32-bit) registers.
- Memory mapping offers more flexibility in protection than does I/O mapping. Memory mapped devices are protected by the memory management and protection features. A device can be inaccessible to a task, visible but protected, or fully accessible, depending on where it is mapped. Paging and segmentation provide the same protection levels for 4-KByte pages or variable length segments which can be swapped to the disk or shared between programs. The i486 microprocessor supports pages and segments to provide the designer with maximum flexibility.
- The I/O privilege level of the i486 processor protects I/O-mapped devices by either preventing a task from accessing any I/O devices or by allowing a task to access all I/O devices. A virtual-8086 mode I/O permission bitmap can be used to select the privilege level for a combination of I/O bytes.

7.1.2 Dynamic Bus Sizing

Dynamic data bus sizing allows a direct processor connection to 32-, 16- or 8-bit buses for memory or I/O devices. The i486 microprocessor supports dynamic data bus sizing. Data transfers to or from 32-bit, 16-bit or 8-bit devices are supported by determining the bus width during each bus cycle. The decoding circuitry may assert BS16# for 16-bit devices, or BS8# for 8-bit devices for each bus cycle. For addressing 32-bit devices both BS16# and BS8# are negated. If both BS16# and BS8# are asserted, an 8-bit bus width will be assumed.

Appropriate selection of BS16# and BS8# drives the i486 microprocessor to run additional bus cycles to complete requests larger than 16 or 8-bits. When BS16# is asserted, a 32-bit transfer is converted into two 16-bit transfers (or three transfers if the data is misaligned) Similarly asserting BS8# will convert 32-bit transfers into four 8-bit transfers. The extra cycles forced by the BS16# or BS8# should be viewed as independent cycles. BS16# or BS8# are normally driven active during the independent cycles. The only exception would be if the addressed device can vary the number of bytes that it can return between the cycles.

The i486 microprocessor drives the appropriate byte enables during the independent cycles initiated by BS8# and BS16#. Addresses A2-A31 do not change if accesses are to a 32-bit aligned area. Table 7-1 shows the set of byte enables that will be generated on the next cycle for each of the valid possibilities of the byte enables on the current cycle. BEx# must be ignored for 16-byte cycles to memory mapped devices.

The dynamic bus sizing feature of i486 microprocessor is significantly different than that of 386™ DX microprocessor. The i486 microprocessor requires that the data bytes be driven on the addressed lines only, unlike 386 DX microprocessor which expects both high and low order bytes on D0-D15. The simplest example of this function is a 32-bit aligned BS16# read. When the i486 microprocessor reads the two higher order bytes,

Table 7-1. Next Byte-Enable Values for the BSn# Cycles

Current				Next with BS8#				Next with BS16#			
BE3#	**BE2#**	**BE1#**	**BE0#**	**BE3#**	**BE2#**	**BE1#**	**BE0#**	**BE3#**	**BE2#**	**BE1#**	**BE0#**
1	1	1	0	n	n	n	n	n	n	n	n
1	1	0	0	1	1	0	1	n	n	n	n
1	0	0	0	1	0	0	1	1	0	1	1
0	0	0	0	0	0	0	1	0	0	1	1
1	1	0	1	n	n	n	n	n	n	n	n
1	0	0	1	1	0	1	1	1	0	1	1
0	0	0	1	0	0	1	1	0	0	1	1
1	0	1	1	n	n	n	n	n	n	n	n
0	0	1	1	0	1	1	1	n	n	n	n
0	1	1	1	n	n	n	n	n	n	n	n

NOTE: "n" means that another bus cycle will not be required to satisfy the request.

they must be driven on D16-D31 data bus, and it expects the two low order bytes on D0-D15. The 386 DX microprocessor always reads or writes data on the lower 16-bits of the data bus when BS16# is asserted.

The external system design must provide buffers to allow i486 microprocessor to read or write data on the appropriate data bus pins. Table 7-2 shows the data bus lines where i486 microprocessor expects valid data to be returned for each valid combination of byte enables and bus sizing options. Valid data is driven only on data bus pins which correspond to byte enables signals that are active during write cycles. Other data pins will also be driven but they will not contain valid data. Unlike 386 DX microprocessor, the i486 microprocessor does not duplicate write data on the data bus when corresponding byte enables are negated.

The BS16# and BS8# inputs allow external 16- and 8-bit buses to be supported using fewer external components. The i486 microprocessor samples these pins every clock cycle. This value is sampled on the clock before ready and determines the bus size. When BS8# or BS16# is asserted then only 16- or 8-bits of data are valid. If both BS8# and BS16# are asserted, an 8-bit bus width is valid.

Table 7-2. Valid Data Lines for Valid Byte Enable Combinations

BE3#	BE2#	BE1#	BE0#	w/o BS8#/BS16#	w BS8#	w BS16#
1	1	1	0	D7–D0	D7–D0	D7–D0
1	1	0	0	D15–D0	D7–D0	D15–D0
1	0	0	0	D23–D0	D7–D0	D15–D0
0	0	0	0	D31–D0	D7–D0	D15–D0
1	1	0	1	D15–D8	D15–D8	D15–D8
1	0	0	1	D23–D8	D15–D8	D15–D8
0	0	0	1	D31–D8	D15–D8	D15–D8
1	0	1	1	D23–D16	D23–D16	D23–D16
0	0	1	1	D31–D16	D23–D16	D31–D16
0	1	1	1	D31–D24	D31–D24	D31–D24

Dynamic bus sizing allows the power-up and boot up program to be stored in eight-bit EPROM while high speed program execution uses 32-bit memory.

7.1.2.1 ADDRESS DECODING FOR I/O DEVICES

Address decoding for I/O devices resembles address decoding for memories. The primary difference is that the block size (range of addresses) for each address signal is much smaller. The minimum block size is dependent on the number of addresses used by the I/O device. In most processors, where I/O instructions are separate, I/O addresses are shorter than memory addresses. Typically, microprocessors with 16-bit address bus use 8-bit address for I/O.

One technique for decoding memory-mapped I/O address is to map the entire I/O space of the i486 microprocessor into a 64-Kbyte region of the memory space. The address decoding logic can be reconfigured so that each I/O device responds to a memory address and an I/O address. This configuration is compatible with software that uses either I/O instructions memory-mapped or I/O techniques.

Addresses can be assigned arbitrarily within the I/O or memory space. Addresses for either I/O mapped or memory mapped devices should be selected to minimize the number of address lines needed.

7.1.2.1.1 Address Bus Interface

Figure 7-2 shows the i486 microprocessor address interface to 32-, 16- and 8-bit devices. To address 16-bit devices, the byte enables must be decoded to produce A1, BHE# and BLE# (A0) signal.

To access to 8-bit devices, the byte enable signals must be decoded to generate A0 and A1. Because A0 and BLE# are the same, the same generation logic can be used. For 32-bit memory/mapped devices A2–A31 can be used in conjunction with BE3#–BE0#. This logic is shown in Figure 7-3.

7.1.2.1.2 8-Bit I/O Interface

Due to the presence of dynamic data bus sizing and the variety of byte-enable pin combinations (Table 7-2), byte swapping logic for 32-to-8-bit conversions can be implemented in various ways.

This section discusses an example in which BE0#–BE3# = Low and D0–D7 are used when BS8# is enabled.

Figure 7-4 shows the interfacing of i486 microprocessor to an 8-bit device. This implementation requires seven 8-bit bidirectional data buffers.

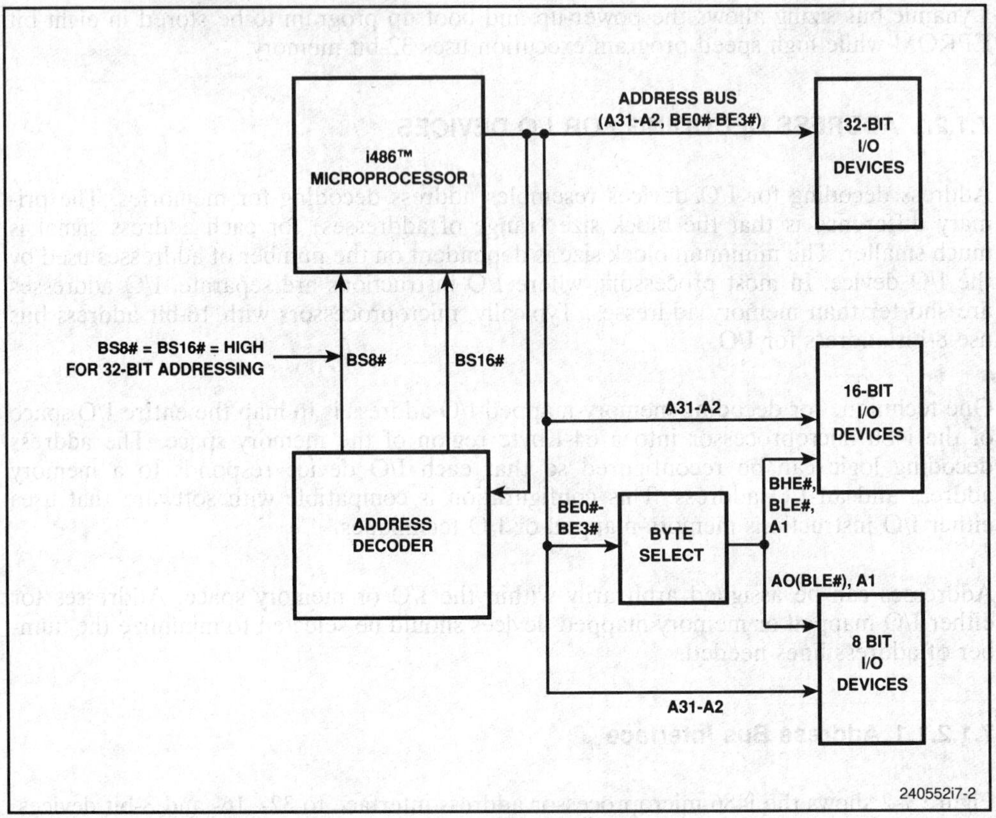

Figure 7-2. Address Interface to 32/16/8-Bit I/O Devices

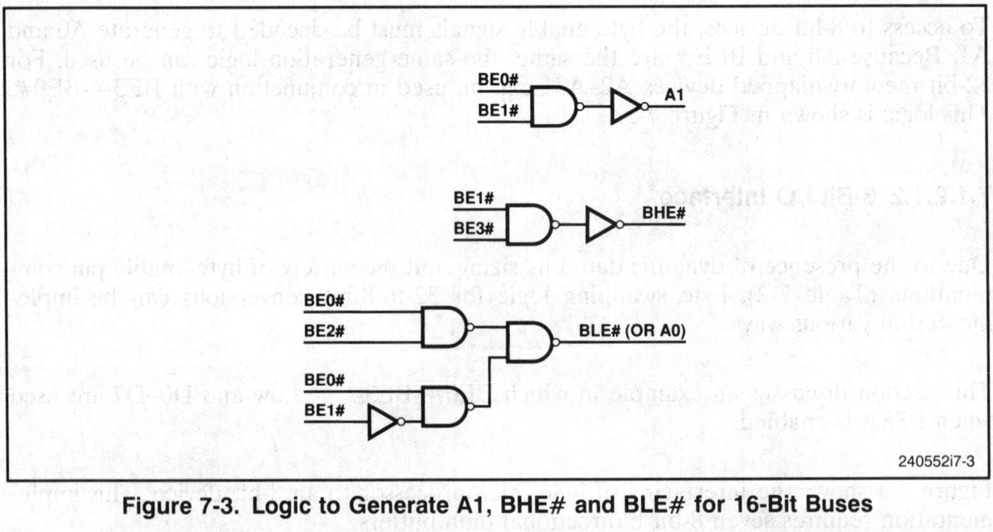

Figure 7-3. Logic to Generate A1, BHE# and BLE# for 16-Bit Buses

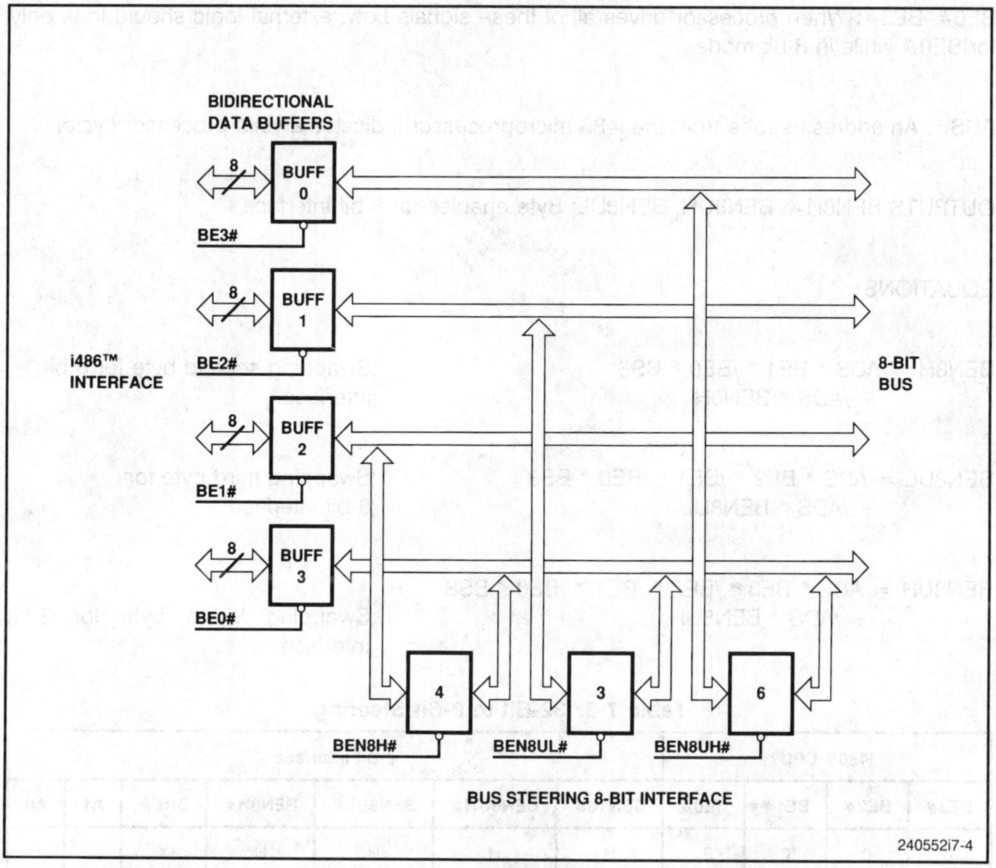

Figure 7-4. i486™ Microprocessor Interface to 8-Bit Device

In this example, in case of 32-bit writes, the BE0#–BE3# are enabled, hence 32 bits of data reside on the data buffer outputs. This is then swapped based on the control signals. Buffers are enabled in the following manner:

For Byte # 0	Buffer 3 is enabled (BE0# is true)
For Byte # 1	Buffer 2 and 4 are enabled (BE1# and BEN8H#)
For Byte # 2	Buffer 1 and 5 are enabled (BE2# and BEN8UL#)
For Byte # 3	Buffer 0 and 6 are enabled (BE3# and BEN8UH#)

Table 7-3 shows the truth table for 8-bit I/O interface to the i486 microprocessor. The table also contains the values of the control signals used to enable the second set of buffers. The PLD equations used to implement these signals are shown below:

PLD Input Signals:

BS8#: The signal is from an 8-bit device or from the system logic that interfaces to an 8-bit device.

BE0#–BE3#: When processor drives all of these signals Low, external logic should look only for BE0# while in 8-bit mode.

ADS#: An address strobe from the i486 microprocessor indicates a valid processor cycle.

OUTPUTS BEN8H#, BEN8UH, BEN8UL: Byte enables for 8 bit interface.

EQUATIONS

```
BEN8H  = ADS * BE1 * /BE0 * BS8                 ;Swapping second byte for 8 bit
         + /ADS * BEN8H                         ;interface

BEN8UL = ADS * BE2 * /BE1 * /BE0 * BS8          ;Swapping third byte for
         + /ADS * BEN8UL                        ;8-bit interface

BEN8UH = ADS * BE3 * /BE2 * /BE1 * /BE0 * BS8
         + /ADS * BEN8UH                        ;Swapping fourth byte for 8-bit
                                                ;interface
```

Table 7-3. 32-Bit to 8-Bit Steering

i486™ CPU				8-Bit Interface						
BE3#	**BE2#**	**BE1#**	**BE0#**	**BEN16#**	**BEN8UH#**	**BEN8UL#**	**BEN8H#**	**BHE#**	**A1**	**A0**
0	0	0	0	H	H	H	H	X	L	L
1	0	0	0	H	H	H	H	X	L	L
0	1	0	0*	H	H	H	H	X	X	X
1	1	0	0	H	H	H	H	X	L	L
0	0	1	0*	H	H	H	H	X	X	X
1	0	1	0*	H	H	H	H	X	X	X
0	1	1	0*	H	H	H	H	X	X	X
1	1	1	0	H	H	H	H	X	L	L
0	0	0	1	H	H	H	L	X	L	H
1	0	0	1	H	H	H	L	X	L	H
0	1	0	1*	H	H	H	L	X	X	X
1	1	0	1	H	H	H	L	X	L	H
0	0	1	1	H	H	L	H	X	H	L
1	0	1	1	H	H	L	H	X	H	L
0	1	1	1	H	L	H	H	X	H	H
1	1	1	1	H	H	H	H	X	X	X
← Inputs →				← Outputs →						

NOTES:
X: Do not care (either L or H).
BHE# (byte high enable) is not needed in 8-bit interface.
*A non-occurring pattern of byte enables; either none are asserted or the pattern has byte enables asserted for non-contiguous bytes.

7.1.2.1.3 16-Bit I/O Interface

16-bit I/O interface byte swap logic requires six eight-bit bidirectional I/O data buffers as shown in Figure 7-5. Buffers 0 through 3 are controlled by BE0–BE3# respectively. Buffers 4 and 5 are monitored by BEN16#.

To transfer data on the lower 16-bits, buffers 2 and 3 are enabled. While the higher 16-bits are transferred through Buffer 0, 1, 4 and 5.

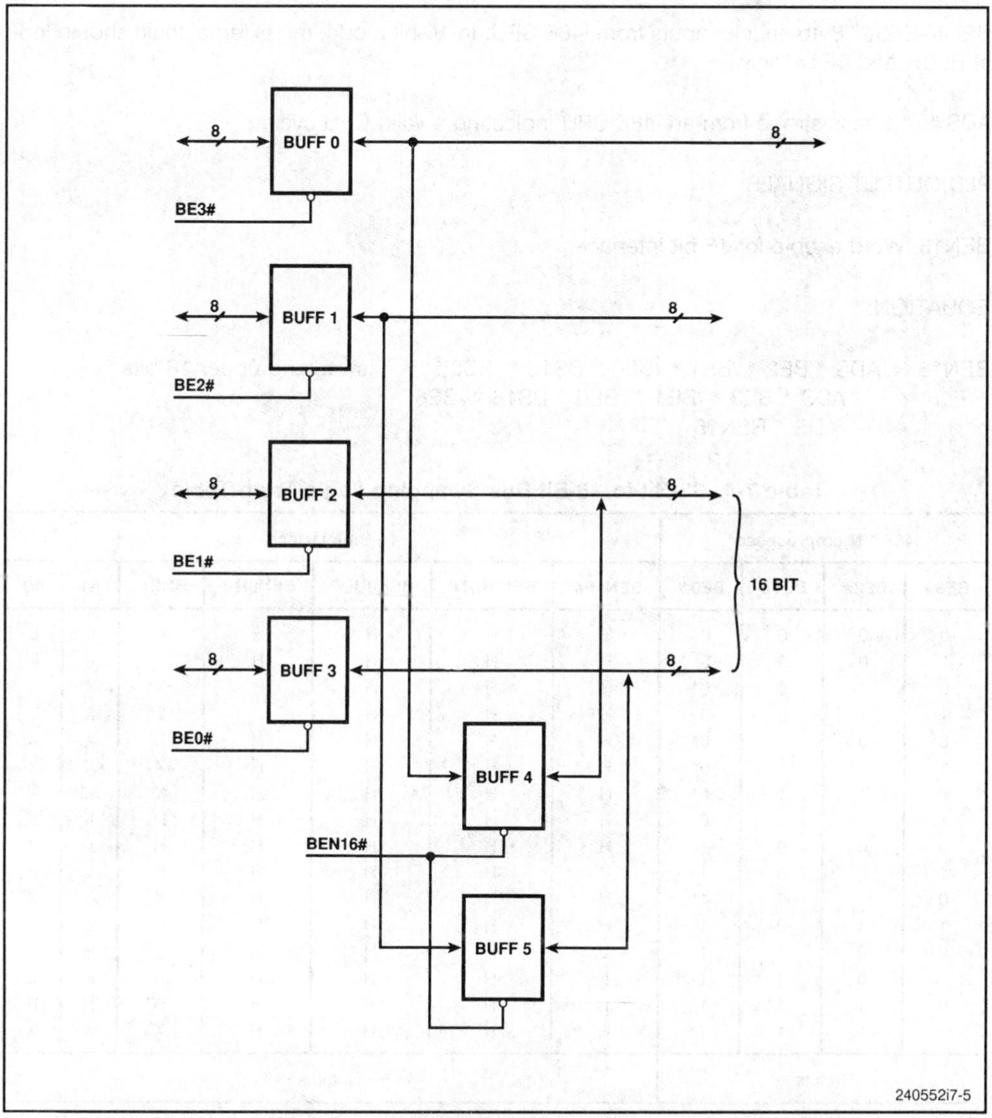

Figure 7-5. Bus Swapping 16-Bit Interface

Table 7-4 shows the truth table for 32-to-16-bit Bus Swapping logic and A0, A1 and BEH# generation.

The PLD equation used to implement 32-bit-to-16-bit byte swap/steer logic is shown below:

PLD INPUT SIGNALS:

BS16#: Either from a 16-bit device or from system logic which indicates a 16-bit transfer.

BE0#–BE3#: Byte enable inputs from i486 CPU. In 16-bit mode, the external logic should look at BE0# and BE1# only.

ADS#: Address strobe from an i486 CPU indicating a valid CPU cycle.

PLD OUTPUT SIGNALS:

BEN16: Word enable for 16-bit interface.

EQUATION:

```
BEN16 = ADS * BE2 * /BE1 * /BE0 * BS16 * /BS8      ;swapping upper 16-bits
        + ADS * BE3 * /BE1 * /BE0 * BS16 * /BS8
        + /ADS * BEN16
```

Table 7-4. 32-Bit to 16-Bit Bus Swapping Logic Truth Table

i486™ Microprocessor				16-Bit Interface						
BE3#	**BE2#**	**BE1#**	**BE0#**	**BEN16#**	**BEN8UH#**	**BEN8UL#**	**BEN8H#**	**BHE#**	**A1**	**A0**
0	0	0	0	H	H	H	H	L	L	L
1	0	0	0	H	H	H	H	L	L	L
0	1	0	0*	H	H	H	H	X	X	X
1	1	0	0	H	H	H	H	L	L	L
0	0	1	0*	H	H	H	H	X	X	X
1	0	1	0*	H	H	H	H	X	X	X
0	1	1	0*	H	H	H	H	X	X	X
1	1	1	0	H	H	H	H	H	L	L
0	0	0	1	H	H	H	H	H	L	H
1	0	0	1	H	H	H	H	H	L	H
0	1	0	1*	H	H	H	H	X	X	X
1	1	0	1	H	H	H	H	H	L	H
0	0	1	1	L	H	H	H	L	H	L
1	0	1	1	L	H	H	H	H	H	L
0	1	1	1	L	H	H	H	H	H	H
1	1	1	1*	H	H	H	H	X	X	X
← Inputs →				← Outputs →						

*A non-occurring pattern of byte enables; either none are asserted or the pattern has byte enables asserted for non-contiguous bytes.

The logic needed to generate the byte swapping control signals for 32-bit-to-8-bit and 32-bit-to-16-bit data transfer can be implemented in PLDs. Propagation delay of the PLD and the bidirectional Buffer propagation delay of 9 ns max must be taken into consideration. This adds into data set-up time for CPU Read cycle and data valid delay for the CPU Write cycle. The byte-swapping and address bit generation logic is shown in Figure 7-6.

7.1.2.1.4 32-Bit Interface

A simple 32-bit I/O interface is shown in Figure 7-7. The example uses only four 8-bit wide bidirectional buffers which are enabled by BE3#–BE0#. Table 7-2 provides different combinations of BE3#–BE0#. To provide greater flexibility in I/O interface implementation, the design should include interfaces for 32-, 16- and 8-bit devices. The truth table for 32-to-32-bit interface is shown in Table 7-5.

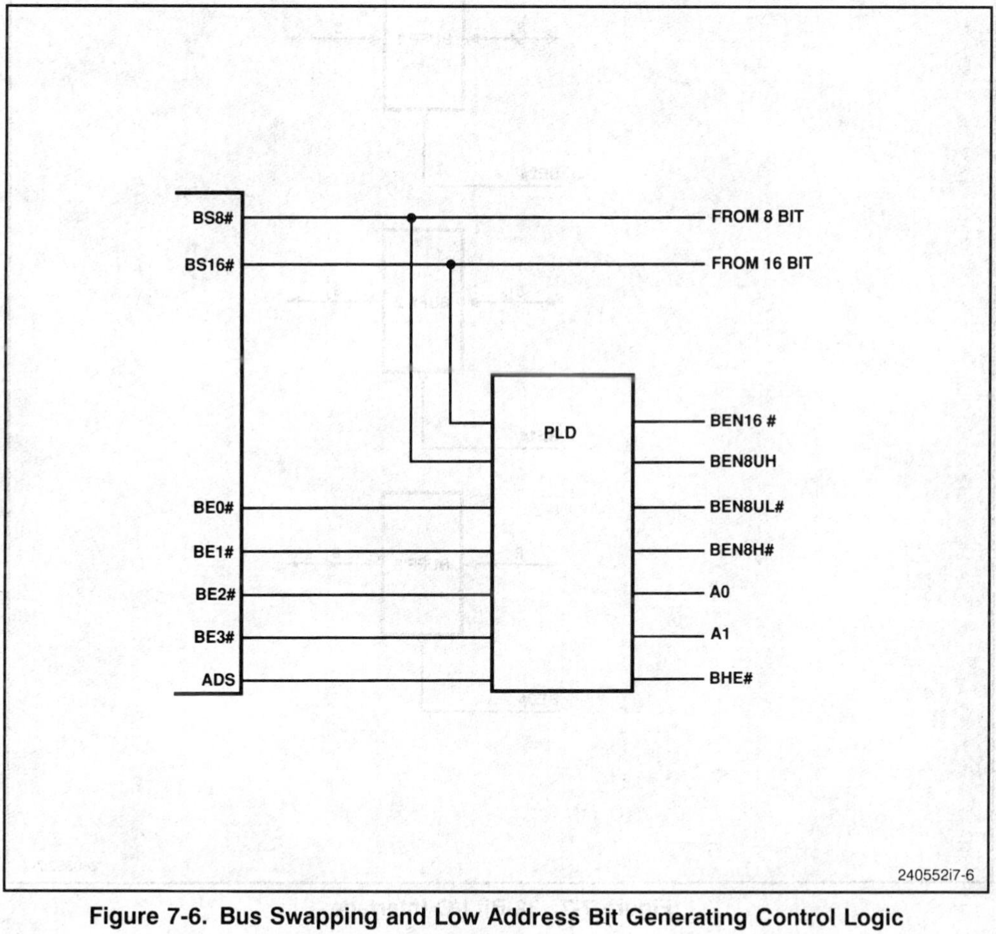

Figure 7-6. Bus Swapping and Low Address Bit Generating Control Logic

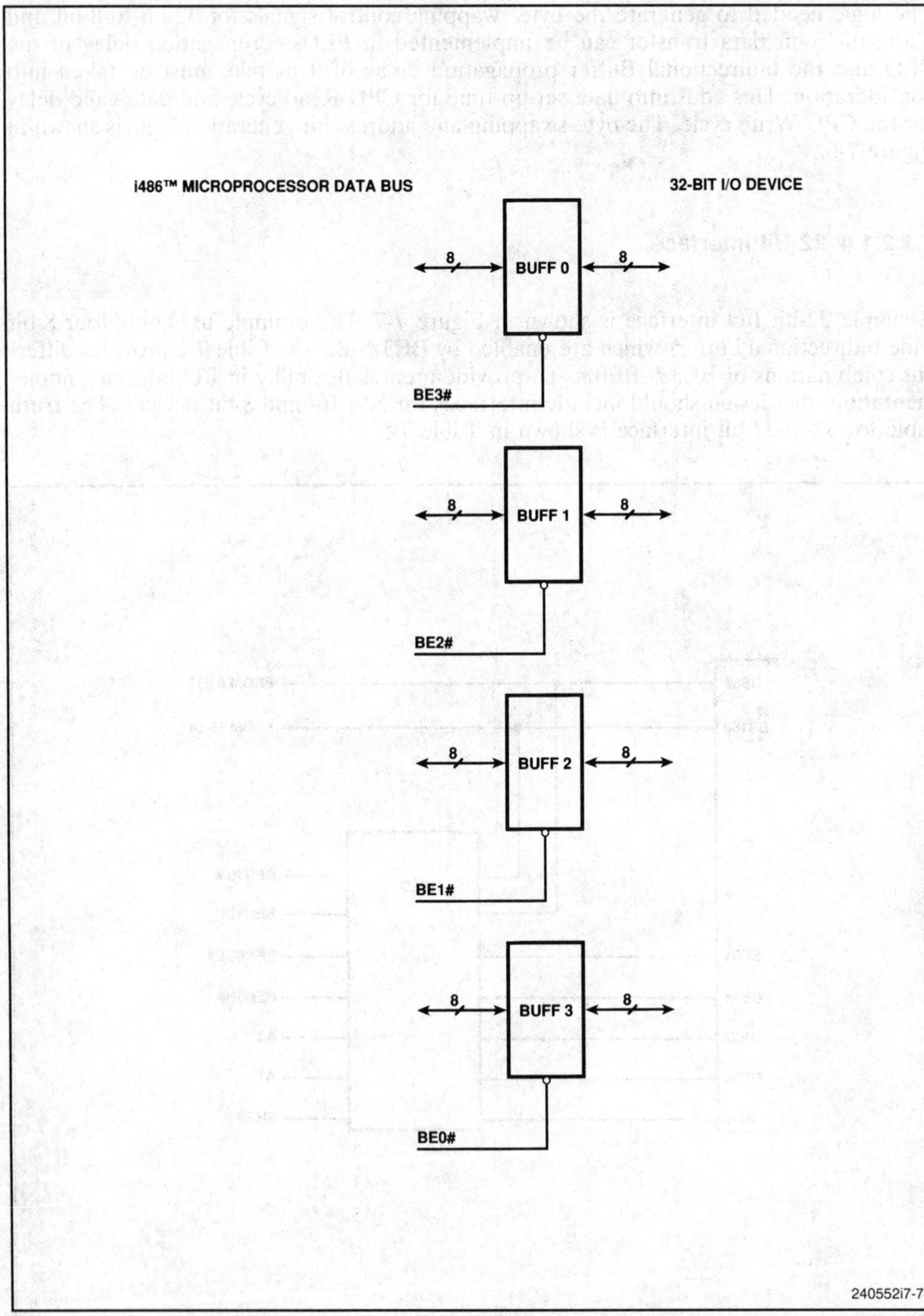

Figure 7-7. 32-Bit I/O Interface

Table 7-5. 32-Bit to 32-Bit Bus Swapping Logic Truth Table

i486™ CPU				32-Bit Interface						
BE3#	BE2#	BE1#	BE0#	BEN16#	BEN8UH#	BEN8UL#	BEN8H#	BHE#	A1	A0
0	0	0	0	H	H	H	H	X	X	X
1	0	0	0	H	H	H	H	X	X	X
0	1	0	0*	H	H	H	H	X	X	X
1	1	0	0	H	H	H	H	X	X	X
0	0	1	0*	H	H	H	H	X	X	X
1	0	1	0*	H	H	H	H	X	X	X
0	1	1	0*	H	H	H	H	X	X	X
1	1	1	0	H	H	H	H	X	X	X
0	0	0	1	H	H	H	H	X	X	X
1	0	0	1	H	H	H	H	X	X	X
0	1	0	1*	H	H	H	H	X	X	X
1	1	0	1	H	H	H	H	X	X	X
0	0	1	1	H	H	H	H	X	X	X
1	0	1	1	H	H	H	H	X	X	X
0	1	1	1	H	H	H	H	X	X	X
1	1	1	1*	H	H	H	H	X	X	X
← Inputs →				← Outputs →						

*A non-occurring pattern of byte enables; either none are asserted or the pattern has byte enables asserted for non-contiguous bytes.

7.2 BASIC PERIPHERAL SUBSYSTEM

All microprocessor systems include a microprocessor, memory and I/O devices which are linked by the address, data and control buses. Figure 7-8 illustrates the system block diagram of a typical i486 microprocessor-based system.

A typical system consists of four subsystems. The heart of the system is the processor core. The memory subsystem is also important and must be efficient and optimized to provide peak system level performance. As described in Chapter 5, it is necessary to utilize the burst-bus feature of the i486 microprocessor for the DRAM control implementation. Cache subsytem as described in Chapter 6 also plays an important role in overall system performance. For many systems however, the on-chip cache provides sufficient performance.

A high-performance i486 microprocessor-based system, requires an efficient peripheral subsystem. This section describes the elements of this system which includes the I/O devices on the expansion bus (the memory bus) and the Local I/O bus. In a typical system a number of slave I/O devices can be controlled through the same local bus interface. Complex peripheral devices which can act as bus masters may require more complex interface.

Although the i486 microprocessor can interface to the peripherals of the earlier architecture (Section 7.5), Intel has added new members to the peripheral subsystem family as shown in Table 7-6.

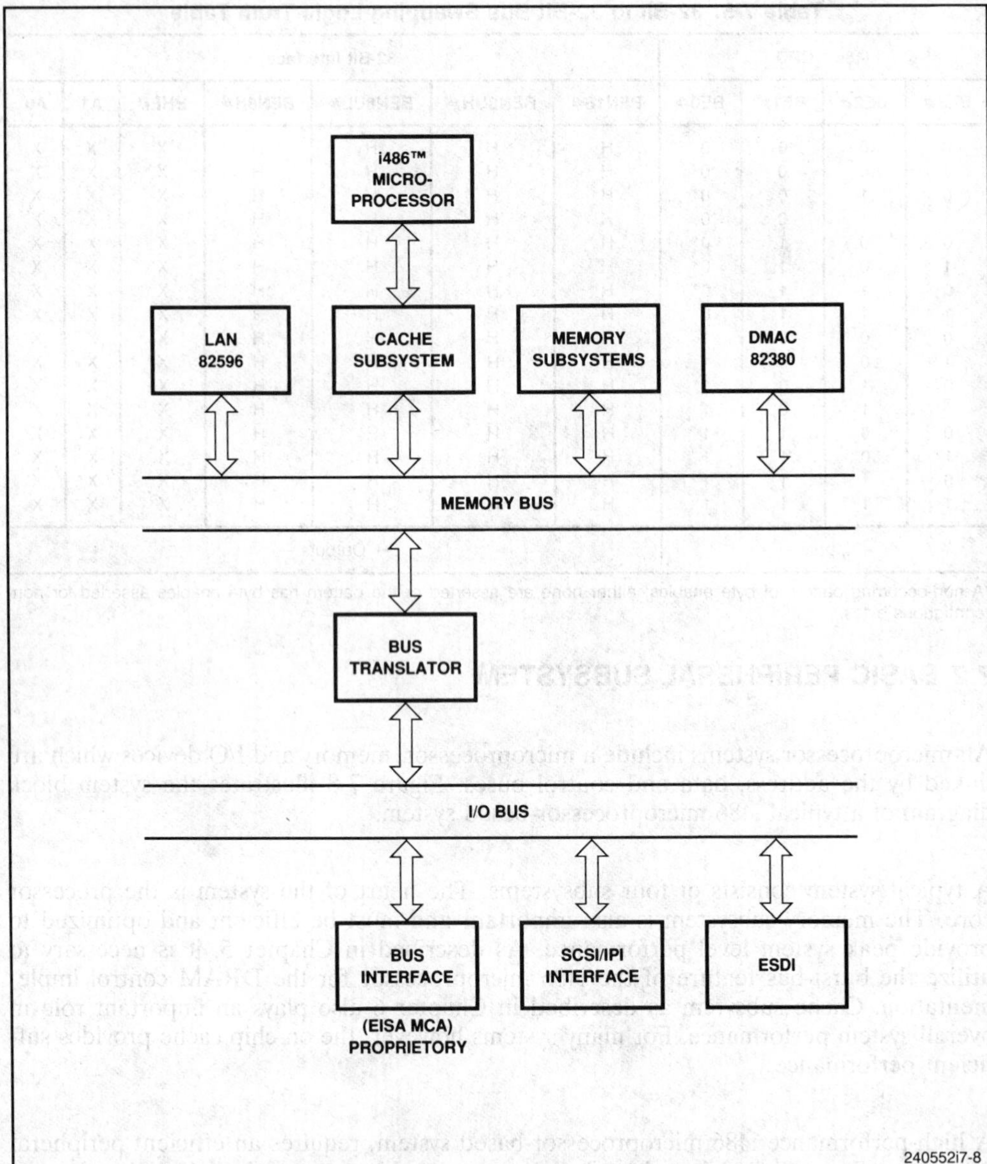

Figure 7-8. System Block Diagram

Table 7-6. i486™ CPU Peripheral Family

Device	# Function
82596	LAN Coprocessor
82350	EISA Peripheral Chip Set

System performance depends upon efficient interfacing and load-sharing between the processor and its peripherals. Intel's 32-bit peripheral devices are designed to provide an optimum system-level performance.

The 82596 LAN coprocessor provides an interface to the i486 microprocessor and a wide variety of networks, including the IEEE 802.3, the IBM PC and the CSMA/CD networks. The 82596 executes high-level commands to control all time-critical LAN functions and performs command chaining and interprocessor communication using memory that it shares with the processor.

EISA peripheral chip set. The 82350 EISA chip-set provides an interface between the i486 microprocessor and the Extended Industry Standard Architecture (EISA) bus. The chip-set includes three motherboard peripherals: a bus controller, an integrated system peripheral, and a bus buffer. A bus master interface chip for EISA bus expansion is also available.

Section 7.6 discusses the 82596-LAN coprocessor and 82350-EISA peripheral chip sets. Chapter 8 details the i486 microprocessor implementation based on the EISA bus.

The basic I/O control logic, wait-state generation logic, and the address decode logic needed in EISA implementation of the i486 microprocessor are provided by 82350 chip set. To achieve compatibility, some workstation designs may require customized bus and control logic. The flexibility of the i486 processor's local bus interface permits this, and the available programmable and semi-custom logic chips simplify the implementation.

The bus interface can control a number of slave devices such as the 82C59A-programmable interrupt controller.

The bus interface control logic can be similar to that used in the memory subsystem. In most systems, the same control and data logic can access memory as well as I/O devices.

The bus interface control logic is shown in Figure 7-9 and consists of three main blocks: the bus control and ready logic, the data transceiver and byte swap logic, and the address decoder.

7.2.1 Bus Control and Ready Logic

A typical peripheral device has address inputs which the processor uses to select the device's internal registers. It also has a chip select (CS#) signal which enables it to read data from and write data to the data bus, as controlled by the READ (RD#) and WRITE (WR#) control signals. For a microprocessor that has separate memory and I/O addressing, either memory or I/O read and write signals can be used. As discussed in Section 7.1.1 when memory read and write signals are used to access the peripheral device, then the device is called a memory-mapped I/O device.

Many peripheral devices also generate an interrupt output which is asserted when a response is required from the microprocessor. Here, the microprocessor must generate an interrupt acknowledge (INTA#) signal.

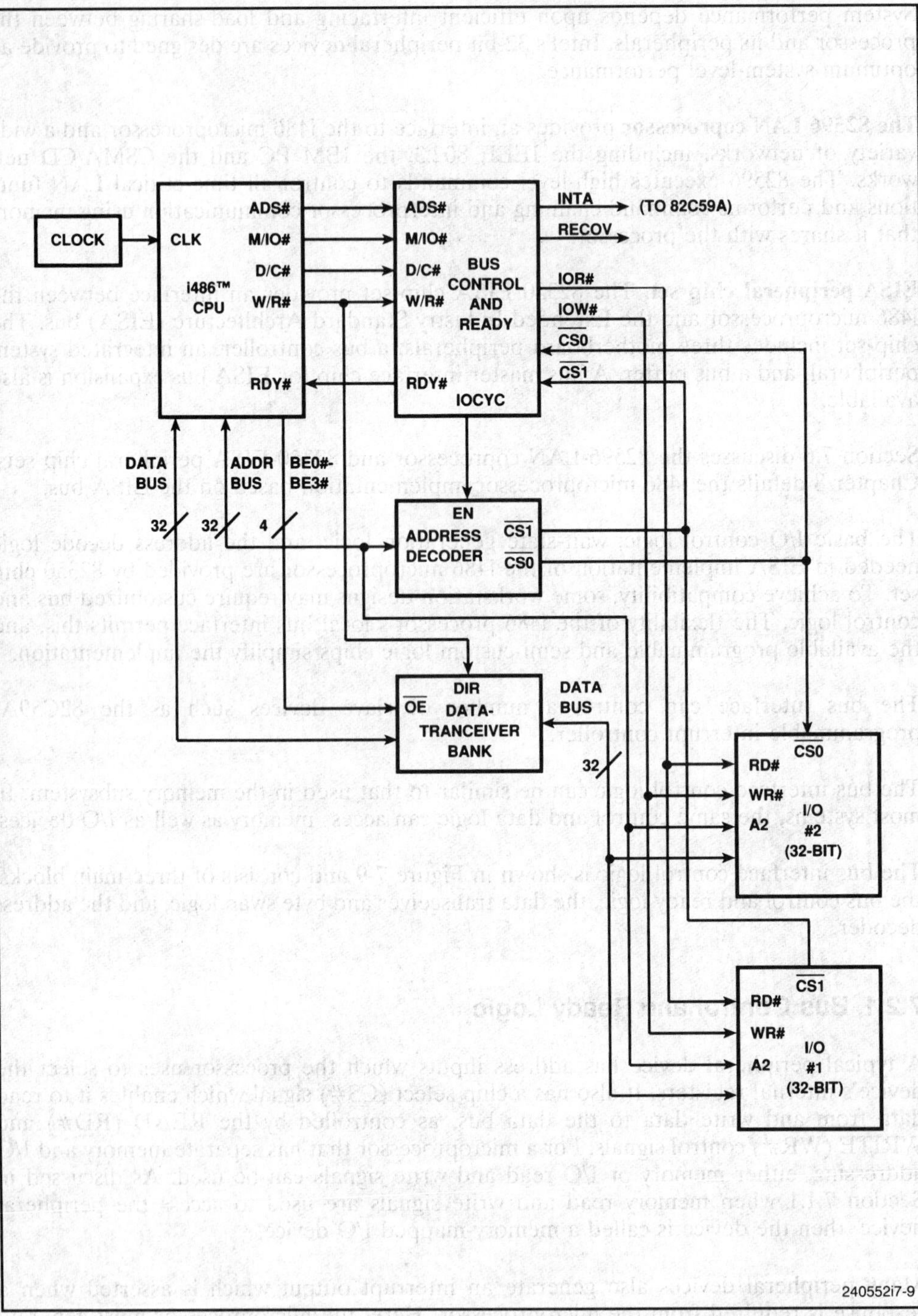

Figure 7-9. Basic I/O Interface Block Diagram

The bus controller decodes the i486 processor's status outputs (W/R#, M/IO# and D/C#) and activates command signals according to the type of bus cycle requested.

The bus controller can be used to do the following:

1. Generate an EPROM data read when the control logic generates a signal such as a memory read command (EPRD#). The command forces the selected memory device to output data. Chapter 8 provides further explanation.

2. Generate the IOCYC# signal which indicates to the address decoder that a valid I/O cycle is taking place. As a result the relevant chip select (CS#) signal should be enabled for the I/O device. Once IOCYC is generated, the IOR# and IOW# signals are asserted according to the decoded i486 microprocessor status signals (explained later).

3. Initiate I/O read cycles when W/R# is Low and M/IO# is Low. The I/O read command (IOR#) is generated. IOR# selects the I/O device which is to output the data.

4. Initiate an I/O Write cycle. When W/R# is High and M/IO# is Low. The I/O write command signal (IOW#) is generated. This signal instructs a selected I/O device to receive data from the i486 microprocessor.

5. Generate a RECOV signal which is used for recovery and to avoid data contention. This signal is detailed in Section 7.2.4.

6. Generates the interrupt acknowledge signal (INTA#). This signal is sent to the 82C59A programmable interrupt controller to enable 82C59A interrupt vector data onto the i486 microprocessor data bus using a sequence of interrupt acknowledge pulses that are issued by the control logic. This signal is detailed in Section 7.5.

The bus control logic may be implemented as shown in Figure 7-10.

7.2.1.1 SIGNAL DESCRIPTION

The following list describes all of the input/output signals for the bus control logic.

7.2.1.1.1 Processor Interface

ADS#—Address Status. This input signal to the bus controller is connected directly to the processor's ADS# output. It indicates that a valid bus cycle definition and address are available on the cycle definition lines and address bus. ADS# is driven active at the same time when addresses are driven.

M/IO#—Memory/Input-Output Signal
D/C#—Data/Control
W/R#—Write/Read (Input signals to bus controller)

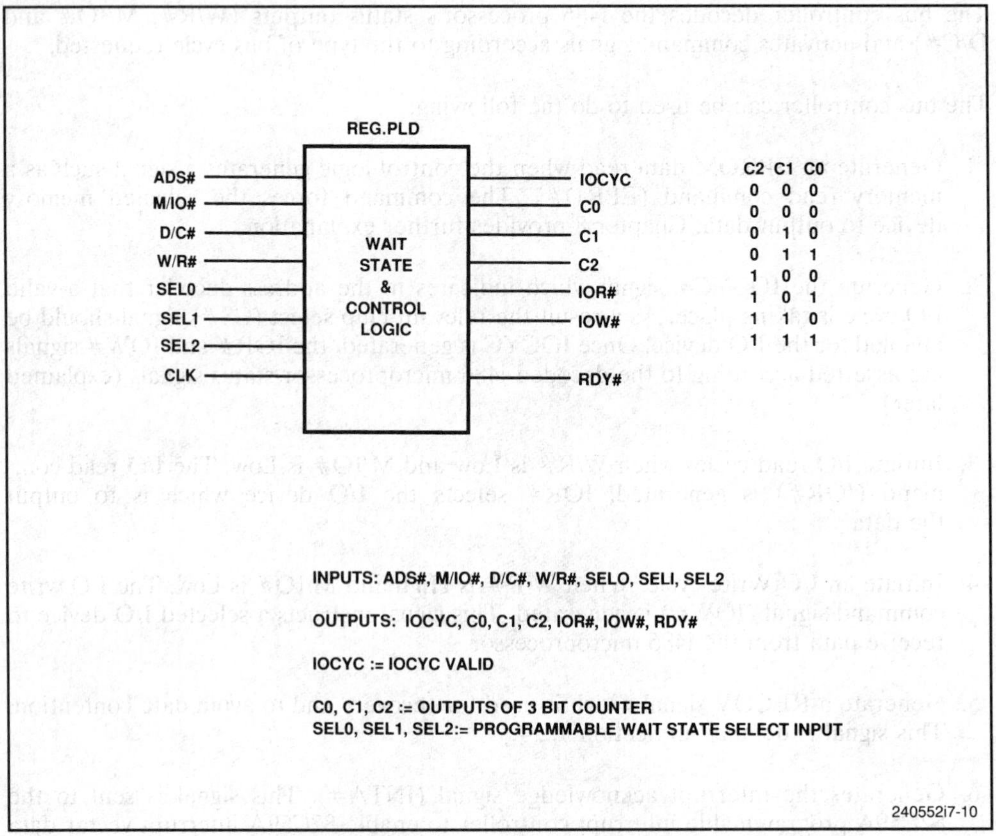

Figure 7-10. Bus Control Logic Implementation

These signals are connected directly to the i486 microprocessor's bus cycle status outputs. For the i486 microprocessor, they are valid when ADS# is asserted. Table 7-7 describes the bus cycles of various combinations of M/IO#, D/C# and W/R# signals.

RDY#—Ready Output Signal. This signal is connected directly to the i486 processor's RDY# input and indicates that the current bus cycle is complete. It also indicates that the I/O device has returned valid data to the i486 microprocessor's data pins following an I/O write cycle. For the i486 microprocessor, RDY# is ignored when the bus is idle and at the end of first clock of the bus cycle. The signal is utilized in wait-state generation which is covered in the next section.

CLK#—Clock Input Signal. This signal provides the fundamental timings for the bus control logic and is synchronous with the processor's clock. All of the external timings are specified with respect to the rising edge of the clock.

IOCYC—I/O Interface Signals. The IOCYCLE OUTPUT signal is generated at the rising clock edge following ADS#, M/IO#, D/C and W/R# being active. The signal indicates that an I/O cycle is taking place and is used to enable the address decoder.

Table 7-7. Bus Cycle Definitions

M/IO#	D/C#	W/R#	Bus Cycle Initiated
0	0	0	Interrupt acknowledge
0	0	1	Halt/special cycle
0	1	0	I/O read
0	1	1	I/O write
1	0	0	Code read
1	0	1	Reserved
1	1	0	Memory read
1	1	1	Memory write

IOR#—The I/O READ Signal. This signal is active low and is generated when the i486 processor's W/R# output signal is low, indicating a read cycle. When IOR# is low, data can be read from the peripheral device. The signal is negated with the rising edge of the RDY# signal.

IOW#—Interrupt Acknowledge Signal. This signal is generated by the controller logic and is active low when W/R# status signal from the i486 processor is high, indicating that the processor will write to the I/O device which has its present address on the address bus. When IOW# is low, data from the i486 processor can be written to the peripheral device. The signal is valid until the rising edge of the RDY# signal.

INTA—Interrupt Acknowledge Signal. This signal is active high and is generated to acknowledge an interrupt from peripheral devices such as 82C59A, etc. The signal function will be discussed in Section 7.5.

7.2.1.1.2 Wait-State Generation Signals

SEL0, SEL1, SEL2. These programmable wait-state select input can be controlled by DIP switches or can be programmed by the processor. In the control logic example, a seven-state wait-state generator is implemented. The purpose and functionality of a wait-state generator is described in the next section.

C0, C1, C2 Counter Outputs 0, 1 and 2. These outputs are internally decoded to generate a RDY# signal, and they represent the number of wait-states implemented by the bus control logic. The wait-state generation logic is used to patch timing differences between the peripheral device and the i486 processor. The next section discusses this issue in detail.

7.2.1.2 WAIT-STATE GENERATOR LOGIC

When the memory subsystem or the I/O device cannot respond to the microprocessor in the optimum time, then wait-states are added to the bus cycles. During wait-states the microprocessor freezes the state of the bus. On the i486 microprocessor, wait-states are activated by the RDY# (when asserted) signal. Additional wait-states are generated as long as RDY# stays deasserted, and microprocessor resumes its operations once RDY# is asserted.

Timing differences between microprocessors and peripheral devices are common, and they can be compensated by using wait-states or some other delay techniques. The following major timing parameters must be accounted for:

1. Minimum pulse width for read and write timings

2. Chip select access time

3. Address access time

4. Access time from read strobe

It is possible to adjust the minimum pulse width and chip select access time by adding wait-states. In the i486 processor, the fastest non-burst cycle requires two clocks. Such cycles are called 2-2 cycles because read and write cycles require two clocks each, with the first 2 referring to the read and the second referring to the write (Figure 7-11).

If an additional wait-state is needed for the read and write, then a 3-3 cycle is created as shown in Figure 7-12.

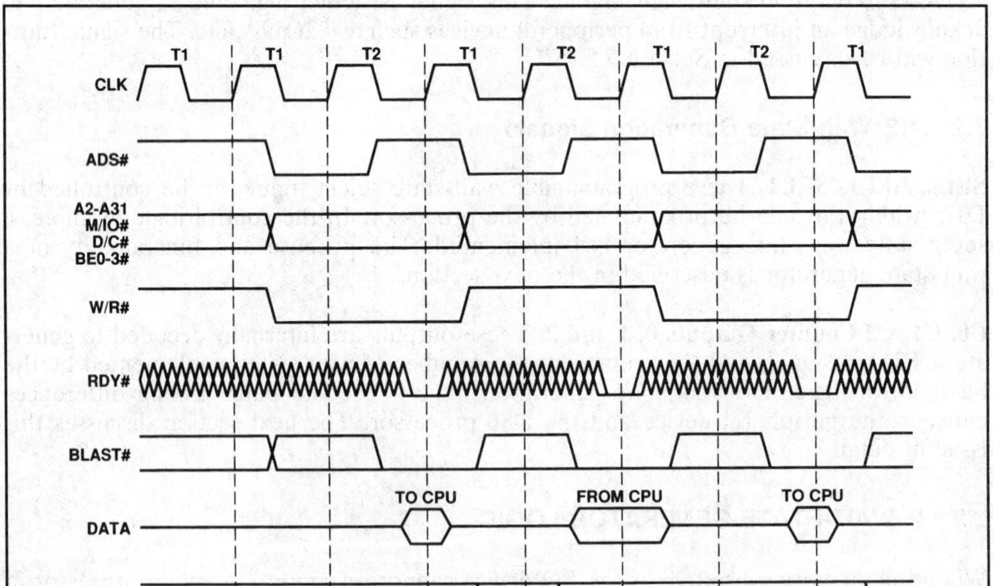

Figure 7-11. Basic 2-2 Cycle

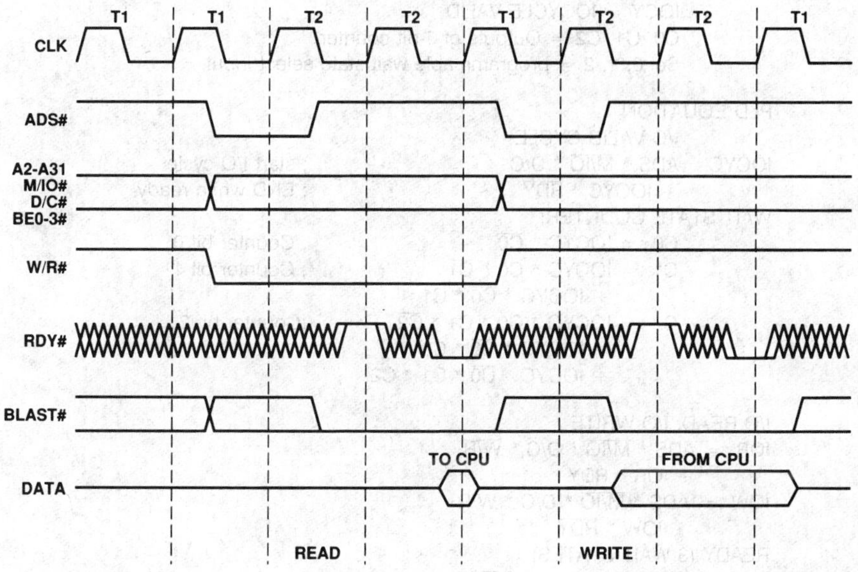

Figure 7-12. Basic 3-3 Cycle

The i486 processor initiates a cycle by asserting the address status signal (ADS#) at the rising edge of the first clock. The presence of ADS# indicates the presence of valid addresses and start of a bus cycle. The non-burst ready signal (RDY#) is returned to the external system in the second clock (for a 2-2 cycle), indicating that the external system has presented valid data to or accepted valid data from the data pins for a read or write cycle. The processor samples the ready signal at the rising edge of the third clock. The cycle is complete if RDY# is active (low). RDY# is ignored when sampled at the end of the first clock (T1) of the bus cycle. If a wait-state is to be inserted, then RDY# should be inactive in the second clock. Wait-states can be added for each subsequent bus cycle in which RDY# is inactive.

Figure 7-13 shows PLD equations for basic I/O control logic. A wait-state generator should be implemented to optimize wait-state generation.

The equation in Figure 7-13 shows an implementation of a seven-state wait-state controller. The wait-state logic inserts the needed wait-states according to the number required by the device being accessed. In a simple design, I/O accesses can be designated as being equal to the number of wait-states required by the slowest device.

Inputs ADS#, M/IO#, D/C#, W/R#, SEL0, SEL1, SEL2
Outputs IOCYC, 0, C1, C2, IOR#, IOW#, RDY#
IOCY = IOCYCLE VALID
C0, C1, C2 = Outputs of 3-bit counter
Sel 0, 1, 2 = programmable wait state select input

PLD EQUATION =
I/O VALID CYCLE;
IOCYC :=ADS * $\overline{\text{M/IO}}$ * D/C ; start I/O cycle
+ IOCYC * $\overline{\text{RDY}}$; END when ready
WAIT STATE COUNTER;
C0 := IOCYC * $\overline{\text{C0}}$; Counter bit 0
C1 := IOCYC * C0 * $\overline{\text{C1}}$; Counter bit 1
+ IOCYC * $\overline{\text{C0}}$ * C1
C2 := IOCYC * C0 * C1 * $\overline{\text{C2}}$;Counter bit 2
+ IOCYC * $\overline{\text{C0}}$ * C2
+ IOCYC * $\overline{\text{C0}}$ * C1 * C2

I/O READ; I/O WRITE
IOR := ADS * $\overline{\text{M/IO}}$ * D/C * $\overline{\text{W/R}}$
+ IOR * RDY
IOW := ADS * $\overline{\text{M/IO}}$ * D/C * W/R
+ IOW * $\overline{\text{RDY}}$
READY (3 WAIT STATES)
RDY = C0 * C1 * $\overline{\text{C2}}$

Figure 7-13. PLD Equations for Basic I/O Control Logic

7.2.2 Address Decoder

The function of the address decoder is to decode the most significant address bits and generate address select signals for each system device. The address space is divided into blocks, and the address select signals indicate whether the address on the address bus is within the predetermined range. The block size usually represents the amount of address space that can be accessed within a particular device and the address select signal is asserted for any address within that range.

Address select signals are asserted within the range of addresses which is determined by by the decoded address lines. The relationship between memory and I/O mapping and address decoding is given by the following equation:

Given that n = bits to decoder
m = bits to I/O or memory

then # of chip selects = 2^n
address range = 2^m = # of least significant address lines

For example, if the address decoder decodes A13 through the most significant address bits, then the least significant 13 address bits A2 to A12 are ignored. Hence the address select can be asserted for a 2^{11} (two-Kbyte) address range.

For I/O mapped devices, the maximum I/O space is 64 Kbytes. Thus when using I/O instructions the block size (range of addresses) for each address select signal is much smaller than the address space of the memory-mapped devices. The minimum block size is determined according to the number of addresses being used by the peripheral device.

A typical address decoding circuit for a basic I/O interface implementation is shown in Figure 7-14. It uses 74X138. Only one output is asserted at a time, the signal corresponding to the binary number present at the A, B and C inputs and value of the gate enable signals.

Figure 7-15 shows the internal logic and truth table of the 74LS138. It has three enable inputs; two are active low, and one is active high. All three inputs must be asserted; otherwise the outputs will be negated. Since all of the outputs are active low, the selected output is low and the others are high.

In Figure 7-14, address lines A8–A15 are ignored to maintain simplicity. Lines A2–A7 are decoded to generate addresses XXE0–XXFC. When a valid cycle begins, ADS# is latched in the flipflop.

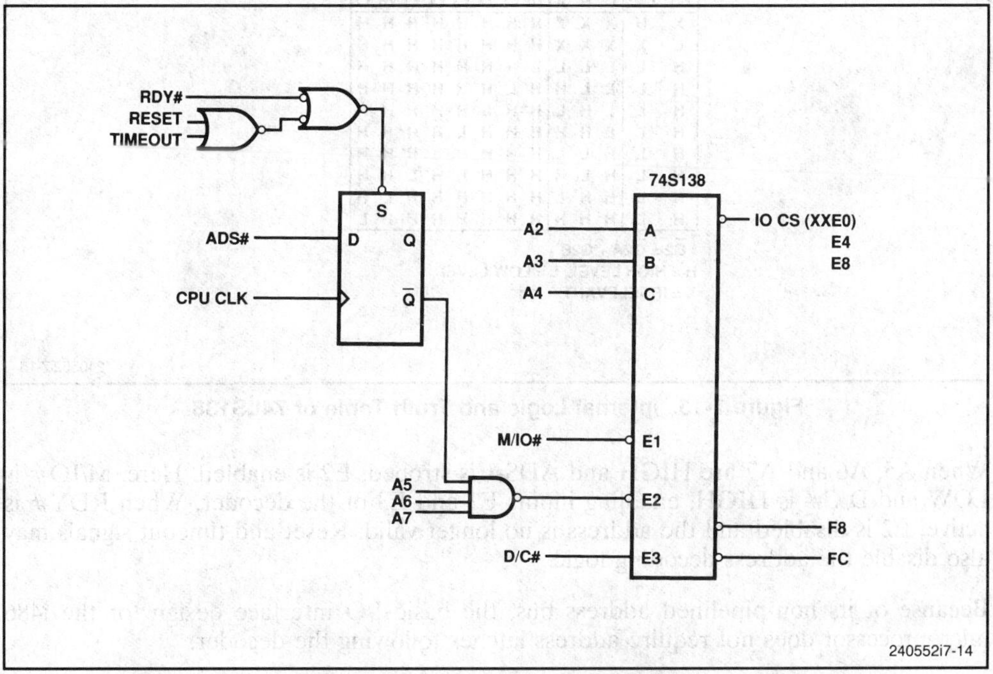

Figure 7-14. I/O Address Example

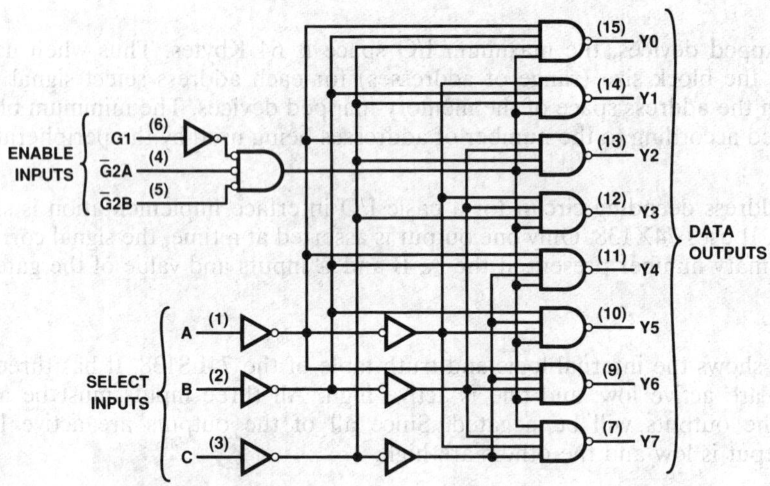

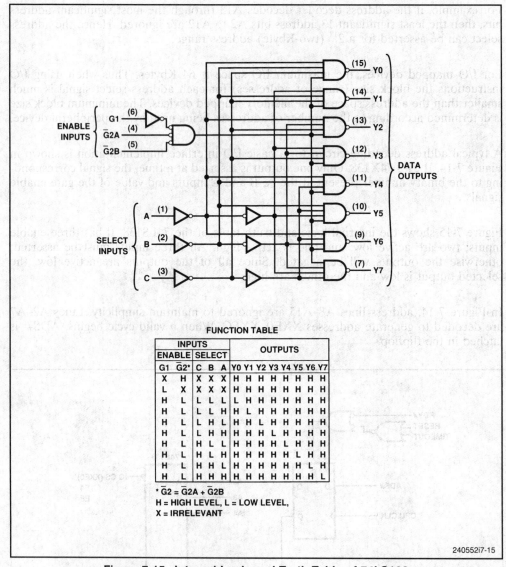

FUNCTION TABLE

INPUTS					OUTPUTS							
ENABLE		SELECT										
G1	G̅2*	C	B	A	Y0	Y1	Y2	Y3	Y4	Y5	Y6	Y7
X	H	X	X	X	H	H	H	H	H	H	H	H
L	X	X	X	X	H	H	H	H	H	H	H	H
H	L	L	L	L	L	H	H	H	H	H	H	H
H	L	L	L	H	H	L	H	H	H	H	H	H
H	L	L	H	L	H	H	L	H	H	H	H	H
H	L	L	H	H	H	H	H	L	H	H	H	H
H	L	H	L	L	H	H	H	H	L	H	H	H
H	L	H	L	H	H	H	H	H	H	L	H	H
H	L	H	H	L	H	H	H	H	H	H	L	H
H	L	H	H	H	H	H	H	H	H	H	H	L

* G̅2 = G̅2A + G̅2B
H = HIGH LEVEL, L = LOW LEVEL,
X = IRRELEVANT

240552i7-15

Figure 7-15. Internal Logic and Truth Table of 74LS138

When A5, A6 and A7 are HIGH and ADS# is strobed, E2 is enabled. Here, M/IO# is LOW and D/C# is HIGH, enabling inputs E1 and E3 of the decoder. When RDY# is active, E2 is disabled and the address is no longer valid. Reset and timeout signals may also disable the address decoding logic.

Because of its non-pipelined address bus, the basic I/O interface design for the i486 microprocessor does not require address latches following the decoder.

The number of decoders needed is usually a factor of memory mapping complexity.

7.2.3 Data Transceivers

Data transceivers are used for isolating the microprocessor's data bus from the external databus and increasing the drive capability for larger fanouts. Transceivers are used to avoid the contention on the data bus caused when slow devices performing delayed read on the databus following a read cycle. When a write cycle follows a read cycle, the i486 processor may drive the data bus before a slow device can remove its outputs from the bus, creating potential bus contention problems. If the load on the i486 microprocessor's data pins meets device specifications, and if the data float time of the device is short enough, the transceivers can be ommitted from the system.

There should be enough transceivers in the bus interface to accommodate the device with the most inputs and outputs on the data bus. Only eight transceivers are needed if the widest device has 16 data bits and if the I/O device addresses are connected only to the lower byte of the data bus.

The 74x245 transceiver is controlled through two input signals:

- Data Transmit/Receive (DT/R#)—The transceiver for write cycles is enabled when this signal is high, and a read cycle is enabled when it is low. This signal is simply a latched version of i486 processor's W/R# output.

- Data Enable (DEN#)—When low, this input enables the tranceiver outputs. It is generated by the byte swapping logic and by the BE0#–BE3# signals.

Data transceivers may be combined with byte swapping logic, depending upon whether a 32-8/16/32 bit transfer is used. The implementation details of this logic has already been discussed in the previous sections.

7.2.4 Recovery and Bus Contention

Although data transceivers help to avoid data bus contention, I/O devices may still require a recovery period between back-to-back accesses. At higher i486 processor clock frequencies, bus contention is more problematic, particularly because of the long float delay of I/O devices which can conflict with read data from other I/O device or write data from the CPU. To ensure proper operation, I/O devices require a recovery time between consecutive accesses. All slave devices stop driving data on the bus on the rising edge of IOR#. After a delay which follows this rising edge, the data bus floats.

If however, other devices drive data on to the bus before the data from the previous access floats, bus contention occurs. The i486 microprocessor has a very fast cycle time (30 ns at 33 MHz), and the probability of bus contention must be addressed.

Bus control logic should implement recovery to eliminate the occurrence of bus contention. The logic generates a RECOV signal until the data from the previous read floats. It may or may not be possible to enforce this recovery with the hardware counter. The hardware counter method may not be feasible when recovery times are too fast for the hardware counter (i.e., when recovery time is in nanoseconds). In this case, recovery time can be enforced in software using NOPs and delay loops or using a programmable timer.

The advantages of using hardware enforced recovery, however, are transparency and reliability. Further when moving to higher processor clock speeds, no change is needed in the I/O device drivers. For these reasons, hardware enforced I/O recovery time is recommended.

7.2.5 Write Buffers and I/O Cycles

The i486 microprocessor contains four write buffers to enhance the performance of consecutive writes to memory. Writes will be driven onto the external bus in the same order in which they are received by the write buffers. Under certain conditions, a memory read will be reordered in front of the writes pending in the write buffer even though the writes occurred earlier in program execution (see Section 2.1.2 for details).

However, I/O cycles must be handled in a different manner by the write buffers. I/O reads are never reordered in front of buffered memory writes. This ensures that the i486 microprocessor will update all memory locations before reading status from an I/O device.

The i486 microprocessor never buffers single I/O writes. When processing an I/O write instruction (OUT, OUTS), internal execution stops until the I/O write actually completes on the external bus. This allows time for the external system to drive an invalidate into the i486 processor or to mask interrupts before the processor continues to the instruction following the Write instruction. Repeated OUTS (REP OUTS) instructions will be buffered, however the next instruction will not be executed until the REP OUTS finishes executing.

7.2.5.1 WRITE BUFFERS AND RECOVERY TIME

The write buffers, in association with the cache, have certain implications for I/O device recovery times. Back to back write recovery times need to be guaranteed by explicitly generating a read cycle to a non-cacheable area in between the writes. Since the i486 microprocessor does not buffer I/O writes, the inserted read will not be allowed to proceed to the bus until the first write is completed. Then, the read cycle will run on the external bus. During this time, the I/O device will recover and allow the next write.

7.2.6 Non-Cacheability of Memory Mapped I/O Devices

To avoid problems caused by I/O "read arounds," memory mapped I/O should not be cached. A read around occurs when a read cycle is reordered in front of a write cycle. If the memory mapped I/O device is cached the possibility of reading the status of the I/O device may occur before all previous writes to that device are completed. This could cause a problem if the read initiates an action requiring memory to be up to date.

An example of when a read around could cause a problem follows:

- The interrupt controller is memory mapped in cacheable memory.
- The write buffer is filled with write cache hits, so a read is reordered in front of the writes.
- One of the pending writes is a write to the interrupt controller control register.
- The read that was reordered (and performed before the write) was to the interrupt controller's status register.

Because the reading of the status register occurred before the write to the control register, the wrong status was read. This can be avoided by not caching memory mapped I/O devices.

7.2.7 i486 Microprocessor On-Chip Cache Consistency

Some peripheral devices can write to cacheable main memory. If this is the case, cache consistency must be maintained to prevent stale data from being left in the on-chip cache. Cache consistency is maintained by adding bus snooping logic to the system and invalidating any line in the on-chip cache that another bus master writes to.

Cache line invalidations are usually performed by asserting AHOLD to allow another bus master to drive the addresss of the line to be invalidated, and then asserting EADS# to invalidate the line. Cache line invalidations may also be performed when BOFF# or HOLD is asserted instead of AHOLD. If AHOLD, BOFF# and HOLD are all deasserted when EADS# is issued, the i486 microprocessor will invalidate the cache line at the address that happens to be on the bus. Cache line invalidations and cache consistency are explained more fully in Sections 3.4.2 and 6.3.3.

7.3 I/O Cycles

The I/O read and write cycles used in system are a factor of the I/O control logic implementation. Figures 7-16 through 7-19 illustrate an I/O read and write cycle for a typical implementation.

7.3.1 Read Cycle Timing

A new i486 processor read cycle is initiated when ADS# is asserted in T1. The address, and status signals (M/IO# = LOW, W/R# = LOW, D/C# = HIGH) also become valid. The IOCYC signal is generated by the control logic by decoding ADS#, M/IO#, W/R# and D/C#. IOCYC indicates to an external device that an I/O cycle is pending. The IOR# signal is asserted in the T2 clock when IOCYC is valid and RECOV is inactive. The RECOV signal indicates that the new cycle must be delayed to meet the I/O device recovery time or to prevent data bus contention. The I/O read signal (IOR#) signal is not asserted until RECOV is deasserted. Data becomes valid after IOR# is asserted, and the timing depending upon the number of wait-states implemented.

TIMING ANALYSIS FOR I/O READ CYCLE

tR_{vd} READ SIGNAL VALID DELAY

$tR_{vd} = t_{PLDpd}$

$= 10$ ns

tD_{su} READ DATA SETUP TIME

$tD_{su} = t_{BUFpd} + t_{su}{}^*$

$= 9 + 5 = 14$ ns

tD_{hd} READ DATA HOLD TIME

$tD_{hd} = t_{hd}{}^* - t_{BUFpd}$

$= 3 - 9 = -6$ ns

* $t_{su} = t_{22}$ i486™ microprocessor time (33 MHz)

t_{hd} = i486 microprocessor read hold time (33 MHz)

Figure 7-16. I/O Read Timing Analysis

In the example, two wait-states are required for the slowest I/O device to do a read, and the bus control logic keeps IOR# active to meet the minimum active time requirement. The worst case timing values are calculated by assuming maximum delay in the decode logic and through data transceivers. The following equations shows the fastest possible cycle implementation. Wait-states should be added to meet the access times of the I/O devices used. Figure 7-16 and 7-17 show the I/O read cycle timing and the critical analysis.

7.3.2 Write Cycle Timings

The I/O write cycle is similar to the I/O read cycle with the exceptions of W/R# being asserted high when sampled rather than low from the i486 processor side. This is shown in Figures 7-18 and 7-19.

The timing of the remaining signals (the address and status signals) is similar to that of I/O read cycle timings. The processor outputs data in T2. The I/O Write signal (IOW#) may be asserted one or two clocks after the chip select with exact delay between the chip select and the IOW# varying according to the write requirements of the I/O device. Data is written into the I/O device on the rising edge of IOW#, and the processor stops driving data once RDY# data is sampled active. The critical timings for the I/O write cycle are shown in Figure 7-19.

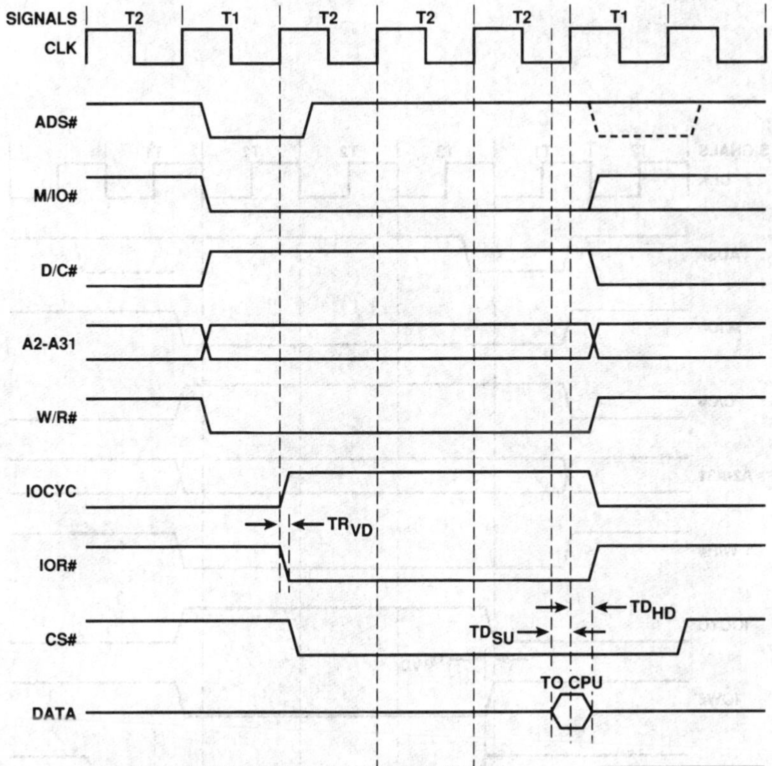

Figure 7-17. I/O Read Timings

Latches and data buffers can improve microprocessor write performance. In Figure 7-20, I/O addresses and data are both latched in a configuration called a posted write. Posted writes help increase system performance by allowing the CPU to complete a cycle without wait-states. Once the data and address are latched, RDY# can be returned to the processor during the first T2 of an I/O write cycle. Thus, the processor operation and the write cycle to the peripheral device can continue simultaneously. This is illustrated in Figure 7-21. The write cycle appears to be only two clocks long (from ADS# to RDY#) because the actual write overlaps other CPU bus cycles.

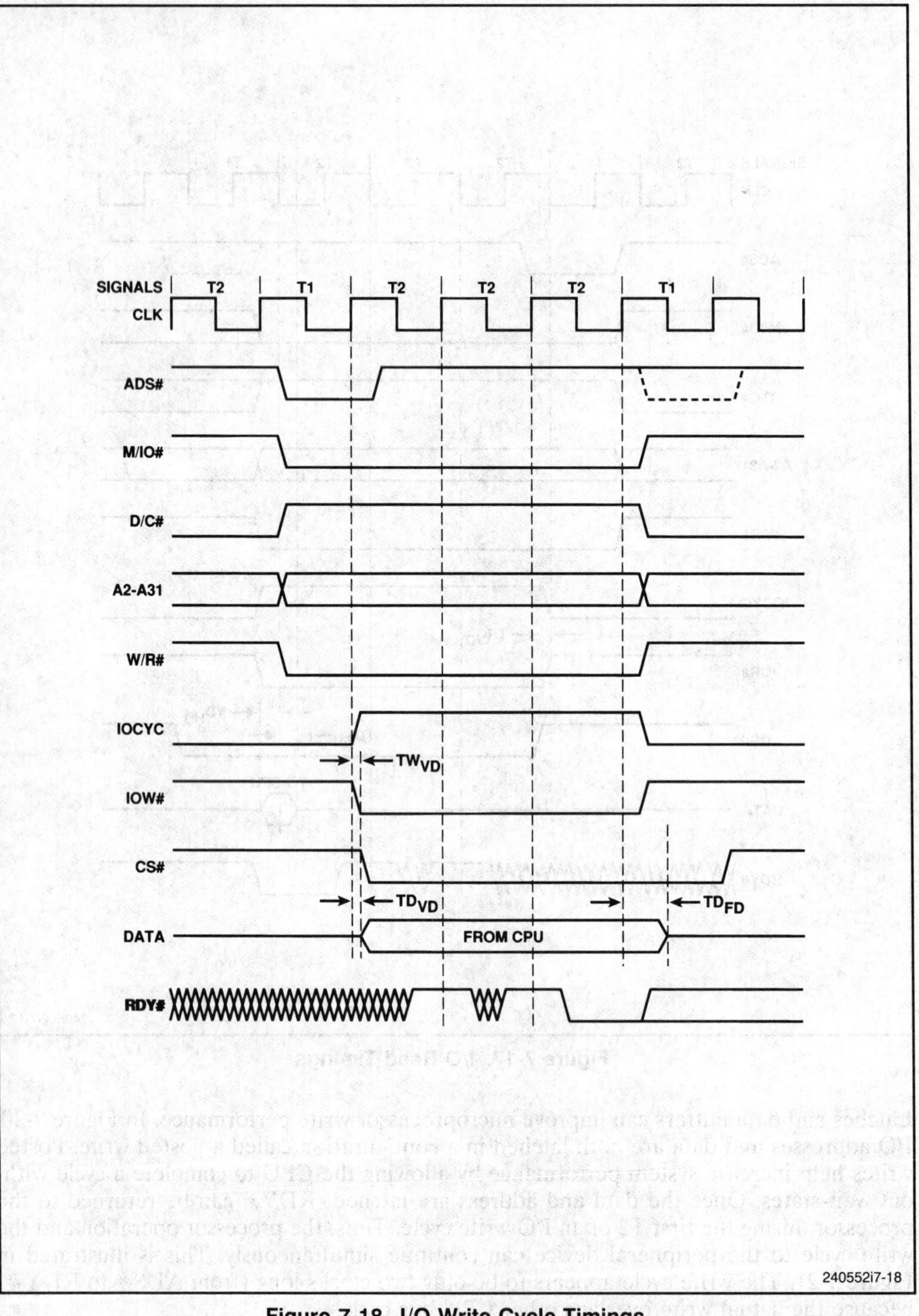

Figure 7-18. I/O Write Cycle Timings

TIMING ANALYSIS FOR I/O WRITE CYCLE

tW_{Vd} WRITE SIGNAL VALID DELAY
$tW_{vd} = t_{PLDpd}$
$= 10$ ns

tD_{vd} WRITE DATA VALID DELAY
$tD_{VD} = t_{Vd}* + t_{BuFpd}$
$= 19 + 9 = 28$ ns

tD_{fd} WRITE DATA FLOAT TIME
$tD_{fd} = t_{fd}* + t_{BUFpd}$
$= 0 + 9 = 9$ ns

$* t_{vd} = t_{10}$ i486™ MICROPROCESSOR WRITE DATA VALID DELAY (33 MHz)
$t_{fd} = t_{11}$ i486™ MICROPROCESSOR WRITE DATA FLOAT DELAY (33 MHz)

Figure 7-19. I/O Write Cycle Timing Analysis

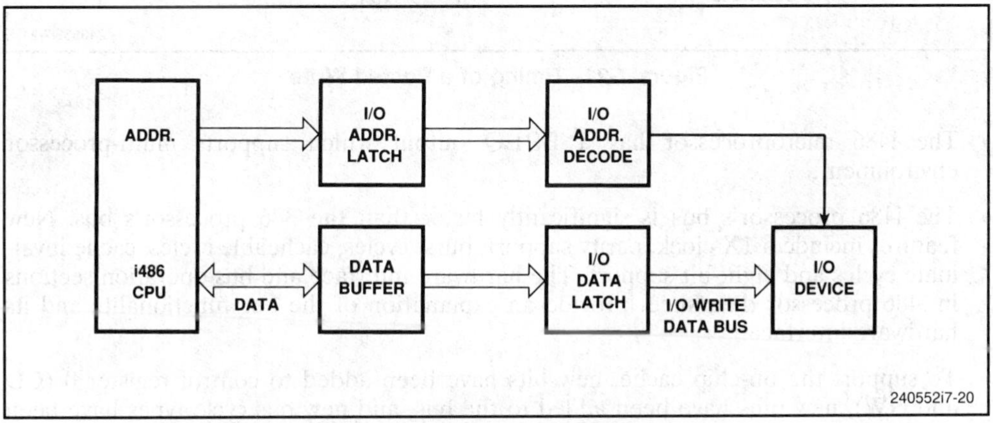

Figure 7-20. Posted Write Circuit

7.4 DIFFERENCE BETWEEN i486 AND 386 MICROPROCESSORS

The i486 microprocessor is integrated chip which is comprised of a CPU, a math coprocessor and a cache controller. It is fully compatible with its predecessor, the 386 DX microprocessor, yet has the following differences:

- i486 microprocessor offers dynamic bus sizing to supports 8, 16 and 32-bit bus sizes and requires external swapping logic. The 386 DX microprocessor supports only 16-bit and 32-bit bus sizes and does not require swapping logic.
- The i486 microprocessor has a burst transfer mode which can transfer four 32-bit words from external memory to the on-chip cache using only five clock cycles. The 386 DX microprocessor requires at least eight clock cycles to transfer the same amount of data.

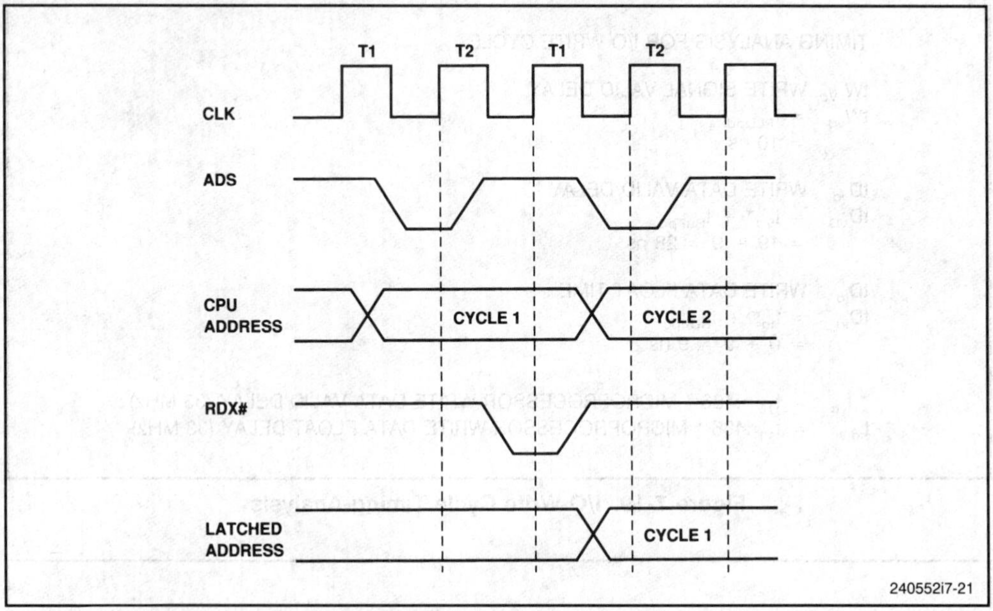

Figure 7-21. Timing of a Posted Write

- The i486 microprocessor has a BREQ output which supports multi-processor environment.
- The i486 processor's bus is significantly faster than the 386 processor's bus. New features include a 1X clock, parity support, burst cycles, cacheable cycles, cache invalidate cycles and eight-bit support. The hardware interface and bus operation sections in i486 processor data sheet provide an explanation of the bus functionality and its hardware interface.
- To support the on-chip cache, new bits have been added to control register 0 (CD and NW), new pins have been added to the bus, and new bus cycle types have been added. The on-chip cache must be enabled after reset by clearing the CD and NW bit in CRO.
- The complete 387™ math coprocessor instruction set and register set have been added. No I/O cycles are performed during floating-point instruction execution. The instruction and data pointers are set to zero after FINIT/FSAVE. Interrupt 9 cannot occur, and interrupt 13 occurs instead.
- The i486 microprocessor supports new floating-point error reporting modes to ensure DOS compatibility. These new modes require a new bit in control register 0 (NE) (see Section 2.1.2.1 of the i486 processor data sheet) as well as new pins (FERR# and IGNNE# see Section 6.2.13 and 7.2.14 of the i486 processor data sheet).
- Six new instructions have been added: Byte Swap (BSWAP), Exchange and Add (XADD), Compare and Exchange (CMPXCHG), Invalidate data cache (INVD), Write-back and Invalidate data Cache (WBINVD) and Invalidate TLB Entry (INVLPG).

- Two new bits are defined in control register 3 for page table entries and page directory entries (PCD and PWT see Section 4.5.2.5. of the i486 processor data sheet).
- A new page protection feature has been added, requiring a new bit in control register 0 (WP—see Section 2.1.2.1 and 4.5.3 of the i486 processor data sheet).
- A new alignment check feature has been added, requiring a new bit in the flags register (AC—see Section 2.1.1.3 of the i486 processor data sheet) and a new bit in the control register 0 (AM—see Section 2.1.2.1 of the i486 processor data sheet).
- The replacement algorithm for the translation lookaside buffer (TLB) is a psuedo-least-recently-used algorithm like the one used in the on-chip cache (see Section 5.5 of the i486 processor data sheet for a description of the algorithm).
- Three new testability registers TR5, TR6 and TR7 have been added for testing of the on-chip cache. TLB testability has been enhanced (see Section 8 in the i486 processor data sheet).
- The prefetch queue has been increased from 16 bytes to 32 bytes. A jump must always execute after code modification to ensure proper execution of the new instruction.
- After reset, the ID in the upper byte of the DX register is 04. The contents of the base register, including the floating-point registers, may be different after reset.

7.5 INTERFACING TO X86 PERIPHERALS

This section discusses the i486 processor interface to two peripheral devices from the X86 family, the two being the 8041, and the 8259A. Not all systems use these separate devices, however the examples explain in detail many of the issues surrounding slave I/O and interrupts.

7.5.1 8042 Interface

The 8041 and 8042 are universal peripheral interface (UPI) devices which allow customized solutions for peripheral device control. These microcontrollers have a slave interface on board and include an eight-bit CPU, ROM, RAM, an I/O timer/counter and a clock. Intel also supplies an EPROM implementation, comprised of the 8741 and 8742. The 8742 has a 2Kx8 ROM and 256Kx8 RAM, an eight-bit timer/counter and 18 programmable I/O pins. It also has an eight-bit status register and two data registers for asynchronous slave-to-master interfacing. The 8742 supports DMA, Interrupt and Polled operations.

The 32-bit i486 microprocessor requires 32-to-8-bit byte-steering logic to interface to the eight-bit 8042 as shown in Figure 7-22. In this implementation, the bus controller logic generates the BS8# signals.

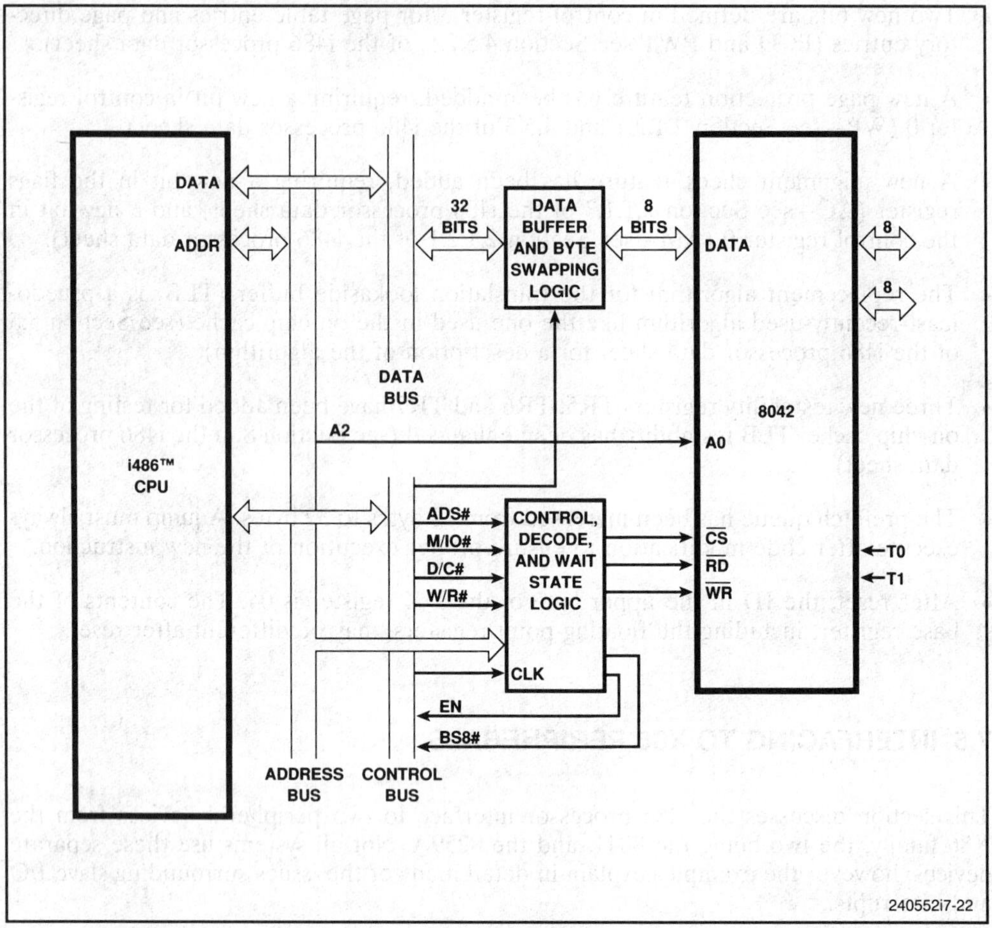

Figure 7-22. 8042 Interface to i486™ Microprocessor

7.5.2 82C59A Interface

The following discussion of interrupt-driven microprocessor environments is a helpful preface to the section on interfacing i486 microcomputer systems to the 82C59A programmable interrupt controller. It also provides a context to review other interrupt controller implementations.

In a microcomputer system, the CPU must service I/O devices such as key-boards and displays efficiently to minimize overhead. One technique is polling, in which the microprocessor tests each device in sequence to determine whether servicing is needed. Unfortunately a large portion of the main program must be devoted to polling, at a cost of system throughput.

Interrupts provide more efficient and desirable alternative for servicing I/O devices. Here a hardware signal can cause the main program to change its execution path. These interrupts are acknowledged only between instructions—with the exception of the bus error signal. The i486 microprocessor reacts to interrupts by saving the program address and then performing special interrupt processing (as explained in the i486 microprocessor data sheet). Once the current program address and flags are saved on a stack, the i486 processor receives an eight-bit vector which identifies an entry in the interrupt table which contains the starting address of the interrupt service routine. The vector interrupt allows a hardware mechanism to select a separate service routine for each interrupt source. Once the interrupt service routine is executed, the previous processor state is restored, and proper program execution resumes. The i486 microprocessor can handle up to 256 interrupts/exceptions. To service these interrupts a table with 256 different interrupt is given in i486 microprocessor data sheet.

The interrupt-driven environment increases system throughput and allows more tasks to be accomplished by the microprocessor, thus increasing overall cost-effectiveness.

The 82C59A is a high performance CMOS programmable interrupt controller which manages the interrupt-driven i486 processor system environment. It accepts requests from peripheral devices and determines device priorities. The 82C59A provides the processor with an eight-bit vector interrupt. The interrupt points to an address in the vector table, and the processor's INTA# signal (generated by the bus controller logic) enables the vector data on the data bus.

Individual 82C59A devices can be cascaded to accommodate up to 64 interrupts, and later sections discuss how to implement such configurations. Intel application note AP-59 details 82C59A configurations.

7.5.2.1 SINGLE INTERRUPT CONTROLLER

Figure 7-23 shows a basic I/O interface between the i486 processor and a single 82C59A device. The address decoder generates the chip select (CS#) signal while the bus control ready logic generates the interrupt acknowledge (INTA#), write (WR#) and read (RD#) signals. In this example, the 82C59A is used in the master mode since the SP/EN# pin is high. The A0 address pin is used to decipher various processor command words and to determine the status that the processor wishes to read. The A0 pin is connected to the processor's A2 pin and is also used to distinguish between two consecutive interrupt acknowledge cycles. The 82C59A register address must therefore be located at two consecutive doubleword boundaries.

An interrupt activates the Interrupt output of the 82C59A which is connected to the INTR input (Interrupt request) of the i486 microprocessor. The processor automatically performs two consecutive interrupt acknowledge cycles. The 82C59A device's timings are as follows:

- Each interrupt acknowledge cycle must be extended by at least one wait-state which is implemented by the wait-state generator logic described in Section 7.2.
- Four idle cycles must be inserted between two interrupt acknowledge cycles.

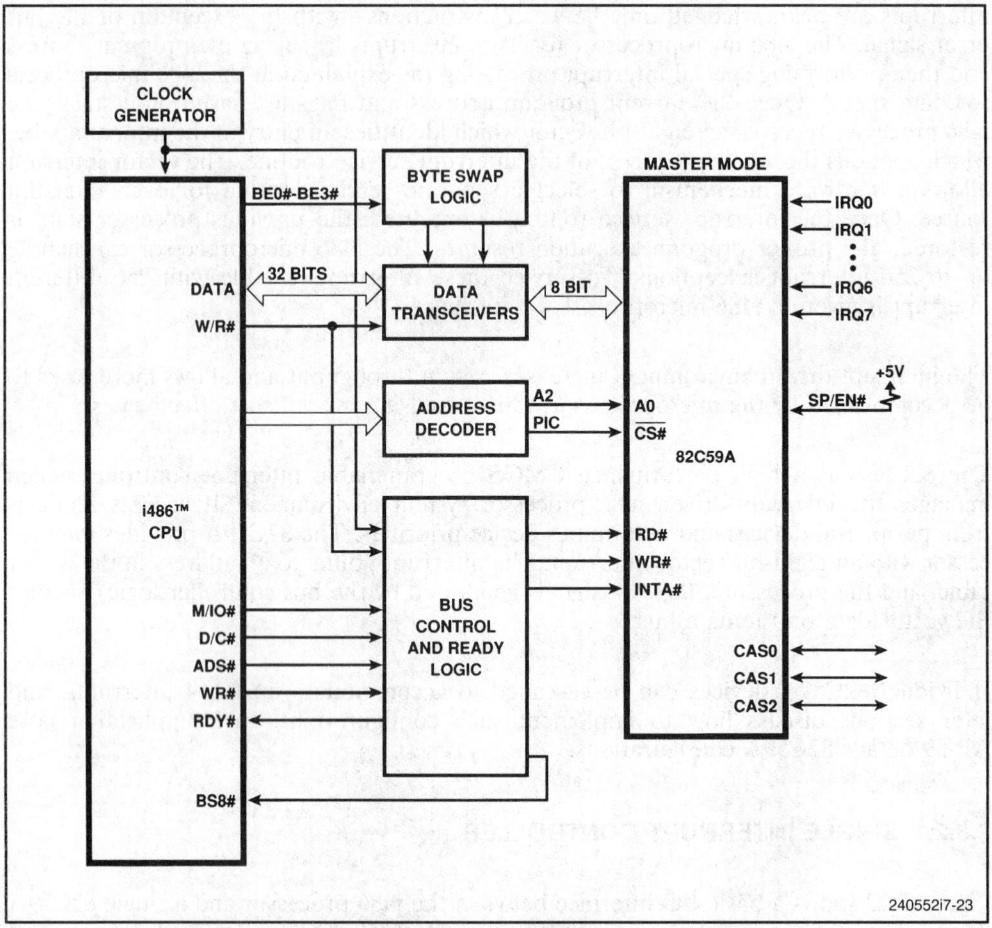

Figure 7-23. i486™ Microprocessor Interface to the 82C59A

7.5.2.2 CASCADED INTERRUPT CONTROLLERS

Figure 7-24 shows how several interrupt controllers can be cascaded to handle up to 64 interrupt requests. Here, one device acts as the master and the rest as slaves. The interface between these devices resembles the single device interface with the following addition of features:

- The cascaded address outputs are used to provide address and chip select signals for the slave controllers.
- The interrupt request lines (IR7–IR0) of the master controller are connected to the INT outputs of the slave devices.

The function of each slave controller is to identify the priorities among eight interrupt requests and generate a single interrupt request for the master controller. The master controller must identify the priorities among eight slave controllers and transmits a single interrupt request to the i486 microprocessor.

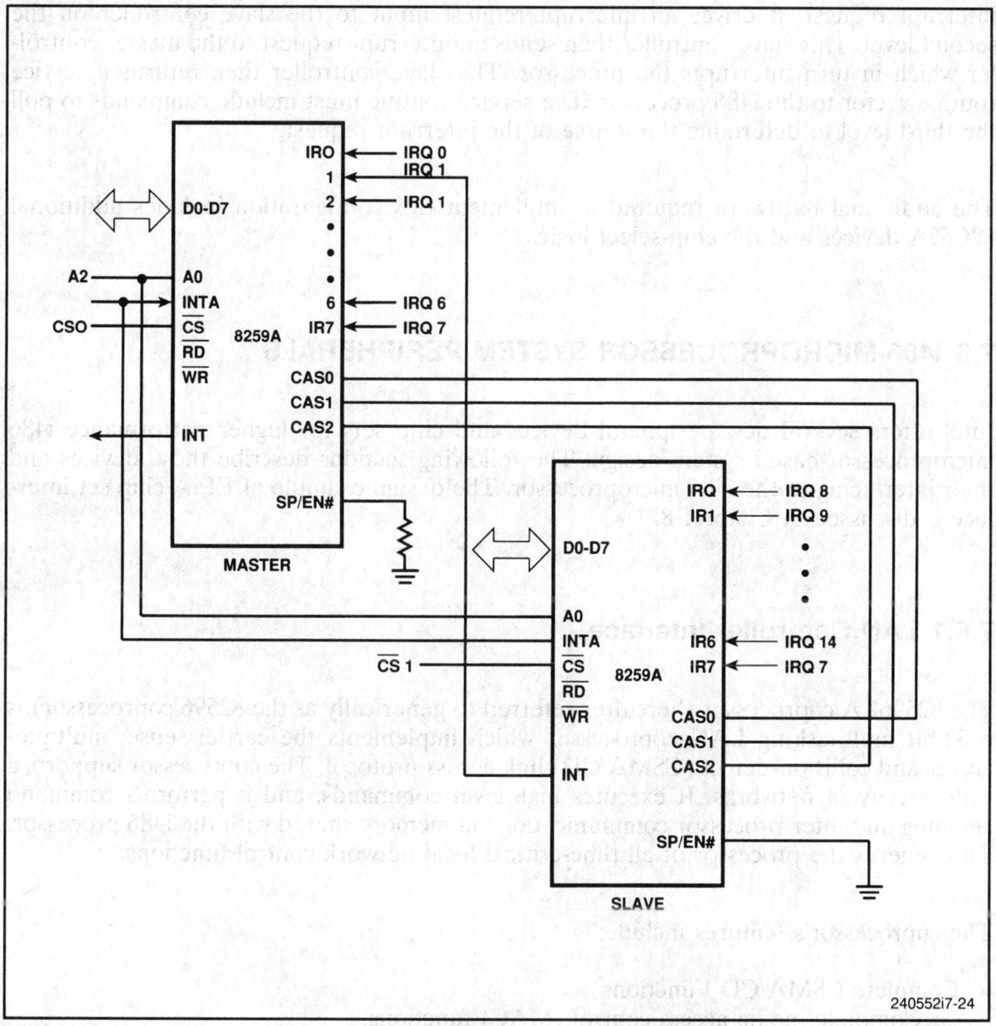

Figure 7-24. Cascaded Interrupt Controller

The timing interface resembles that used for single devices. During the first interrupt acknowledge cycle, all the 82C59As devices freeze the states of their interrupt request inputs. The master controller outputs the cascaded address to select the slave controller that is generating the request with the highest priority. During the second interrupt-acknowledge cycle, the selected slave controller outputs an interrupt vector to the i486 microprocessor.

7.5.2.3 HANDLING MORE THAN 64 INTERRUPTS

If an i486 microprocessor-based system requires more than 64 interrupt request lines, a third 82C59A device level in polled mode is added to the configuration shown in Figure 7-23. Here, once the third level receives an Interrupt Controller receives an interrupt request, it drives an interrupt request input to the slave controller on the second level. This slave controller then sends an interrupt request to the master controller which in turn interrupts the processor. The slave controller then returns a service routine vector to the i486 processor. The service routine must include commands to poll the third level to determine the source of the interrupt request.

The additional hardware required to implement this configuration includes additional 82C59A devices and the chip-select logic.

7.6 i486 MICROPROCESSOR SYSTEM PERIPHERALS

Intel offers several new peripheral devices and chip sets for higher performance i486 microprocessor-based system design. The following sections describe these devices and their interfacing to the i486 microprocessor. The design example of EISA chip set interface is discussed in Chapter 8.

7.6.1 LAN Controller Interface

The 82596CA coprocessor (hereafter referred to generically as the 82596 coprocessor) is a 32-bit multitasking LAN coprocessor which implements the carrier-sense, multiple-access and collision-detect (CSMA/CD) link access protocol. The coprocessor supports a wide variety of networks. It executes high-level commands, and it performs command chaining and inter-processor communication via memory shared with the i486 processor. This relieves the processor of all time-critical local-network control functions.

The coprocessor's features include:

- Complete CSMA/CD Functions
  - Complete media access control (MAC) functions.
  - High-level command interface.
  - Manchester encoding or NRZ encoding and decoding.
  - IEEE 802.3 or CCITT HDLC frame delimiting.
- Industry-Standard Network Support
  - IEEE 802.3 (Ethernet, Ethernet Twisted Pair, Cheapernet, StarLAN, etc.).
  - IBM PC Network (baseband and broadband).
  - Proprietary CSMA/CD networks up to 20 Mbits/second.
  - HDLC frame delimiting.
- Compatible i486 Processor Interface
  - Optimized interface to the i486 processor bus.
  - Shared i486 processor bus signals and memory timing.
  - Support for i486 processor byte ordering.

- Architectual Features
  - On-chip DMA.
  - Bus Throttle.
  - 128-byte receive FIFO, 64-byte transmit FIFO.
  - On-chip memory management.
  - Network management and diagnostics.
  - 82586 software-compatible mode.

- Performance Features
  - 9.6 msec interframe spacing for back-to-back frame transmission and reception.
  - 80/106 Mbytes/second bus transfer rate (burst) at 25/33 MHz.
  - 50/66 Mbytes/second bus transfer rate (non-burst) at 25/33 MHz.

Figure 7-25 is a block diagram of the 82596 coprocessor. A serial subsystem interfaces to the physical-layer device for the network. This subsystem performs CSMA/CD media-access-control and channel-interface functions. It supports the the full set of IEEE 802.3

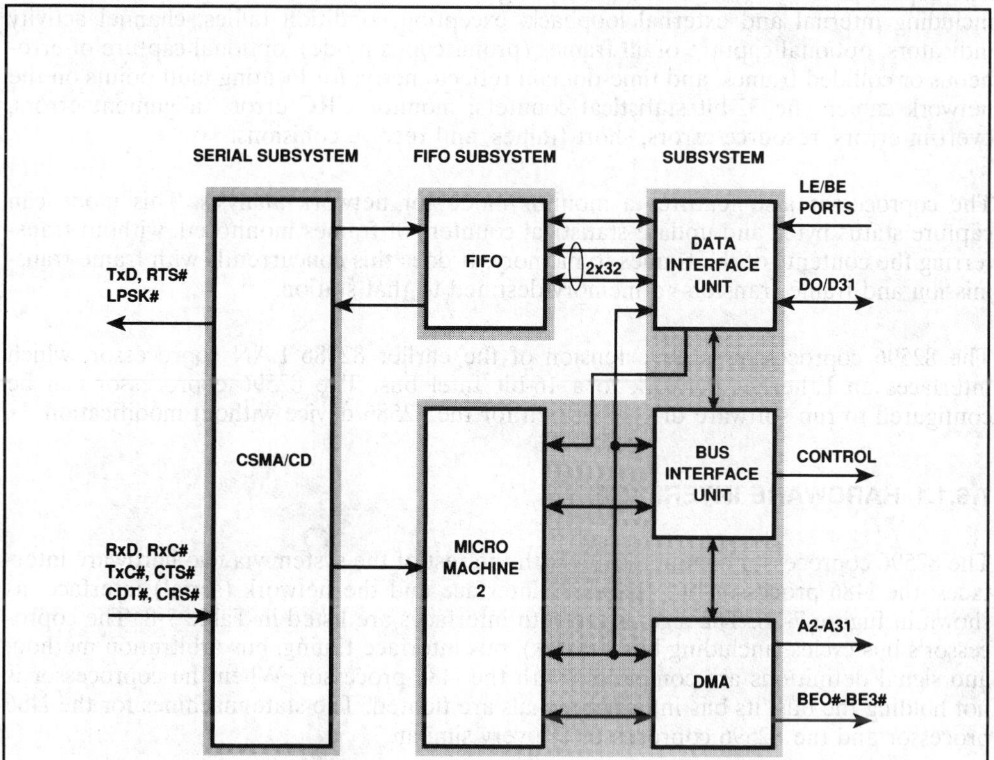

Figure 7-25. 8259CA Coprocessor Block Diagram

and other industry-standard and proprietary network functions. A parallel subsystem interfaces to the i486 processor. This subsystem contains a data interface unit, a bus interface unit, a 4-channel DMA unit, and a micro-machine command processor. A FIFO subsystem connects the serial and parallel subsystems, allowing them to run asynchronously to one another through a 128-byte receive FIFO and a 64-byte transmit FIFO.

The coprocessor can be used in either baseband or broadband networks. It can be configured for maximum network efficiency (minimum contention overhead) for networks of any physical cable length operating at any data rate up to 20 Mbits/second. It features a highly flexible CSMA/CD unit, supporting address lengths from zero to six bytes. It supports 16- or 32-bit CRC. The CRC field can optionally be transferred directly to memory on receive and dynamically inserted on transmit. The CSMA/CD unit can also be configured for full duplex operation or for CSMA/DCR (deterministic collision resolution).

The coprocessor provides a rich set of diagnostic and network management functions, including internal and external loopback, exception condition tallies, channel activity indicators, optional capture of all frames (promiscuous mode), optional capture of erroneous or collided frames, and time-domain reflectometry; for locating fault points on the network cable. The 32-bit statistical counters; monitor CRC errors, alignment errors, overrun errors, resource errors, short frames, and receive collisions.

The coprocessor also features a monitor mode for network analysis. This mode can capture status bytes and update statistical counters of frames monitored, without transferring the contents of the frames to memory. It does this concurrently with frame transmission and frame transfers to memory destined to that station.

The 82596 coprocessor is an extension of the earlier 82586 LAN coprocessor, which interfaces an Ethernet network to a 16-bit Intel bus. The 82596 coprocessor can be configured to run software drivers written for the 82586 device without modification.

7.6.1.1 HARDWARE INTERFACE

The 82596 coprocessor communicates with the rest of the system via two hardware interfaces: the i486 processor bus (parallel) interface and the network (serial) interface, as shown in Figure 7-26. The signals for both interfaces are listed in Table 7-8. The coprocessor's bus cycles (including burst cycles), bus interface timing, bus arbitration method, and signal definitions are compatible with the i486 processor. When the coprocessor is not holding the bus, its bus interface signals are floated. The state machines for the i486 processor and the 82596 coprocessor are very similar.

These similarities between the i486 processor and the 82596 coprocessor simplify bus arbitration when the processor and the coprocessor are the only two bus masters on the processor bus. The HOLD and HLDA signals can be used for handshake arbitration and BREQ from the processor can trigger the coprocessor's bus throttle timers when needed, as shown in Figure 7-27.

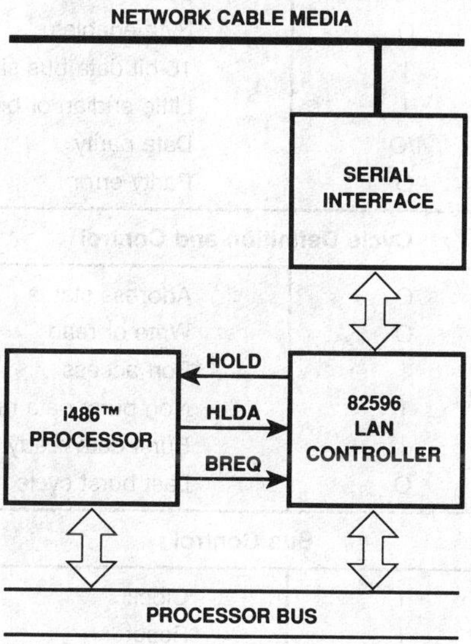

Figure 7-26. 82596CA Application Example

Access to memory and I/O resources can be overlapped between the processor and the coprocessor with the bus backoff (BOFF#) output to the processor. The BOFF# overlapping method avoids the need for a time-consuming bus hold arbitration (HOLD and HLDA) and it is done without the risk of deadlock.

The coprocessor signals have the same significance as on the i486 processor bus, except for the AHOLD signal. Because there is no internal cache to invalidate on the coprocessor, this input is used to release the coprocessor address bus when an external cache controller needs to perform a cache invalidation cycle.

7.6.1.2 PROCESSOR AND COPROCESSOR INTERACTION

The 82596 coprocessor interacts with the processor bus as either a bus master or a slave (port access mode). In normal operation, it is a bus master which moves data between

Table 7-8. 82596 Signals

Signal	Type	Description
Address and Data Buses		
A2-A31	O	Address
D0-D31	I/O	Data
BE0#–BE3#	O	Byte-enables
BS16#	I	16-bit data bus size
LE/BE#	I	Little endian or big endian byte ordering
DP0–DP3	I/O	Data parity
PCHK#	O	Parity error
Cycle Definition and Control		
ADS#	O	Address status
W/R#	O	Write or read
PORT#	I	*Port access
RDY#	I	Non-burst data ready
BRDY#	I	Burst data ready
BLAST#	O	Last burst cycle
Bus Control		
CLK	I	Clock
RESET	I	*Reset
INT/INT#	O	Interrupt
BREQ	I	Bus request
HOLD	O	Bus hold request
HLDA	I	Bus hold acknowledgement
AHOLD	I	*Address hold request
BOFF#	I	Bus backoff
LOCK#	O	Bus lock
CA	I	*Channel Attention
Network (Serial) Interface		
TxD	O	*Transmit data
TxC#	O	*Transmit clock
LPBK#	O	*Loopback
RxD	I	*Receive data
RxC#	I	*Receive clock
RTS#	O	*Request to send
CTS#	I	*Clear to send
CRS#	I	*Carrier sense
CDT#	I	*Collision detect

*Signals marked with an asterisk are not included on, or operate differently than, the i486™ processor bus.

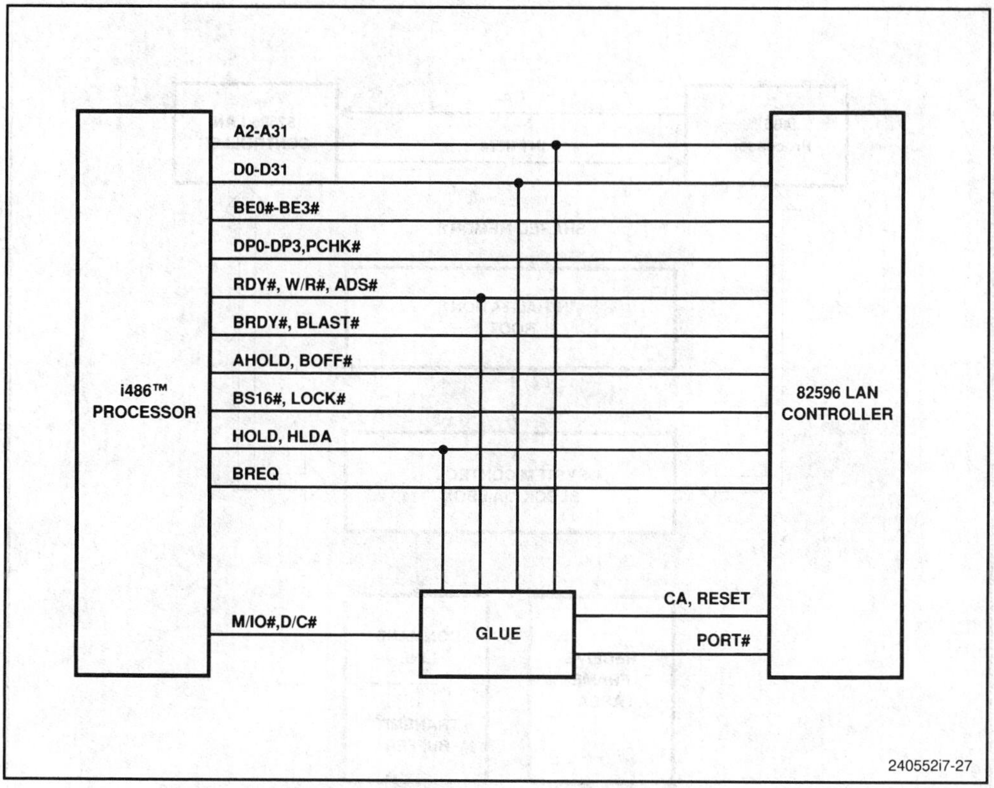

Figure 7-27. 82596-to-Processor Interfacing

the system memory and the coprocessor's control registers or internal FIFOs. The coprocessor can use the same burst cycles, bus hold, address hold, bus backoff, and bus lock operations that the i486 processor uses.

The coprocessor and the processor communicate through shared memory, as shown in Figure 7-28. The processor and the coprocessor normally use the interrupt (INT/INT#) and channel attention (CA) signals to initiate communication, using a system control block of memory for command and status storage. INT/INT# alerts the processor to a change of contents in the system control block. By asserting CA, the processor causes the coprocessor to examine the system control block contents for the change.

The coprocessor executes its command list from shared memory and, in parallel, receives frames from the network and places them in shared memory. The processor manages the shared memory, which contains command chains and bidirectional data chains. The coprocessor executes the command chains. An on-chip DMA controls four channels, which allow autonomous transfers of data blocks independently of the processor. Buffers containing erroneous or collided frames can be automatically recovered without processor intervention. The processor becomes involved only after a command sequence has finished executing, or after a sequence of frames has been received and stored, ready for processing.

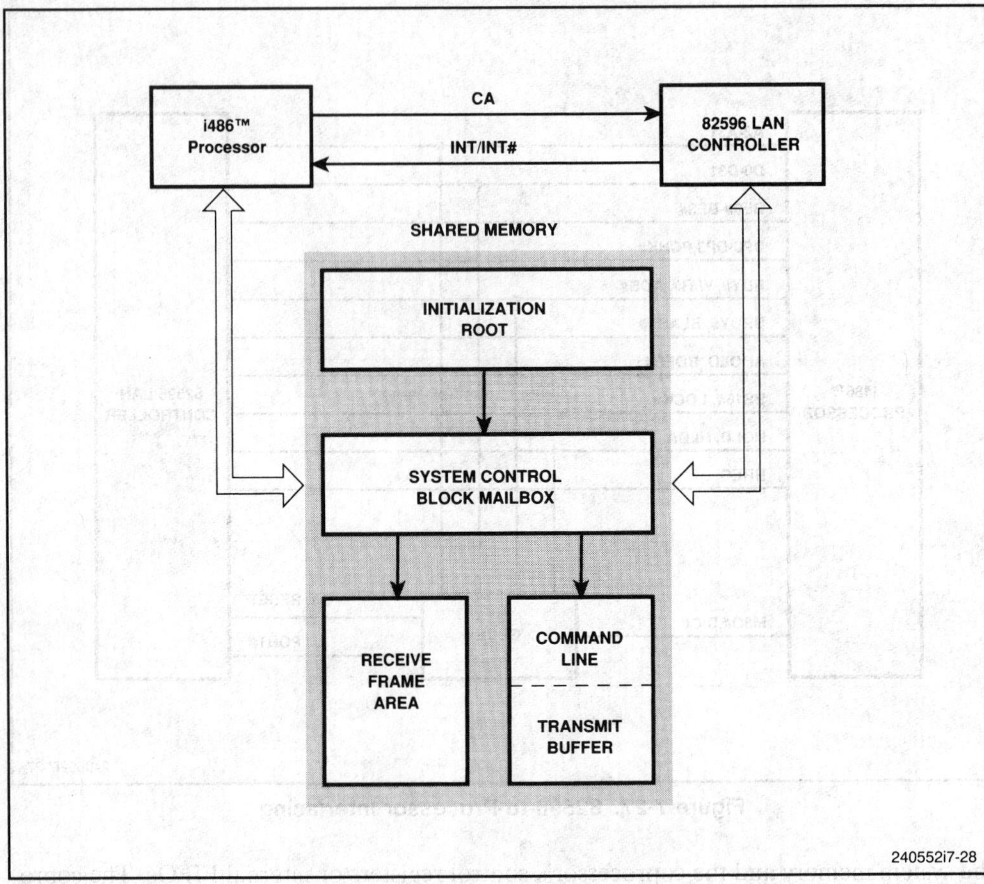

Figure 7-28. 82596 Shared Memory

In addition to this normal operating mode, the processor can initiate a port access in the coprocessor. This mode may be entered whenever the coprocessor is not actively driving the bus. It allows the processor to write an alternate system configuration pointer, write an alternate dump command and pointer (used for troubleshooting a no-response problem), perform a software reset, or perform a self-test.

7.6.1.3 MEMORY STRUCTURE

The memory shared by the processor and coprocessor consists of four parts.

- Initialization root.
- System control block.
- Command list (including transmit buffer).
- Receive frame area.

The command list functions as a program. Individual commands are placed in blocks of memory called command blocks. These command blocks contain the parameters and status of high-level commands used by the processor to control the operation of the coprocessor.

One of three memory addressing modes can be used:

- 82586 Mode: Uses 24-bit addresses with all shared memory structures residing in one 64-Kbyte segment.
- 32-bit Segmented Mode: Uses 32-bit addresses with all shared memory structures residing in one 64-Kbyte segment.
- Linear Mode: Uses 32-bit addresses with no restrictions on the placement of any shared memory structure.

Big-endian and little-endian byte ordering schemes are supported. For compatibility with the i486 processor, the little-endian scheme should be used.

7.6.1.4 MEDIA ACCESS

The 82596 coprocessor accesses the cable-media network through the serial subsystem. This subsystem performs the full set of IEEE 802.3 CSMA/CD media access control (MAC) sublayer and channel interface functions, including framing, preamble generation and stripping, source address generation, destination address checking, short-frame (runt packet) detection, and automatic-length field handling. Data rates up to 20 Mbits/second on the cable media are supported. IEEE 802.3 and HDLC CRC generation and checking is supported.

The following media access methods are supported:

- CSMA/CD
- Deterministic collision resolution
- Full duplex

The following IEEE standards are supported:

- 1BASE5
- 10BASE5
- 10BASE2
- 10BROAD36
- Proposed 10BASE-F
- Proposed 10BASE-T

7.6.1.5 TRANSMIT AND RECEIVE OPERATION

Most of the bus traffic initiated by the coprocessor consists of DMA transfers of frame data. The coprocessor transmits data as a series of frames by executing a series of high-level commands from the command list in memory. These commands are fetched by the coprocessor and executed in parallel with processor operations. A single transmit command contains all the information necessary to prepare and execute the transmission of one or more data frames.

The data consists of a buffer descriptor and a data buffer containing the actual data. These may also be chained into a linked list of buffer descriptors and associated data buffers. A frame with a long data field can therefore be transmitted using several shorter buffers chained together. This is useful when assembling frames which include nested headers generated by independent software modules.

In order for the coprocessor to receive frames, the processor must first dedicate an area of memory as a receive buffer space and enable the coprocessor for reception. Frames arrive at the coprocessor network interface unsolicited. The coprocessor must always be prepared to store them in an buffer area of memory known as the free frame area. The receive frame area is a list of free frame descriptors and a list of user-prepared buffers. The coprocessor fills the buffers as frames are received, and it reformats the free buffer list into received frame structures. The frame structure stored is the same as that for frames to be transmitted. The data contained in the buffers is transferred by means of the on-chip DMA controller. This allows bidirectional, autonomous transfer of data blocks partitioned as buffers or chained into frames. Buffers which contain errors are recovered automatically without processor intervention.

The coprocessor monitors the frames presented on the serial interface for a destination address which corresponds to its own unique address, one or more multicast addresses, or the broadcast address. When a match is found, the frame's destination, source addresses, and length field are stored, and the data field is placed in the next available buffer. As one buffer is filled, the device automatically links the next available buffer until the entire frame is stored. This technique accommodates buffer sizes which are much shorter than the maximum permitted frame length.

When a frame has been received without error, several housekeeping tasks are performed by the coprocessor. If a frame error occurs, the coprocessor re-initializes the DMA pointers and reclaims any buffers to which the frame had been allocated.

7.6.1.6 BUS THROTTLE TIMERS

The coprocessor's use of the processor bus is regulated with the coprocessor's bus throttle timer logic. These timers are independently programmed and can be triggered internally or externally. The operation of the timers is shown in Figure 7-29. Two timers are associated with the bus throttle function:

- TON Timer: Defines the maximum time the coprocessor can remain bus master.
- TOFF Timer: Defines the minimum time the coprocessor must wait before re-asserting the HOLD output to request the bus again.

If the timers are configured to be triggered internally, the coprocessor monitors the length of time that the HLDA input is held asserted. When this time exceeds the time programmed in the TON timer, the coprocessor relinquishes the bus by de-asserting HOLD; and starts the TOFF timer.

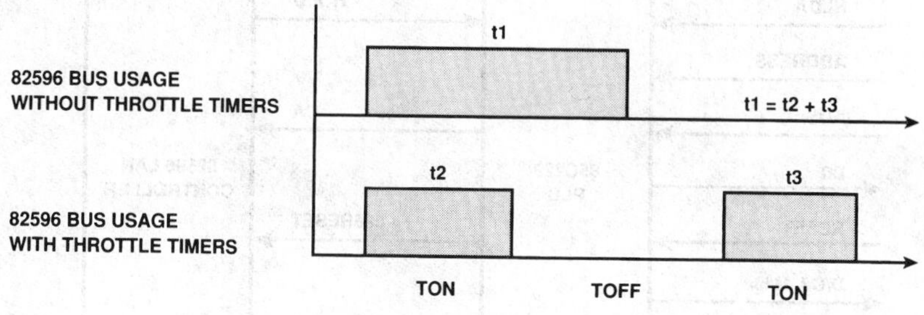

Figure 7-29. Bus Throttle Timers

If the timers are configured externally, assertion of the BREQ; input causes the coprocessor to start the TON timer. Upon timeout, the coprocessor relinquishes the bus and starts the TOFF timer. This latter configuration is particularly useful in the i486 processor environment, where the processor's BREQ output can be tied directly to the coprocessor's BREQ input.

7.6.1.7 DESIGN CONSIDERATIONS

The glue logic for interfacing the 82596 coprocessor to the i486 processor can be contained in a single Intel 85C220 PLD, as shown in Figure 7-30. This logic provides four functions:

- Generate channel attention (CA) input to the coprocessor.
- Generate reset (RESET) input to the coprocessor.
- Generate processor port access (PORT#) input to the coprocessor.
- Drive the M/IO# and D/C# processor bus signals when the coprocessor is bus master.

The coprocessor's RESET input is referred to in Figure 7-30 and the text below as "596RESET" to distinguish it from the processor's RESET.

To assert the CA or 596RESET signals, the processor drives a memory-mapped I/O cycle. During such a cycle, address decode is done while monitoring CLK, ADS#, HLDA, and D0 to distinguish CA from 596RESET. A similar memory-mapped cycle is

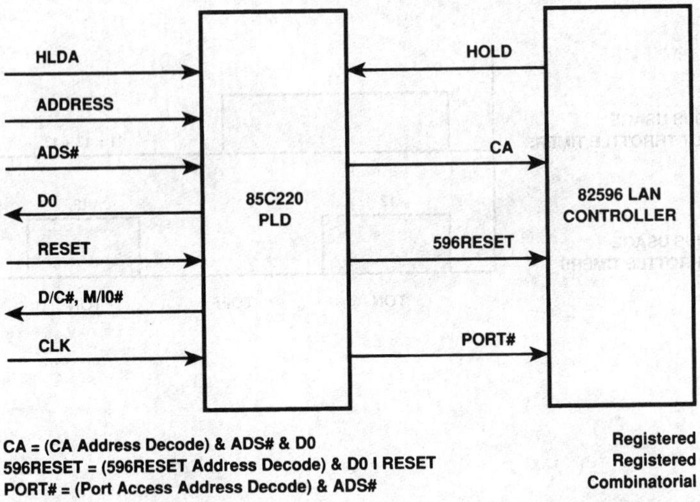

Figure 7-30. 596RESET, CA, and PORT# Equations

used to de-assert the signal. The HLDA input to the 85C220 PLD gates the logic, so that CA or 596RESET is generated only when HLDA is de-asserted (i.e., when the coprocessor is not bus master).

The PORT# input to the coprocessor can be generated by combinatorial logic which has an address decode qualified by ADS# and CLK. This asserts the PORT# output for one clock. While PORT# is asserted, the coprocessor will treat the data bus as containing slave control information. System software must ensure that the coprocessor is idle while the processor executes a port access. This guarantees that the coprocessor will not attempt to acquire the bus by asserting HOLD. Failure to comply with this restriction may result in the coprocessor entering an undefined state.

The CA, 596RESET, and PORT# signals are generated according to the equations shown in Figure 7-30. The M/IO# and D/C# signals are also generated by the glue logic. When both HOLD and HLDA are asserted, indicating that the coprocessor has requested and been granted the bus, M/IO# and D/C# must be driven high.

Caching of the coprocessor memory structures in the i486 internal cache may be disadvantageous, because these memory structures are not directly executable by the processor. Typically, most coprocessor bus activity consists of receiving and transmitting frames, managing the receive frame area, and prefetching descriptor pointers. The system control block is typically accessed only once by the processor for every update of this area made by the coprocessor. The processor gains no advantage from caching locations which are used only once. Also, each time a cached memory location is written to by the coprocessor, a cache invalidation cycle must be performed.

For systems in which caching is obligatory, external logic must monitor ADS# and W/R# and to drive the EADS# cache invalidation input to the processor.

7.6.1.8 PERFORMANCE

With a 25-MHz clock, the 82596 coprocessor can transfer data at up to 80 Mbytes/second in burst cycles, or 50 Mbytes/second in non-burst cycles. With a 33-MHz clock, the rates are 106 Mbytes/second for burst and 66 Mbytes/second for non-burst. Most transfers in a i486 processor environment can be in the burst mode. Ethernet provides data at a maximum instantaneous rate of 1.25 Mbytes/second. The coprocessor, however, requires approximately 0.25 Mbytes/second additional bandwidth for frame processing, updating various command blocks and descriptors. This brings the maximum bus bandwidth requirement to approximately 1.5 Mbytes/second. The coprocessor therefore requires only a small fraction of the available processor bus bandwidth.

Several variables affect the total bandwidth required. The main factors are:

- Use of burst cycles for memory transfers.
- Number of memory wait states per transfer.
- Processor bus clock (CLK) frequency.
- Frame and buffer size.

Table 7-9 compares the percentage of 32-bit bus bandwidth used under some of these conditions. These are worst-case numbers and over-estimate typical network loading. Typical bus utilization numbers at non-peak rates will be lower.

Table 7-9. 82596 Bus Bandwidth Utilization

Bus Frequency	Frame Size	Burst (0 ws)	Non-Burst (0 ws)	Non-Burst (1 ws)
25 MHz	64 bytes	3.33%	4.05%	5.65%
	1,518 bytes	1.70%	2.63%	3.90%
33 MHz	64 bytes	2.52%	3.07%	4.29%
	1,518 bytes	1.29%	1.99%	2.95%

7.6.2 Extended Industry Standard Architecture (EISA) Peripherals (82350)

The Extended Industry Standard Architecture (EISA) is a superset of the functionality and performance provided by ISA (PC/AT-compatible) systems. Intel's 82350-family of peripherals interfaces the i486 processor to an EISA bus. The chip set includes three motherboard peripherals (one of which is used in triplicate) and one peripheral for EISA-bus expansion boards:

Motherboard peripherals:

- EISA Bus Controller (EBC) 82358
- Integrated System Peripheral (ISP) 82357
- EISA Bus Buffer (EBB) 82352 (three required)

EISA-bus peripherals:

- Bus Master Interface Controller (BMIC) 82355

Figure 7-31 shows a general system diagram. The EISA standard maintains full compatibility with the existing ISA standard (also known as the AT standard). The EISA expansion board connector is a superset of the ISA expansion board connector. This allows existing 8- and 16-bit ISA boards to be installed in EISA slots.

7.6.2.1 EISA BUS CONTROLLER (EBC)

The 82358 EISA bus controller (EBC) sits between the processor bus and the 8-MHz EISA bus. It performs functions common to all peripherals connected to the bus, including:

- Cycle translation, including translations among processor, EISA, and ISA cycles.
- Data-buffer control and byte-swap logic.
- Processor-bus arbitration.
- Data assembly for mismatched cycles.

The bus controller is tightly coupled with the EISA integrated system peripheral (ISP), described in the next section. The bus controller handles address and data buffers between buses and inserts delays between back-to-back I/O cycles from the processor bus to the EISA bus. The controller also subdivides bus cycles, so that transfers between buses of varying sizes or transfers with misaligned addresses can be performed correctly. Data byte swap logic and address buffer control signals are generated directly from the bus controller.

The EISA bus controller generates both EISA and ISA bus control signals. Most of the processor bus control signals connect directly to the EBC for translation of i486 processor bus cycles to EISA or ISA bus cycles.

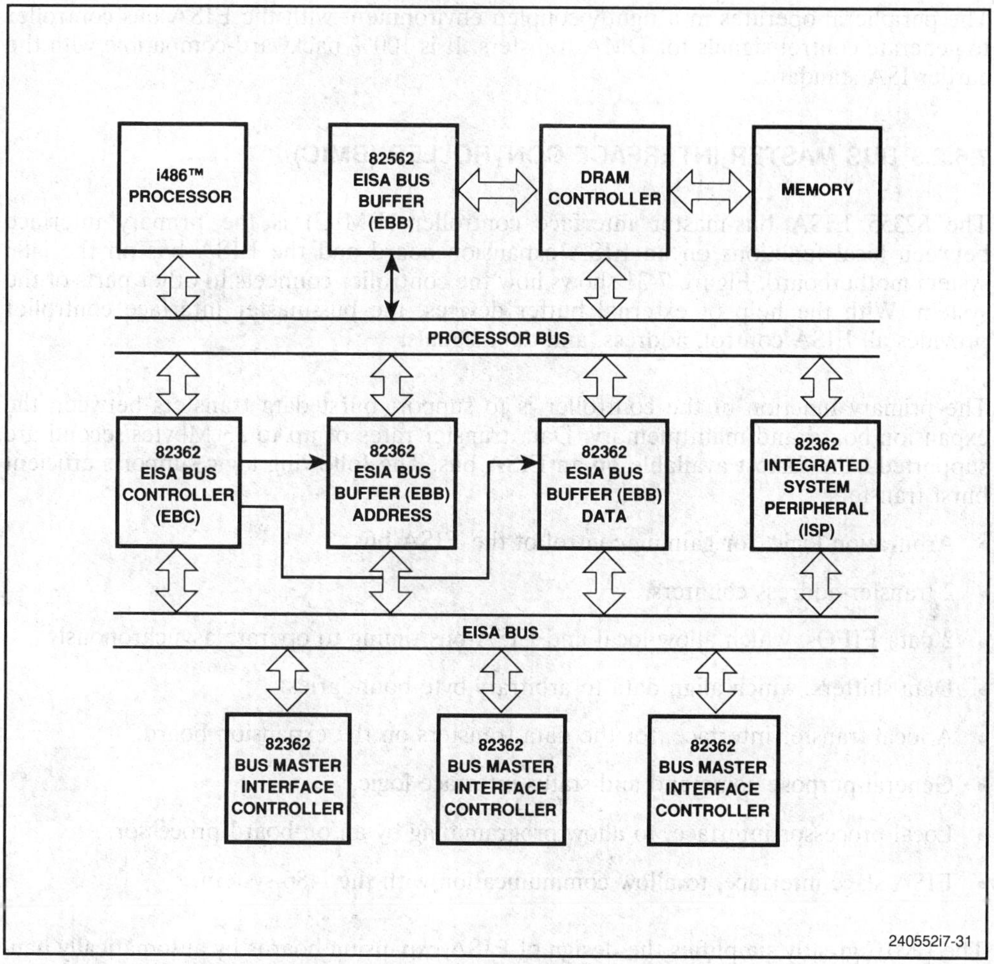

Figure 7-31. EISA System Diagram

7.6.2.2 INTEGRATED SYSTEM PERIPHERAL (ISP)

The 82357 EISA integrated system peripheral (ISP) contains most of the EISA-specific peripheral functions, including:

- 32-bit, seven-channel programmable DMA controller.
- EISA bus arbiter.
- 2 eight-channel, 15-level programmable interrupt controllers.
- Non-maskable interrupt logic for multiple NMI control and generation.
- 5 counter/timers.
- DRAM refresh address generation and control.

The peripheral operates in a tightly coupled environment with the EISA bus controller to generate control signals for DMA transfers. It is 100% backward-compatible with the earlier ISA standard.

7.6.2.3 BUS MASTER INTERFACE CONTROLLER (BMIC)

The 82355 EISA bus-master interface controller (BMIC) is the primary interface between local functions on an EISA expansion board and the EISA bus on the i486 system motherboard. Figure 7-31 shows how the controller connects to other parts of the system. With the help of external buffer devices, the bus-master interface controller provides all EISA control, address, and data signals.

The primary function of the controller is to support burst data transfers between the expansion board and main memory. Data transfer rates of up to 33 Mbytes/second are supported—the fastest available on an EISA bus. The following logic supports efficient burst transfers:

- Arbitration logic, for gaining control of the EISA bus.
- 2 transfer-address counters.
- 2 data FIFOs, which allow local and EISA bus timing to operate asynchronously.
- Data shifters, which align data to arbitrary byte boundaries.
- A local transfer interface, for the data transfers on the expansion board.
- General-purpose command and status interface logic.
- Local processor interface, to allow programming by an on-board processor.
- EISA slave interface, to allow communication with the i486 system.

The BMIC greatly simplifies the design of EISA expansion boards by automatically handling the full EISA bus-master protocol. With the controller, a board can be implemented with simple logic similar to that used in traditional ISA DMA designs. However, the EISA standard also allows designs with 32-bit data and address buses, burst transfers, and automatic configuration.

The general-purpose command and status interface allows a variety of software control protocols to be used by a local expansion-board processor. Data transfers on the local transfer-interface bus are similar to traditional DMA transfer protocols. Address-generation support logic for the local data transfer buffer is provided on-chip. If a local processor is not used, the local processor interface can be connected to the 8-bit ISA bus. Local logic can use a high-speed local clock. The EISA bus-master interface controller handles all synchronization with the EISA bus. A FIFO within the controller eliminates performance degradation on burst transfers caused by synchronization delays. Local processors are supported with the ability to access individual locations in system memory or I/O space; this peek-and-poke feature allows the expansion board to communicate easily with, or control, other devices in the system.

Two independent transfer channels are supported by the chip. The on-chip data shifters automatically handle misaligned doubleword transfers with no performance penalty. The EISA expansion board ID function is provided. A set of programmable address comparators that drive external chip selects on the expansion board assist local devices in decoding I/O address ranges. The complete state of the bus-master interface controller can be read by software during context switching.

7.6.2.4 BUS BUFFERS

Three 82352 EISA bus buffers are used—one for EISA address buffering, one for EISA data buffering, and one for local DRAM data buffering. The same chip is strapped in three different ways to obtain the three configurations. These three chips, as a group, integrate the logic and buffers that normally require approximately 17 chips. They support some of the EISA timing requirements that are difficult to implement with discrete components. They also eliminate excess electromagnetic interference for FCC testing requirements.

7.7 IMPLEMENTATION EXAMPLE

This section describes the AT compatible control signals and the PLD code to generate them.

7.7.1 AT Compatible Signals

Before discussing the generation of the AT compatible control signals (MEMR#, MEMW#, IOR# and IOW#), there is one major difference in the implementation of I/O interfacing. In the old 80286 microprocessor-based AT machines, the CPU only does word (16 bits) transfer. Therefore when interfacing to the 8-bit bus, external logic is used to provide the 16-bit to 8-bit conversion and vice versa.

Since the i486 microprocessor supports the dynamic byte sizing, interfacing to 8- and 16-bit buses can be accomplished by decoding the BS8# and BS16# inputs. Thus the CPU provides extra cycles if the request is longer than 8 or 16 bits. The conversion is no longer required although bus swapping has to be provided and address bits A0, A1 and BHE# have to be generated (refer to Bus Swapping logic Section 7.1).

Eight bit device on the AT bus is the I/O device connected on the Xbus and on the system (AT) bus when either IOCS16# or MEMCS16# is not true.

To generate AT control signals, the inputs from the i486 microprocessor are as follows:

ADS#	Indicating a valid CPU cycle.
M/IO#	High when it is memory, low when it is I/O.
W/R#	High when it is write cycle, low when it is a read.
D/C#	High when data, low when code.

AT motherboard inputs are as follows:

ENDCYC#	Indicating the end of the CPU cycle.		
	For 16 bit device:		
	OWS = low	0 wait state	2 sysclk cycles
	Standard	1 wait state	3 sysclk cycles
	For 8 bit device:		
	OWS = low	2 wait states	4 sysclk cycles
	Standard	4 wait states	6 sysclk cycles
Q1	Indicating 1 wait state.		
Q4	Indicating 4 wait states.		
OWS	Indicating 0 wait state.		
CMDLY	Delay the command output when it is I/O and/or 8-bit cycle.		
ARDY#	Indicating end of cycle of non on-board memory.		
RESET	System reset.		
DATACON#	True (low) indicating 8-bit device. False (hi) indicating 16-bit device.		

The following inputs are generated in the memory decoding section of the i486 microprocessor:

MEMSEL#	Indicating the on-board memory cycle.
MEMRDY#	Indicating the on-board memory ready.

The following signals are generated by the 2 PLDs:

VALCYC#	Indicating the start of a valid cycle.
ALEO	Address latch enable 0.
ALE1	Address latch enable 1.
ALE	Address latch enable. It will not get out of the system (AT) bus during an on-board memory cycle (when MEMSEL# is low).
BS8#	Byte size select 8.
BS16#	Byte size select 16.

CNTO — CPUCLK counter bit 0; for OWS cycle use only. The counter is present because at zero wait state (OWS# = low):

* For 16-bit transfer:
  2 sysclks = 8 cpuclks is needed for READY0# output.

* For 8-bit transfer:
  4 sysclks = 16 cpuclks is needed for READ0# output.

CNT1	CPUCLK counter bit 1
CNT2	CPUCLK counter bit 2
CNT3	CPUCLK counter bit 3

READY0#	Indicating cycle ready for non on-board memory.
IOR#	I/O read cycle.
IOW#	I/O write cycle.
MEMR#	Memory read cycle.
MEMW#	Memory write cycle.

The following signals should also be generated. Refer to Byte Swapping section for details.

SA0	Address bit 0.	Refer to Byte Steering
SA1	Address bit 1	Logic section for details.
SBHE#	Byte high enable.	

Refer to AT schematics for more details.

The PLD implementation of the AT control signal is shown in Figure 7-32 and Figure 7-33. The equations follow.

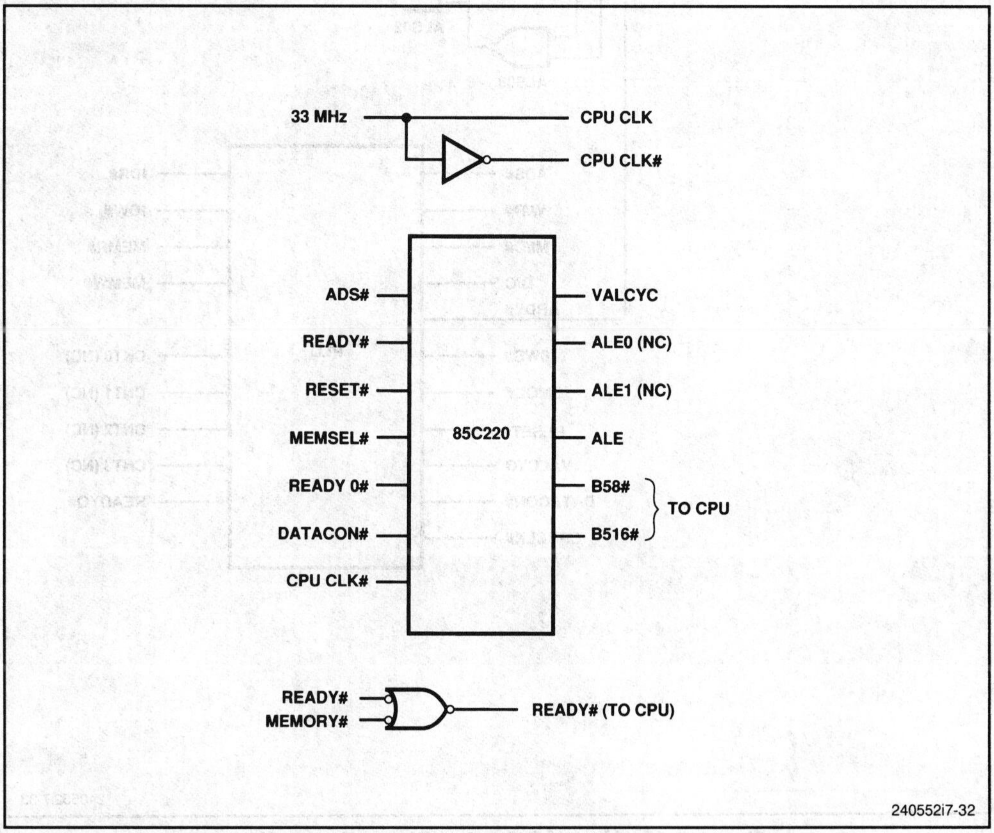

Figure 7-32. AT Control Signal Generation

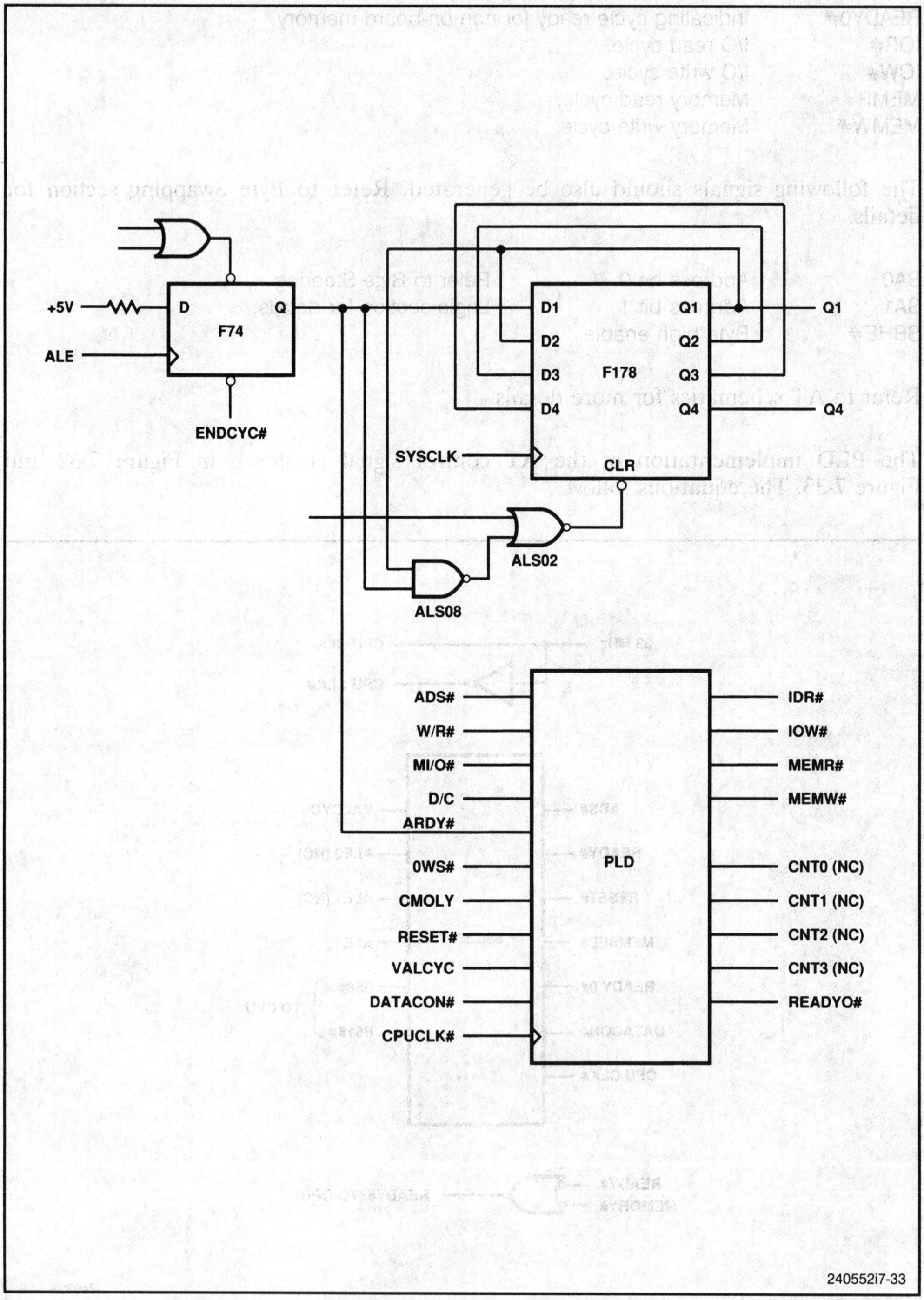

Figure 7-33. More AT Control Signal Generation

Equation:

```
ALEO       := ADS      *   /RESET
LE1        := ALEO     *   /RESET
ALE        := ALE1     *   /MEMSEL      * /RESET     ;Output ALE only if
                                                     ;non on-board mem.

VALCYC     := ADS      *   /READY0      * /RESET     ;Valid cycle.
            + VALCYC   *   /READY0      */RESET      ;until READY goes
                                                     ;away

BS8        DATACONV
BS16       = /DATACONV
```

Counter outputs for 0 wait state (8 CPUCLK = 2 SYSCLK)
(16 CPUCLK = 4 SYSCLK)

```
CNTO       := VALCYC   *   /CNTO                     ;bit 0 of count
NT1        := VALCYC   *   CNTO * /CNT1              ;bit 1 =
            + VALCYC   *   /CNTO * CNT1

CNT2       := VALCYC   *   CNTO * CNT1               ;bit 2 =
            + VALCYC   *   /CNT1 * CNT2
            + VALCYC   *   /CNTO * CNT1 * CNT2

CNT3       := VALCYC   *   CNTO * CNT1 * CNT2 * /CNT3   ;bit 3

            + VALCYC   *   /CNT2 * CNT3
            + VALCYC   *   /CNT1 * CNT2 * CNT 3
            + VALCYC   *   /CNTO * CNT1 * CNT2 * CNT3

READY0     = ARDY
            + OWS * CNTO * CMT1 * CNT2 * /CNT3 * /DATACONV
                                                     ;8 counts for 16 bit
            + OWS * CNTO * CNT1 * CNT2 * CNT3 * DATACONV
                                                     ;16 counts for 8 bit
```

The following control signals are for the AT compatible system using i486 microprocessor as the motherboard CPU.

```
IOR        := ADS * /MIO * /WR * DC * /CMDLY * /RESET
            + IOR * /READY0 * /RESET

IOW        := ADS * /MIO * WR * DC * /CMDLY * /RESET
            + IOW * /READY0 * /RESET

MEMR       := ADS * MIO * /WR * DC * /CMDLY * /RESET
            + MEMR * /READY0 * /RESET

MEMW       := ADS * MIO * WR * DC * /CMDLY * /RESET
            + MEMW * /READY0 * /RESET
```

System Design 8

CHAPTER 8
SYSTEM DESIGN

8.1 INTRODUCTION

With the increasing speed of microprocessors there is an inherent need for efficient input/output devices (such as disks, video controllers, local area network controllers, etc.). The key to successfully supporting I/O options is to have a standard means of connecting them to the motherboard. Each computer supports a standard system bus. Examples of system buses are ISA, MCA, EISA, MBII, etc. To exercise the full potential of the i486™ microprocessor 32-bit system buses, supporting 32-bit I/O devices are required. This chapter discusses the EISA (Extended Industry Standard Architecture) system bus in detail. This is one of the latest standards supported by i486 microprocessor class of machine.

A typical i486 CPU system consists of a system bus connecting various subsystems. Each subsystem can have its own local bus with local resources and can share global resources. This approach allows each subsystem to perform operations simultaneously on their respective local buses to yield a significant throughput improvement over single-bus systems.

i486 CPU system designs may be divided into several subsystems. The first level is the CPU core which consists of CPU and second level cache subsystem memory, cache and I/O control. Each of these subsystems have been described in detail in the previous chapters. The system bus is the vehicle by which the i486 CPU can communicate with other processing subsystems which perform operations simultaneously on their individual local buses.

A major concern when designing a system with various subsystems is how to divide the allocated resources. A designer has to decide which resources should be shared by all the subsystems on the system bus and which should be located on the local bus. The choice is based on the individual system's needs in the areas of reliability, integrity, throughput, and performance. Duplicating resources on each local bus, for example, may increase system integrity and local bus performance but duplication increases system cost.

This chapter introduces an i486 processor system and it separates an i486 CPU system into functional block diagrams and then elaborates each block separately.

8.2 MICROPROCESSOR CONTROL SUBSYSTEM

A single i486 microprocessor system with memory and I/O is shown in Figure 8-1. The memory and the I/O are both controlled by the decode and control logic block. In the system in Figure 8-1, the processor controls the memory and I/O devices. A typical system consists of four subsystems. A high-performance i486 processor-based system

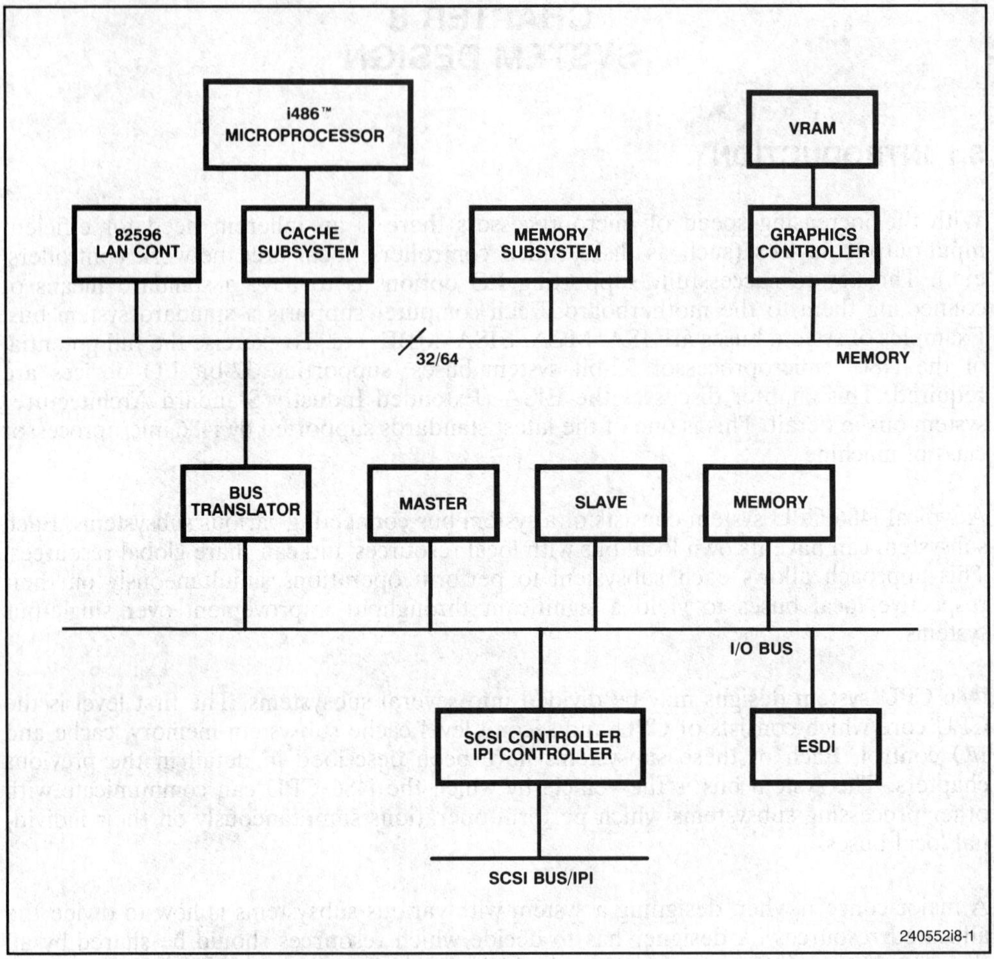

Figure 8-1. Single-Processor i486™ CPU System

requires an efficient memory subsystem and peripheral subsystem. In a typical system a number of slave I/O devices can be controlled on the same bus interface. Complex peripheral devices may require more complex interface.

The 82586 LAN Coprocessor and 82350 EISA Peripheral Chip Set ease the interface design and provide optimum load sharing between the processor and the peripherals. The 82596 LAN coprocessor provides an interface between the i486 processor and a wide variety of networks, including IEEE802.3, the IBM PC, and CSMA/CD networks. The 82596 executes high level commands to control all time-critical LAN functions and performs command chaining and interprocessor communication using memory that it shares with the processor. The EISA peripheral chip set that is discussed in greater detail in this chapter provides an interface between the i486 processor and the Extended Industry Standard Architecture (EISA). The I/O control, wait state generation logic, and the address decode logic in the EISA implementation are provided by the 82350 chip set. A graphics controller resides on the system bus that controls the Video RAM memory.

A more complex system is shown in Figure 8-2. The i486 processor is connected to the memory, I/O and other peripherals via the local bus. Another processor with a second-level cache such as the 485Turbocache Module also resides on the local bus. Both processors can access the system bus via the system bus interface, the arbitration logic, or the interrupt control logic. The system bus can have other masters, slave memory, and system I/O devices.

Figure 8-3 shows an even more complex i486 CPU system. In this application multiple i486 processors reside on the system bus. They have their own local caches and share a global memory as well. In this application higher speed I/O devices, and controllers supporting Enhanced System Device Interface (ESDI), Intelligent Peripheral Interface (IPI), and Small Computer System Interface (SCSI) reside on the I/O bus.

8.3 CLOCK AND RESET CIRCUITS

Analysis of the i486 processor system design begins with the two signals most critical to proper operation clock and reset and proceeds to the memory interface which is used by the i486 CPU immediately after reset.

8.3.1 Clock Circuit

The clock and the reset logic generate the clock and reset signals for the i486 CPU and are also distributed to the peripheral devices. The i486 processor uses a 1X clock which must satisfy TTL levels. The clock goes to most logic areas so it must be distributed in a way to minimize skew and distortion while maintaining drive requirements.

8.3.2 Reset Circuit

The reset signal to the i486 processor must meet the set-up and hold time requirements referenced to the clock signal. The system requires RESET to be asserted approximately one msec to boot up from a cold start and at least 15 clock cycles to reboot from a warm start.

8.3.3 Self Test Operation

The i486 processor has a means of testing 60% of the on-chip logic automatically after reset. It is the Built-In Self Test, BIST. The clock, reset and AHOLD signals are used to initiate the BIST. BIST tests the non-random logic, the control ROM, the translation lookaside buffer and the on-chip cache memory.

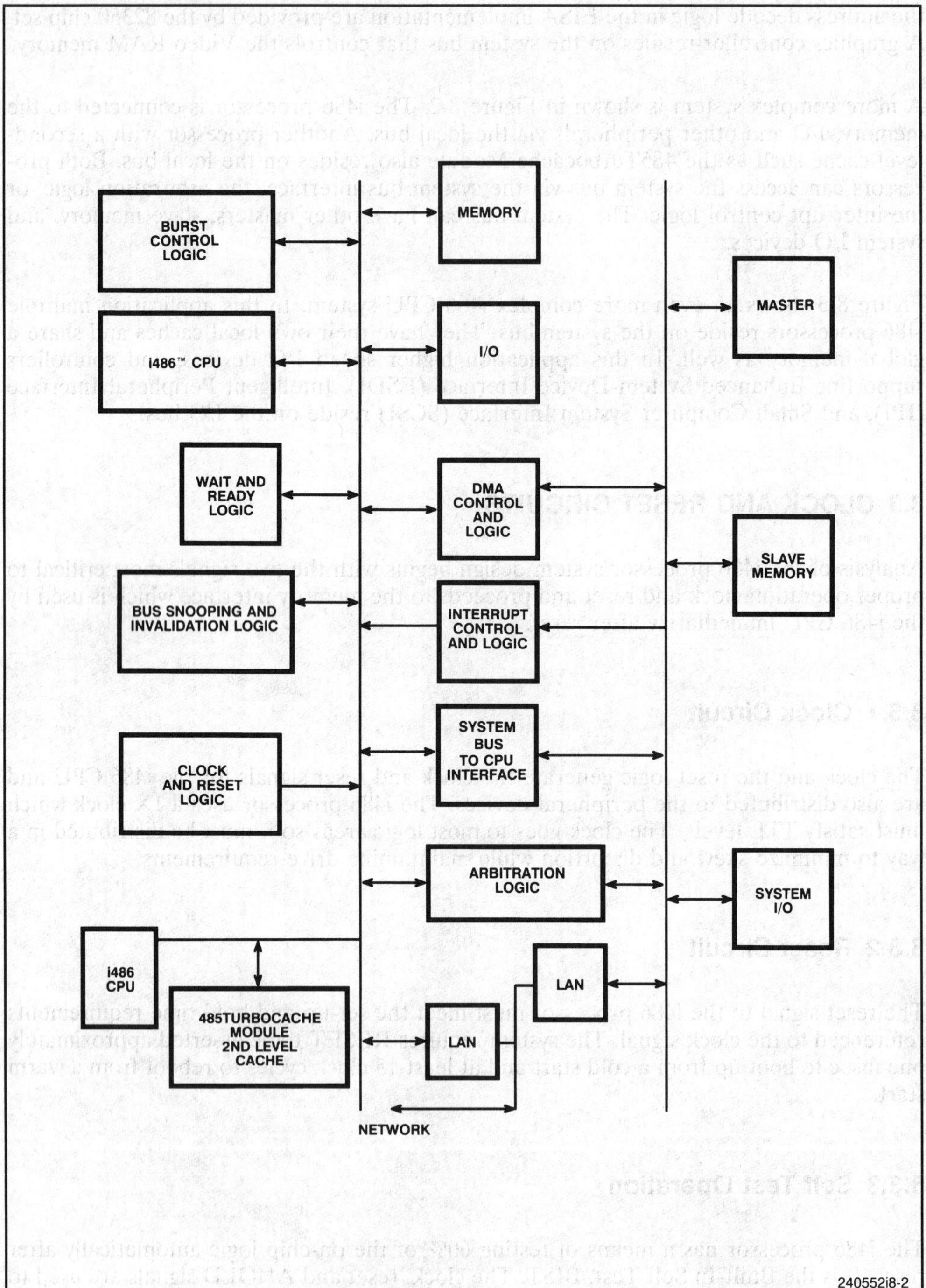

Figure 8-2. Multiple-Processor i486™ CPU System

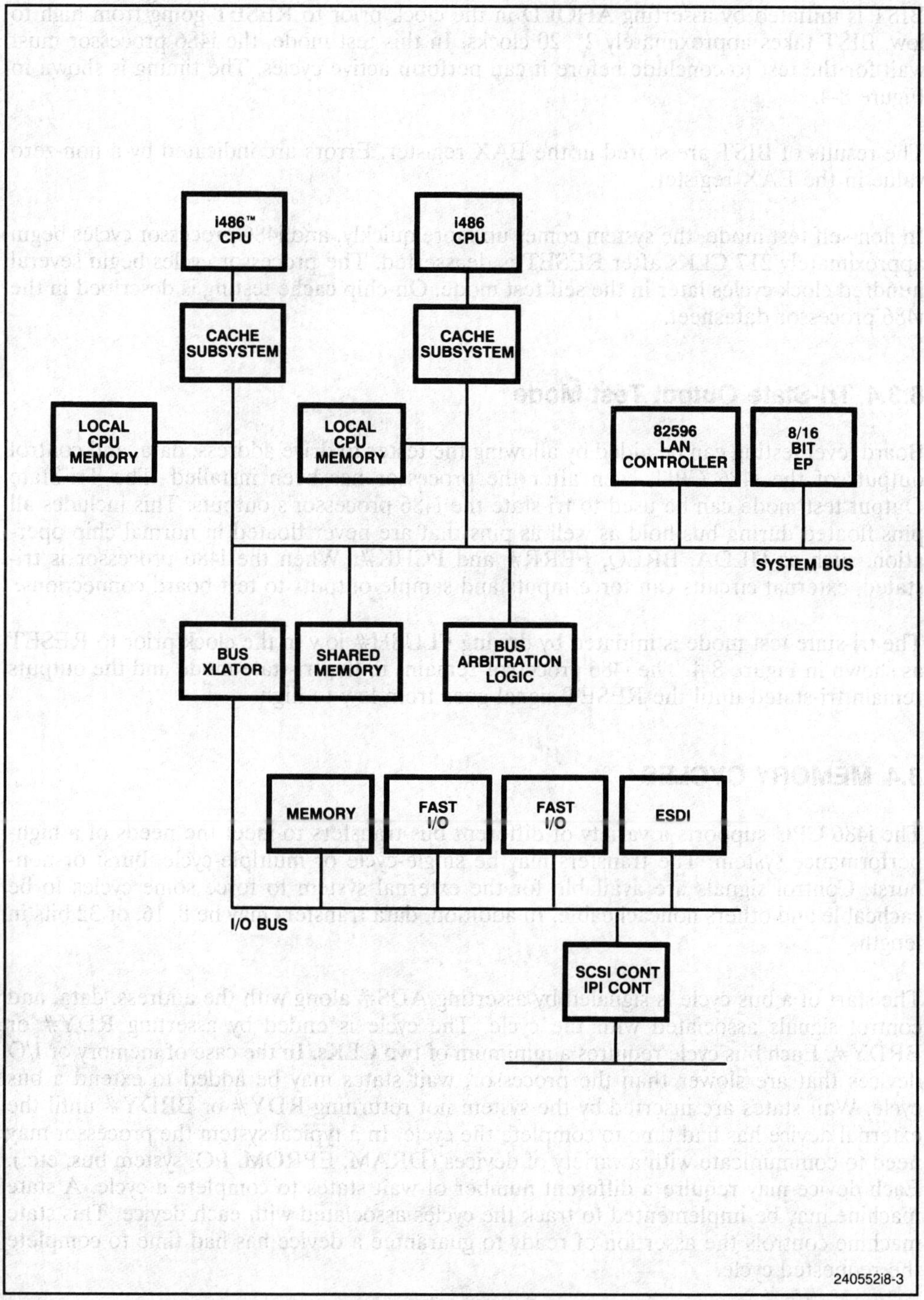

Figure 8-3. Multiple-Processor/Cache/Memory i486™ CPU System

BIST is initiated by asserting AHOLD in the clock prior to RESET going from high to low. BIST takes approximately 2**20 clocks. In this test mode, the i486 processor must wait for the test to conclude before it can perform active cycles. The timing is shown in Figure 8-4.

The results of BIST are stored in the EAX register. Errors are indicated by a non-zero value in the EAX register.

In non-self test mode, the system comes up more quickly, and i486 processor cycles begin approximately 217 CLKs after RESET is deasserted. The processor cycles begin several hundred clock cycles later in the self test mode. On-chip cache testing is described in the i486 processor datasheet.

8.3.4 Tri-State Output Test Mode

Board level testing can be aided by allowing the tester to drive address, data, and control outputs of the i486 CPU, even after the processor has been installed. The Tri-State Output test mode can be used to tri-state the i486 processor's outputs. This includes all pins floated during bus hold as well as pins that are never floated in normal chip operation, such as HLDA, BREQ, FERR# and PCHK#. When the i486 processor is tri-stated, external circuits can force inputs and sample outputs to test board connections.

The tri-state test mode is initiated by driving FLUSH# low in the clock prior to RESET as shown in Figure 8-4. The i486 processor remains in the tri-state mode and the outputs remain tri-stated until the RESET signal goes from low to high.

8.4 MEMORY CYCLES

The i486 CPU supports a variety of different bus transfers to meet the needs of a high-performance system. The transfers may be single-cycle or multiple-cycle, burst or non-burst. Control signals are available for the external system to force some cycles to be cacheable and others noncacheable. In addition, data transfers may be 8, 16, or 32 bits in length.

The start of a bus cycle is signaled by asserting ADS# along with the address, data, and control signals associated with the cycle. The cycle is ended by asserting RDY# or BRDY#. Each bus cycle requires a minimum of two CLKs. In the case of memory or I/O devices that are slower than the processor, wait states may be added to extend a bus cycle. Wait states are inserted by the system not returning RDY# or BRDY# until the external device has had time to complete the cycle. In a typical system the processor may need to communicate with a variety of devices (DRAM, EPROM, I/O, system bus, etc.). Each device may require a different number of wait states to complete a cycle. A state machine may be implemented to track the cycles associated with each device. This state machine controls the assertion of ready to guarantee a device has had time to complete the requested cycle.

To enhance performance, the i486 CPU supports a type of cycle called a burst transfer.

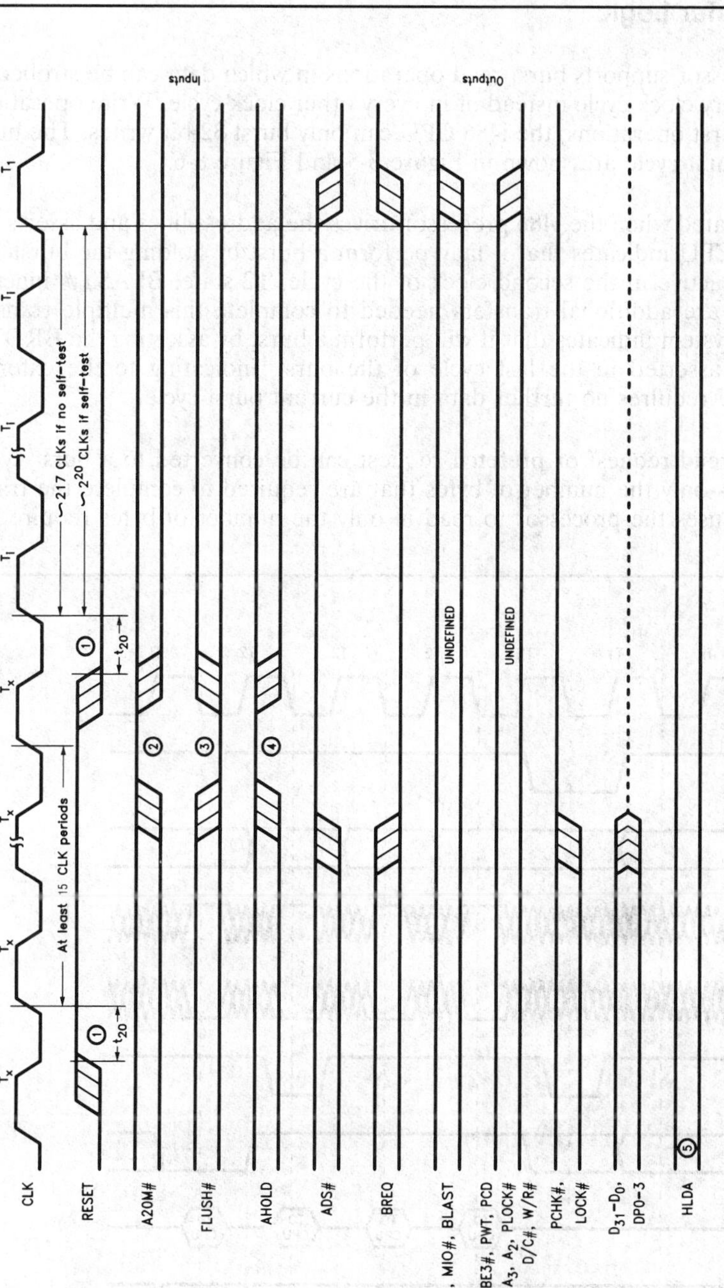

NOTES:
1. RESET is an asynchronous input. t_{20} must be met only to guarantee recognition on a specific clock edge.
2. High on this clock edge for correct operation of the part.
3. Low on this clock edge if tri-state output test mode is to be entered.
4. High on this clock edge to initiate self-test.
5. Hold is recognized normally during RESET.

240552i8-4

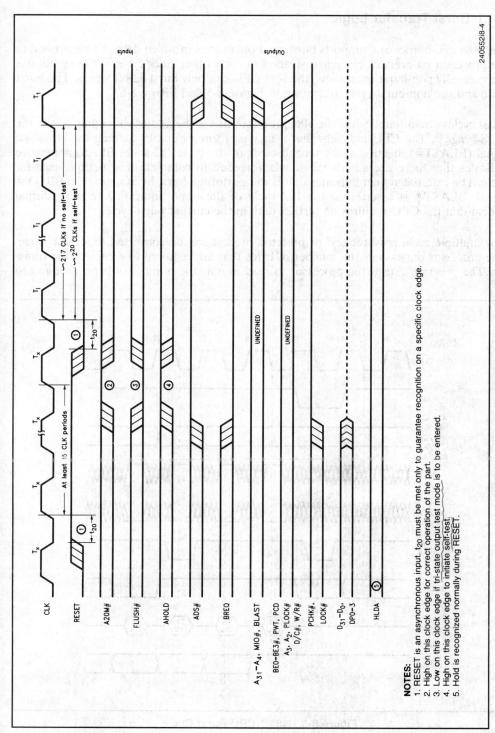

Figure 8-4. i486™ CPU Reset Sequence

8.4.1 Burst Transfer Logic

The i486 microprocessor supports burst read operations in which data can be strobed to the processor on every clock cycle instead of in every other clock cycle. Write operations are generally non-burst operations; the i486 CPU can only burst 32-bit writes. The burst cycle and the non-burst cycle are shown in Figure 8-5 and Figure 8-6.

Burst cycles are initiated when the i486 processor drives the address lines and asserts the ADS# signal. The CPU indicates that it may perform a burst by holding the burst last signal (BLAST#) inactive in the second clock of the cycle, T2 state. BLAST# inactive indicates that there are additional transfers needed to complete this multiple transfer cycle. The external system indicates that it will perform a burst by asserting the BRDY# signal. BLAST# is asserted in the last cycle of the burst, indicating to the external system that the CPU requires no further data in the current burst cycle.

Any multiple cycle read request or prefetch request can be converted to a burst cycle. The processor bursts only the number of bytes that are required to complete the transfer. The program causes the processor to read in only the number of bytes required to

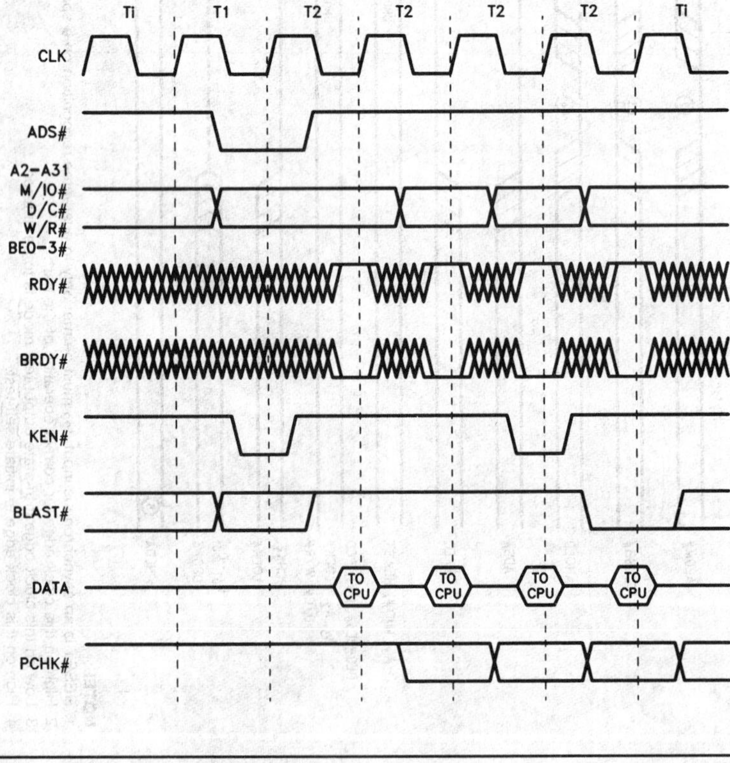

Figure 8-5. i486™ CPU Burst Cycle

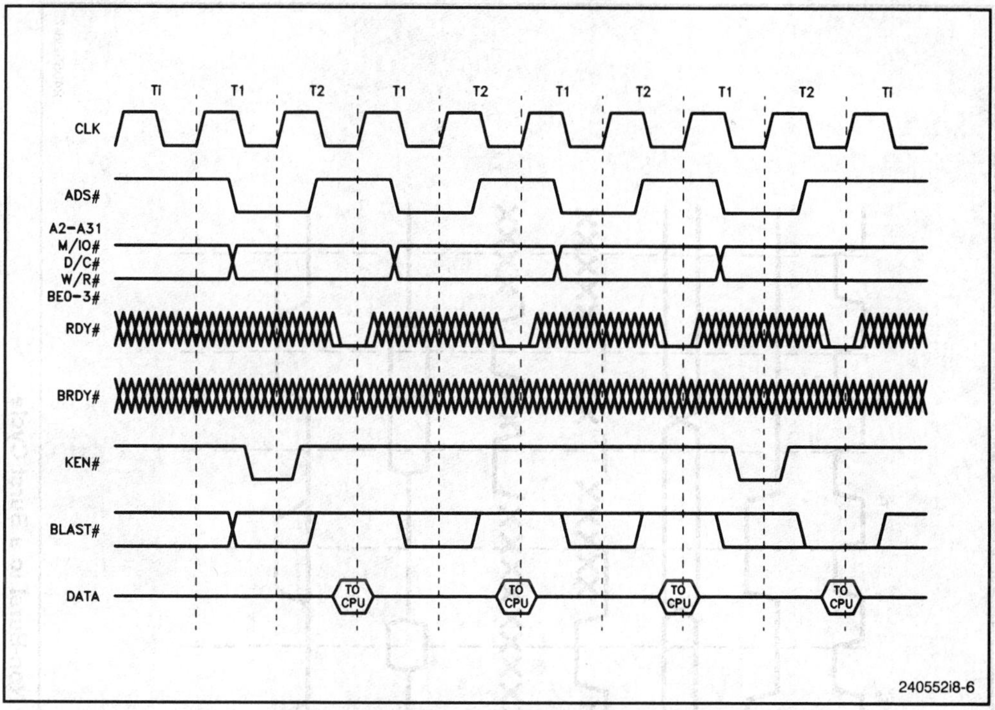

Figure 8-6. i486™ CPU Non-Burst Cycle

complete the instruction. For a 64-bit floating point instruction two doublewords will be read and these can be read in a burst mode if they are 8-byte aligned. For write operations, bursts are limited to four byte operand.

For write operations 32-bit operands are non-burst operations. However, writes of 8-bit and 16-bit operands can be executed as burst cycles when the corresponding memory is organized as 8-bit or 16-bit sizes.

The external system can acknowledge that it will perform a burst by asserting BRDY# (rather than RDY#) in the first cycle. BRDY# is ignored if both RDY# and BRDY# are returned in the same clock. However, the external system can return either RDY# or BRDY# to end the cycle and indicate that the data is present. If BRDY# is returned and BLAST# is asserted in that cycle, BRDY# ends the cycle as though RDY# was returned. Since no additional transfers are needed a burst cycle is not initiated.

When the processor receives a RDY# signal it indicates nonburst operation, and when the processor receives a BRDY# signal it indicates burst operation. However, one can switch between these two modes. For example, if a processor is accessing four doublewords, and the first two doublewords are read with two RDY# pulses. If BRDY# is asserted on the third word while RDY# is high, then CPU reads the third word. The next time BRDY# is asserted, while RDY# is high, the fourth word is read. This is shown in Figure 8-7.

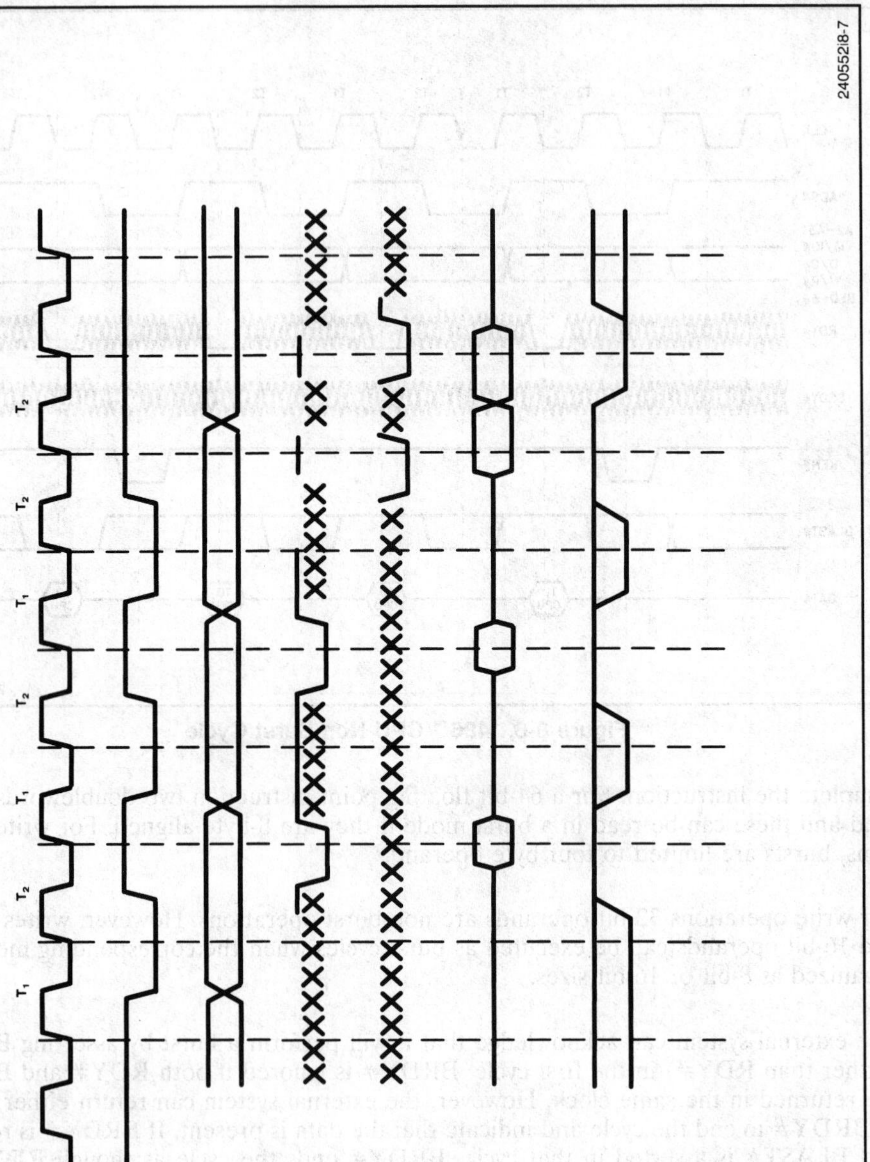

Figure 8-7. Changing from a Non-Burst to a Burst Cycle

In burst operations, the processor addresses A4 to A31 do not change but the processor toggles the addresses A2 and A3 and memory is accessed for the second doubleword. The address sequence for an address beginning with 104 is shown in Figure 8-8. The microprocessor presents each request for data in an order determined by the first address. Table 8-1 shows the Burst address sequence for the four different possibilities. Timing may not permit data to be accessed on the next clock edge if A2 and A3 are used directly to access the external memory. To allow single-cycle bursts and to minimize wait states, the system designer must use logic that can implement the values taken on by A2 and A3 during a burst cycle. Further, the memory banks may be interleaved to allow additional time for accessing consecutive words. Details of the memory subsystem implementation are in Chapter 5.

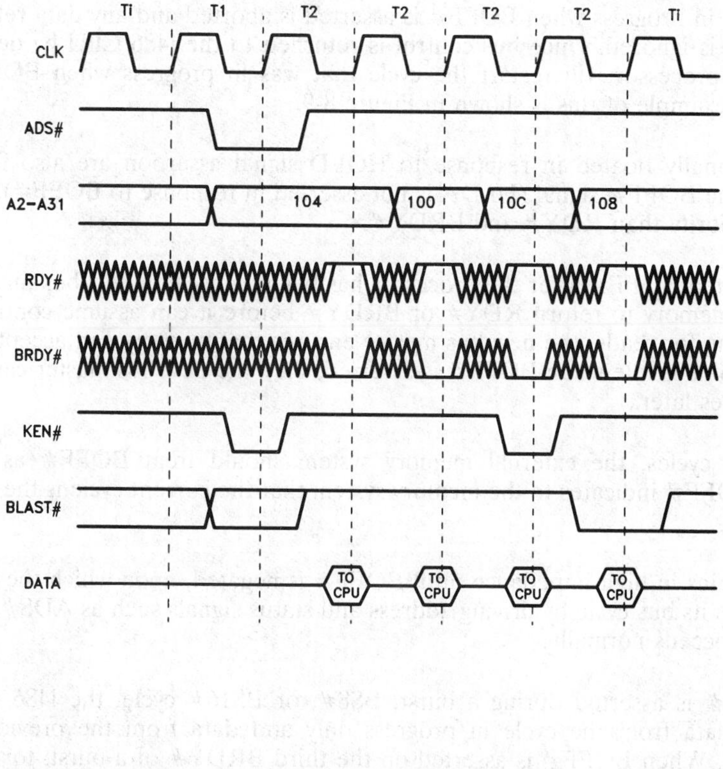

Figure 8-8. Burst Cycle Beginning at Address 104

Table 8-1. Burst Order

First Addr.	Second Addr.	Third Addr.	Fourth Addr.
0	4	8	C
4	0	C	8
8	C	0	4
C	8	4	0

8.5 BUS RESTART LOGIC

In multi-master systems, another bus master may need to gain control of the bus and prevent the i486 processor from completing the current bus access. In this case, the i486 processor must restart its bus cycle once the other bus master has completed its bus transaction.

A bus cycle is aborted if the external system has asserted the backoff (BOFF#) input to gain access to the bus. The i486 processor samples the BOFF# input every cycle; and when it is asserted, the address, data, and status pins are floated as shown in Figure 8-9. Any bus cycle in progress when BOFF# is asserted is aborted and any data returned to the processor is ignored. Once bus control is returned to the i486 CPU by deasserting BOFF#, the processor will restart the cycle that was in progress when BOFF# was asserted. An example of this is shown in Figure 8-9.

The pins normally floated in response to HOLD signal assertion are also floated in response to the BOFF# signal (HLDA is not asserted in response to BOFF#). BOFF# has higher priority than RDY# and BRDY#.

If it has asserted BOFF# after the processor has begun a cycle, a new bus master must wait for the memory to return RDY# or BRDY# before it can assume control of the bus. By waiting for ready, the new bus master ensures that memory can accept new bus cycles. If the bus is idle when BOFF# is asserted, then the new bus master can start its cycle two cycles later.

During burst cycles, the external memory system should treat BOFF# as it treats BLAST#. BOFF# indicates to the memory system that the current cycle is the last cycle in a transfer.

The bus remains in high impedance until BOFF# is negated, upon which the i486 processor restarts its bus cycle by driving address and status signals such as ADS#. The bus cycle then proceeds normally.

When BOFF# is asserted during a burst, BS8#, or BS16# cycle, the i486 processor ignores the data from the cycle in progress only and data from the previous cycles remains valid. When BOFF# is asserted on the third BRDY# of a burst, for example, the processor assumes that data received upon the first and second BRDY# is valid and it receives the third word associated with the third BRDY# when the cycle is later restarted after BOFF# is deasserted.

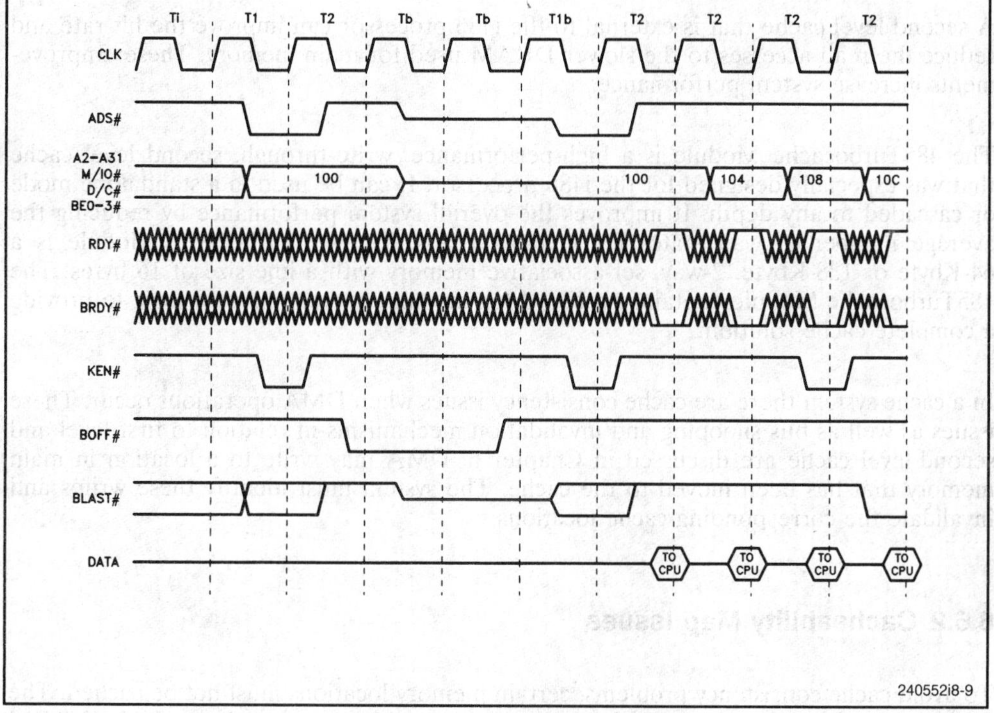

Figure 8-9. i486™ CPU Backoff

When BOFF# is asserted in the same clock as ADS#, the i486 processor floats its bus as long as ADS# is low in the next clock. As ADS# goes low, it may indicate to a peripheral that the bus cycle is in progress even though the cycle was aborted. There are two ways to solve this problem. The first method is to have devices recognize the BOFF# condition and ignore ADS# until ready is returned. The second is to generate a two-clock back-off, wherein AHOLD is asserted in the first clock and BOFF# is asserted in the second clock. These methods ensure that ADS# will not be at a low, and they are only required in systems where BOFF# is asserted in the same clock as ADS#.

8.6 CACHE SUBSYSTEM

Chapter 6 describes the cache subsystem in detail. Two aspects of the subsystem, the cacheability map and multi-masters, are discussed in this section.

8.6.1 On-Chip Cache and Second-Level Cache

The i486 processor's on-chip cache is organized as a 4-way set associative cache with a line size of 16 bytes. The 8-Kbyte cache is organized as four 2-Kbyte ways. Each 2-Kbyte way is comprised of 128 sets. Each set contains 4 16-byte lines. With 4-way associativity, the user can achieve a high hit rate. The cache is transparent, so that the i486 processor is easy to use.

A second level cache that is external to the i486 processor can improve the hit rate and reduce the read accesses to the slower DRAM used for main memory. These improvements increase system performance.

The 485Turbocache Module is a high-performance, write-through, second level cache that was especially designed for the i486 processor. It can be used in a standalone mode or cascaded to any depth. It improves the overall system performance by reducing the average number of wait states for memory reads. The 485Turbocache Module is a 64-Kbyte or 128-Kbyte, 2-way, set-associative memory with a line size of 16 bytes. The 485Turbocache Module contains on-board tag memory and comparator logic to provide a complete cache solution.

In a cache system there are cache consistency issues when DMA operations occur. These issues as well as bus snooping and invalidation mechanisms in relation to first-level and second-level cache are discussed in Chapter 6. DMA may write to a location in main memory that has been moved to the cache. The system must identify these writes and invalidate the corresponding cache locations.

8.6.2 Cacheability Map Issues

To avoid cache consistency problems, certain memory locations must not be cached. The PC architecture has several special memory areas which may not be cached. If ROM locations on add-in cards are cached, for example, write operations to the ROM can alter the cache while main memory contents remain the same. Further, if the mode of a video RAM subsystem is switched, it can produce altered versions of the original data when a read-back is performed. Expanded memory cards may change their mapping and hence memory contents with an I/O write operation. LAN or disk controllers with local memory may change it independent of the i486 CPU. This altering of certain memory locations can cause a cache consistency problem. For these reasons the video RAM, shadowed BIOSROMs, expanded memory boards, add-in cards, and shadowed expansion ROMs should be non-cacheable locations. Depending on the system design, ROM locations may be cacheable in a secondary cache if write protection is allowed.

8.6.3 Cache and Multi-Masters

The i486 processor is designed for multiple-processor applications. The BREQ output permits a simple hardware interface for bus arbitration. The on-board and secondary caches have a high hit rate and reduce main memory accesses for reads. Further, the address bus on the i486 processor and the 485Turbocache Module bus controller are bidirectional to allow cache invalidation on system bus memory writes by other masters.

Each microprocessor may have its own local cache or all the microprocessors may share a global cache. With multi-masters bus utilization is critical. When a write-back cache is used the bus utilization is reduced as compared to a write-through cache for write operations.

Figure 8-10 shows two processors and a DMA controller that are connected over the system bus. The arbitration logic arbitrates between the processors and the DMA controller. The CPUs and their secondary cache monitor the system bus to identify cache writes and the system must have the mechanisms to support invalidation cycles and to ensure consistency between the contents of the two caches and memory. Coherency is achieved by snooping the address bus. When a write is identified by one processor to a location contained in the other's cache, an invalidation cycle must be generated by asserting AHOLD and EADS# to the second processor and its cache. This type of invalidation is true for the write-through cache like the one shown in Figure 8-10. If the caches are write-back caches the invalidation protocol may be different.

8.7 INTERRUPT CONTROLLER AND LOGIC

Complex system consist of multiple interrupt sources. Logic must be contained in the system to control or coordinate these interrupts. Chapter 7 contains a description of this logic.

8.8 DMA CONTROLLER AND LOGIC

8.8.1 Impact of DMA on System Performance

DMA functions can be implemented in many ways, and DMA implementations can impact system performance. In some cases, DMA is needed for software compatibility even though it degrades system performance. For example, transfers may have to be done in eight-bit increments, even though the system supports 32-bit transfers. This smaller bus size translates into more cycles and degrades system performance.

Some of the factors that have to be considered in hardware implementations are bus request and latency, bus arbitration, arbitration processing, DMA data transfer type, bus bandwidth, and programming ease. Further information regarding DMA controllers may be found in Chapter 7.

8.9 LAN CONTROLLER AND LOGIC

Connection to a Local Area Network (LAN) is a logical extension of an i486 CPU system. This connection requires logic to control the transfer of information. Chapter 7 provides more details on the logic required for a LAN controller.

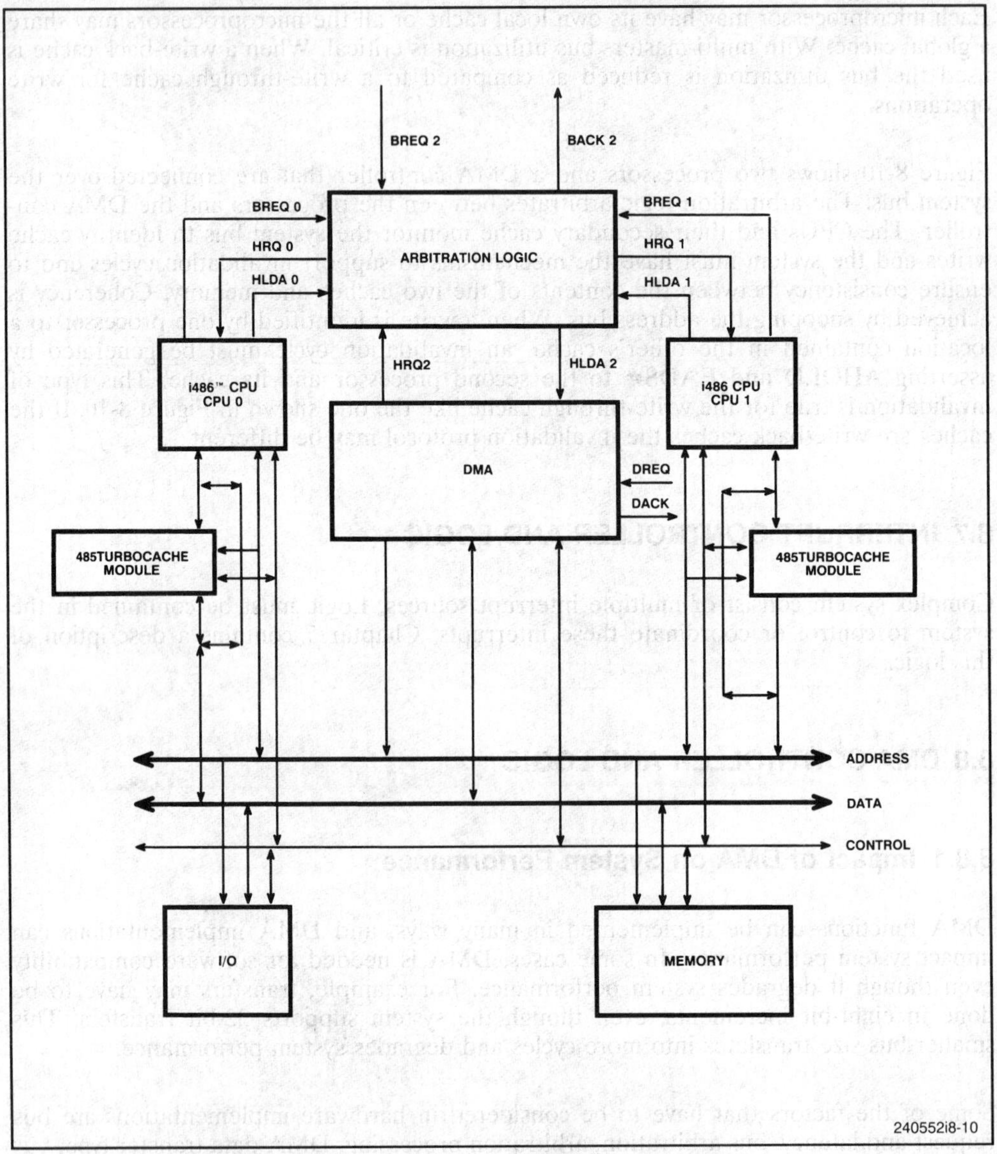

Figure 8-10. i486™ CPU System Arbitration

8.10 BUS ARBITRATION LOGIC

Bus arbitration logic is needed with multiple bus masters. Hardware implementations range from single-master designs to those with multiple masters and DMA devices.

Figure 8-11 shows a simple system in which only one master controls the bus and accesses the memory and I/O devices. Here, no arbitration is required.

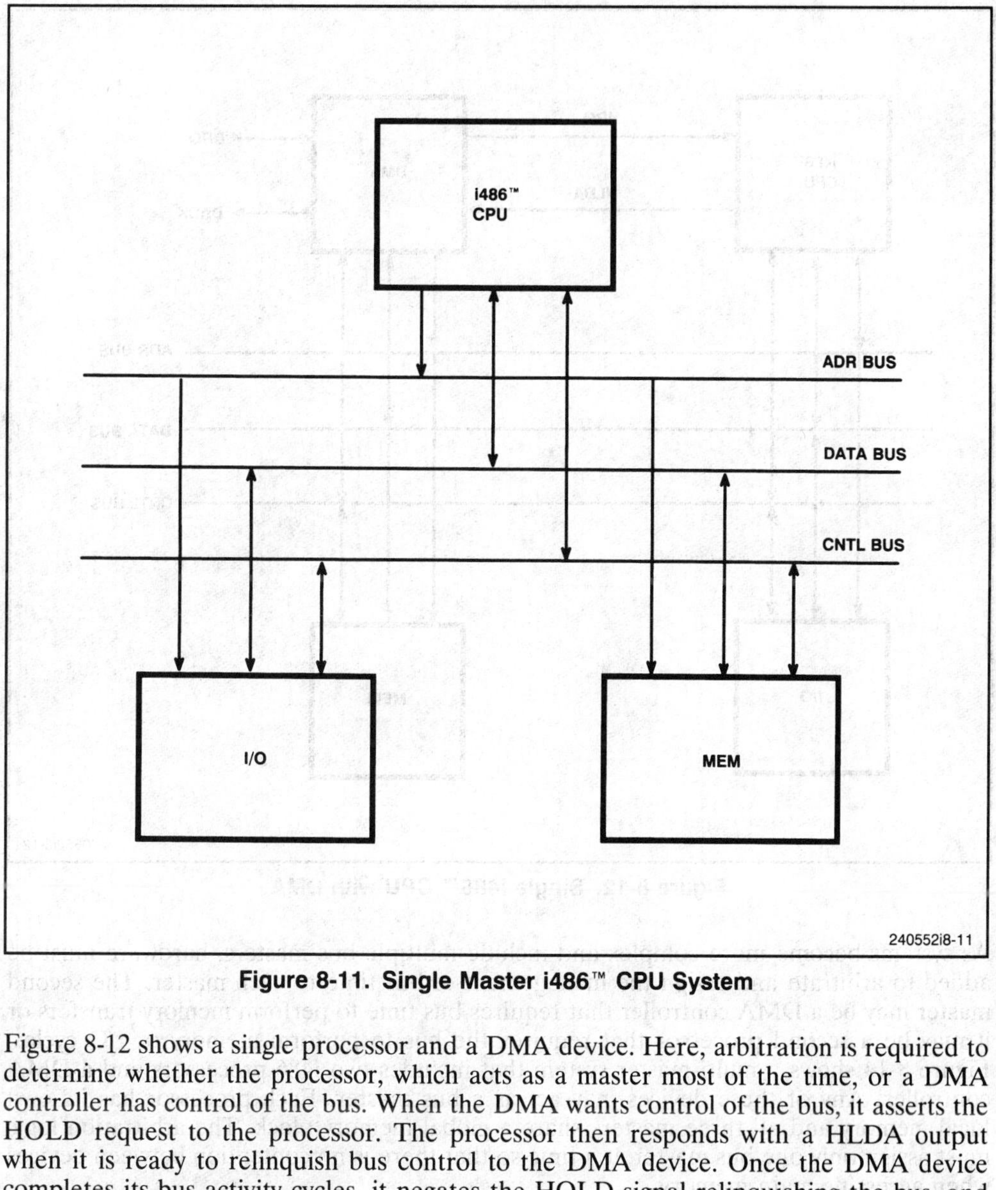

Figure 8-11. Single Master i486™ CPU System

Figure 8-12 shows a single processor and a DMA device. Here, arbitration is required to determine whether the processor, which acts as a master most of the time, or a DMA controller has control of the bus. When the DMA wants control of the bus, it asserts the HOLD request to the processor. The processor then responds with a HLDA output when it is ready to relinquish bus control to the DMA device. Once the DMA device completes its bus activity cycles, it negates the HOLD signal relinquishing the bus, and the processor resumes control.

Figure 8-13 shows more than one primary bus master and two secondary masters, and the arbitration logic is more complex. The arbitration logic resolves bus contention by ensuring that all device requests are serviced one at a time using either a fixed or a rotating scheme. The arbitration logic then passes information to the i486 processor which ultimately releases the bus. The arbitration logic receives bus control status information via the HOLD and HLDA signals and relays it to the requesting devices.

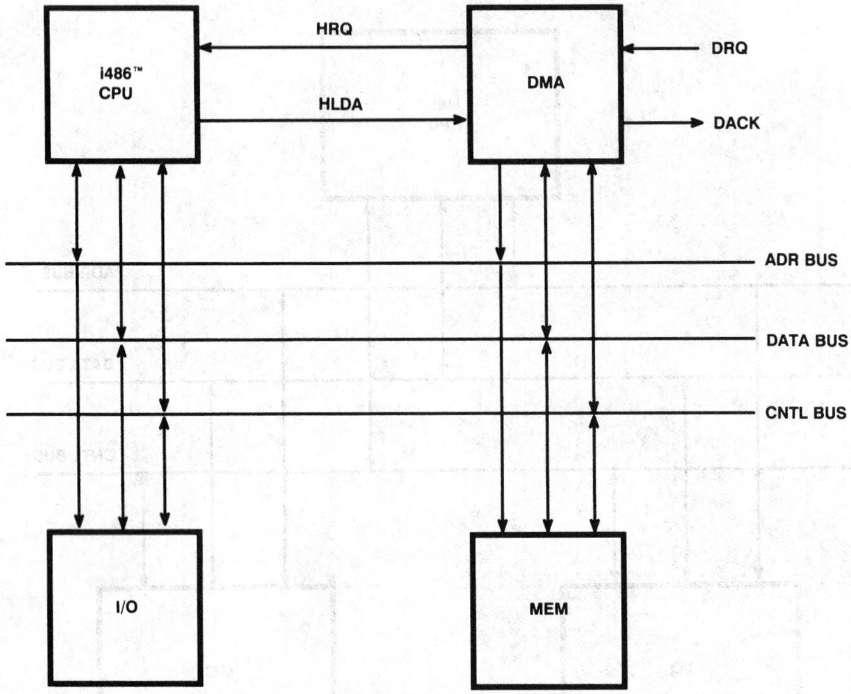

Figure 8-12. Single i486™ CPU with DMA

As systems become more complex and include multiple bus masters, hardware must be added to arbitrate and assign the management of bus time to each master. The second master may be a DMA controller that requires bus time to perform memory transfers or it may be a second processor that requires the bus to perform memory or I/O cycles. Figure 8-14 shows a multi-master system that includes two i486 processors and a DMA controller. Any of these devices may act as a bus master. Each processor has its own local memory and all three masters share a global memory block. The arbitration logic must assign only one bus master at a time so that there is no contention between devices when accessing main memory.

The arbitration logic may be implemented in several different ways. The first technique is to round-robin or to time slice each master. Each master is given a block of time on the bus to match their priority and need for the bus.

Another method of arbitration is to assign the bus to a master when the bus is needed. Assigning the bus requires the arbitration logic to sample the BREQ or HOLD outputs from the potential masters and to assign the bus to the requestor. A priority scheme

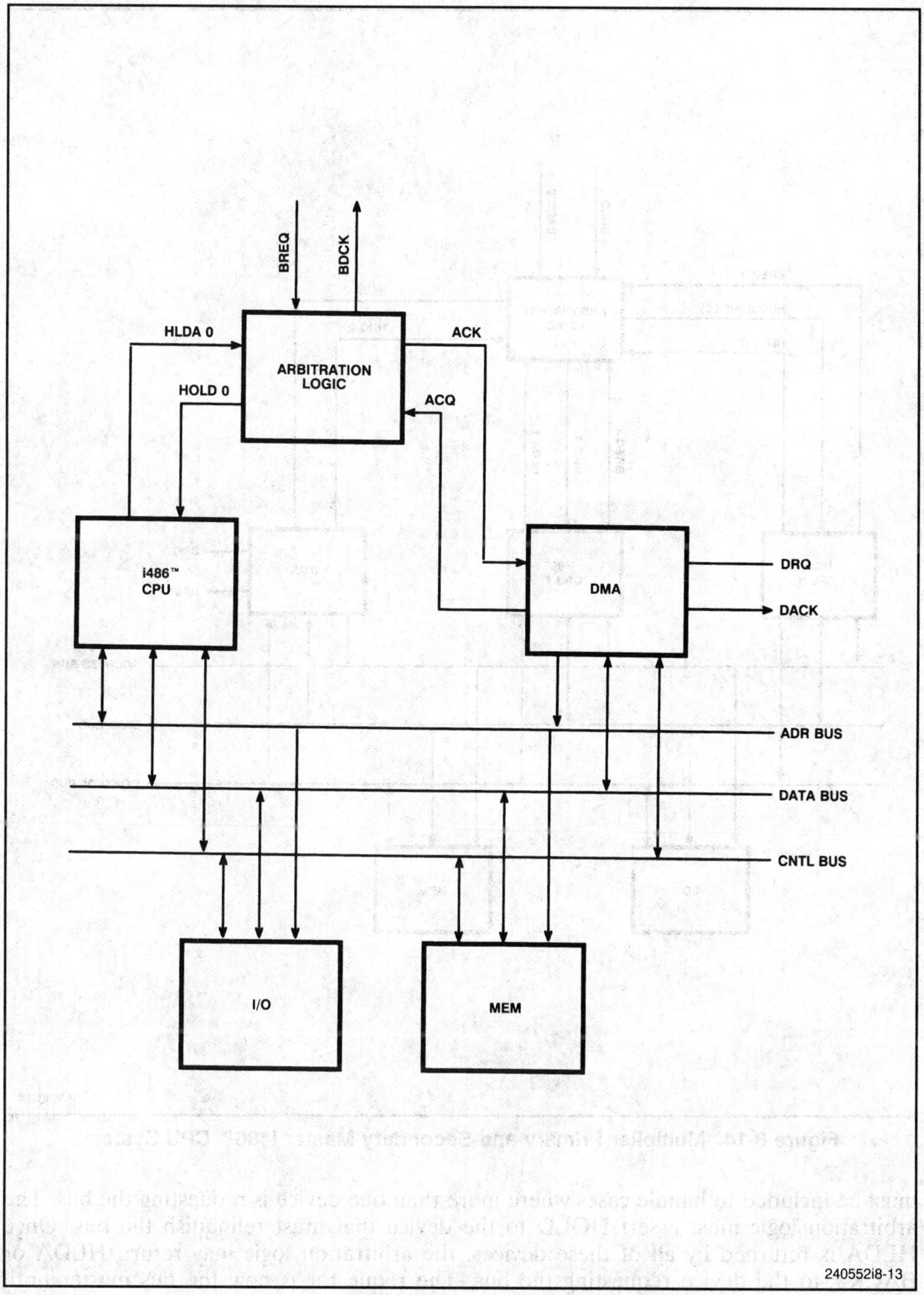

Figure 8-13. Single i486™ CPU with Multiple Secondary Masters

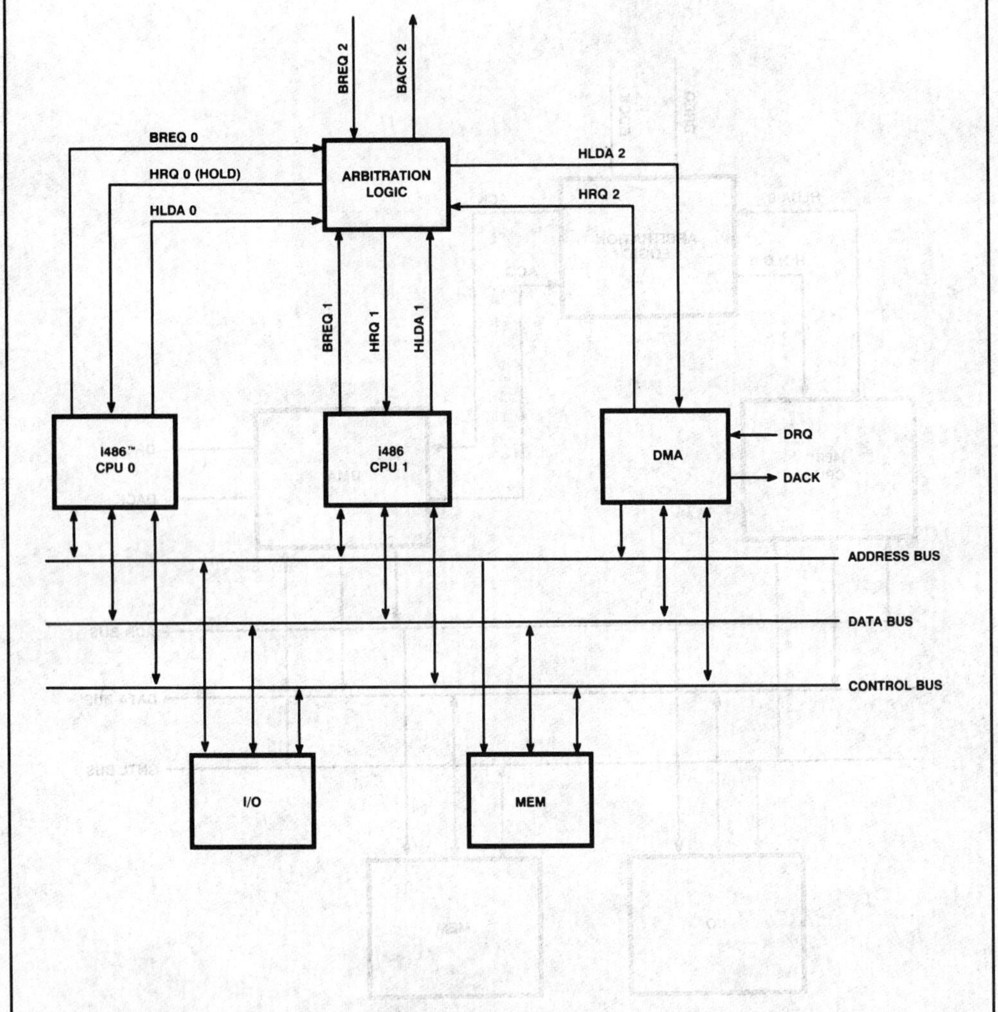

Figure 8-14. Multiplier Primary and Secondary Master i486™ CPU System

must be included to handle cases where more than one device is requesting the bus. The arbitration logic must assert HOLD to the device that must relinquish the bus. Once HLDA is returned by all of these devices, the arbitration logic may return HLDA or BACK# to the device requesting the bus. The requestor is now the bus master until another device needs the bus.

These two arbitration techniques can be combined to create a more elaborate arbitration scheme that is driven by a device that needs the bus but guarantees every device will get time on the bus. It is important that an arbitration scheme be selected to best fit the needs of each system's implementation.

From the processor's viewpoint, the i486 processor asserts BREQ when it requires control of the bus. BREQ notifies the arbitration logic that the processor has pending bus activity and requests the bus. When its HOLD input is inactive and its HLDA signal is deasserted, the i486 CPU can acquire the bus. Otherwise if HOLD is asserted, then the i486 processor has to wait for HOLD to be deasserted before acquiring the bus. If the i486 processor does not have the bus, then its address, data, and status pins are tri-stated. However, the processor can execute instructions out of the internal cache or instruction queue, and does not need control of the bus to remain active.

The address buses shown in Figure 8-12, Figure 8-13 and Figure 8-14 are bidirectional to allow cache invalidations to the processors during memory writes on the bus.

8.11 SYSTEM BUS INTERFACE

The processing subsystems described must communicate with one another. Each may be able to stand alone as a processing unit but must share information. The system bus is the vehicle by which information may be transferred. In addition a standard system bus provides a format for all vendors to follow when building boards or subsystems. This standard allows boards from multiple suppliers to be used in a system. For a subsystem to access the system bus, the protocol signals associated with that bus must be provided. In addition buffers and drivers are needed to provide the necessary AC and DC drive capability for the address, data, and control signals.

There are several standard bus architectures for the system designer to choose from. The following section explains the implementation for one of these buses, EISA (Extended Industry Standard Architecture).

8.12 i486 PROCESSOR SYSTEM DESIGN EXAMPLE USING THE EISA BUS

8.12.1 Introduction to the EISA Architecture

EISA (Extended Industry Standard Architecture) is a superset of the Industry Standard Architecture (ISA). It extends the ISA capabilities and maintains compatibility with ISA expansion boards and software. EISA provides the following important enhancements:

- 32-bit address bus for CPU, DMA and bus masters
- 32-bit data transfers for CPU, DMA, I/O devices and bus masters
- High Speed synchronous bus transfers of 1.5 cycles per doubleword
- Automatic translation of bus cycles between EISA and ISA master and slaves

- Up to 33 Mbyte/second transfer rates for bus masters and DMA devices interrupts are programmable to be edge- or level-sensitive
- Support of intelligent bus master peripheral controllers

The EISA bus is designed to handle wider address and data buses than those of ISA. All EISA connector, performance, and function enhancements are a superset to those of ISA. EISA maintains full compatibility with ISA expansion boards and software.

Bus masters and multiple processors on the EISA bus can be synchronized to a common clock, for greater performance. Burst cycles can be executed at 33 Mbytes/sec transfer rate and a standard EISA cycle can transfer data in two cycles. CPUs are permitted to generate a 1.5 clock "compressed" cycles for slaves that request such a cycle however.

EISA systems can support DMA transfers with 32-bit addressability, and with 8-, 16-, or 32-bit data. 32-bit DMA devices can transfer data at 33 Mbytes/sec using burst cycles.

EISA-based computers support a bus master architecture for intelligent peripherals. The bus master provides a high-speed channel with data rates up to 33 Mbytes/sec. The bus master provides localized intelligence with a dedicated I/O processor and local memory to relieve the host of sophisticated memory access functions. Applications that can disk controllers, LAN interfaces, data acquisition systems and certain classes of graphic controllers.

The EISA bus provides a mechanism for data size translation which is useful when it is transferring data between 16-bit ISA bus masters and 8-bit or 16-bit memory, I/O slaves, or DMA devices. The system board also provides a mechanism for transactions between 16-bit ISA devices and 32-bit EISA devices.

EISA systems provide a centralized arbiter that allows efficient bus sharing between multiple EISA bus masters and DMA devices. An active bus master or DMA device may be preempted when another device needs the bus. Further, if a device does not release the bus once it has been preempted, then the centralized arbiter can reset the device. The EISA arbitration method grants the bus to DMA devices, memory controller for DRAM refreshes, bus masters, and the host CPU in an efficient rotational manner. The rotational scheme provides shorter latencies for DMA devices, to assure compatibility with ISA devices. Bus masters and CPUs have longer latencies, because often they have buffers.

8.12.2 Intel's EISA Chip Set

Figure 8-15 shows a high-performance system with an i486 processor residing on the host bus. Three EISA support devices from Intel, 82358 EISA bus controller (EBC), 82357 integrated system peripheral (ISP), and 82352 EISA bus buffers (EBB), interface between the host bus and the EISA bus and the three devices also communicate with each other.

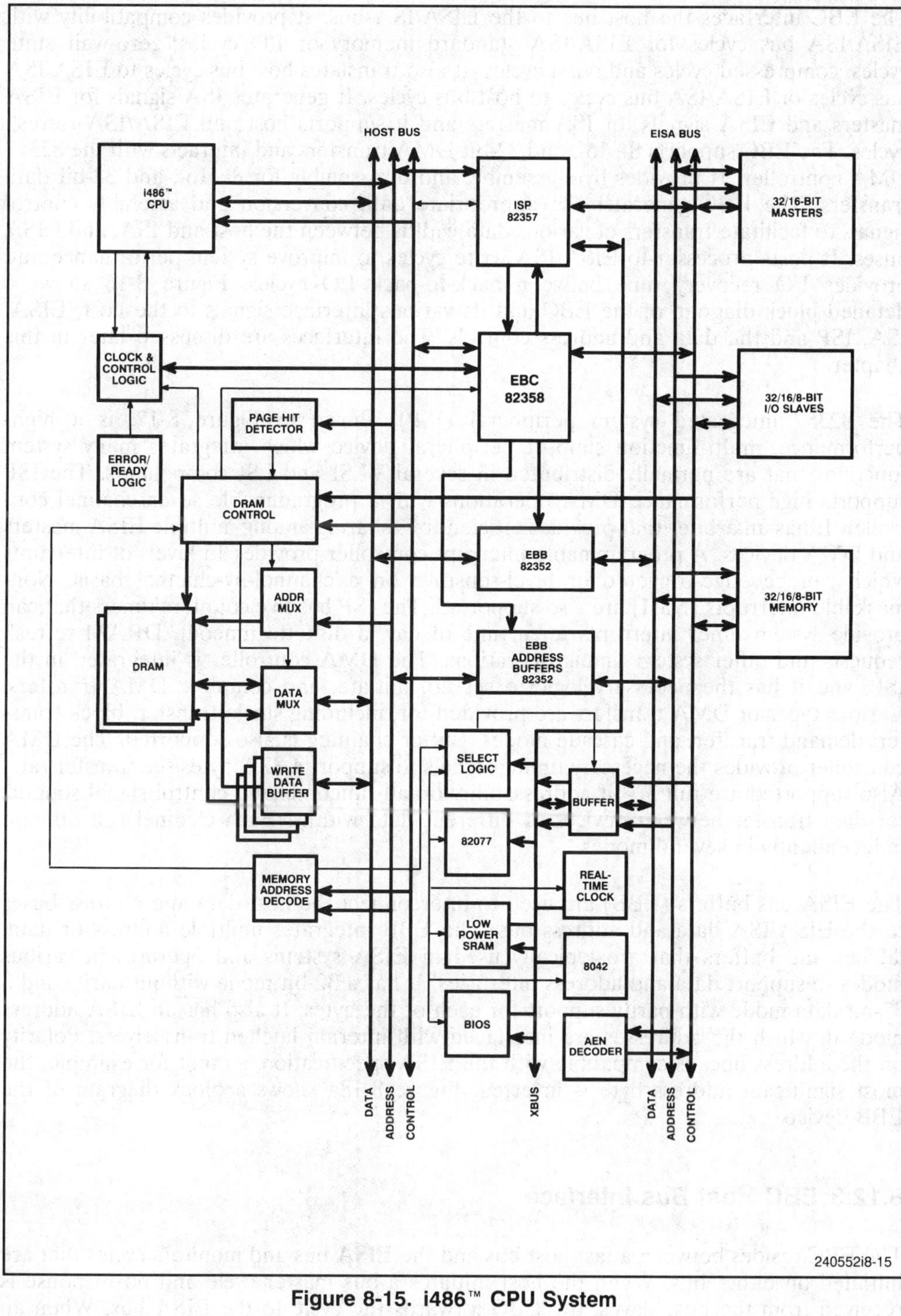

Figure 8-15. i486™ CPU System

The EBC interfaces the host bus to the EISA/ISA bus. It provides compatibility with EISA/ISA bus cycles for EISA/ISA standard memory or I/O cycles, zero-wait state cycles, compressed cycles and burst cycles. It also translates host bus cycles to EISA/ISA bus cycles or EISA/ISA bus cycles to host bus cycles. It generates ISA signals for EISA masters and EISA signals for ISA masters and it supports host and EISA/ISA refresh cycles. The EBC supports 8-, 16-, and 32-bit DMA transfers and interacts with the 82357 DMA controller. It provides byte-assembly and disassembly for 8-, 16-, and 32-bit data transfers. The EBC generates the appropriate data conversion and assembly control signals to facilitate transfers of various data widths between the host and ISA, and EISA buses. It posts processor-to-EISA/ISA write cycles to improve system performance and provides I/O recovery time between back-to-back I/O cycles. Figure 8-16 shows a detailed block diagram of the EBC and its various interface signals to the host, EISA, ISA, ISP and the data and address controls. The interfaces are discussed later in this chapter.

The 82357 integrated system peripheral (ISP), shown in Figure 8-17, is a high-performance, multi-function support peripheral device which integrates many system functions that are normally distributed in several VLSI and LSI components. The ISP supports high-performance DMA operations with a programmable seven-channel controller. It has an arbiter that provides efficient bus sharing among multiple EISA masters and DMA devices. A programmable interrupt controller provides 15 levels of interrupts which can be edge-triggered or level-sensitive on a channel-by-channel basis. Non-maskable interrupts (NMI) are also supported. The ISP has five counters/timers that can provide system timer interrupts for a time of day, a diskette timeout, DRAM refresh requests and other system timing operations. The DMA controller is integrated in the ISP, and it has the necessary logic to set up, initiate, and complete DMA transfers. Various types of DMA transfers are provided for, including single transfer, block transfer, demand transfer, and cascade modes. Buffer chaining is also supported. The DMA controller provides the necessary timing signals to support a 33 Mbytes/sec transfer rate. Also supported are full 32-bit addressability on all functions and control signal support for data transfer between devices of different data widths. Each channel can operate independently in several modes.

The EISA bus buffers (EBB) are used to interconnect the host data and address buses to the EISA/ISA data and address bus. The EBB integrates multiple address or data, latches and buffers that are typically used in EISA systems and operates in various modes to support data and address interfaces. It has a 32-bit mode without parity and a 32-bit data mode with parity support for each of the bytes. It also has an EISA address mode in which the addresses are interfaced with internal latched transceivers. Polarity on the address lines is compatible with the EISA specification, so that for example, the most significant address byte is inverted. Figure 8-18a shows a block diagram of the EBB device.

8.12.3 EBC Host Bus Interface

The EBC resides between a fast host bus and the EISA bus and monitors cycles that are initiated on either bus. When the host initiates a bus master cycle and no response is received from the host slaves, the EBC forwards the cycle to the EISA bus. When an

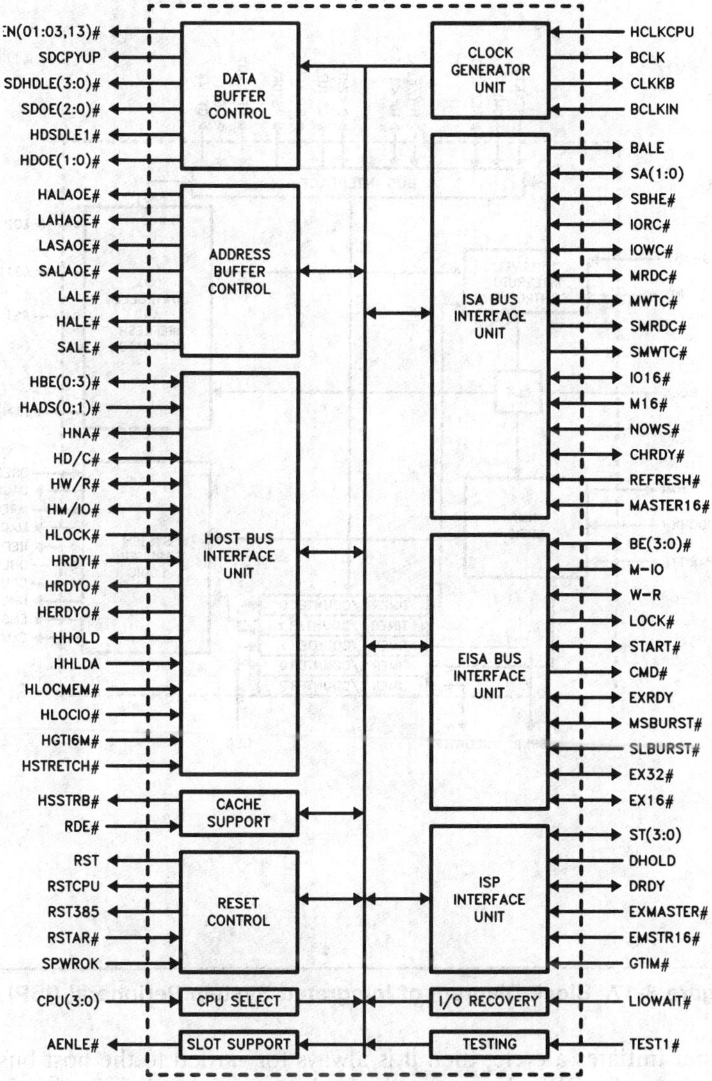

Figure 8-16. Block Diagram of EISA Bus Controller (EBC)

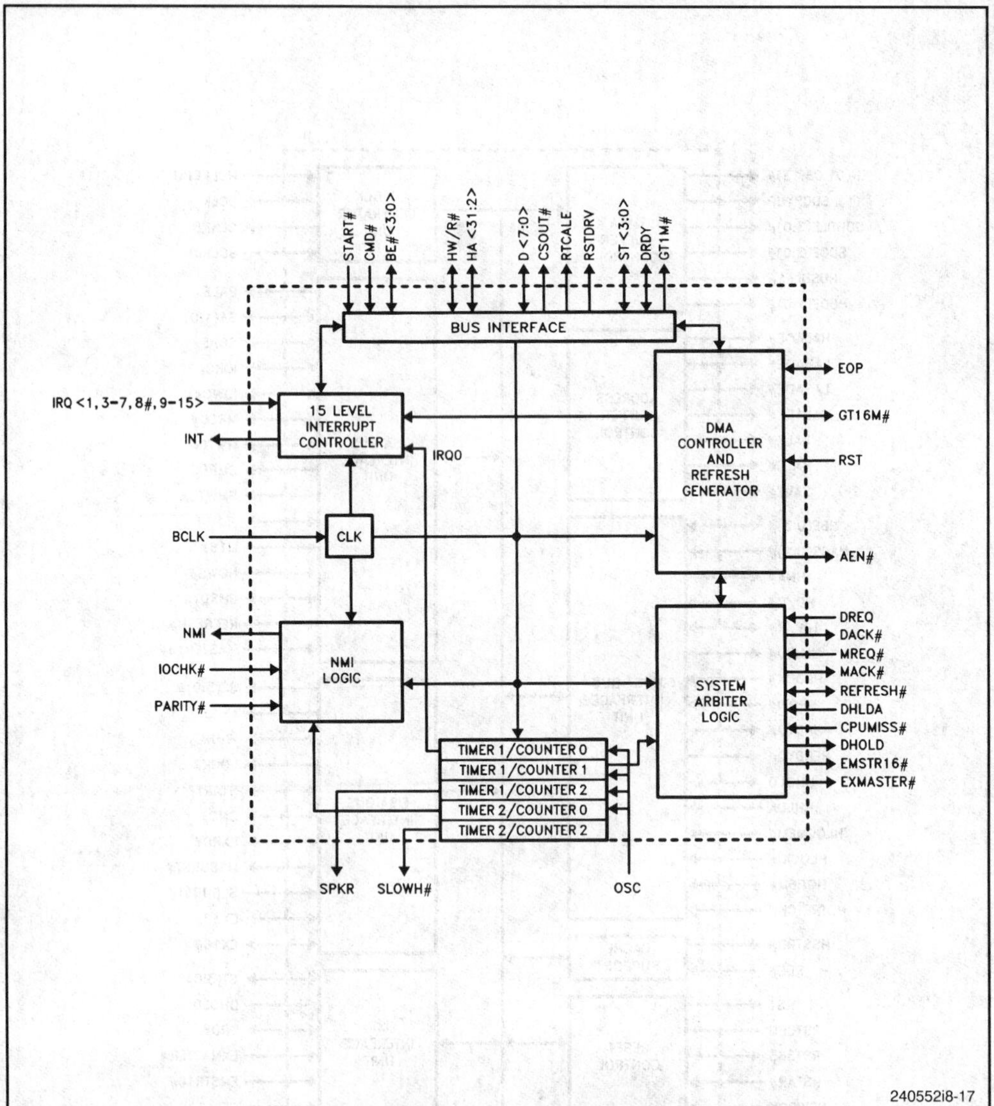

Figure 8-17. Block Diagram of Integrated System Peripheral (ISP)

EISA bus master initiates a cycle, then it is always forwarded to the host bus. The EBC provides controls to the EBB device for the address and the data buffers between the two buses. The EBC also inserts delays between back-to-back I/O cycles between the host and the EISA bus.

Figures 8-18b and 8-18c show a brief description of the interface signals between the host and the EBC.

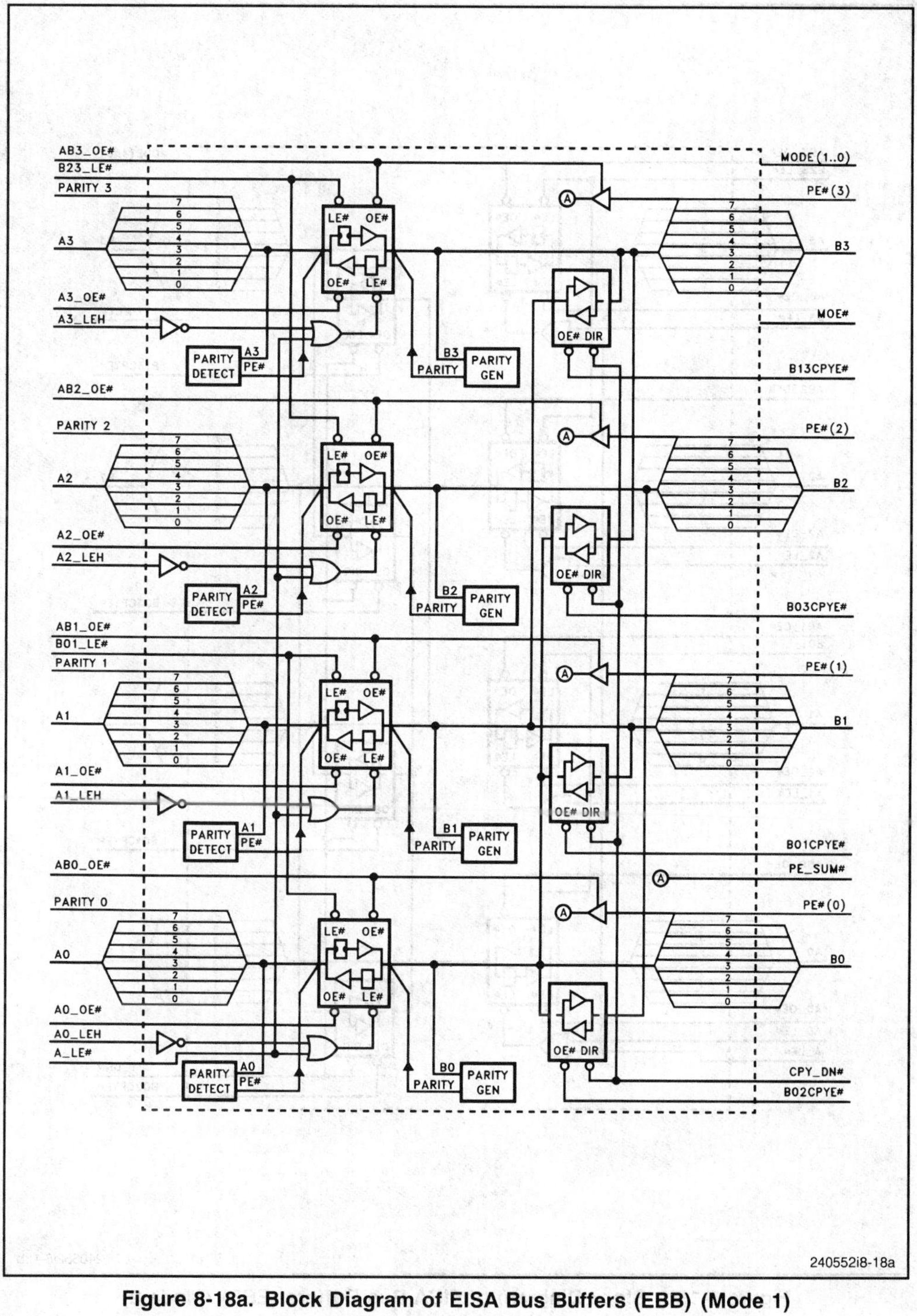

Figure 8-18a. Block Diagram of EISA Bus Buffers (EBB) (Mode 1)

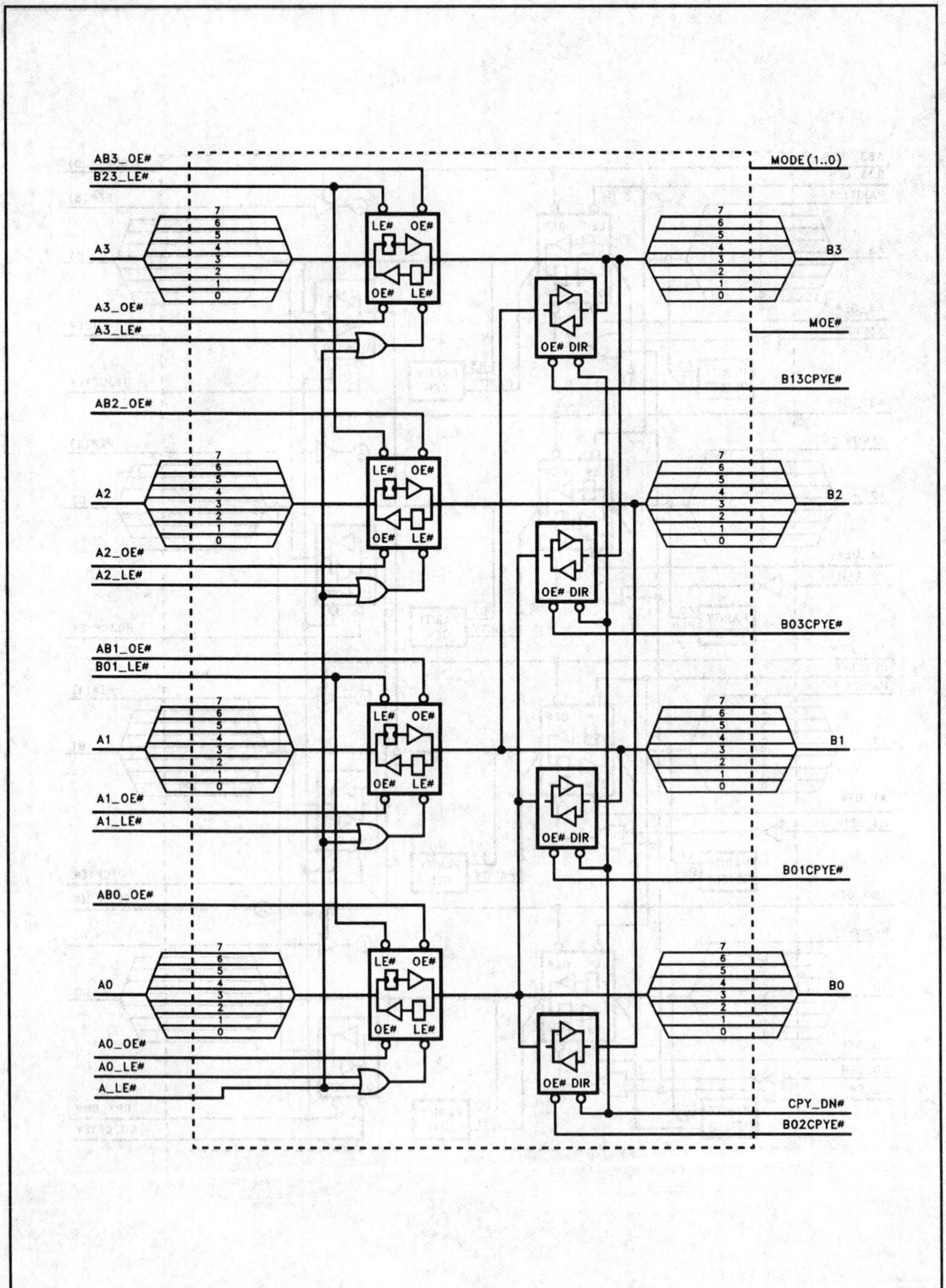

Figure 8-18b. Block Diagram of EISA Bus Buffers (EBB) (Mode 2)

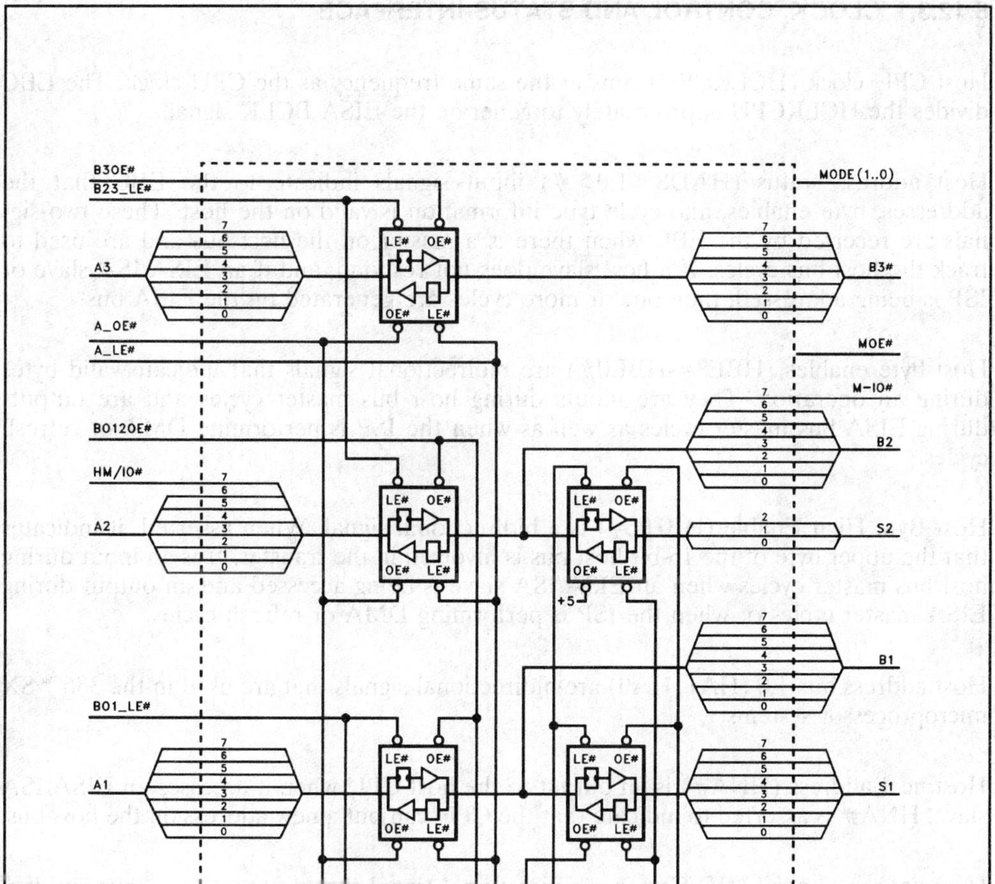

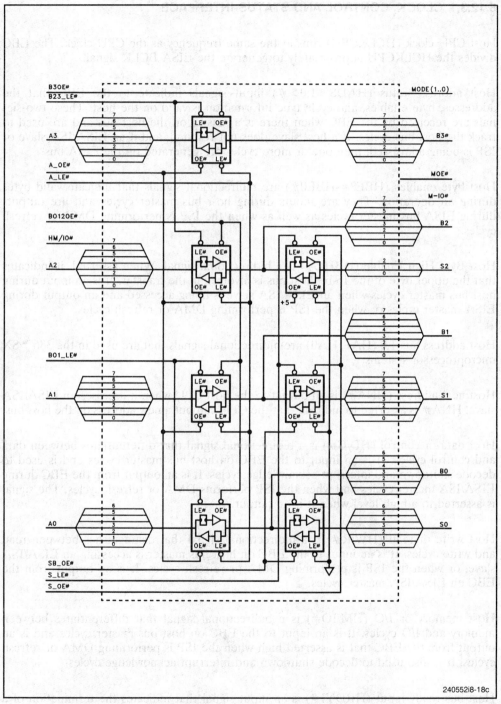

Figure 8-18c. Block Diagram of EISA Bus Buffers (EBB) (Mode 3)

8.12.3.1 CLOCK, CONTROL AND STATUS INTERFACE

Host CPU clock (HCLKCPU) runs at the same frequency as the CPU clock. The EBC divides the HCLKCPU appropriately to generate the EISA BCLK signal.

Host address status (HADS<1:0>#) input signals indicate to the EBC that the addresses, byte enables, and cycle type information is valid on the host. These two signals are received by the EBC when there is a master on the host bus and are used to track the host bus cycles. If a host slave does not respond, and if an EISA/ISA slave or ISP is being addressed, then one or more cycles are generated on the EISA bus.

Host byte enables (HBE3#-HBE0#) are bidirectional signals that indicate valid bytes during an operation. They are inputs during host bus master cycles and are outputs during EISA bus master cycles as well as when the ISP is performing DMA or refresh cycles.

Host Byte High Enable (HBHE#) is a bidirectional signal. When asserted, it indicates that the upper byte of the 16-bit host bus is involved in the transfer. It is an input during host bus master cycles when an EISA/ISA slave is being accessed and an output during EISA master cycles or when the ISP is performing DMA or refresh cycles.

Host address bits 1,0 (HA1, HA0) are bidirectional signals that are used in the 386™ SX microprocessor systems.

Host next address (HNA#) is an output to the host CPU when it accesses an EISA/ISA slave. HNA# is asserted to indicate that the CPU can put a new address on the host bus.

Host data or control (HD/C#) is a bidirectional signal that differentiates between data and control cycles. It is an input to the EBC on host bus master cycles and is used to decode shutdown and interrupt acknowledge cycles. It is an output from the EBC during EISA/ISA master cycles and when the ISP performs DMA or refresh cycles. The signal is asserted to a high level when it is an output.

Host write or read (HW/R#) is a bidirectional signal that distinguishes between read and write cycles. It is an input to the EBC on host bus master is accessing an EISA/ISA slave, or when the ISP is performing DMA or refresh cycles. It is an output from the EBC on EISA/ISA master cycles.

Host memory or I/O (HM/IO#) is a bidirectional signal that differentiates between memory and I/O cycles. It is an input to the EBC on host bus master cycles and is an output from the EBC that is asserted high when the ISP is performing DMA or refresh cycles. It is also used to decode shutdown and interrupt acknowledge cycles.

Host bus ready input (HRDYI#) is an input signal that indicates the termination of a cycle on the host bus.

Host bus ready output (HRDYO#) is an output signal indicating that the EBC has completed a cycle. It is asserted when the host is addressing an EISA/ISA slave, and the cycle has completed by appropriate inputs from EXRDY, CHRDY, NOWS#, and DRDY.

Host bus early ready output (HERDYO#) is an early version of the ready output from the EBC for situations in which HRDYO# does not provide enough set-up time.

8.12.3.2 HOST LOCAL MEMORY AND I/O INTERFACE

Host bus local memory (HLOCMEM#) is an input signal which indicates that a host bus memory slave has decoded the current address as its own without preconditioning the HMI/O# signal. If this signal is asserted on host bus master memory cycles, it prevents EISA bus cycle from initiating. This signal is used to determine if the memory is being accessed on the host bus during EISA/ISA master memory cycles, or during DMA cycles.

Host bus local I/O (HLOCIO#) is an input signal which indicates that a host bus I/O slave has decoded the current address as its own without preconditioning the HMI/O# signal. If this signal is asserted on host bus master I/O cycles, it prevents EISA bus cycle from initiating. This signal is used to determine if the I/O device is being accessed on the host bus during EISA/ISA master I/O cycles.

Host bus stretch (HSTRETCH#) is an input used by host bus slaves during EISA/ISA master cycles to run zero (EISA) wait state cycles. This input can be used during DMA cycles and EISA/ISA bus master cycles to stretch the low period of the BCLK during the CMD# portion of the cycle. BCLK remains low until HSTRETCH# is sampled high. This produces a "stalling" effect of the EISA/ISA master without adding BCLK wait states. If the host memory subsystem is capable of performing EISA cycles without wait states, then the HSTRETCH# can be pulled high and no CPU clock-based logic will be required for bus master or DMA cycles.

8.12.3.3 HOST BUS ACQUISITION AND RELEASE

Host bus hold request (HHOLD) is an output signal which is asserted by the EBC to indicate a hold request to the host. This occurs when the ISP asserts DHOLD to indicate that an EISA/ISA bus master wants control or that a DMA device requires service.

Host hold acknowledge (HHLDA) is an input signal to the EBC from the bus master to indicate that it has relinquished control.

8.12.3.4 LOCK, SNOOP, AND ADDRESS GREATER THAN 16 MBYTES

Host bus lock (HLOCK#) is an input signal which is asserted by the host master when a locked bus cycle is in progress. If the addressed device is on the EISA bus the signal is propagated to the LOCK# signal on the EISA bus.

Host snoop strobe (HSSTRB#) is an output signal which is driven by the EBC during any write cycle on the host bus. It is asserted during I/O to memory DMA cycles, EISA/ISA bus master memory write cycles and CPU write cycles to host memory.

8.12.4 EISA/ISA Bus Interface to the EBC

The EBC translates cycles from EISA masters that can be handled by ISA slaves and translates cycles between ISA masters that can be handled by EISA slaves. It also facilitates transfers between 32-bit and 16-bit EISA devices and 16-bit and 8-bit ISA devices.

Most of the EISA and ISA bus signals connect directly to the EBC or ISP without buffers. The direct connection assumes a worst case load of 300 pF and an IOL of 24 mA, with a worst case clock-to-output propagation delay of 30 ns. Only the AEN8 control signal lacks a direct connection to EISA/ISA. AENx is a slot specific signal that is decoded and asserted for a specific slot of a particular address. The ISP unit provide a global AEN# that is decoded with the LA bus address bit to generate the AENx signals. This is shown in Table 8-2.

The following is a brief functional description of the interface signals between the EISA/ISA bus and the EBC.

8.12.4.1 EBC AND EISA BUS INTERFACE SIGNALS

Byte enables (BE3#-BE0#) are bidirectional signals that indicate which bytes are involved in the current cycle. They are outputs during host bus master cycles and are inputs during ISA bus master cycles. They are inputs during EISA bus master cycles and when the ISP is performing DMA or refresh cycles.

Memory or I/O cycle (M/IO#) is an output signal that distinguishes between memory and I/O EISA cycles. It is an output during ISA master cycles and during host bus master-to-EISA/ISA slaves cycles. The signal floats during CPU, DMA or EISA bus master cycles.

Table 8-2. AENx Decode Table

Address	AEN#	AENx					
		1	2	3	4	5	6
xxxx	1	1	1	1	1	1	1
00xx, 04xx, 08xx, 0Cxx	0	1	1	1	1	1	1
01xx-03xx, 05xx-07xx, 09xx-0Bxx, 0Dxx-0Fxx	0	0	0	0	0	0	0
10xx, 14xx, 18xx, 1Cxx	0	0	1	1	1	1	1
20xx, 24xx, 28xx, 2Cxx	0	1	0	1	1	1	1
30xx, 34xx, 38xx, 3Cxx	0	1	1	0	1	1	1
40xx, 44xx, 48xx, 4Cxx	0	1	1	1	0	1	1
50xx, 54xx, 58xx, 5Cxx	0	1	1	1	1	0	1
60xx, 64xx, 68xx, 6Cxx	0	1	1	1	1	1	0

Write or read cycle (W/R#) is a bidirectional signal that is an input during EISA bus master cycles. It is an output of the EBC during host bus master to EISA/ISA slave cycles, and during ISA master cycles.

Start cycle (START#) is a bidirectional input signal to the EBC which starts cycles on the host bus. It is an output from the EBC on host master cycles when no responses are received from the host slaves. It is an output during ISP requests for DMA and refresh cycles. It is also an output during ISA master I/O cycles to eight-bit devices and when the EBC translates a 32-bit or 16-bit EISA bus master into cycles for an EISA/ISA slave with a smaller data bus size.

Command (CMD#) is an output which provides timing control within cycles. It is asserted simultaneously with the negation of START# and remains asserted until the cycle terminates. It is generated by the EBC during any EISA cycle.

Master burst (MSBURST#) is a bidirectional, open-collector output asserted by an EISA master to indicate that it is capable of supporting a burst operation in the next cycle. It is an input during EISA bus master cycles and an output during DMA cycles, when a burst mode DMA has been selected, and when memory is capable of supporting burst operations.

Slave burst (SLBURST#) is a bidirectional open-collector signal that is asserted by EISA slaves to indicate that they can accept burst cycles. It is an input when the ISP requests burst cycles and an output from the EBC when an EISA master is in control. It is asserted if the host memory is accessed and has asserted HSLBURST#.

EISA 32-bit device (EX32#) is a bidirectional, open-collector signal that is asserted by 32-bit EISA slaves to indicate 32-bit bus size. The signal is used to determine matched or unmatched data sizes on masters and slaves. Once the sizes are determined the EBC assembles and disassembles data and performs multiple EISA or ISA cycles when necessary.

EISA 16-bit device (EX16#) is a bidirectional, open-collector signal that is asserted by 16-bit EISA slaves to indicate 16-bit bus size. The signal is used to determine matched or unmatched data sizes on masters and slaves. Once the sizes are determined the EBC assembles and disassembles data and performs multiple EISA or ISA cycles when necessary.

EISA ready (EXRDY) is a bidirectional, open-collector signal which indicates that a slave is ready to terminate a cycle. It is an input to the EBC on host master cycles which access EISA or ISA slaves and is propagated to the host as the HRDY# signal. It is also an input for performing DMA or refresh cycles and is propagated as DRDY. It is an output from the EBC when an EISA master is accessing a host bus slave or the ISP. It is an output from the EBC during EISA master cycles to ISA slaves and is derived from CHRDY. It is an output for CPU cycles to ISA slaves for which an EISA cycle has been initiated.

Locked cycle (LOCK#) is an output signal which indicates to EISA slaves that the host CPU is executing a locked cycle. It is asserted by the EBC when the HLOCK# signal is asserted.

8.12.4.2 EBC AND ISA BUS INTERFACE SIGNALS

Bus address latch enable (BALE) is an output from the EBC which indicates that a valid address is present on the latched address (LA) address bus.

Bus clock (BCLK) is an output signal derived from the host CPU clock (HCLKCPU). The HCLKCPU can be divided by 3, 4, 5, 6 or 8 to give clock frequencies ranging between 8.0 and 8.33 MHz. The high or low time of BCLK can be stretched to synchronize it to four conditions, as outlined in the Intel 82358 datasheet.

16-bit master (MASTER1#16) is an input that indicates that a 16-bit EISA or ISA master has control of the EISA bus. It is sampled twice, at the beginning and at the end of START#. If negated at the first sampling time but asserted at the second sampling time, then it indicates to the EBC that a 32-bit EISA master is translating to 16 bits in order to perform burst operations.

16-bit memory (M16#) is a bidirectional open-collector signal that the ISA memory is capable of performing 16-bit transfers. It is an output during ISA master cycles and a host slave or EISA memory slave is accessed. It is an input during host bus master cycles and the EISA/ISA bus is accessed. It is an input during EISA master cycles.

Standard memory read control strobe (SMRDC#) is an output signal that commands the ISA memory to place data on the data bus. It is asserted during CPU, DMA or EISA/ISA master read cycles to 16-bit or 8-bit ISA memory slaves when the address range is less than one megabyte. It behaves like the MRDC# signal.

Standard memory write control strobe (SMWTC#) is an output signal that commands the ISA memory slave to accept data from the data bus. It is asserted during CPU, DMA or EISA/ISA master write cycles to a 16-bit or 8-bit ISA memory slaves when the address range is less than one megabyte.

Channel ready (CHRDY) is a bidirectional, open-collector signal which is used by the ISA slaves to insert wait states. It is an output during ISA master cycles and accesses host bus slaves or EISA slaves.

No wait states (NOWS#) is an input asserted by ISA slaves to request compressed standard wait states, and by EISA bus slaves to request compressed or 1.5 BCLK cycles.

System address bits 1 and 0 (SA1, SA0) are the least significant bits of the latched EISA address bus. They are inputs during ISA bus master and generate appropriate EISA bus or host bus controls. They are outputs during host bus master cycles and access EISA/ISA slaves. Further, they are outputs during EISA master cycles to ISA slaves and during DMA accesses to ISA memory.

System byte high enable (SBHE#) is a bidirectional signal that indicates the validity of the high byte on the EISA bus. It is an input during ISA bus master cycles and an output during host accesses to EISA/ISA slave. Further, it is an output during EISA master cycles to ISA slaves and during DMA accesses to ISA memory.

Refresh (REFRESH#) is an input which indicates that the ISP is performing a refresh-cycle. During refresh cycles the EBC generates the MRDC#, CMD# and other host bus signals to refresh the entire system's DRAM memory.

8.12.5 EBC and ISP Interface

The EBC and ISP have a tightly coupled interface, and they interact with the host bus requests, DMA status and EISA bus master size and other control and status signals which are described below:

- ISP hold request (DHOLD) is an input from the ISP which is used to request the host bus on behalf of ISA/EISA masters or when a DMA device requests service. DHOLD is used to generate HHOLD.
- ISP ready (DRDY) is a bidirectional signal. It is an input to the EBC when the ISP is in the slave mode. It is an output from the EBC during DMA cycles and refresh cycles.
- Greater than one megabyte (GT1M#) is an input to the EBC that indicates that the current address is above the 00000000h to 000FFFFFh range. If it is not asserted during a host bus master or during EISA/ISA bus master cycle, or during DMA cycles on accessing ISA memory slave, then the EBC generates SMRDC# or SMWTC# signals. The ISP generates the GT1M# signals for all cycles including DMA and non-DMA cycles.
- Host address greater than 16 megabytes (HGT16M#) is an input signal which indicates that the address of the current cycle is than 00FFFFFFh. It is driven on DMA cycles, based on the address from the ISP. This signal is used by the EBC during DMA cycles to determine whether to generate the ISA memory command signals, MRDC# and MWTC#. MRDC# and MWTC# are generated during DMA cycles but are inhibited when HGT16M# is active.
- DMA status (ST3-ST0) are bidirectional signals. They are inputs to the EBC during DMA and refresh cycles. They indicate the timing that has been programmed for the current cycle and the size of the I/O device involved in the DMA transfer. They are outputs form the EBC when the ISP is not a bus master. The four signals function as address strobe for the ISP, memory or I/O cycle indicator, interrupt acknowledge cycle indicator, and EISA bus master cycle indicator, respectively.
- EISA master (EXMASTER#) is an input signal to the EBC, which indicates that a 16-bit or 32-bit EISA master has control of the EISA bus. It is used with the MASTER16# signal to differentiate between 32-bit EISA masters, 16-bit EISA masters, and 16-bit ISA masters.
- Early indication of 16-bit ISA Master (EMSTR16#) is an input signal to the EBC which indicates that a 16-bit master is in control is or about to assume control of the EISA bus.

8.12.6 EBC and EBB Data and Address Buffer Controls

The host data and address buses are connected to the EISA/ISA data and address buses using the EISA bus buffer (EBB). The EBB has internal latches and the outputs can be controlled in either direction. Data from the EISA bus, can flow to the host bus on port B and and on an individual byte basis on port A. Data can be stored using the provided control signal. Data can also flow from the host bus to the EISA/ISA bus.

The EBB controls byte assembly. Bytes can be transferred as shown in Figure 8-19. The EBC provides signals used to copy the individual bytes. For multiple cycle operations the octal registered transceivers are used to temporarily store the data until an entire word or doubleword is assembled. Following assembly, the word or doubleword is transferred to the destination. Byte assembly logic is used for all bus size mismatches and non-aligned address translations between the host bus, a 32-bit or a 16-bit EISA bus and a 16-bit ISA bus. The EBC generates controls to steer the data buses, and to latch the address and data.

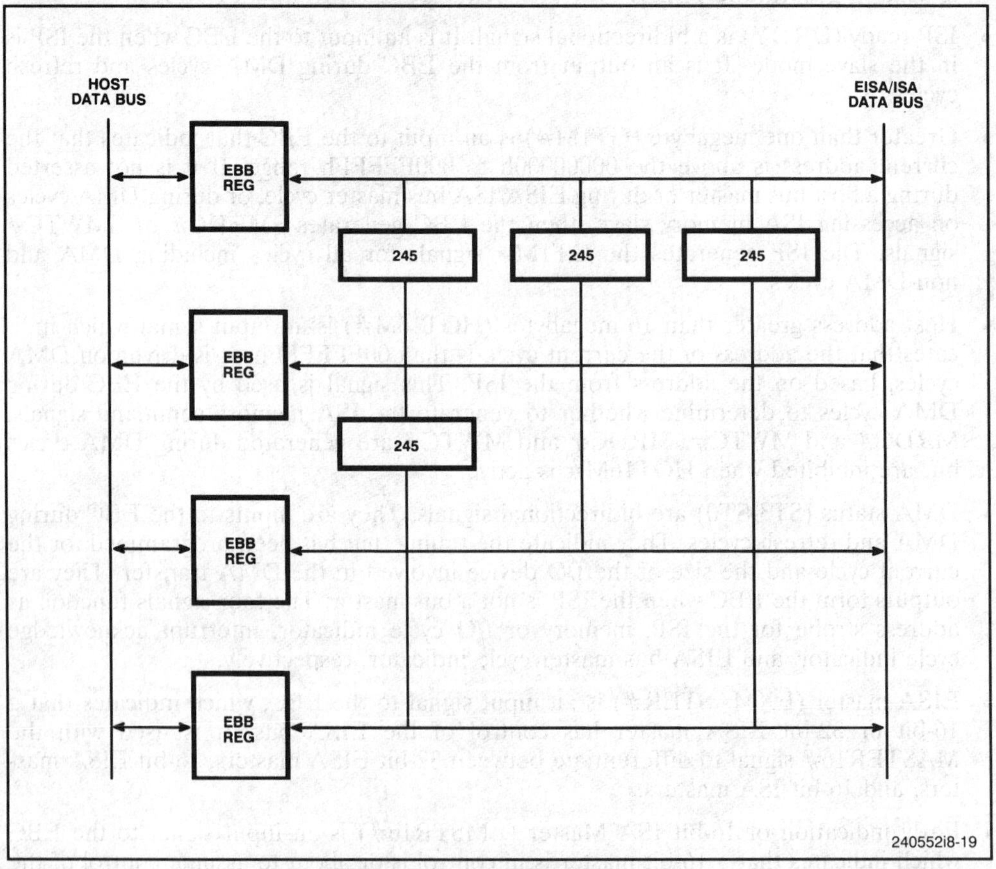

Figure 8-19. EBB Byte Transfer

Copy enable between bytes (SDCPYEN01#-03#, 13#) are output controls that enable the byte copy transceivers between the EISA bus bytes 0, 1, 2 and 3. Data bits 0-7 can be copied between data bits 8-15, 16-23 and 24-31. Data bits 8-15 can be copied between data bits 24-31.

Copy up (SDCPYUP) is an output that controls the direction of the byte copy transceivers, to copy the lower bytes to the higher bytes and vice versa.

System (EISA) to host data latch enables (SDHDLE3-0#) are outputs that control the latching of data from the EISA bus to the host bus.

System (EISA) data output enable (SDOE2-0#) are output enables to data buffers on the EISA bus.

Host data to system (EISA) data latch enables (HDSDLE1-0#) are outputs that control the latching of data from the host data bus to the EISA data bus.

Host data output enables (HDOE1#, 0#) are output enables to the host data bus buffers.

Host address bus to EISA LA bus output enable (HALAOE#) is an output signal which enables the output of the address buffers for host address bus bits 31-2 on to the EISALA bus bits 31-2. The signal is asserted during CPU, DMA and refresh cycles along with HALAOE#.

Host address latch enable (HALE#) is an output signal which latches the LA address bus on to the host address bus. The latch closes on the trailing edge, and the host address bus is held until the slave terminates the cycle.

EISA LA to EISA SA output enable (LASAOE#) is an output signal which enables the EISA LA bus bits 19-2 on the EISA SA bus. It is asserted during CPU, EISA bus master, DMA and refresh cycles.

EISA LA to host address output enable (LAHAOE#) is an output signal which enables address buffers from the EISA LA bits to the host address bus. It is asserted during EISA/ISA bus master cycles.

LA latch enable (LALE#) is an output signal which latches the host address bus on to the LA address bus. It is useful when the CPU operates in burst mode or when additional address pipelining is required on the host bus.

EISA SA to EISA LA output enable (SALAOE#) can be used to the output of the address buffers from the EISA SA bus bits 16-2 on to the EISA LA bus 16-2. It is asserted during ISA bus master cycles.

SA latch enable (SALE#) is an output signal which latches the LA address bus on to the SA address bus. It can be asserted during EISA master, CPU, regular DMA, and DMA burst cycles.

8.12.6.1 FUNCTIONS OF THE ISP

The ISP provides system arbitration, DMA control, interrupt control, and counting by using interval timer/counters.

The system arbiter on the ISP evaluates requests from several sources including DMA channels, EISA devices, refresh requesters, and the host CPU: DREQ is generated by 8-, 16-, or 32-bit devices that require DMA service; MREQ# is generated by 16-bit or 32-bit EISA device; and CPUMISS# is generated by the host CPU. Refresh requests are generated internally using the timers. Request priority is assigned on different levels, and at each level, devices are given rotating priority. Examples of priorities and assignments are shown in the ISP datasheet. The arbiter determines which requester receives the bus from EISA masters, DMA slaves, refresh requesters and the host CPU.

The on-chip DMA controller is functionally equivalent to two 8237 DMA controllers. Seven independent channels can be programmed. 8-, 16-, and 32-bit data widths are supported as are ISA compatible, ISA/EISA compatible, type A/type B modes, and EISA type C mode. Single, block, demand, or cascade transfer modes are supported. The DMA controller provides refresh address generation, and buffer chaining.

The ISP provides an ISA-compatible interrupt controller and the functionality of two 8259 interrupt controllers. The ISP can handle fourteen external interrupts and two internal interrupts. The internal interrupts are for internal functions only and not available externally. A non-maskable interrupt can be generated by hardware or software.

The ISP has five interval timers. The counter timers are addressed as if they are contained in two separate 8254 timers.

The ISP operates as a slave device or as a master device. In slave mode, the ISP monitors the address lines and decodes all bus cycles. Here, an EISA master or host bus master can read or write to any of the ISP registers. 16-bit ISA masters can read and write to any of the non-DMA registers and to some of the non-8237/PC AT compatible registers. In the master mode, the ISP becomes the bus master and can perform DMA or refresh cycles.

8.12.6.2 ISP-TO-HOST INTERFACE

Host addresses HA31-HA2 are tri-stateable address signals which connect to the host bus. HA31-HA20 and HA15-HA2 are bidirectional, while HA19-16 are outputs. In master mode all of the address lines are outputs. In slave mode HA15-2 and HA31-2 are inputs. Upon reset these lines are tri-stated and configured as inputs.

Byte enables (BE3#-BE0#) are tri-stateable EISA bus byte enables. In slave mode the BE2#-BE0# are inputs and are used to access ISP internal registers. In master mode BE3#-BE0# are outputs. BE3# is always an output.

Host write/read (HW/R#) is a bidirectional signal which indicates a read or write cycle. It is an input during slave mode and an output during master mode. It is sent to the EBC which propagates the appropriate read/write signals to the EISA bus. Upon reset this signal is tri-stated and configured as an input.

Slow down host CPU (SLOWH#) is an output from CPU slowdown timer 2, which is used to slow down the host CPU.

CPU cache miss (CPUMISS#) is an input signal from the host CPU, or the cache controller subsystem which indicates that a host bus cycle is pending and must contend for the next bus arbitration.

Hold acknowledge (DHLDA) is an input signal which indicates that the system has granted ISP to the host bus.

Interrupt (INT) is an output signal which indicates that an interrupt request is pending and must be serviced. Once asserted, it remains asserted until it receives the first INTA# pulse via the ST2# signal. Upon reset, the state of INT is undefined.

Non-maskable interrupt (NMI) is an output used to force a non-maskable interrupt to the host CPU. Once asserted, it remains asserted until the CPU reads to one of the NMI registers. Upon reset this signal is low.

Parity (Parity#) is an input from the system board which indicates a main memory parity error.

8.12.7 ISP to EISA Interface

DMA requests (DMA 7-5, 3-0) are inputs to the ISP, which indicate requests for control of the system bus. They are generated externally by DMA subsystems or by 16-bit masters.

DMA acknowledge (DACK 7-5, 3-0) are outputs from the ISP which indicate that the bus has been granted to the respective requester.

Master requests (MREQ 5-0) are slot-specific inputs to the ISP, which are used by EISA masters to request bus access.

Master acknowledges (MACK# 5-0) are outputs from the ISP that acknowledge that the bus has been granted to a requesting EISA master.

Refresh (REFRESH#) is a bidirectional signal. It is an output during refresh cycles and should be used to refresh the entire system memory at once. It is an output only when the ISP DMA is a bus master, while an internal request for a refresh cycle is generated in the ISP. The REFRESH# is an input when an expansion bus adapter acts as a 16-bit ISA bus master.

Start of cycle (START#) is an input which connects to the EISA START# signal. Command (CMD#) is an input connects directly to the EISA CMD# signal. It is used to tri-state the data buffers following a read cycle.

End of process (EOP) is a bidirectional signal which is directly connected to the TC signal of the ISA/EISA bus. It is used in three modes: as an input in one mode, it is used by DMA slaves to stop DMA transfers; as an input from a slave in a second mode, as a terminal count; as an output in a third mode, and it indicates that a chain buffer has expired and that a new chain buffer must be programmed. Interrupt request (IRQ 15-3,1) are interrupt inputs to the ISP.

Byte enables (BE 3-0) are the EISA bus byte enables. BE2-0 are bidirectional, and BE0 is output only. In master mode, the ISP drives these lines. In slave mode the BE2-0 are inputs to the ISP and are used to access the internal registers.

Ready signal (DRDY) is a bidirectional signal. In slave mode, it is an output which is driven when the ISP detects a slave write to its registers. In master mode, it is an input which indicates to the DMA controller that the current cycle has completed and that the DMA controller must pipeline addresses for DMA burst transfers.

Data (D7-0) are bidirectional signals that function as outputs when the ISP is in the slave mode. These signals are not used in the master mode. The pins are in a output mode when CSOUT# is asserted during an I/O read or interrupt acknowledge cycle.

Slave mode selected (CSOUT#) is an output from the ISP which indicates that it is accessed in the slave mode.

Address enable (AEN#) is an output signal, which indicates whether the host, EISA, or ISA is the current bus master.

I/O check bus error (IOCHK#) is an input from the ISA bus and is used for parity error checks and for other high priority interrupts. It can be programmed to cause a non-maskable interrupt.

MULTIBUS II System Interface

9

CHAPTER 9
MULTIBUS II SYSTEM INTERFACE

Industry-standard system bus interfaces provide compatibility between existing and newly developed technology. This compatibility safeguards hardware investments against obsolescence. The original MULTIBUS I interface provided this expansion path for early systems. The newer MULTIBUS II interface extends Intel's Open Systems design strategy to the world of 32-bit systems.

Among the features supported by Intel's MULTIBUS II architecture are:

- 32-bit multiplexed data and address bus.
- 40-Mbytes-per-second throughput.
- Processor-independent system architecture.
- Four address spaces:

  Two Processor Address Spaces – memory and I/O
  Two MULTIBUS II Address Spaces – interconnect and message
- Optimized interprocessor data transfer and communication.
- Implementation of the IEEE/ANSI 1296 standard in silicon (82389).
- Bounded interrupt response time.
- Software-defined interconnection for easy system configuration and integration.
- Parity protection.

MULTIBUS II board designs can be greatly simplified with Intel's 82389 *message passing coprocessor* (MPC) interface chip. The 82389 MPC can easily be designed into MULTIBUS II microcomputer boards. This basic board design can be augmented in firmware to include many of the ease-of-use features of MULTIBUS II architecture, such as configuration, initialization, and diagnostics.

This chapter focuses on the interface between the i486 processor and the MULTIBUS II parallel system bus using the 82389 MPC. The design examples assume some familiarity with the MULTIBUS II architecture described in the *IEEE 1296 High Performance Synchronous 32-bit Bus Standard Handbook*.

9.1 PARALLEL SYSTEM BUS (PSB)

The system interface (system bus) for the MULTIBUS II architecture is called the *parallel system bus* (PSB). This bus implements the signals of the IEEE/ANSI 1296 standard. The bus has a 32-bit multiplexed data and address path capable of 40-Mbyte-per-second throughput. The bus provides the bounded worst-case interrupt latency and high bus availability needed for high-performance systems. Multiple processors can communicate over the bus with a high-speed data packet transfer scheme called *message passing*.

Microprocessor-based MULTIBUS II boards from all vendors are implemented with the same bus interface component – the message passing coprocessor (MPC). The result is a high degree of compatibility across different vendors' boards. Moreover, the MPC greatly simplifies the hardware design of message passing boards.

The boards are based on the Eurocard format. This format, commonly called a 6U board, is shown in Figure 9-1 with typical devices populating the board. The standard size is 233.35 mm x 220 mm deep. The board has two DIN connectors, P1 and P2. All

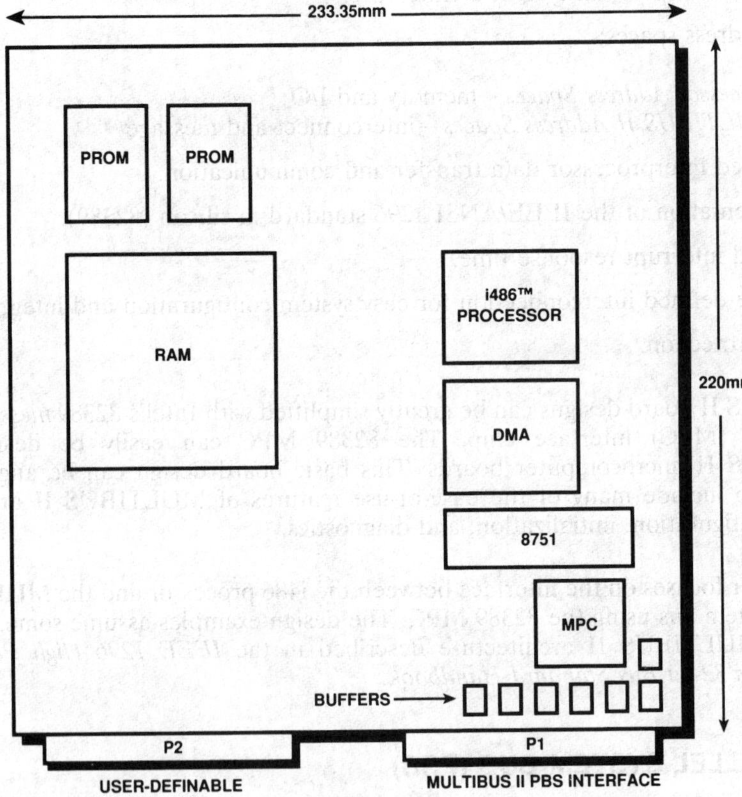

Figure 9-1. Example MULTIBUS II Architecture Board Layout

PSB connections are satisfied by P1, a 96-pin DIN connector. P2 is user-definable; it may be used for such purposes as memory expansion, additional power requirements, or specialized I/O. P2 would be an excellent candidate for the tightly-coupled interface between the i486 processor and its off-board memory. In this architecture, an application-optimized bus can be coupled with an open-system bus. Using this architecture, system components such as terminal I/O, disk drive interface and LAN boards residing on the PSB are unaffected by processor changes.

Other features make the MULTIBUS II architecture an excellent basis for complex systems. These features include ease of system configuration and integration provided by the interconnect address space (see Section 9.5) and high reliability provided by the parity protected data and control signals. Many I/O, memory, general-purpose processing, and dedicated-function boards based on the MULTIBUS II architecture are available from Intel and other manufacturers.

9.1.1 PSB Interface

The parallel system bus (PSB); is optimized for interprocessor data transfer and communication. Its burst transfer capability provides a maximum sustained bandwidth of 40 megabytes per second for high-performance data transfers. A functional subsystem board interfaced to the PSB is called a *bus agent*. The PSB supports four address spaces per bus agent:

- *Traditional Processor-Supported Address Spaces*:

  Memory space.
  I/O space.

- *New MULTIBUS II Address Spaces*:

  Interconnect space.
  Message space.

The 255-address message space supports interprocessor message passing. The IEEE 1296 message passing protocol has been standardized and implemented in hardware for high performance. A processor typically performs interprocessor communications inefficiently. The 82389 MPC is an intelligent bus interface component capable of message passing. It allows two bus agents to exchange a block of data at full bus bandwidth without supervision from a processor. This shifts the burden of interprocessor communication away from the processor and enhances system performance.

The interconnect space allows geographic addressing, which identifies bus agents by slot number. Every MULTIBUS II system contains a *central services module* (CSM);. The CSM provides system services such as uniform initialization and bus timeout detection, for all bus agents on the PSB bus. The CSM; may use the registers of the interconnect space of each bus agent to configure the agent dynamically. Stake pin jumpers, DIP switches, and other hardware-configuration devices can be eliminated. Because the i486 processor can access only memory space or I/O space, the message space and interconnect space may be mapped into the memory space or the I/O space. Decoding logic can provide chip-select signals for the devices implementing the message space and the interconnect space, as well as for devices in the memory and I/O space.

9.1.2 PSB Operation

Operations on the PSB are performed as one of three bus cycles:

- Arbitration cycles.
- Transfer cycles.
- Exception handling cycles.

Arbitration cycles determine the next owner of the bus. These cycles consist of a resolution phase, in which competing bus agents determine priority for bus control, and an acquisition phase, in which the bus agent with the highest priority initiates a transfer cycle.

Transfer cycles perform a data transfer between the bus owner and another bus agent. This cycle consists of a request phase, in which address and control signals are driven, and a reply phase, in which the two agents perform a handshake to synchronize the data transfer. The reply phase is repeated and data transfers continue until the bus owner ends the transfer cycle.

Exception cycles indicate that an error has occurred during a transfer cycle. This cycle consists of a signal phase, in which an exception signal from one bus agent causes all other bus agents to terminate any arbitration or transfer cycles in progress, and a recovery phase, in which the exception signals go inactive. A new arbitration cycle can begin on the clock after the recovery phase.

9.2 THE 82389 MESSAGE PASSING COPROCESSOR (MPC)

MULTIBUS II boards from all manufacturers are implemented with the same bus controller—a message passing coprocessor (MPC). This ensures a high degree of compatibility across different manufacturers' boards. Moreover, the MPC chip greatly simplifies the hardware design of message passing boards and reduces the software burden by assisting data movement. To further reduce the software complexity Intel has defined a higher-level data communication protocol above the standard MPC bus interface called *MULTIBUS II Transport*. This communication protocol is analogous to the OSI transport layer.

Intel's 82389 MPC is a 70,000-transistor VLSI device whose functional block diagram is shown in Figure 9-2. This MPC implements the MULTIBUS II parallel system bus (PSB) specification.

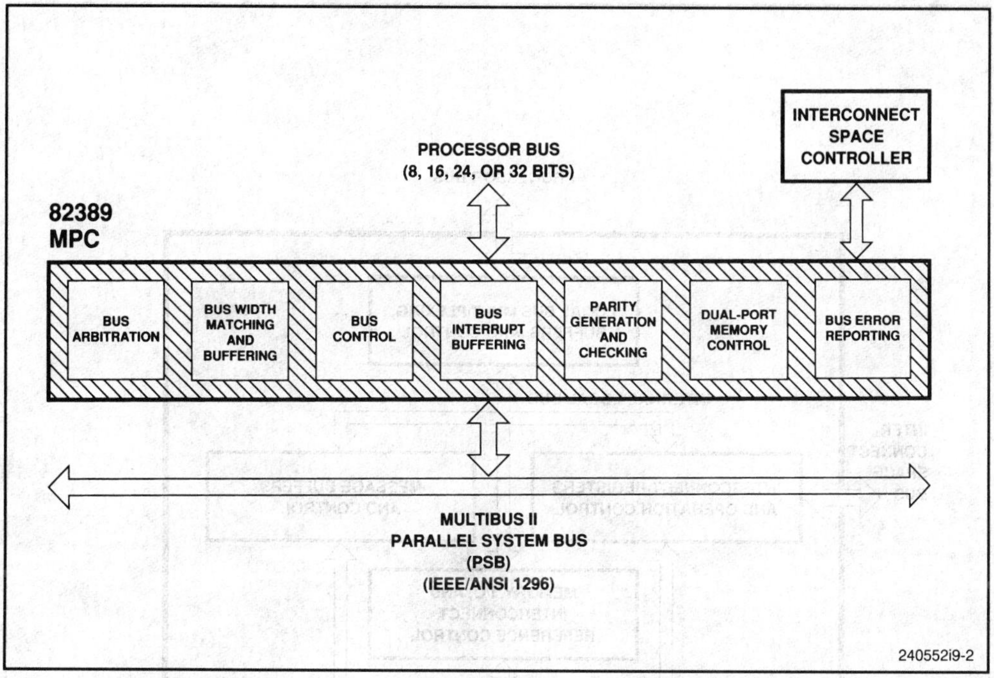

Figure 9-2. Message Passing Coprocessor (MPC) Block Diagram

The MPC contains almost all of the logic needed to interface any microprocessor to the parallel system bus. A complete MULTIBUS II interface can be assembled from the MPC, some bus transceivers, and a microcontroller such as the Intel 8751. Figure 9-3 shows how the interface signals of the MPC are partitioned to support four major interfaces:

- PSB bus interface.
- Processor bus (local bus) interface.
- Interconnect space bus.
- Dual-port memory control interface.

With the 82389 MPC, the PSB bus interface is very straightforward. This simplifies board design and ensures compatibility with other boards. The processor bus interface offers board designers more options. For example, an 8-, 16-, 24-, or 32-bit local processor may be used. There are also signals to control DMA or assist in dual-port memory operations. Optional external logic to support dual-port memory selection and off-board memory and I/O references may be included if needed.

All of Intel's MULTIBUS II boards use an 8751 microcontroller working in association with the MPC to implement the interconnect space. However, some board manufacturers have chosen to implement this function using the host processor or a simple state machine.

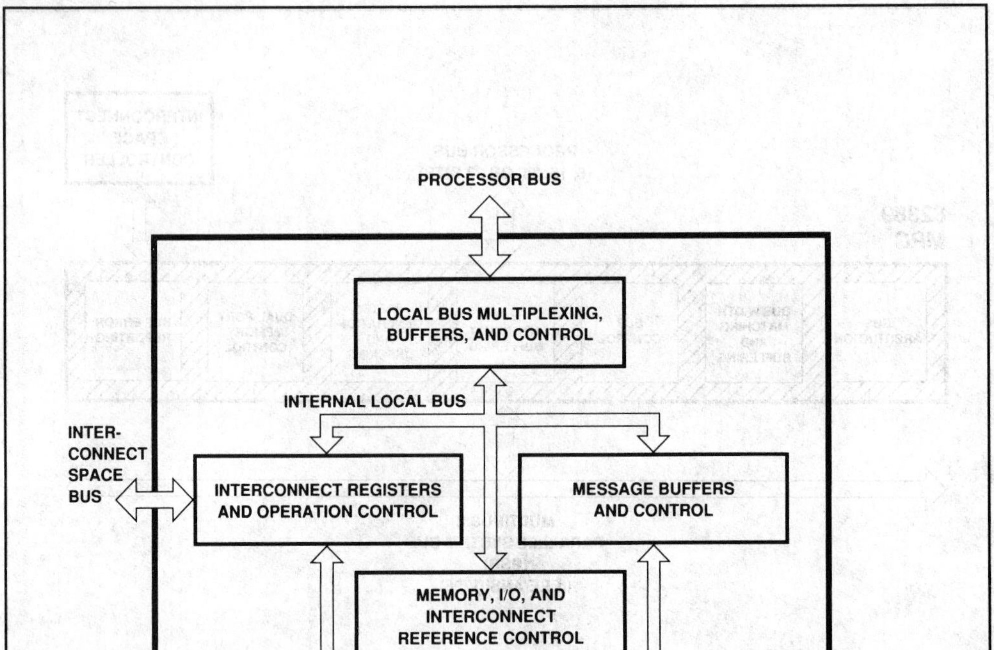

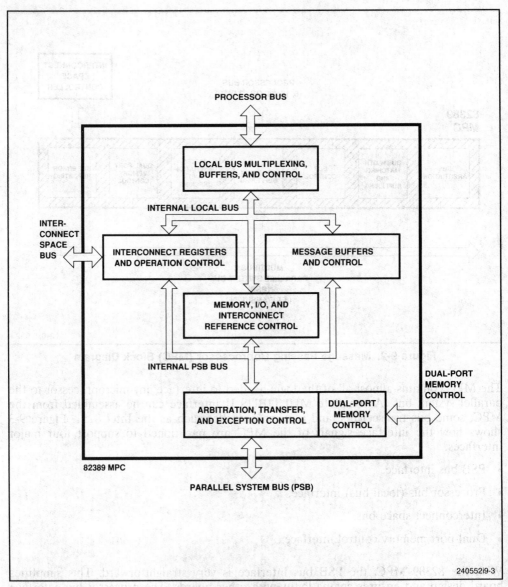

Figure 9-3. MPC Device Interface

9.3 AN MPC INTERFACE EXAMPLE

The MPC bus controller is by far the simplest, easiest, and least expensive method of implementing an intelligent MULTIBUS II PSB interface. The MPC as defined by the MULTIBUS II standard is a processor-independent device; any processor can interface to the MPC and, through the MPC, to the MULTIBUS II PSB system bus. The remainder of this chapter focuses specifically on the Intel 82389 MPC and the i486 processor.

9.3.1 CPU-to-MPC Interface

A block diagram of the MPC interfacing directly to the i486 processor bus is shown in Figure 9-4. Since the processor uses a 32-bit data bus, all byte-enable signals are connected directly between the chips. All of the processor's data signals are also connected directly to the MPC data signals.

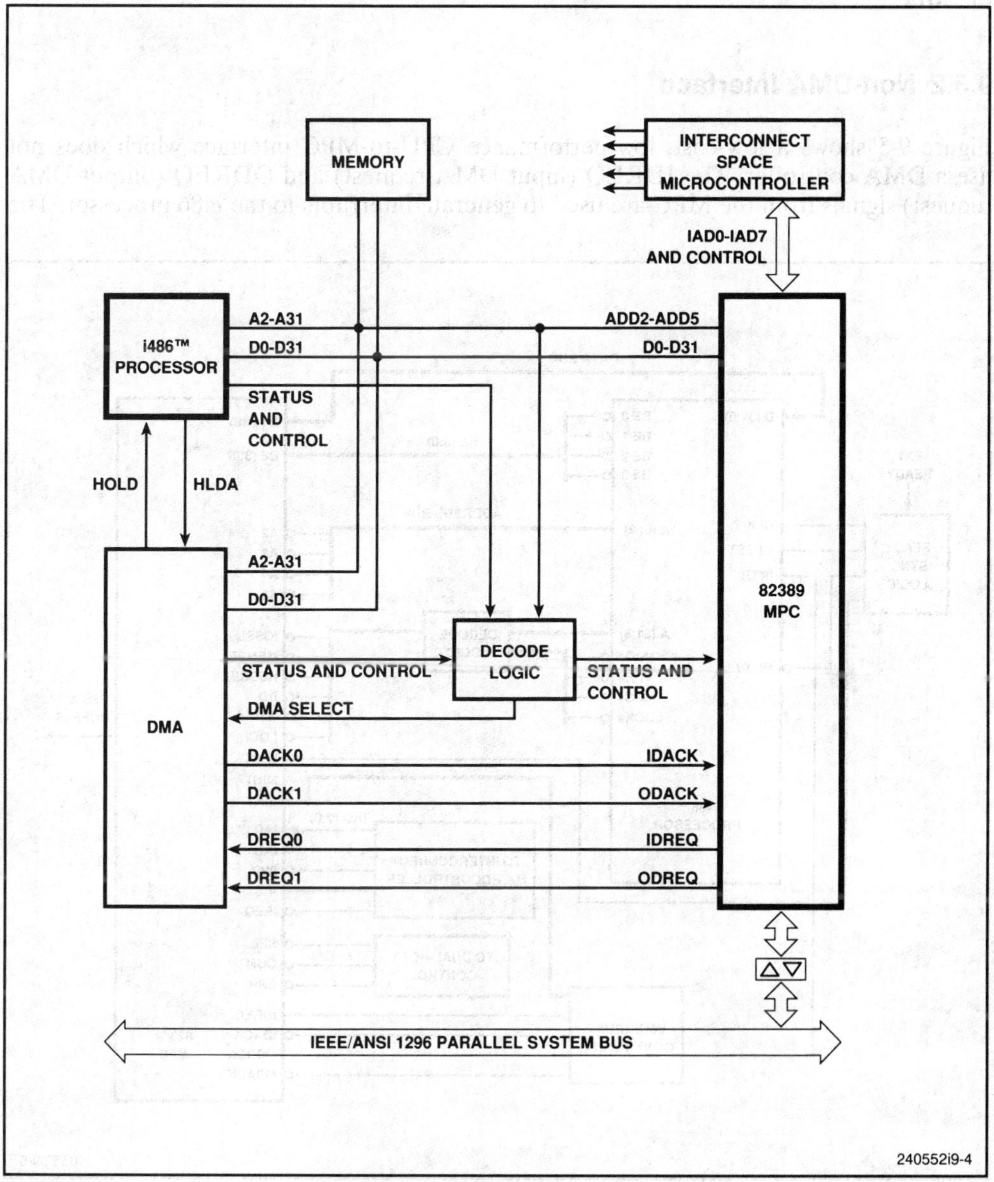

Figure 9-4. MPC Interface Example

The i486 processor has 30 address signals, A2-A31. Signals A2-A5 from the processor connect directly to A2-A5 on the MPC. The timing of these signals is controlled within the processor. The remaining address signals (A6-A31), the cycle definition signals (W/R#, M/IO#, and D/C#), and the LOCK# signal are routed through decode logic which determines whether the address is to PSB memory, PSB I/O, or an MPC register. The cycle definition and LOCK# signals are also used to determine the type of operation the i486 processor is performing—e.g. locked or unlocked cycles, or WAIT# to the MPC.

9.3.2 Non-DMA Interface

Figure 9-5 shows a low-cost, low-performance CPU-to-MPC interface which does not use a DMA controller. The IDREQ (input DMA request) and ODREQ (output DMA request) signals from the MPC are used to generate interrupts to the i486 processor. The

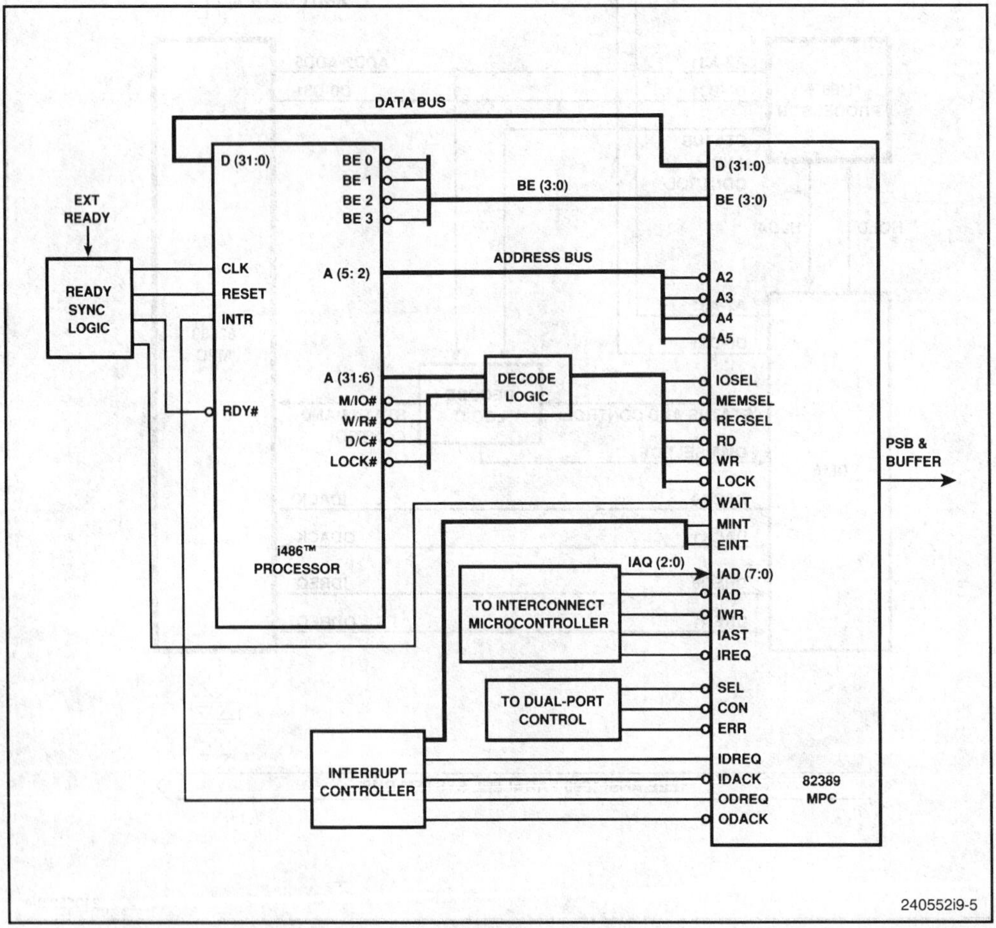

Figure 9-5. CPU-to-MPC Interface without DMA

processor's string-move instructions can be used to load or unload the MPC's message FIFOs within interrupt service routines. There are two bits within the MPC status register which assist this process. The SOCMP bit indicates successful transmission of a solicited message. The SICMP bit indicates successful reception of a solicited message.

The state of the completion bits, SOCMP and SICMP, can be checked by one of two methods: (1) polling the status register, or (2) enabling the message interrupt signal, MINT, by setting the SOCIE (for transmitting) or SICIE (for receiving) bit in the status register. On the completion of a message transfer or reception, the MINT signal is asserted and can be used to interrupt the processor.

9.3.3 DMA Interface

If a DMA controller is used (shown in Figure 9-6), the MPC initiates a DMA operation by asserting its IDREQ (input DMA request) or ODREQ (output DMA request) signal to the DMA controller. IDREQ indicates a data transfer from the PSB bus to a device on the processor bus; ODREQ indicates a transfer in the opposite direction.

When the DMA controller has received a request from the MPC, the DMA arbitrates for the processor bus and sends an acknowledge signal back to the MPC indicating that access to the processor bus has been obtained. The acknowledge signals are IDACK# and ODACK#. When the MPC receives the acknowledge signal, the DMA controller starts the DMA operation. The MPC request signal to the DMA stays asserted until the entire DMA operation is finished. However, the DMA acknowledge signal to the MPC may go inactive at various times during the operation because the DMA controller can give up and regain the bus during a transfer.

A DMA controller can transfer data between memory or I/O and the MPC faster than the i486 processor can. The i486 processor cannot do direct (flyby) memory-to-I/O or memory-to-memory transfers; instead it must read data into its registers before writing it out again. A DMA controller that supports burst operations is the most efficient choice. With burst transfers, every memory address generated by the DMA controller reads or writes 16 bytes of data. The i486 processor, by contrast, can burst 16 bytes during memory reads, but it can only burst 4 bytes during memory writes (and then only on 8- or 16-bit data buses).

9.3.4 DMA Duty Cycle

Some DMA controllers have a programmable duty cycle; or bus throttle. This is a mechanism which disables the DMA channels periodically to limit their bus usage. If processor-bus latency is a concern (as in a real-time environment), a duty-cycle control within the DMA is necessary to limit the DMA from consuming all of the processor bus bandwidth.

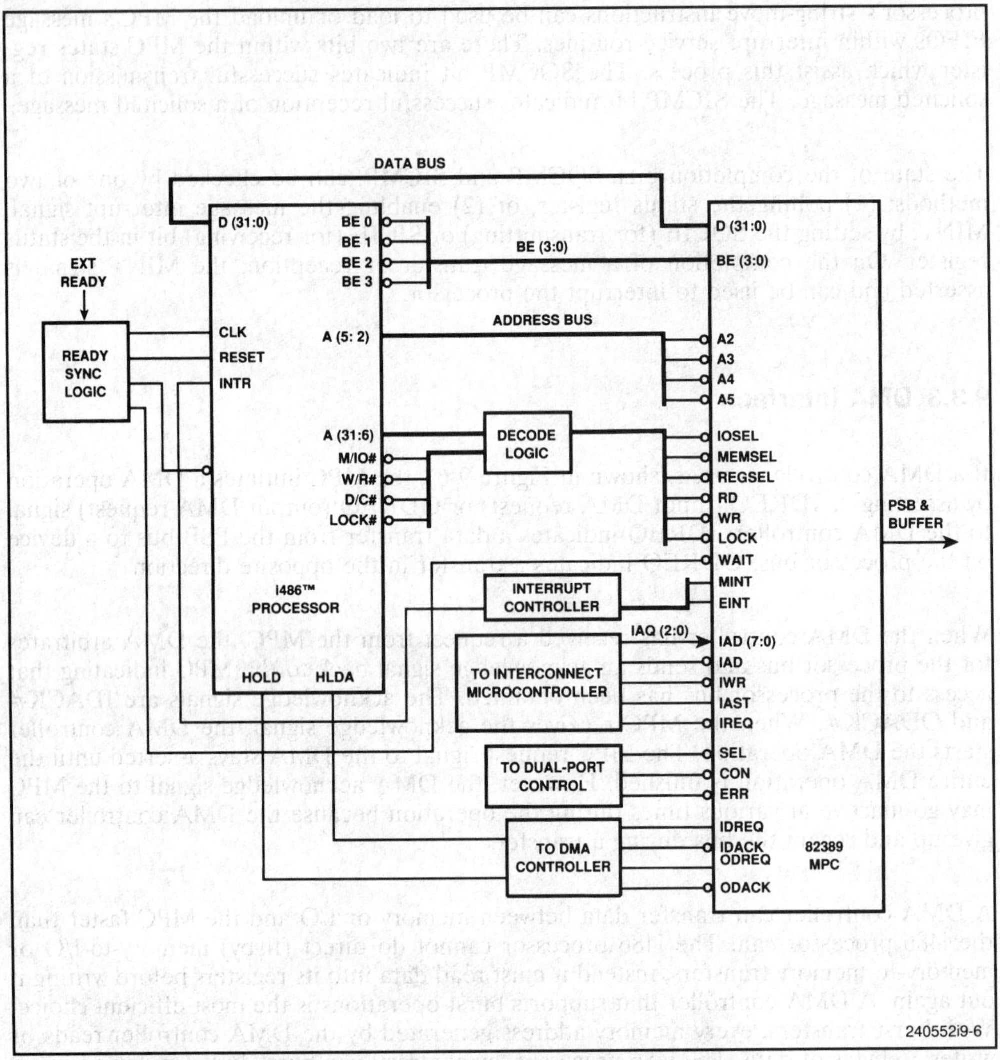

Figure 9-6. CPU-to-MPC Interface with DMA

The MPC also has a bus throttle which is used to control the duty cycle on the PSB. The MPC throttle is used when a fast board is sending messages to a slow board. The receiving MPC tells the sending MPC to insert delays between messages by giving it a duty-cycle parameter. This allows the receiving MPC in the slow board to unload its message before the next one is received.

9.4 PSB INTERFACE AND OPERATION EXAMPLES

All of the complex timing and control logic necessary to connect the MPC to the PSB are contained within the MPC. It is not necessary to understand all the PSB signals on the

P1 connector. For the actual definition and operation of these signals, refer to the *IEEE 1296 High Performance Synchronous 32-bit Bus Standard Handbook*.

The specification for the maximum printed circuit board metal-trace length to bus drivers at the P1 connector is important. The IEEE/ANSI 1296 specification defines a backplane which ensures reliable transmission of signals for a 10-MHz clock in a 2-to-21 slot system. To ensure that individual boards do not disturb the characteristics of the backplane, each board must have its bus driver components within 2.5 metal-trace inches of the connector.

Because of the maximum trace-length; requirement to P1, and the simplicity of the buffering logic from the MPC to the PSB, many manufacturers' boards look very similar in this corner of the board.

9.4.1 Minimal P1 Interconnection

The interface between the MPC and the P1 connector consists primarily of bidirectional bus drivers, buffers, and straight connections. The address/data, parity, and system control signals all need bidirectional buffering. The MPC generates all of these signals and the necessary direction controls to point the buffers in the right directions in a transfer cycle. The arbitration signals, bus request, bus error, and reset-not-complete are all driven on the bus directly by the MPC.

There are 32 buffered address/data (BAD) signals on P1. All 32 must be buffered even if an 8- or 16-bit processor is used. The IEEE/ANSI 1296 specification requires all MULTIBUS II boards to decode the full 32-bit range of the memory address space. This eliminates all possible address-aliasing problems that can be encountered with boards that address less than the full 32 bits. The full 32-bit bus-drive capability is also always needed for message passing.

The bidirectional signals need 48 to 64mA of current sinking capability. The 74F245 transceiver—an octal bidirectional device with three-state inputs and outputs—is recommended for this purpose. Seven of these devices (5 for BAD and 2 for control signals) are necessary to connect the MPC to the PSB. Figure 9-7 shows this buffering between P1 and the MPC.

9.4.2 Memory and I/O Referencing on the PBS

If the board only communicates with other boards via message passing, the implementation shown in Figure 9-7 is adequate. However, if memory and I/O cycles are performed on the system bus additional logic is needed to put addresses on the PSB.

Because the i486 processor bus is de-multiplexed, the MPC does not provide the path to the multiplexed PSB for the address of memory or I/O cycles. To multiplex the address onto the PSB, a set of 74AS240 buffers is used to pass the local address (LA) around the MPC to the 74F245 transceivers. This is shown in Figure 9-8.

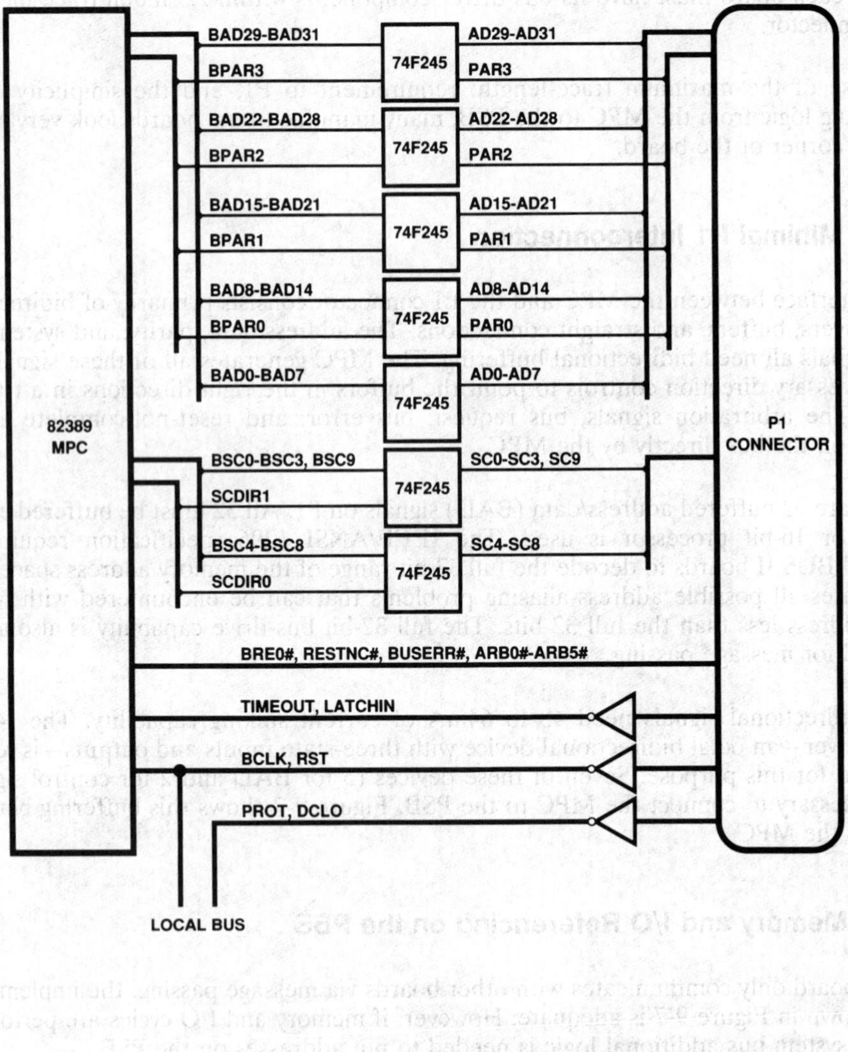

Figure 9-7. Minimal P1 Interconnection Example

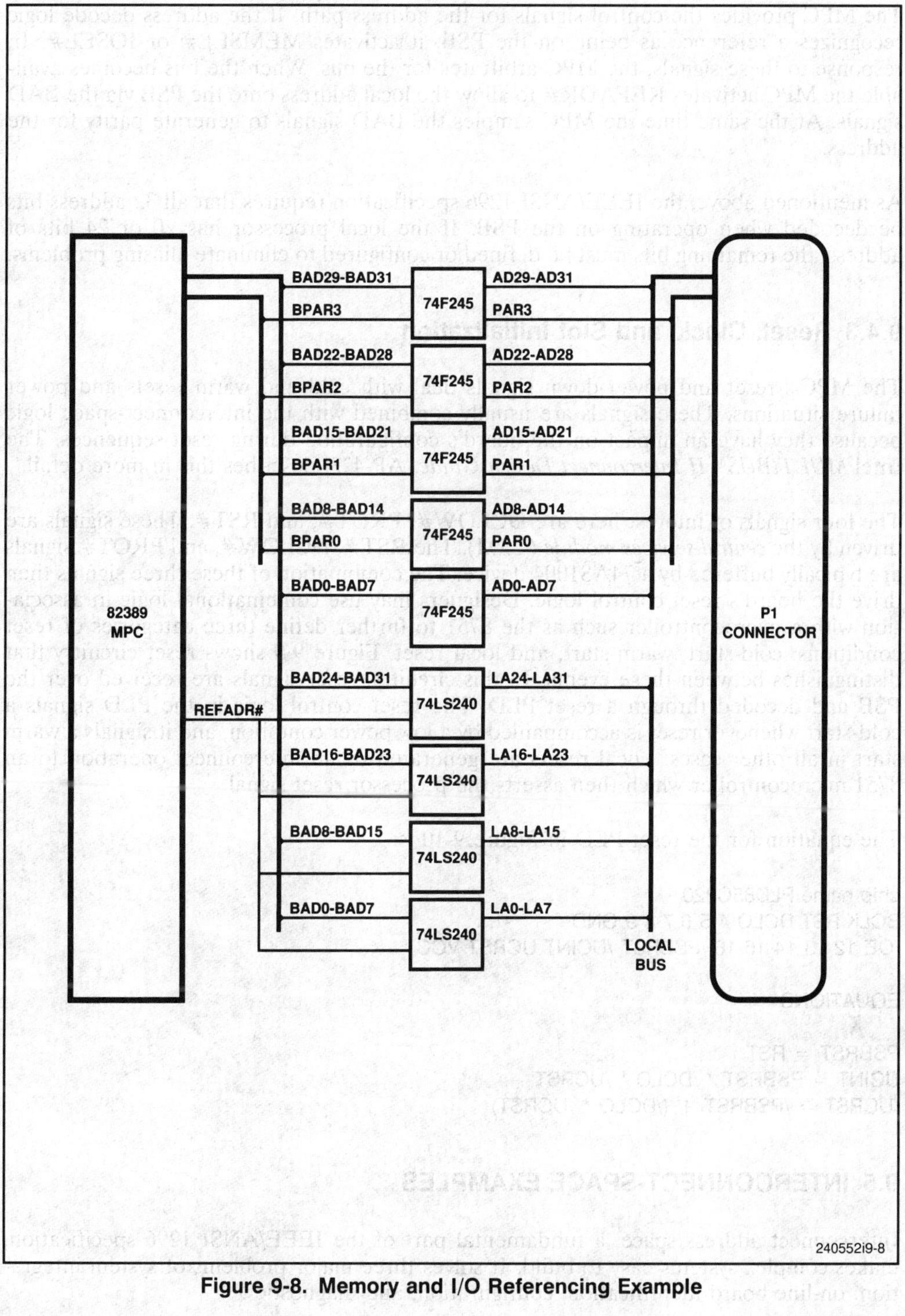

Figure 9-8. Memory and I/O Referencing Example

The MPC provides the control signals for the address path. If the address decode logic recognizes a reference as being on the PSB, it activates MEMSEL# or IOSEL#. In response to these signals, the MPC arbitrates for the bus. When the bus becomes available the MPC activates REFADR# to allow the local address onto the PSB via the BAD signals. At the same time the MPC samples the BAD signals to generate parity for the address.

As mentioned above, the IEEE/ANSI 1296 specification requires that all 32 address bits be decoded when operating on the PSB. If the local processor has 20 or 24 bits of address, the remaining bits must be defined or configured to eliminate aliasing problems.

9.4.3 Reset, Clock, and Slot Initialization

The MPC's reset and power-down signals deal with cold and warm resets and power failure situations. These signals are usually combined with the interconnect-space logic because they have an impact on the board's configuration during reset sequences. The Intel *MULTIBUS® II Interconnect Design Guide*, AP-423, describes this in more detail.

The four signals of interest here are DCLOW#, PROT#, and RST#. These signals are driven by the *central services module* (CSM). The RST#, DCLOW#, and PROT# signals are typically buffered by a 74AS1004 device. The combination of these three signals then drive the board's reset control logic. Designers may use combinational logic in association with a microcontroller such as the 8751 to further define three categories of reset conditions: cold-start, warm-start, and local reset. Figure 9-9 shows reset circuitry that distinguishes between these events. In this circuitry, reset signals are received over the PSB and decoded through a reset PLD. The reset control logic in the PLD signals a cold-start whenever reset is accompanied by a low power condition, and it signals a warm start in all other cases. Local resets are generated by an interconnect operation to an 8751 microcontroller which then asserts the processor reset signal.

The equation for the reset PLD in Figure 9-10 is:

```
chip name PLD85C220
BCLK RST DCLO 4 5 6 7 8 9 GND
/OE 12 13 14 15 16 /PSBRST /UCINT UCRST VCC

EQUATIONS

PSBRST = RST
UCINT = PSBRST * /DCLO * /UCRST
/UCRST = /PSBRST + (/DCLO * /UCRST)
```

9.5 INTERCONNECT-SPACE EXAMPLES

Interconnect address space, a fundamental part of the IEEE/ANSI 1296 specification, makes complex systems easy to build. It solves three major problems of system integration: on-line board identification, configuration, and diagnostics.

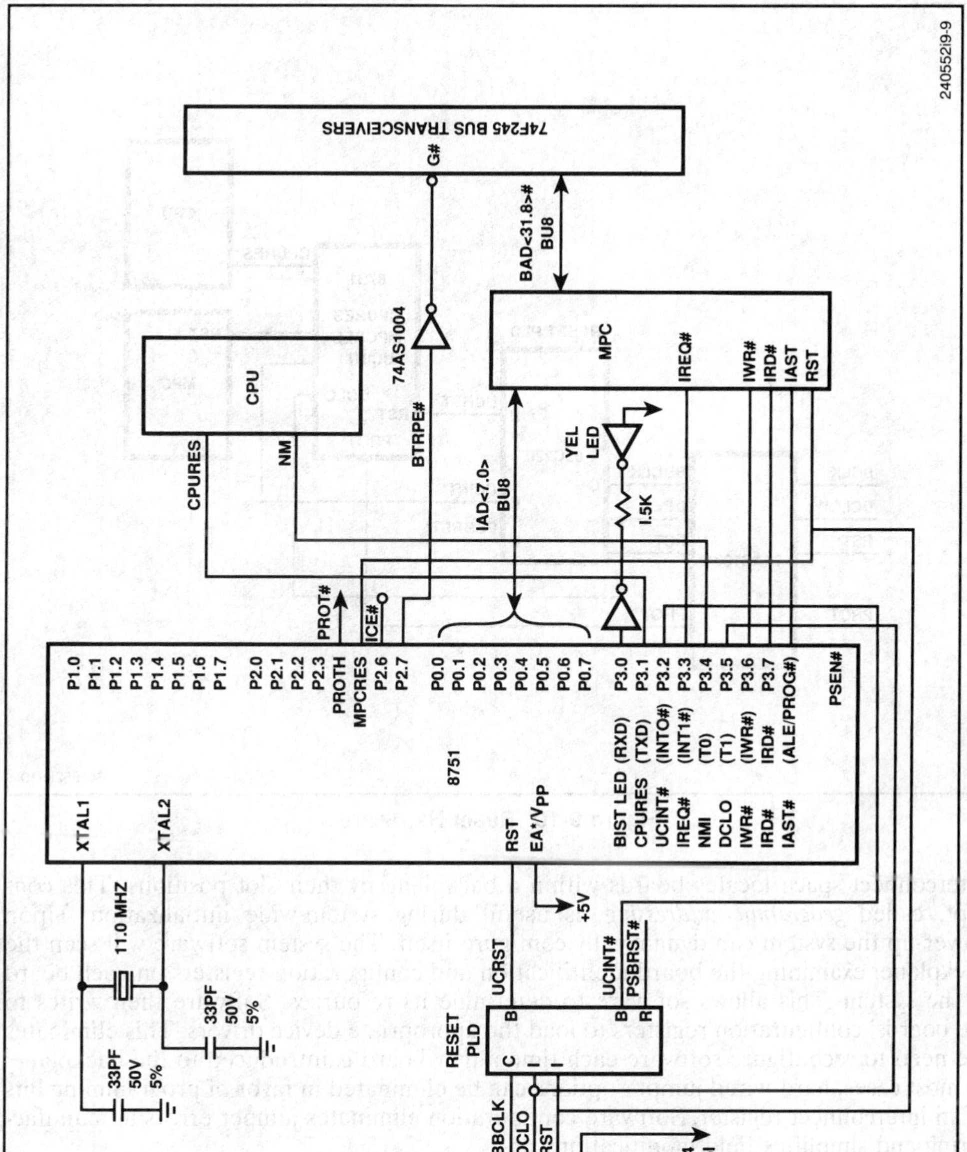

Figure 9-9. Microcontroller-to-MPC Interconnection

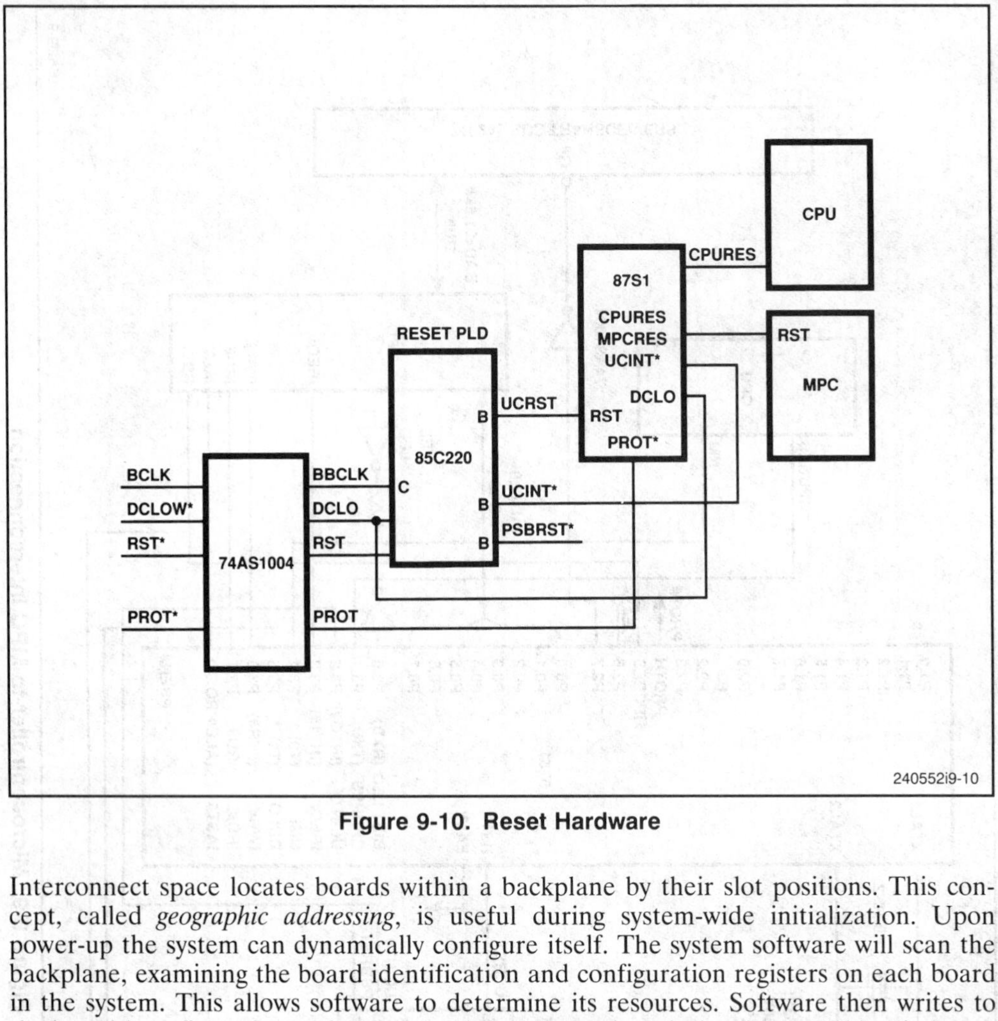

Figure 9-10. Reset Hardware

Interconnect space locates boards within a backplane by their slot positions. This concept, called *geographic addressing*, is useful during system-wide initialization. Upon power-up the system can dynamically configure itself. The system software will scan the backplane, examining the board identification and configuration registers on each board in the system. This allows software to determine its resources. Software then writes to the boards' configuration registers to load the appropriate device drivers. This eliminates the need to reconfigure software each time a new board is introduced to the backplane. In most cases, hard-wired jumper options can be eliminated in favor of programming bits in an interconnect register. Software configuration eliminates jumper errors in manufacturing and simplifies field modifications.

The usefulness of interconnect-space standardization is demonstrated in Intel's standard diagnostic philosophy. In this philosophy, each board has the capability to test itself and report error status in its interconnect space if problems exist. A subset of the complete on-board diagnostics are run during power-on initialization and extensive testing can be invoked from the operator's console. Several provisions have been made within the Intel MPC bus controller to allow implementation of cost-effective interconnect space. On Intel boards, an 8751 microcontroller is used together with an MPC bus controller to implement interconnect space. In other designs, the host processor or a simple state machine may also implement interconnect space. For more information on interconnect-space hardware and software, see Intel Application Note AP-423.

9.5.1 8751 Microcontroller Implementation

An 8751 microcontroller implementation of interconnect space is efficient from a real-estate point of view and it adds to the functionality of the interconnect space. The microcontroller resets the processor, configures resources on the board, and runs board diagnostics in conjunction with the processor. The microcontroller also translates complex functions into what appear as a uniform set of registers. Other boards can then access these uniform registers to learn the interconnect configuration or request the execution of diagnostics.

The MPC provides a directly compatible multiplexed address and data bus requiring no logic external to the 8751 microcontroller. Figure 9-9 shows typical microcontroller-to-MPC interconnect circuitry. The eight multiplexed address and data signals, IAD0-IAD7, are taken directly from Port 0 (P0) of the microcontroller. The address and data transfer operations are controlled by the microcontroller's interconnect address strobe (IAST), interconnect read (IRD#), and interconnect write (IWR#) signals. While the primary purpose of the IAD bus is to provide a communication path between the MPC and the interconnect subsystem, the MPC will remain at high impedance for addresses 0 through 7FH. This condition presents an opportunity for I/O port expansion, as discussed later in this section.

From a hardware viewpoint, the MPC is a slave to the 8751 microcontroller. The MPC supplies an external interrupt (IREQ#) whenever it needs service and the microcontroller satisfies the request. A typical interconnect operation is triggered by the MPC recognizing an interconnect-space address from the i486 processor or the PSB. The MPC then sends an interrupt request to the microcontroller, requesting an interconnect access. The microcontroller then reads the address and data off the IAD bus and executes the appropriate interconnect service routine. Eight signals of port 3 (P3) and four signals of port 2 (P2) are reserved, in addition to the IAD bus on P0, for support of the core interconnect design.

9.5.2 Configuration Through Interconnect Space

Hardware options allow users to configure or access on-board resources through the interconnect space. For boards that contain user-supplied optional devices, it is desirable to include an interconnect status register to report whether or not the device is present. If present, system software can program the device with the appropriate driver. Intel's iSBX™ Single-Board Extension Bus and MULTIMODULE™ compatible numeric processors are examples of products which provide these hardware options.

One common technique for detecting a module's presence is to have the 8751 microcontroller; read a port pin that ties to ground. The microcontroller's 8-bit P1 and P2 ports are pulled up internally, indicating that the addressed modules are not present. A jumper can be installed to override the pull-up and allow verification of the module's presence.

The simplest method for interfacing additional devices to an 8751 microcontroller is to connect the device directly to a microcontroller pin. Even a modest interconnect scheme can exceed the available port resources of the microcontroller, especially when a byte-wide data path is needed. Many port expansion techniques exist for such applications. The design criteria for using a particular technique include board-space requirements, cost, bidirectionality, and ease of programming.

An example of interfacing a complex, bidirectional peripheral to the 8751 IAD bus is shown in Figure 9-11.

9.6 Related Documentation

For more information on the MULTIBUS II architecture and interfacing, see the following documents:

- *MSA Bootstrap Specification* (Order # 455975).
- *MULTIBUS® II Initialization & Diagnostics Specification* (Order # 454077).
- *MULTIBUS® II Transport Protocol Specification & Designers Guide* (Order # 453508).
- *MULTIBUS® II Interconnect Interface Specification* (Order # 149299).
- *IEEE 1296, High Performance Synchronous 32-bit Bus Standard Handbook.*

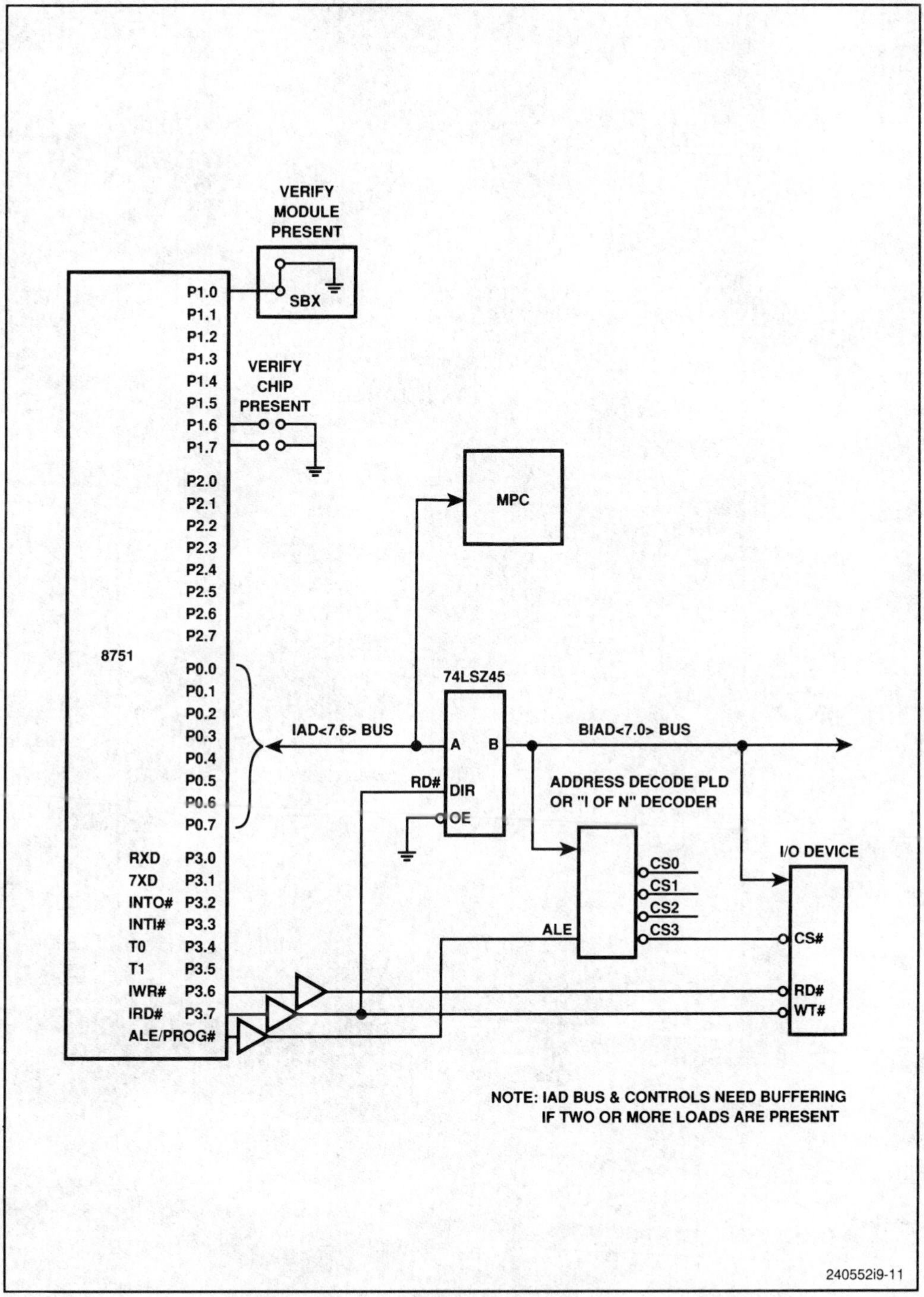

Figure 9-11. On-Board Resource Configuration Example

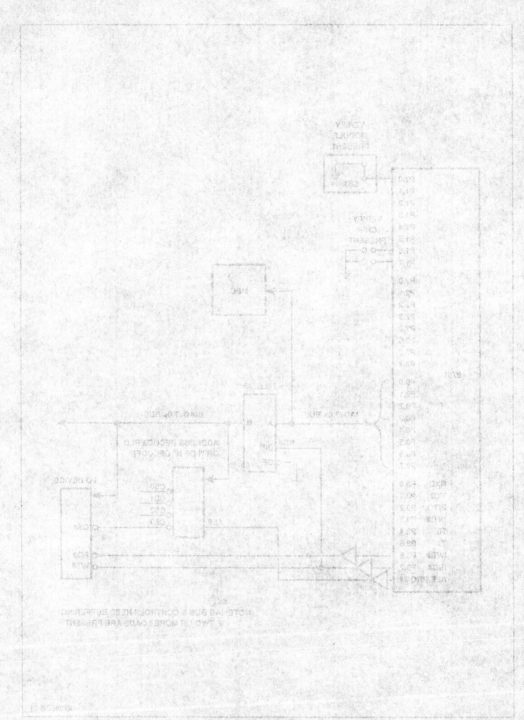

Physical Design and System Debugging

10

CHAPTER 10
PHYSICAL DESIGN AND SYSTEM DEBUGGING

Designing with the i486™ microprocessor is like designing with any other processor. A high-performance i486 processor system can easily be implemented by using standard interface logic, DRAMs, EPROMs and I/O devices.

The higher clock speeds of i486 processor systems requires some design guidelines. This chapter outlines the basic design issues, ranging from power and ground issues to achieving proper thermal environment for i486 CPU.

10.1 GENERAL DESIGN GUIDELINES

The proper operation of any high-speed system greatly depends upon proper physical layout. This section gives a brief overview of general issues and design guidelines for layout which are significant to both higher- and lower-frequency system design implementation.

The ever-increasing improvement of integrated circuit technology has led to an enormous increase in the number of functions that are being implemented on a single chip. Improved technology allows higher clock frequencies. The i486 microprocessor, with operating frequencies of 25 MHz/33 MHz and corresponding high edge rates, presents a challenge to the conventional interconnection technologies which to date have been adequate for interconnecting less sophisticated VLSI devices only. This challenge applies especially to system designers who are responsible for providing suitable interconnections at the systems level.

At higher frequencies, the interconnections in a circuit behave like transmission lines which degrade system's overall speed and distort its output waveforms.

In laying out a conventional printed circuit board, there is freedom in defining the length, shape and sequence of interconnections. But with high-speed devices like the i486 processor this task should be carried out with careful planning, evaluation and testing of the wiring patterns. It is also critical to understand the physical properties of transmission lines because interconnection at high edge rates is analogous to a broadcasting transmission line.

10.2 POWER DISSIPATION AND DISTRIBUTION

The i486 microprocessor uses fast one-micron CHMOS IV process. The main difference between the previous HMOS microprocessors and the new ones is that power dissipation is primarily capacitive and that there is almost no DC power dissipation. As power dissipation is directly proportional to frequency, accommodating high-speed signals on printed circuit boards and through the interconnections is very critical. The power dissipation of the VLSI device in operation is expressed by the sum of the power dissipation of the circuit elements, which include internal logic gates, I/O buffers and cache RAMs. It is also a function of the operating conditions.

The worst-case power dissipation of any VLSI device is estimated in the following manner:

1. To estimate typical power dissipation for each circuit element:
   P_G : Typical power dissipation for internal logic gates (mW)
   $P_{I/O}$: Typical power dissipation for I/O buffers (mW)
   P_{CRAM} : Typical power dissipation for instruction/data cache RAMs (mW)

2. To estimate total typical power dissipation:
   $P_T = P_G + P_{I/O} + P_{CRAM}$ (mW) .... (1)
   where P_T is the total typical power dissipation (mW)

3. To estimate the worst case power dissipation:
   $P_d = P_T \times C_v$ (mW) ....(2)
   where P_d is the worst case power dissipation (mW) and C_v is a multiplier that is dependent upon power supply voltage.

Internal logic power dissipation varies with operating frequency and to some extent with wait states and software. It is directly proportional to the supply voltage. Process variations in manufacturing also affect the internal logic power dissipation, although to a lesser extent than with the NMOS processes.

The I/O buffer power dissipation, which accounts for roughly 10 to 25 percent of the overall power dissipation, varies with the frequency and the supply voltage. It is also affected by the capacitive bus load. The capacitive bus loadings for all output pins is specified in the i486 processor data sheet. The i486 processor's output valid delays will increase if these loadings are exceeded. The addressing pattern of the software can affect I/O buffer power dissipation by changing the effective frequency at the address pins. The frequency variations at the data pins tends to be smaller; thus, a varying data pattern should not cause a significant change in the total power dissipation.

To calculate the total power dissipated by the board, the following formulas can be used to calculate the maximum statistical power:

$$P_{typical1} + P_{typical2} + ...(P_{max1} \quad P_{typical1})^2 + (P_{max2} \quad P_{typical2})^2.....$$

where $P_{typical1}$ and P_{max1} are the typical and maximum power dissipation of each of the integrated circuits on the board. The i486 processor should be placed closer to a fan or where the airflow is unrestricted.

10.2.1 Power and Ground Planes

Today's high-speed CMOS logic devices are susceptible to the ground noise and the problems that this noise creates in digital system design. This noise is a direct result of the fast switching speed and high drive capability of these devices, which are requisites in high-performance systems. Logic designers can use techniques designed to minimize this problem. One technique is to reduce capacitance loading on signal lines and provide optimum power and ground planes.

Power and ground lines have inherent inductance and capacitance, which affect the total impedance of the entire system. Higher impedances reduce current and therefore offer reduced power consumption, while low impedance (ground planes) minimizes problems like noise and cross talk. Hence, it is very important for a designer to have a controlled impedance design where high speed signals are involved. The formula for impedance is as follows:

$$\text{Impedance} = (L/C)^{1/2}$$

The total characteristic impedance for the power supply can be reduced by adding more lines. The effect of adding more lines to reduce impedance is illustrated in Figure 10-1 which shows that two lines in parallel has half the impedance of a single line. To reduce

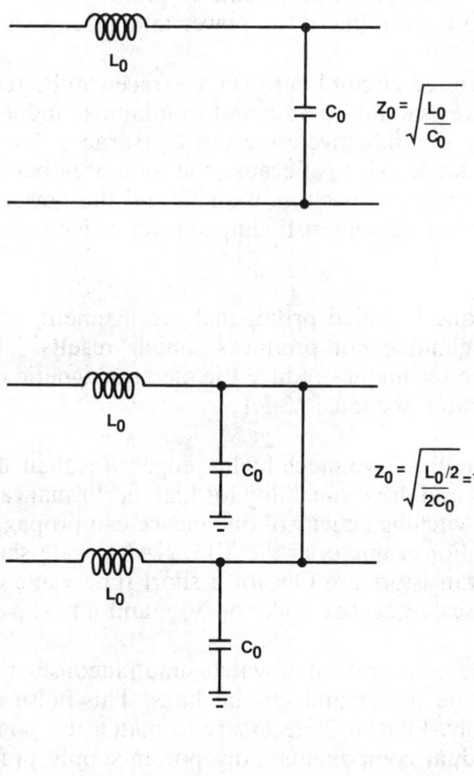

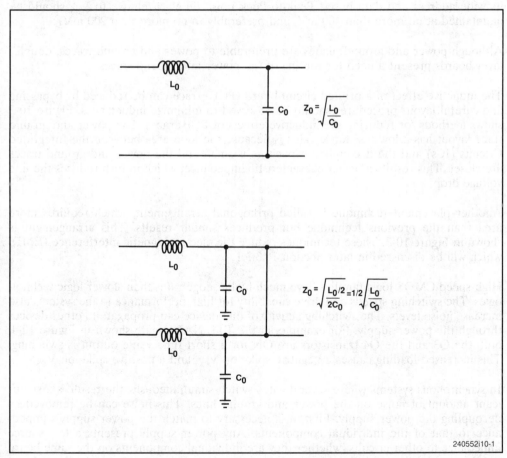

Figure 10-1. Reduction in Impedance

impedance even further, more lines should be added. To lower the impedance infinite number of lines or plane should be used. Planes also provide the best distribution of power and ground.

For multi-layer boards, power and ground planes must be used in the i486 microprocessor designs. The ground plane allows best performance at high speeds. It serves two purposes. First it provides a constant characteristic impedance to signal interconnections. Secondly, it provides a low impedance path for ground currents on the V_{CC} supply. The advantage of power plane is to reduce crosstalk. For example, when adjacent signal lines are switching, signal line crosstalk may occur. The power plane is used to separate excessive layers of signal lines, thus reducing crosstalk.

The i486 microprocessor has 24 power (V_{CC}) and 27 ground (V_{SS}) pins. All power and ground pins must be connected to their respective planes. Ideally, the i486 microprocessor should be placed at the center of the board to take full advantage of these planes. Although i486 CPU generally demands less power than the conventional devices, the possibility of power surges is increased due to processors higher operating frequency and its wide address and data buses. Peak-to-Peak noise on V_{CC} relative to V_{SS} should be maintained at no more than 400 mV, and preferably to no more than 200 mV.

Although power and ground planes are preferable to power and ground traces, double-layer boards present a need for routing of the power and ground traces.

The inductive effect of a printed-circuit board (PCB) trace can be reduced by bypassing and careful layout procedures should be observed to minimize inductances. Figure 10-2 shows methods for reducing the inductive effects of PCB traces. The power and ground trace layout has a low resistance. This is because the loop area between the Integrated Circuits (ICs) and the decoupling capacitors is small and the power and ground traces are closer. This results in lower characteristic impedance, which in turn reduces the line voltage drop.

Another placement technique is called orthogonal arrangement, which requires more area than the previous technique but produces similar results. This arrangement is shown in Figure 10-3. These techniques reduce the electromagnetic interference (EMI), which will be discussed in later Section 10.3.3.1.

High-speed CMOS logic families have much higher edge rates than slower logic technologies. The switching speeds and drive capability for high performance to the systems also increase noise levels. The switching activity of one device can propagate to other devices through the power supply. For example, in the TTL NAND gate shown in Figure 10-4, both the Q3 and the Q4 transistors are ON for a short time while output is switching. This increased loading causes a negative spike on V_{CC} and a positive spike on V_{SS}.

In synchronous systems where several gates switch simultaneously, the result is a significant amount of noise on the power and ground lines. This noise can be removed by decoupling the power supply. First, it is necessary to match the power supply's impedance to that of the individual components. Any power supply presents a low source impedance to other circuits, whether they are individual components on the same board or other boards in a multi-board system. It is necessary to match the supply's impedance

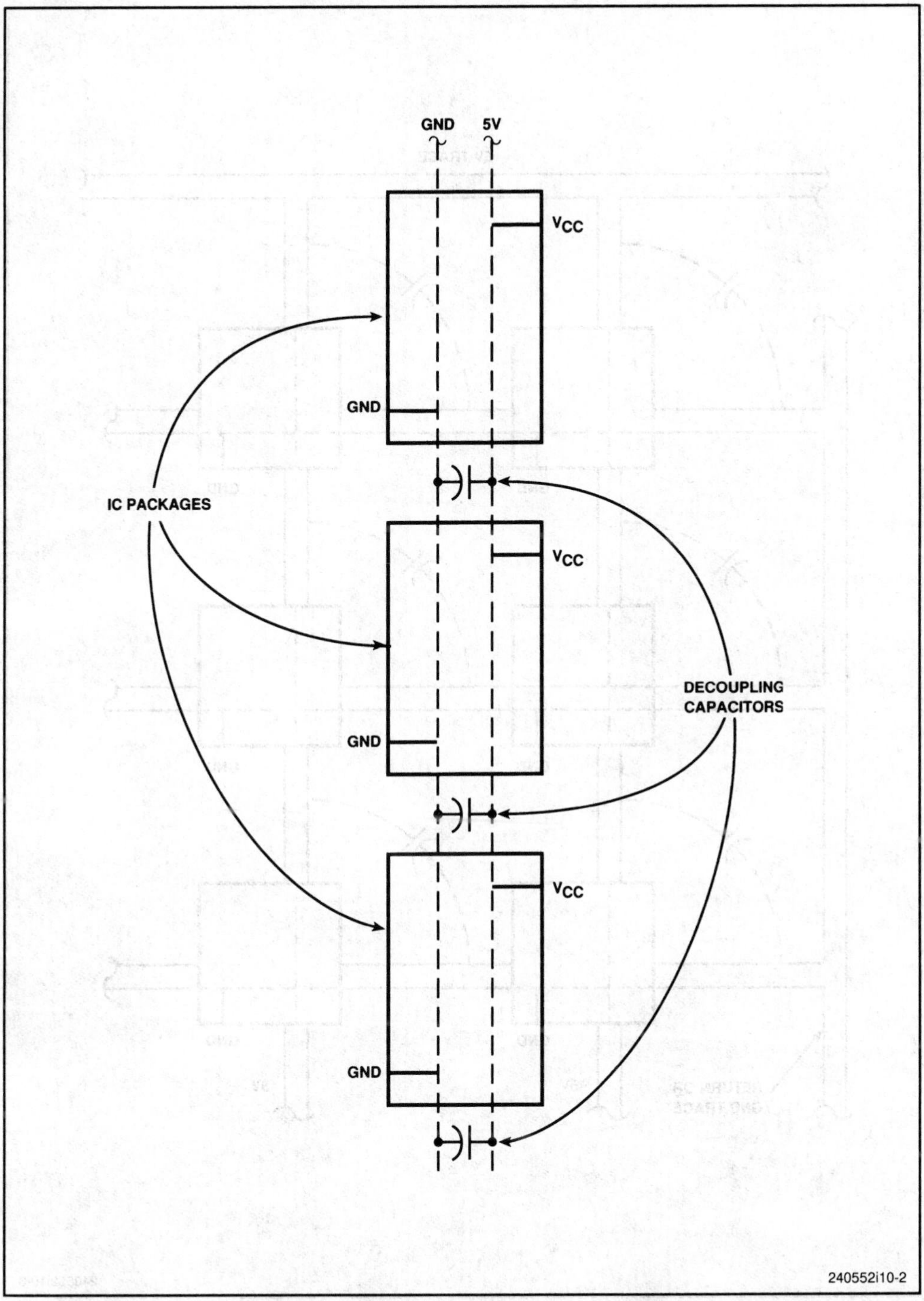

Figure 10-2. Typical Power and Ground Trace Layout for Double-Layer Boards

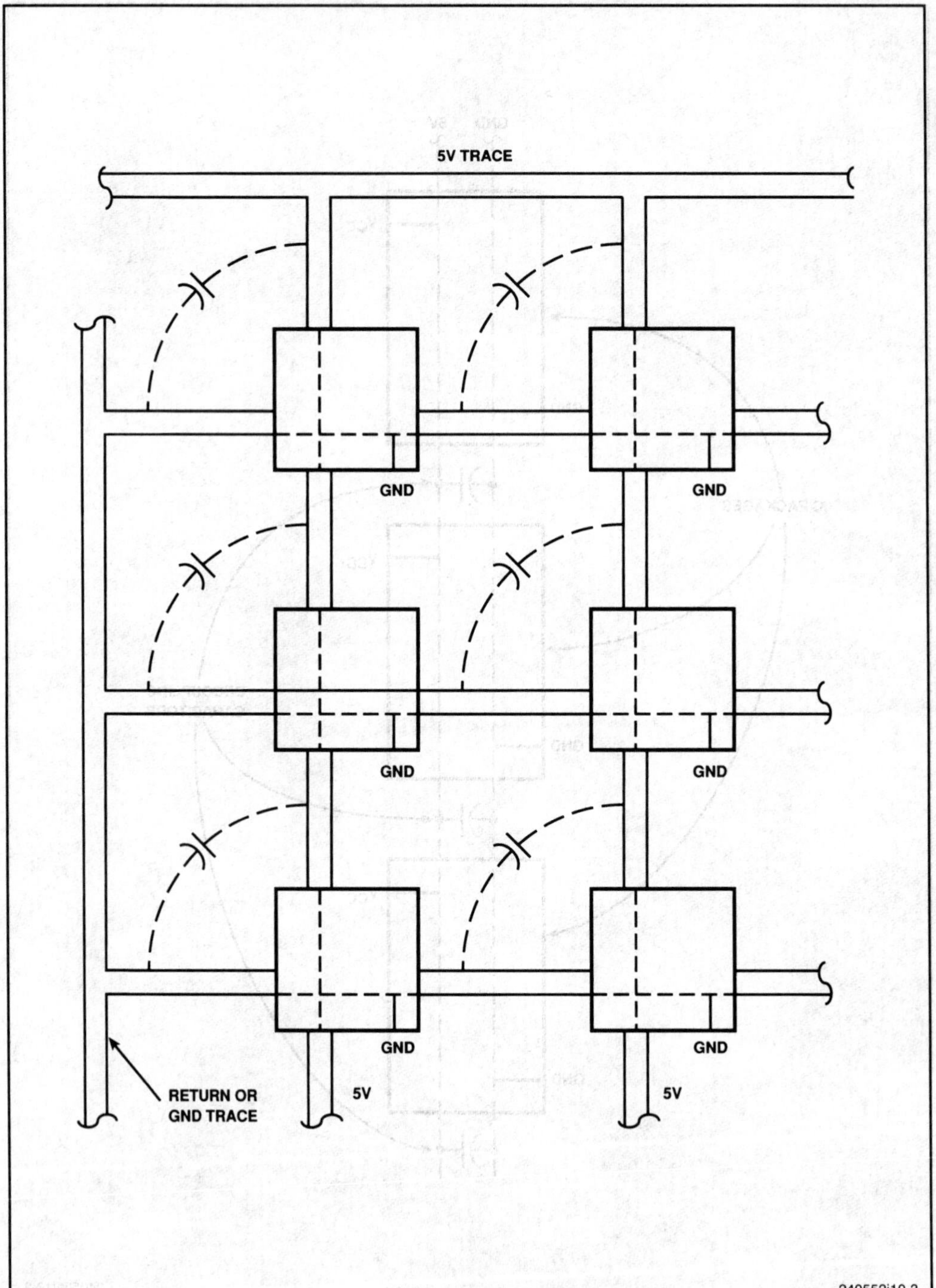

Figure 10-3. Decoupling Capacitors

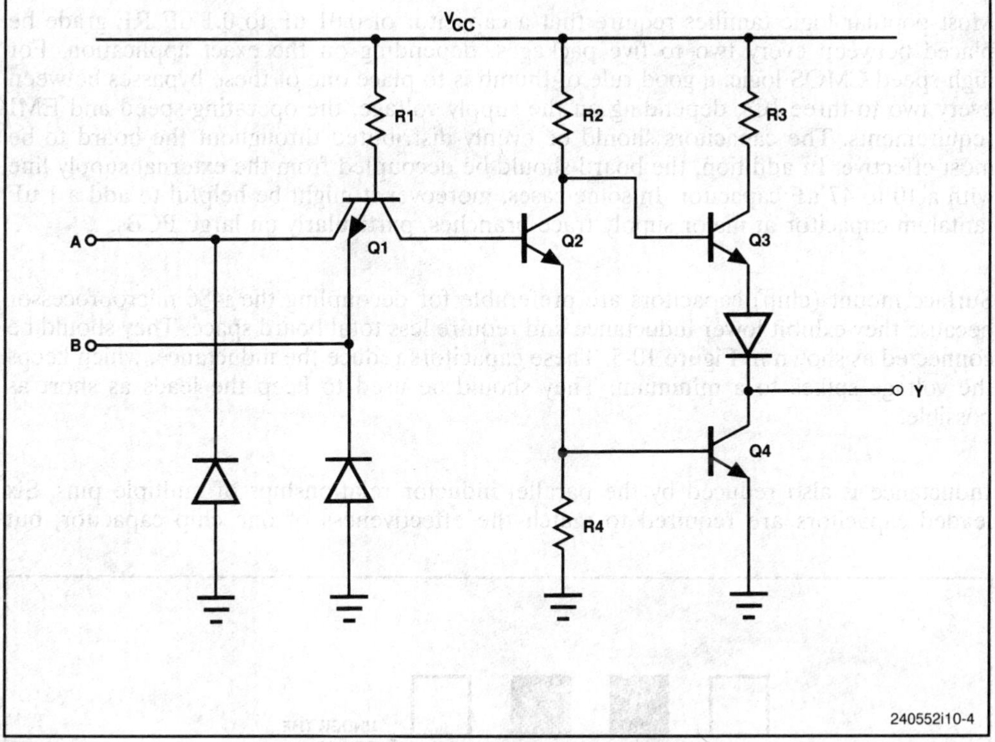

Figure 10-4. Circuit without Decoupling

to that of the components in order to lessen the potential for voltage drops that can be caused by IC edge rates, ground- or signal-level shifting, noise induced currents or voltage reflections.

This mismatch can be minimized by using a suitable high-frequency capacitor for bulk decoupling of major circuitry sections, or for decoupling entire pc boards in multi-board systems. This capacitor is typically placed at the supply's entry point to the board. It should be an aluminum or tantalum-electrolytic type capacitor having a low equivalent series capacitance and low equivalent series inductance. This capacitor's value is typically 10 to 47 uF. An additional 0.1 uF capacitor may be needed if supply noise is still a problem.

A second type of decoupling is used for the rest of the ICs on the board. Additional decoupling capacitors can be used across the devices between V_{CC} and V_{SS} lines. The voltage spikes that occur due to switching of gates are reduced as the extra current required during switching is supplied by the decoupling capacitors. These capacitors should be placed close to their devices as the inductance of lengthier connection traces reduce their effectiveness.

Most popular logic families require that a capacitor of 0.01 uF to 0.1 uF RF grade be placed between every two to five packages, depending on the exact application. For high-speed CMOS logic, a good rule of thumb is to place one of these bypasses between every two to three ICs, depending on the supply voltage, the operating-speed and EMI requirements. The capacitors should be evenly distributed throughout the board to be most effective. In addition, the board should be decoupled from the external supply line with a 10 to 47 uF capacitor. In some cases, moreover it might be helpful to add a 1 uF tantalum capacitor at major supply trace branches, particularly on large PCBs.

Surface mount (chip) capacitors are preferable for decoupling the i486 microprocessor because they exhibit lower inductance and require less total board space. They should be connected as shown in Figure 10-5. These capacitors reduce the inductance, which keeps the voltage spikes to a minimum. They should be used to keep the leads as short as possible.

Inductance is also reduced by the parallel inductor relationships of multiple pins. Six leaded capacitors are required to match the effectiveness of one chip capacitor, but

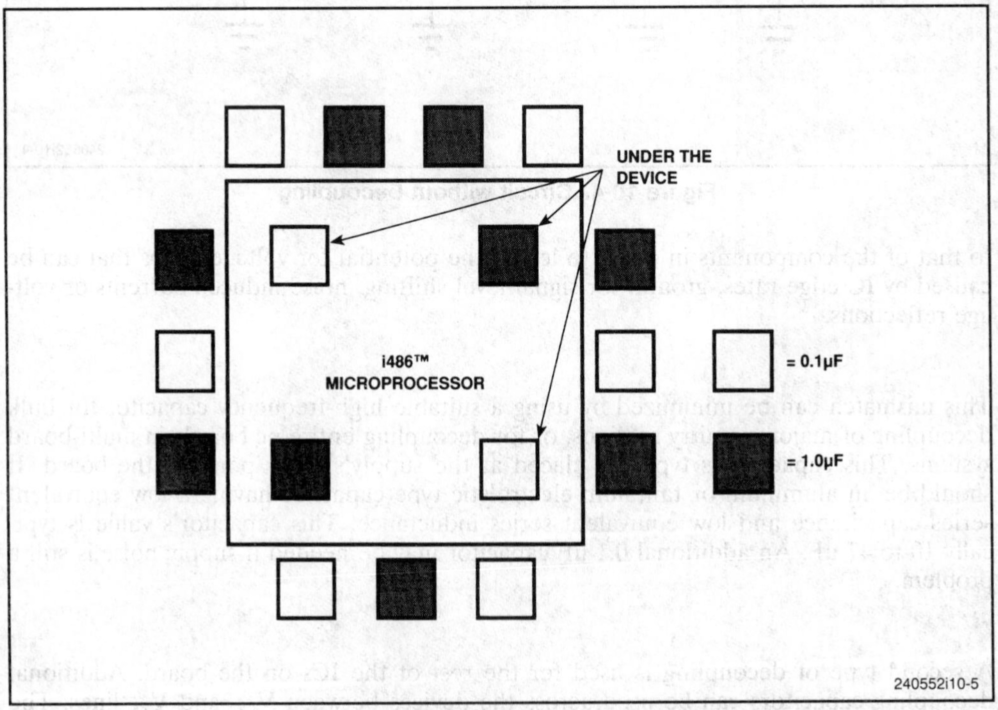

Figure 10-5. Decoupling Chip Capacitors

because only a limited number can fit around i486 CPU, the configuration shown in Figure 10-6 is recommended.

10.3 HIGH-FREQUENCY DESIGN CONSIDERATIONS

The overwhelming concern in dealing with high speed technologies is the management of transmission lines. As the edge rates of the signal increases, the physical interconnections between devices behave like transmission lines. Although transmission line theory is straightforward, the difference between ordinary interconnection and transmission line is fairly complex. Transmission lines have distributed elements which are hard to define and designers tend to over compensate for the effects of these elements.

Efficient i486 CPU designs requires the identification of the transmission lines over backplane wiring, printed circuit board traces, etc. Once this task is accomplished, designer's next concern should be to deal with three major problems which are associated with electromagnetic propagation, impedance control, propagation delay and coupling.

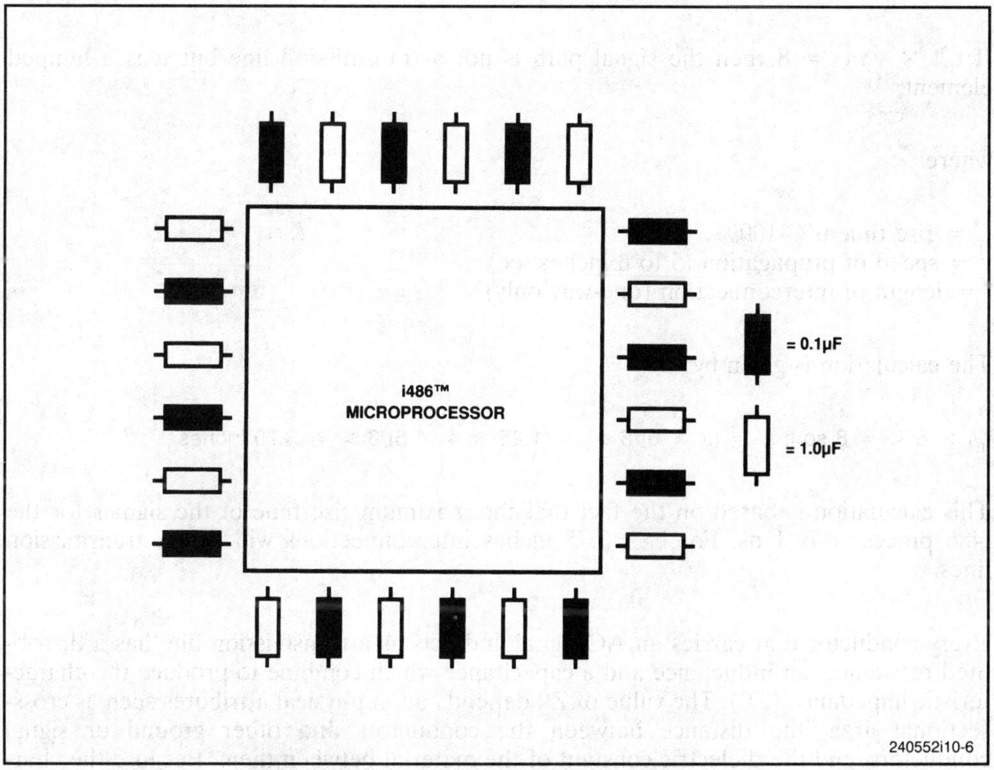

Figure 10-6. Decoupling Leaded Capacitors

The following sections discuss the negative effects of a transmission line that occur when operating at higher frequencies. In higher frequency design the reflection and cross talk effects are inevitable. It is impossible to design optimum systems without accounting for these effects. Later sections include a discussion of techniques that can minimize these effects.

10.3.1 Transmission Line Effects

As a general rule, any interconnection is considered a transmission line when the time required for the signal to travel the length of the interconnection is greater than one-eighth of the signal rise time (Reference 1.). The rise time can be either rise time or fall time, whichever is smaller, and it corresponds to the linear ramp amplitude from 0% to 100%. Normally the rise times are specified between 10% to 90% or 20% to 80% amplitude points. The respective values are multiplied by 1.25 or 1.67 to obtain the linear-ramp duration from 0% to 100% amplitude.

For example in a PCB using G-10 and polymide (the two main dielectric systems available for printed circuit boards) signals travel at approximately 5 to 6 inches per nanosecond (ns).

If $t_r/l \times v <= 8$ then the signal path is not a transmission line but it is a lumped element,

where:

t_r = rise time 0%–100%
v = speed of propagation (5 to 6 inches/sec)
l = length of interconnection (one-way only)

The calculation is given by:

$t_r/l \times 6 <= 8$ so $l >= (tr \times 6)/8 >= (1.25 \times 4 \times 6)/8 >= 3.75$ inches

This calculation is based on the fact that the maximum rise time of the signals for the i486 processor is 4 ns. For $l >= 3.75$ inches interconnections will act as transmission lines.

Every conductor that carries an AC signal and acts as a transmission line has a distributed resistance, an inductance and a capacitance which combine to produce the characteristic impedance (Z0). The value of Z0 depends upon physical attributes such as cross-sectional area, the distance between the conductors and other ground or signal conductors, and the dielectric constant of the material between them. Because the characteristic impedance is reactive, its effect increases with frequency.

10.3.1.1 TRANSMISSION LINE TYPES

Although many different types of transmission lines (conductors) exist, those most commonly used on the printed circuit boards are microstrip lines, strip lines, printed circuit traces, side-by-side conductors and flat conductors.

10.3.1.1.1 Micro Strip Lines

The micro strip trace consists of a signal plane that is separated from a ground plane by a dielectric as shown in Figure 10-7. G-10 fiber-glass epoxy, which is most common, has an $e_r = 5$,

where:

e_r is the dielectric constant of the insulation
w is the width of signal line (inches)
t is the thickness of copper (.0015 inches for 1 oz. Cu/.003 inches for 2 oz. Cu)
h is the height of dielectric for controlled impedance (inches)

The characteristic impedance Z0, is a function of dielectric constant and the geometry of the board. This is theoretically given by the following formula:

$$ZO = [87/\sqrt{(e_r + 1.41)}] \ln (5.98h/.8W + t) \text{ ohms}$$

where e_r is the relative dielectric constant of the board material and h, w and t are the dimensions of the strip. Knowing the line width, the thickness of Cu and the height of dielectric, the characteristic impedance can be easily calculated.

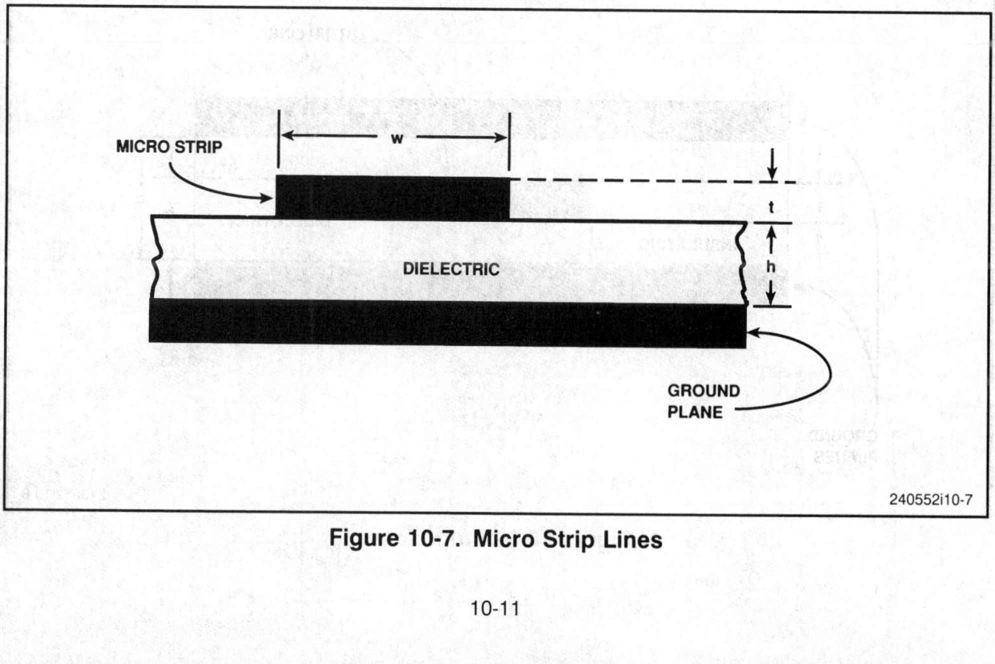

Figure 10-7. Micro Strip Lines

The propagation delay (tpd) associated with the trace is a function of the dielectric only. This is calculated as follows:

$$tpd = 1.017 \sqrt{(0.475e_r + 0.67)} \text{ ns/ft}$$

For G-10 fiber-glass epoxy boards ($e_r = 5.0$), the propagation delay of microstrip is calculated to be 1.77 ns/ft.

10.3.1.1.2 Strip Lines

A strip line is a strip conductor centered in a dielectric medium between two voltage planes. The characteristic impedance is given theoretically by the equation below (Reference 3):

$$ZO = [60/\sqrt{e_r}] \ln (5.98b/\pi (0.8W + t)) \text{ ohms}$$

where b = distance between the planes for controlled impedance as shown in Figure 10-8.

The propagation delay is given by the following formula

$$tpd = 1.017 \sqrt{e_r} \text{ ns/ft}$$

For G-10 fiberglass epoxy boards ($e_r = 5.0$), the propagation delay of the strip lines is 2.26 ns/ft.

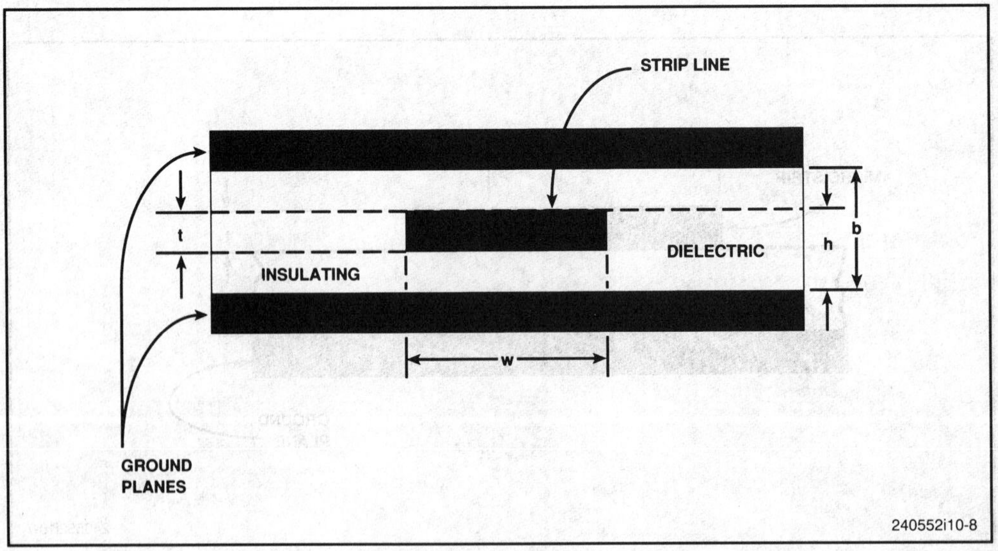

Figure 10-8. Strip Lines

Typical values of the characteristic impedance and propagation delay of these types of lines are as follows:

ZO = 50 ohms
tpd = 2 ns/ft (or 6″/nsec)

The three major effects of transmission line phenomenon are impedance mismatch, coupling and skew.

The following section will discuss them briefly and provide solutions to minimize their effects. A book about high frequency design considerations can provide more details, if necessary (Reference 2).

10.3.2 Impedance Mismatch

As mentioned earlier the impedance of a transmission line is a function of the geometry of the line, its distance from the ground plane, and the loads along the line. Any discontinuity in the impedance will cause reflections.

Impedance mismatch occurs between the transmission line characteristic impedance and the input or output impedances of the devices that are connected to the line. The result is that the signals are reflected back and forth on the line. These reflections can attenuate or reinforce the signal depending upon the phase relationships. The results of these reflections include overshoot, undershoot, ringing and other undesirable effects.

At lower edge rates, the effects of these reflections are not severe. However at higher rates, the rise time of the signal is short with respect to the propagation delay. Thus it can cause problems as shown in Figure 10-9.

Overshoot occurs when the voltage level exceeds the maximum (upper) limit of the output voltage, while undershoot occurs when the level exceeds the minimum (lower) limit. These conditions can cause excess current on the input gates which results in permanent damage to the device.

The amount of reflection voltage can be easily calculated. Figure 10-10 shows a system exhibiting reflections.

The magnitude of a reflection is usually represented in terms of a reflection coefficient. This is illustrated in the following equations:

$T = v_r/v_i$ = Reflected voltage/Incident voltage
T_{load} = (Zload ZO)/ (Zload + ZO)
T_{source} = (Zsource ZO)/ (Zsource + ZO)

Reflection voltage v_r is given by v_i, the voltage incident at the point of the reflection, and the reflection coefficient.

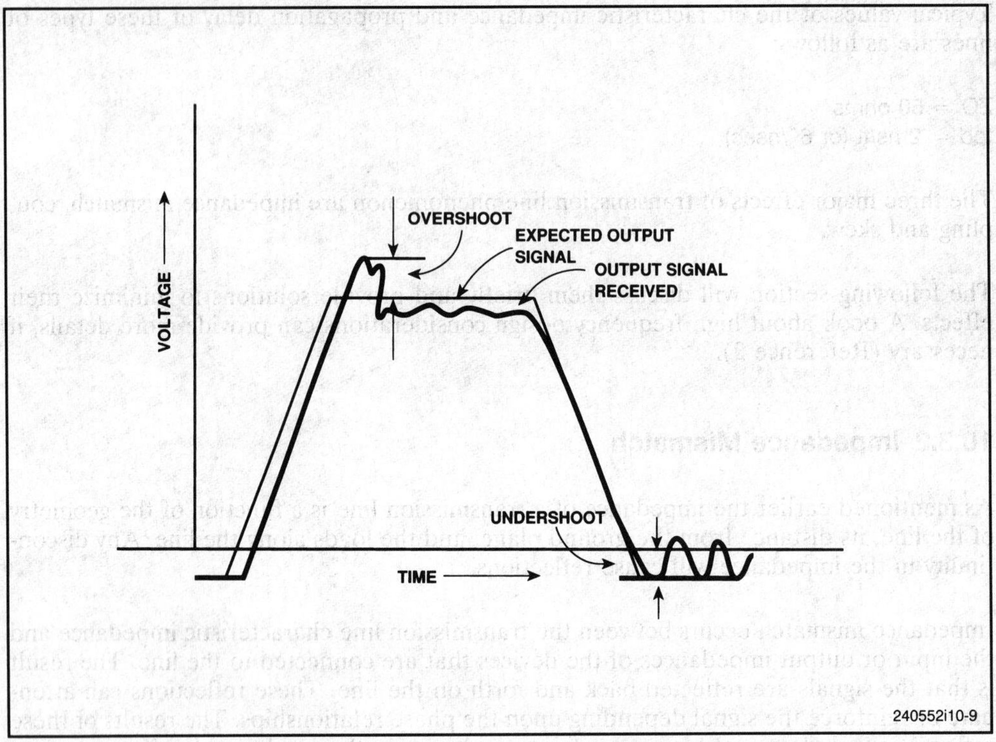

Figure 10-9. Overshoot and Undershoot Effects

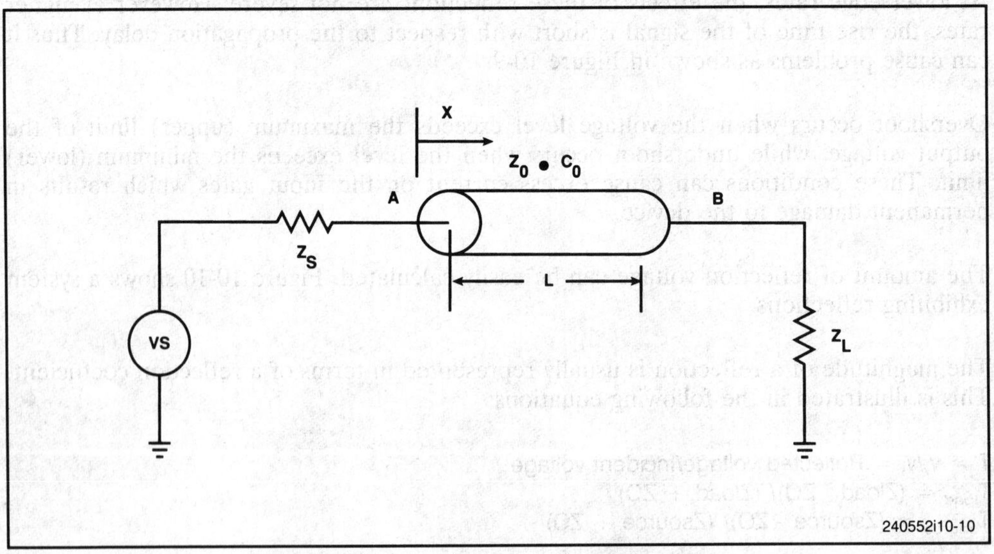

Figure 10-10. Loaded Transmission Line

The model transmission line can now be completed. In Figure 10-10, the voltage seen at point A is given by the following equation:

$$V_a = V_s * Z0/(Z0 + Z_s)$$

This voltage V_a enters the transmission line at "A" and appears at "B" delayed by tpd.

$$V_b = V_a(t-x/v)\ H(t-x/v)$$

where x = distance along the transmission line from point "A" and H(t) is the unit step function. The waveform encounters the load Z_L, and this may cause reflection. The reflected wave enters the transmission line at "B" and appears at point "A" after time delay (tpd):

$$V_{r1} = T_{load} \cdot V_b$$

This phenomenon continues infinitely, but it is negligible after 3 or 4 reflections. Hence:

$$V_{r2} = T_{source} \cdot V_{r1}$$

Each reflected waveform is treated as a separate source that is independent of the reflection coefficient at that point and the incident waveform. Thus the waveform from any point and on the transmission line and at any given time is as follows:

$$\begin{aligned} V(x,t) = {} & (Z0/(Z0 + Z_s))\{[V_s(t\text{-}x/v)H(t\text{-}x/v)] \\ & + T_l\ [V_s(t\text{-}(2L\text{-}x)/v)]\ [H(t\text{-}(2L\text{-}x)/v)] \\ & + T_l\ T_s\ [V_s(t\text{-}(2L + x)/v)]\ [H(t\text{-}(2L + x)/v)] \\ & + T_1^2\ T_s\ [V_s(t\text{-}(4L\text{-}x)/v)]\ [H(t\text{-}(4L\text{-}x)/v)] \\ & + T_1^2\ T_s^2\ [V_s\ (t\ (4L+x)/v)]\ [H(t\ (4L\ +x)/v)] \\ & + \ldots\ldots\ldots\ldots \} \end{aligned}$$

Each reflection is added to the total voltage through the unit step function H(t). The above equation can be rewritten as follows:

$$\begin{aligned} V(x,t) = {} & Z0/(Z0+Z_s)\{\ [V_s(t\ t_{pd}x)H(t\ t_{pd}x)] \\ & + T_l\ [V_s(t\ t_{pd}\ (2L\ x))H(t\ t_{pd}(2L\ x))] \\ & + T_l\ T_s\ [V_s\ (t-t_{pd}(2L+x))H(t\ t_{pd}(2L+x))] \\ & + \ldots\ldots\ldots\ldots\ldots \} \end{aligned}$$

This can be further explained by an example.

Let $Vs = \sin(2\ \pi\ 10^9\ t)$
Zs = 35 ohms
ZL = 20 ohms
Z0 = 50 ohms
L = 14 in
x = 6 inches
tpd = 2 ns/ft = .17 ns/in
v = [2 ns/ft) = .5 ft/ns = 6 in/ns

TL = (20 50)/20 + 50 = .43
Ts = .18
at t = .5 ns
V(x,t) = V(6 in, .5 ns)
$= 50/(50+35)\{\sin(2\pi 10^9(0.5-0.17\text{ns/in}(6\text{in}))\text{ns})\}$
$+(-0.43)\{\sin(2\pi 10^9(0.5-0.17(6))\text{ns})H(0.5-0.17(6))\}$
$= .59\{\sin(-1.04\pi)+0\}$ at t=5 nsec

Voltage at A with the transmission line properties accounted for. There is no reflection yet.

V(x,t) = V(6 in, 5 nsec)
$= [50/50 + 35]\ \{\ \sin(2\pi\ 10^9\ (5-\ (.17)(6))$
$+\ (-.43)\{\sin\ (2\ \pi\ 10^9\ (5-\ .17\ (28\ -\ 6)))\ H\ (5-.17\ (28-6))\}$
$+\ (-.43)(-.18)\{\sin\ (2\ \pi\ 10^9\ (5-.17\ (28+6)))\ H\ (5-.17(28+6))\}$
$=\ .59\ \{\sin\ (-1.04\ \pi)\ -.43\ \sin\ (2.52\ \pi)\ +\ .08\ \sin\ (-1.56\ \pi)\}$

The lattice diagram is a convenient visual tool for calculating the total voltage due to reflections as described in the equations previously. Two vertical lines are drawn to represent points A and B on the horizontal dimension, x. The vertical dimension then represents time.

A waveform will travel back and forth between points A and B of the transmission line in time, producing the lattice diagram shown in Figure 10-11. The voltage at a given point is the sum of all the individual reflected voltages upto that time. Notice that at each endpoint, two waves are converging, the incident wave and the reflected wave. Therefore, the voltage at the end points A and B at the time of the waveform reflection would be calculated by summing both the incident and reflected waves up to and including the point in question.

As an example, let the simple configuration shown in Figure 10-10 be assumed. Assume the following:

Vs = 3.70 H(t)v
Zo = 75 ohms
Zsource = 30 ohms
Zload = 100 ohms

The appropriate reflection coefficients can be calculated as follows:

source = (30 75)/(30+75) = 0.42857
load = (100 75)/(100+75) = 0.14286

Va = Vs.{75/(75+30)} = 2.64286 V
Vr1 = 2.64286 × 0.14286 = 0.37755 V
Vr2 = 0.37755 × 0.42875 = − 0.16181 V
Vr3 = −0.16181 × 0.14286 = − 0.02312 V
Vr4 = −0.02312 × − 0.42857 = 0.00991 V

Vr5 = 0.00991 × 0.14286 = 0.00142 V
Vr6 = 0.00142 × − 0.42857 = −0.00061 V
Vr7 = −0.00061 × 0.14286 = −0.00009 V

Figure 10-12 shows the corresponding lattice diagram.

Impedance discontinuity problems are managed by imposing limits and control during the routing phase of the design. Design rules must be observed to control trace geometry, including specification of the trace width and spacing for each layer. This is very important because it ensures the traces are smooth and constant without sharp turns.

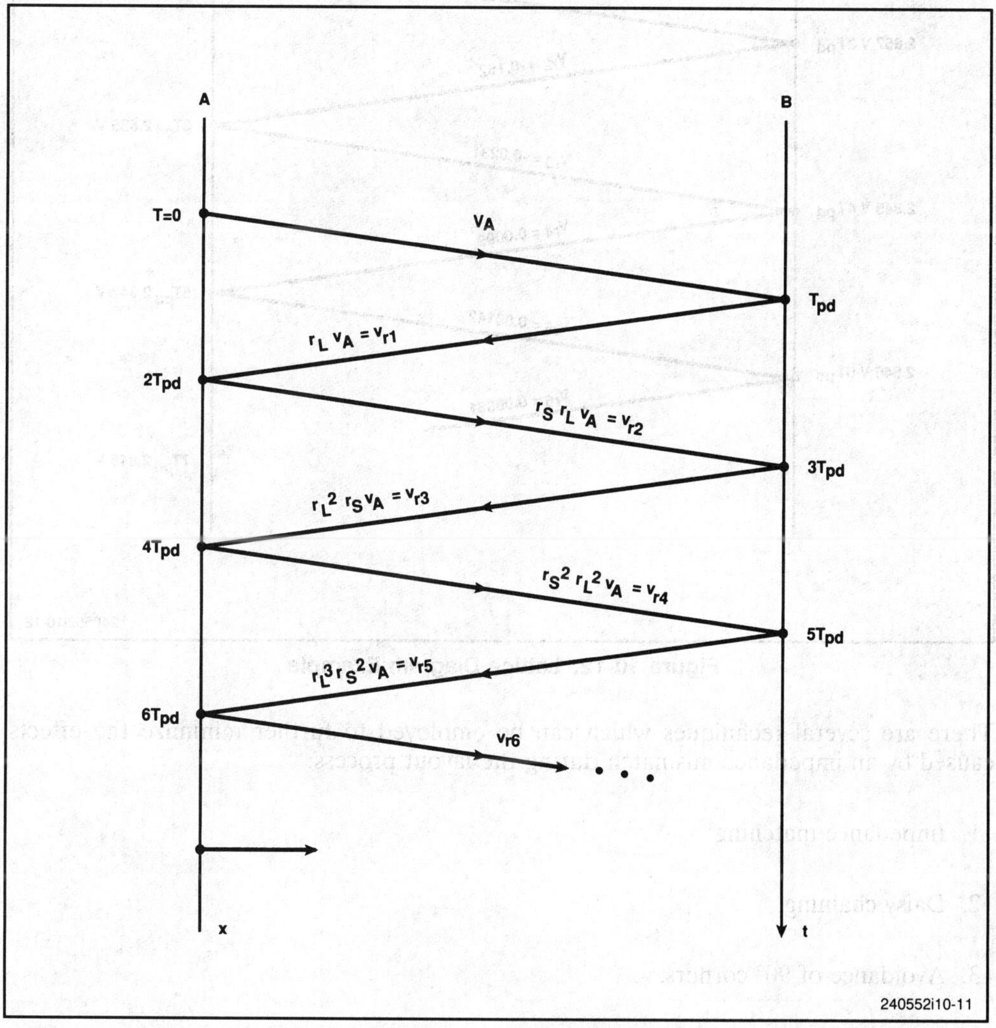

Figure 10-11. Lattice Diagram

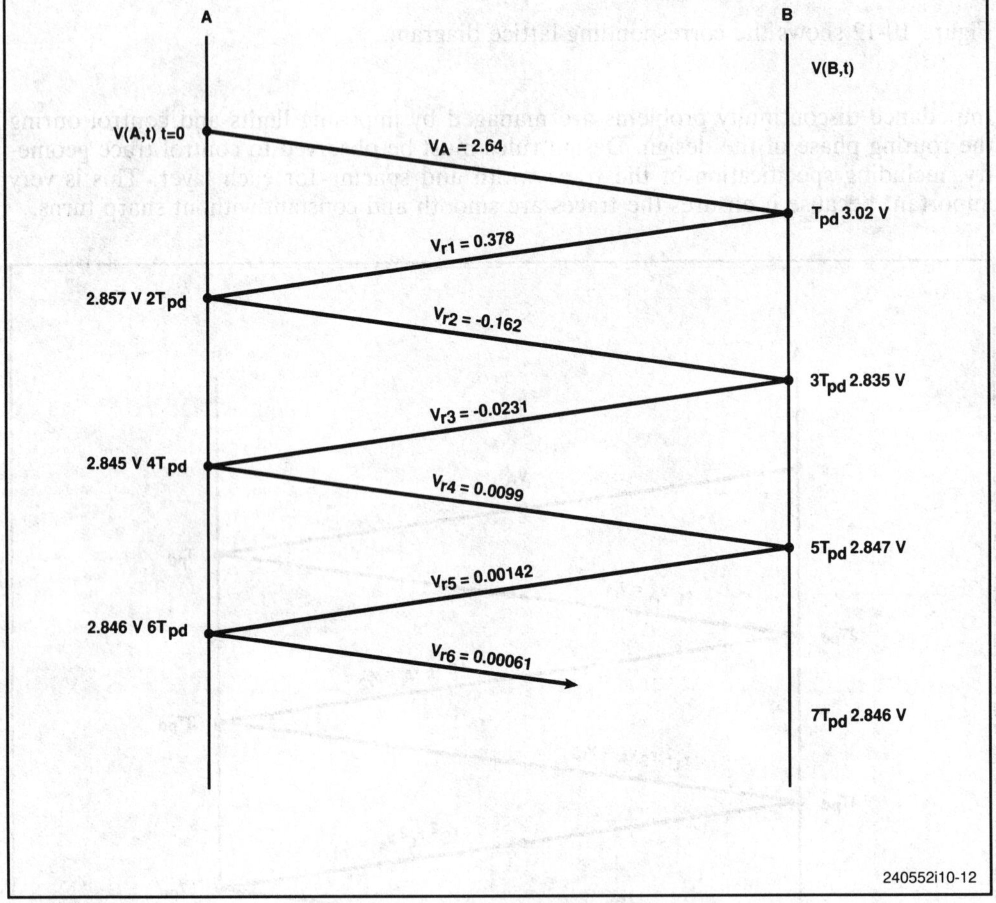

Figure 10-12. Lattice Diagram Example

There are several techniques which can be employed to further minimize the effects caused by an impedance mismatch during the layout process:

1. Impedance matching
2. Daisy chaining.
3. Avoidance of 90° corners.
4. Minimization of the number of Vias.

10.3.2.1 IMPEDANCE MATCHING

Impedance matching is the process of matching the impedance of the source or load with that of the trace and it is accomplished with a technique called termination. The reflection, overshoot and undershoot of signals are reduced by terminating the remote end of the transmission line from the source. The terminating impedance combines with the destination input circuitry to produce a load that closely matches the characteristic impedance of the line (board traces have characteristic impedances in the range of 30 ohms to 200 ohms).

The calculation of characteristic impedance was already discussed. Impedance of the printed circuit board backplane connectors have the impedance in the same range as the traces (i.e., 30–200 ohms).

Depending upon the length of the conductors or when using twisted pairs of coaxial cable in place of PC traces, the characteristic impedance of a backplane may change. Backplane impedance is also affected by the number of boards plugged into the backplane.

10.3.2.1.1 Need for Termination

The transmission line should be terminated when the tpd exceeds one-third of tr (rise-time). If the tpd < 1/3 tr (rise time), line can be left unterminated, provided the capacitive coupling between the traces does not cause crosstalk.

Termination thus eliminates impedance mismatches, increases noise immunity, suppresses RFI/EMI and helps to ensure that signals reach their destination with minimum of distortion. There are five methods for terminating traces on the board:

1. Series

2. Parallel

3. Thevenin

4. A.C.

5. Active

Terminations usually cost money, because they require additional components and power. In the case of passive terminations, extra drivers are needed to deliver more current to the line. In case of active terminations extra power is needed which increases the power dissipation of the system.

10.3.2.1.2 Series Termination

One way of controlling ringing on longer lines is with the series termination technique also known as damping. This is accomplished by placing a resistor in series with the transmission line at the driving device end. The receiver has no termination. The value of the impedance looking into the driving device ($R_{driver} + R_{Line} = Z_0$) should approximate the impedance of the line as closely as possible. In this circuit the ringing dampens out when the reflection coefficient goes to zero. Figure 10-13 illustrates the series termination.

One main advantage of series termination is that only logic power dissipation results so that lower overall power is required. There is one penalty, however, in that the distributed loading along the transmission line cannot be used because only half of the voltage waveform is travelling down the line. There is no limit on the number of loads that can be placed at the end of the series terminated connection. However, the drop in voltage across series terminating resistor limits loading to maximum 10.

10.3.2.1.3 Parallel Terminated Lines

Parallel termination is achieved by placing a resistor of an appropriate value between the input of the loading device and the ground as shown in Figure 10-14. To determine an appropriate value, the currents required by all inputs and the leakage currents of the drivers should be summed. A resistor should be selected so that its addition to the circuit does not exceed the output capacity of the weakest driver. For the type of termination shown in Figure 10-14, only high logic levels need to be calculated.

Since the input impedance of the device is high as compared to the characteristic line impedance, the resistor and the line function as a single impedance with a magnitude that is defined by the value of the resistor.

When the resistor matches the line impedance, the reflection coefficient at the load approaches zero, and no reflection will occur. One useful approach is to place the termination as close to the loading device as possible.

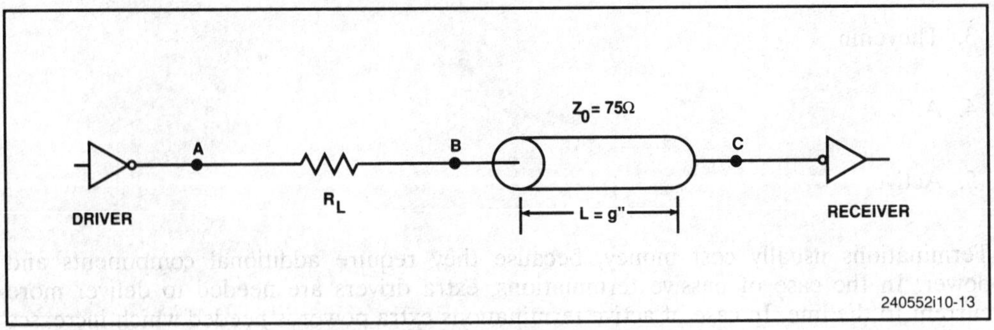

Figure 10-13. Series Termination

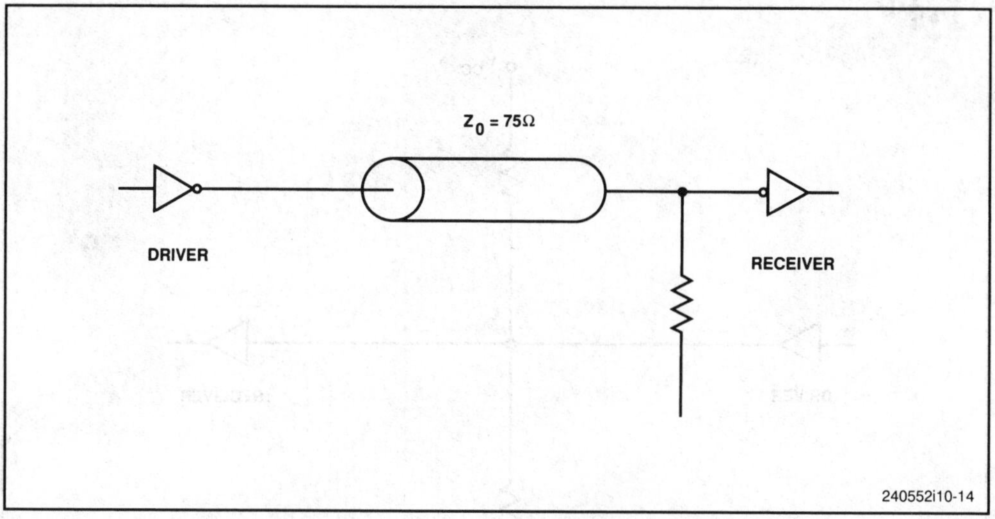

Figure 10-14. Parallel Termination

Parallel terminated lines are used to achieve optimum circuit performance and to drive distributed loads which is an important benefit of using parallel terminations.

There are two significant advantages of using the parallel termination. First, it provides an undistributed waveform along the entire line. Second, when a long line is loaded in parallel termination, it does not affect the rise and fall time or the propagation delay of the driving device. Note that parallel termination can also be used with wire wrap and backplane wiring where the characteristic impedance is not exactly defined. If the designer approximates the characteristic impedance, the reflection coefficient will be very small. This results in minimum overshoot and ringing. Parallel termination is not recommended for characteristic impedances of less than 100 ohms because of large d.c current requirements.

10.3.2.1.4 Thevenins Equivalent Termination

This technique is an extension of parallel termination technique. It consists of connecting one resistor from the line to the ground and another from the line to the V_{CC}. Each resistor has a value of twice the characteristic impedance of the line, so the equivalent resistance matches the line impedance. This scheme is shown in Figure 10-15.

If there were no logic devices present, the line would be placed half way between the V_{CC} and the V_{SS}. When the logic device is driving the line, a portion of the required current is provided by the resistors, so the drivers can supply less current than needed in parallel termination. The resistor value can be adjusted to bias the lines towards the V_{CC} or V_{SS}. Ordinarily it is adjusted such that the two are equal, providing balanced performance. The Thevenins circuit provides good overshoot suppression and noise immunity.

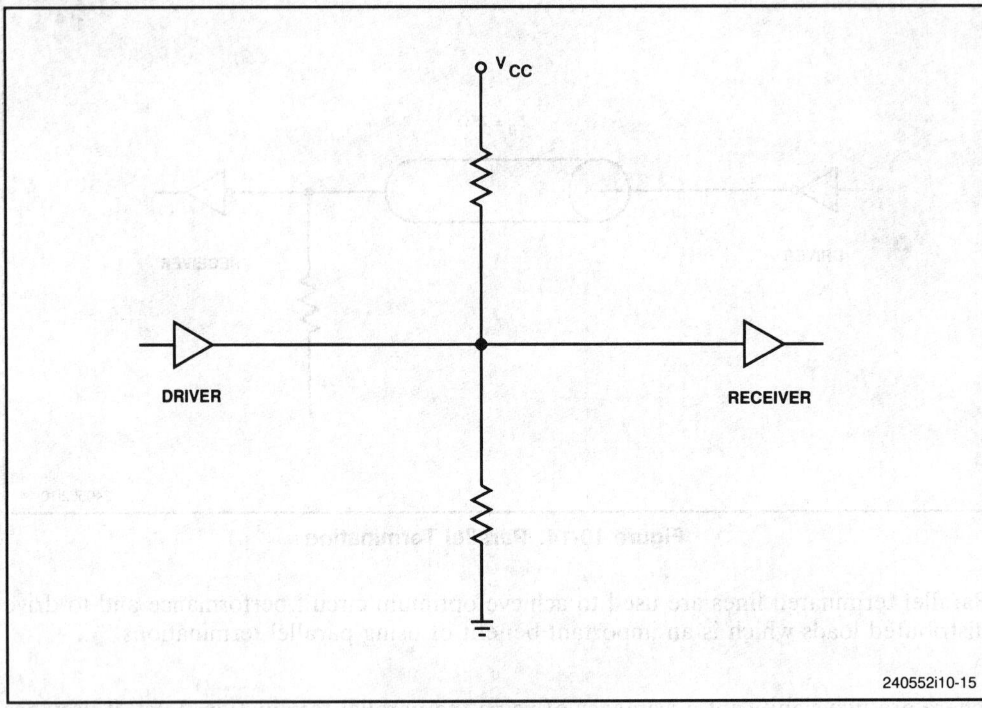

Figure 10-15. Thevenins Equivalent Circuit

Due to power dissipation, this technique is best suited for bipolar and mix MOS devices and is not suitable for pure CMOS implementations. The reasons for not having Thevenins equivalent for the pure CMOS system design are as follows:

- First CMOS circuits have very high impedance to both ground and V_{CC} and their switching threshold is 50% of the supply voltage. Besides dissipating more power, multiple input crossing may occur which creates output oscillations.
- The main problem is high power dissipation through the termination resistors in relationship to the total power consumption of all of the CMOS devices on the board. For this reason, most designers prefer series terminations for CMOS to CMOS connections as this does not introduce any additional impedance from the signal to the ground. The main advantage of the series termination technique, apart from its reduced power consumption, is its flexibility. The received signal amplitude can be adjusted to match the switching threshold of the receiver simply by changing the value of the terminating resistor. This is a very useful technique for interconnecting the logic devices with long lines.

10.3.2.1.5 A.C. Termination

Another technique which can be used for designs which cannot tolerate high power dissipation of parallel termination and delays created by series termination is a.c termination. It consists of a resistor and a capacitor connected in series from the line to the ground. It is similar to the parallel termination technique in functionality except that the capacitor blocks the d.c component of the signal and thus reduces the power dissipation. This technique is shown in Figure 10-16.

The main disadvantage of this technique is that it requires two components. Further the optimum value of the RC time constant of the termination network is not easy to calculate. It usually begins as a resistive value which is slightly larger than the characteristic line impedance. It is critical to determine the capacitor value. If the value of RC time constant is small, the RC circuit will act as an edge generator and will create overshoots and undershoots. Increasing the capacitor value reduces the overshoot and undershoot, but it increases power consumption. As a rule of thumb, RC time constant should be greater than twice the delay line. The power dissipation of the ac termination is a function of the frequency.

10.3.2.1.6 Active Termination

These terminations consist of resistors that are connected between the inputs and outputs of a buffer driver as shown in Figure 10-17.

The main advantage of this technique is that it can tolerate large impedance variations and this tolerance is valuable when tri-state drivers are connected to backplane buses. However, the terminations are costly, and the signals that are produced are not as clean as other terminations. A common solution is to place active terminations at both ends of the bus. This helps to maintain the uniform drive levels along the entire length of the bus, and it reduces crosstalk and ringing.

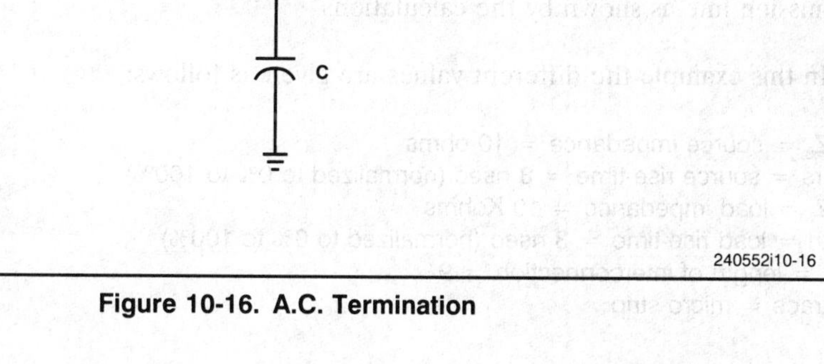

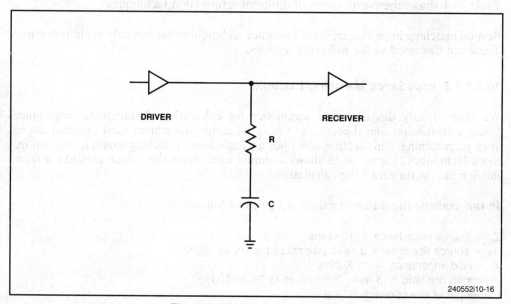

Figure 10-16. A.C. Termination

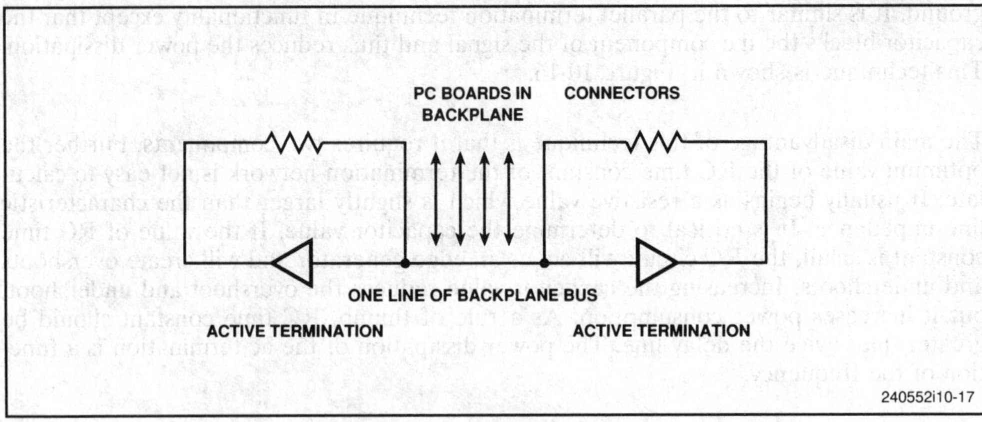

Figure 10-17. Active Termination

Table 10-1. Comparison of Various Termination Techniques

Termination	# of Extra Components	R_L Power Consumption		Prop Delay
Series	1	$Z_0 - Z_{OUT}$	Low	Yes
Parallel	1	Z_0	High	No
Thevenin	2	$2Z_0$	High	No
AC*	2	$2Z_0$	Medium	No
Active	1	$2Z_0$	Medium	No

Table 10-1 shows the comparisons of different termination techniques.

Beyond matching impedances, there are other techniques that can help avoid reflections. These are discussed in the following sections.

10.3.2.1.7 Impedance Matching Example

We have already discussed the techniques for calculating characteristic impedances (using transmission line theory) and the termination procedures used to avoid impedance mismatching. This section describes an impedance matching example that utilizes these techniques. Figure 10-18 shows a simple interconnection which acts like a transmission line as shown by the calculations.

In this example the different values are given as follows:

Z_s = source impedance = 10 ohms
trs = source rise-time = 3 nsec (normalized to 0% to 100%)
Z_l = load impedance = 10 Kohms
trl = load rise-time = 3 nsec (normalized to 0% to 100%)
l = length of interconnection = 9″
trace = micro-strip

e_r = dielectric constant = 5.0
h = .008″
w = .01″
t = .0015″ (1 oz. Cu)
v = 6″/nsec

The interconnection will act as a transmission line if (as was shown in Section 10.3.1).

$l >= (tr \times v) / 8 >= (3 \times 6)/8 >= 3''$.

The value of l = 9″, thus the interconnection acts like a transmission line.

The impedance of the transmission line is calculated as follows:

$$Z0 = 87 / \sqrt{(e_r + 1.41)} \times \ln (5.98h/(.8w + t))$$
$$= 34.39 \ln 5.05 = 55.6 \text{ ohms}$$

Since Z_s = 10 ohms, hence the termination techniques described previously will be needed to match the difference of 45.6 ohms. One method is to use a series terminating resistor of 45.6 ohms or use a.c termination where R = 55.6 ohms and C = 300 pF. The terminated circuit of Figure 10-18 is shown in Figure 10-19.

10.3.2.2 DAISY CHAINING

In laying out PC boards, a stub or T-connection is another source of signal reflection. These types of connections act as inductive loads in the signal path. In daisy chaining, a single trace is run from the source, and the loads are distributed along this trace. This is shown in Figure 10-20.

An alternative way to this technique is to run multiple traces from the source to each load. Each trace will have unique reflections. These reflections are then transmitted down other traces when they return to the source. In such cases a separate termination is required for each branch. To eliminate these T-connections, high-frequency designs are routed as daisy chains.

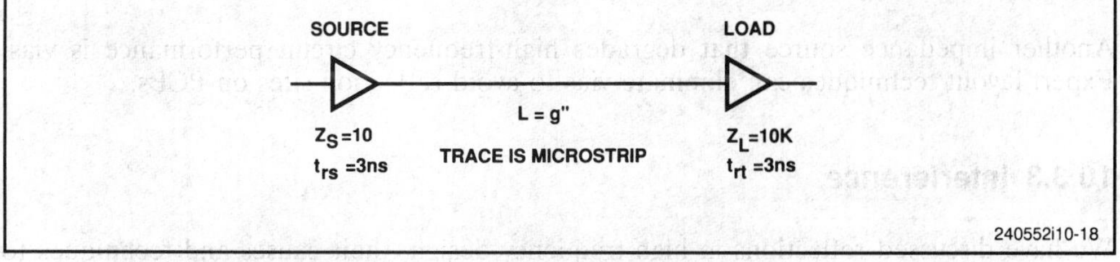

Figure 10-18. Impedance Mismatch Example

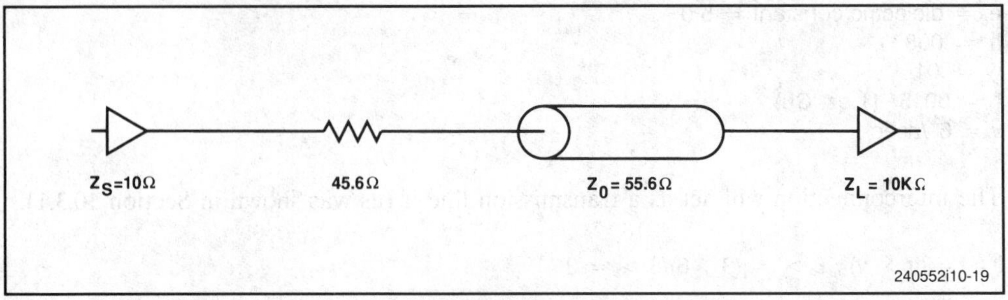

Figure 10-19. Use of Series Termination to Avoid Impedance Mismatch

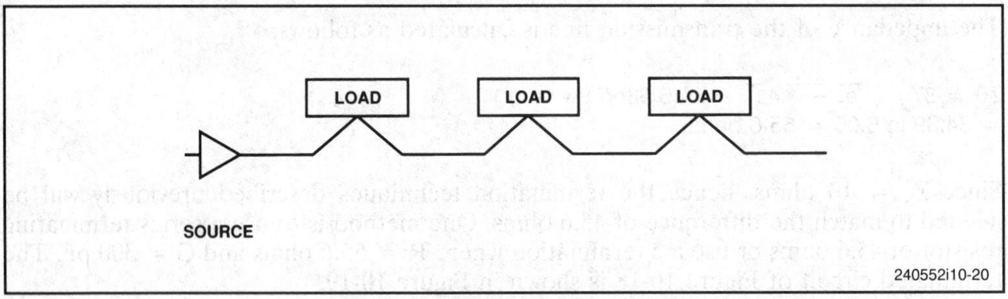

Figure 10-20. Daisy Chaining

Along the chain, each gate provides its own impedance load, thus it is necessary to distribute these loads evenly along the length of the chain. Hence, the impedance along the chain will change in a series of steps and it is easier to match. The overall speed of this line is faster and predictable. Also all loads should be placed at equal distances (regular intervals).

10.3.2.3 90-DEGREE ANGLES

Another major cause of reflections are 90-degree angles in the signal paths, which cause an abrupt change in the signal direction. It promotes signal reflection. For high-frequency layout of designs, avoid 90-degree angles and use 45- or 135-degree angles as shown in Figure 10-21.

10.3.2.4 VIAS (FEED-THROUGH CONNECTIONS)

Another impedance source that degrades high-frequency circuit performance is vias. Expert layout techniques can eliminate vias to avoid reflection sites on PCBs.

10.3.3 Interference

We have discussed reflections in high-frequency design, their causes and techniques to minimize them. In the following sections, we will discuss additional issues related to

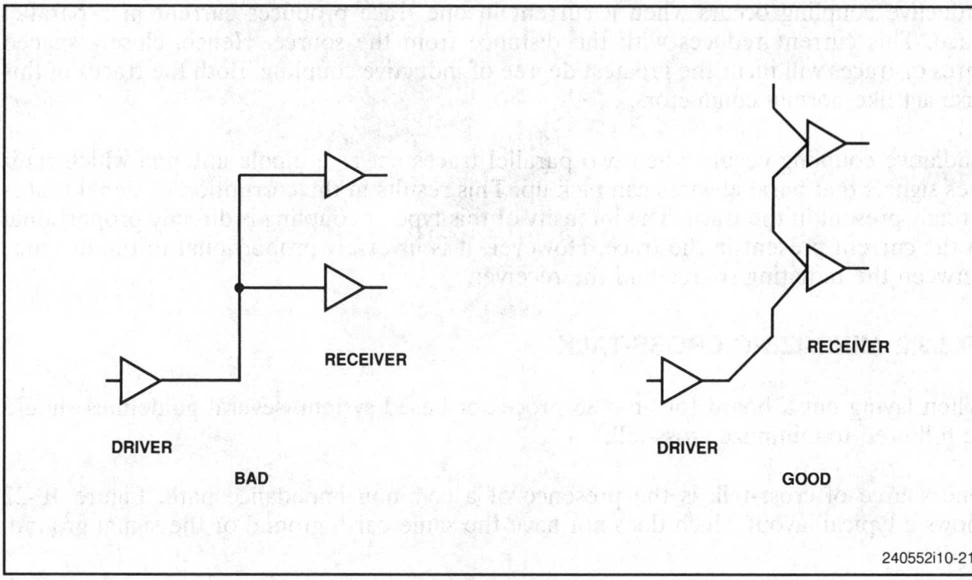

Figure 10-21. Avoiding 90-Degree Angles

high-frequency design, including interference. In general interference occurs when electrical activity in one conductor causes transient voltage to appear in another conductor. Two main factors increase the interference in any circuit:

1. Variation of current and voltage in the lines causes frequency interference. This interference increases with the frequency.

2. Coupling occurs when conductors are in close proximity.

Two types of interference are observed in high-frequency circuits:

1. Electromagnetic Interference (EMI)

2. Electrostatic Interference (ESI)

10.3.3.1 ELECTROMAGNETIC INTERFERENCE (CROSS-TALK)

Cross-talk is a problem at high operating frequencies: when operating frequency increases, signal wavelength becomes comparable to the lengths of some of the interconnections on the PC board. Cross-talk is a phenomenon of a signal in one trace which induces another similar signal in an adjacent trace. There are two types of couplings between parallel traces which determines the amount of cross-talk in a circuit. These are called the inductive coupling and the radiative coupling.

Inductive coupling occurs when a current in one trace produces current in a parallel trace. This current reduces with the distance from the source. Hence, closely spaced wires or traces will incur the greatest degree of inductive coupling. Both the traces in this case act like normal conductors.

Radiative coupling occurs when two parallel traces act as a dipole antenna which radiates signals that parallel wires can pick up. This results in the corruption of signal that is already present in the trace. The intensity of this type of coupling is directly proportional to the current present in the trace. However, it is inversely proportional to the distance between the radiating source and the receiver.

10.3.3.2 MINIMIZING CROSS-TALK

When laying out a board for an i486 processor-based system, several guidelines should be followed to minimize cross-talk.

One source of cross-talk is the presence of a common impedance path. Figure 10-22 shows a typical layout which does not have the same earth ground or the signal ground.

To reduce cross-talk, it is necessary to minimize the common impedance paths, which are Z2, Z3 and Z4 shown primarily as ground impedances. During current switching, the ground line voltage drops causing noise emission. By enlarging the ground conductor

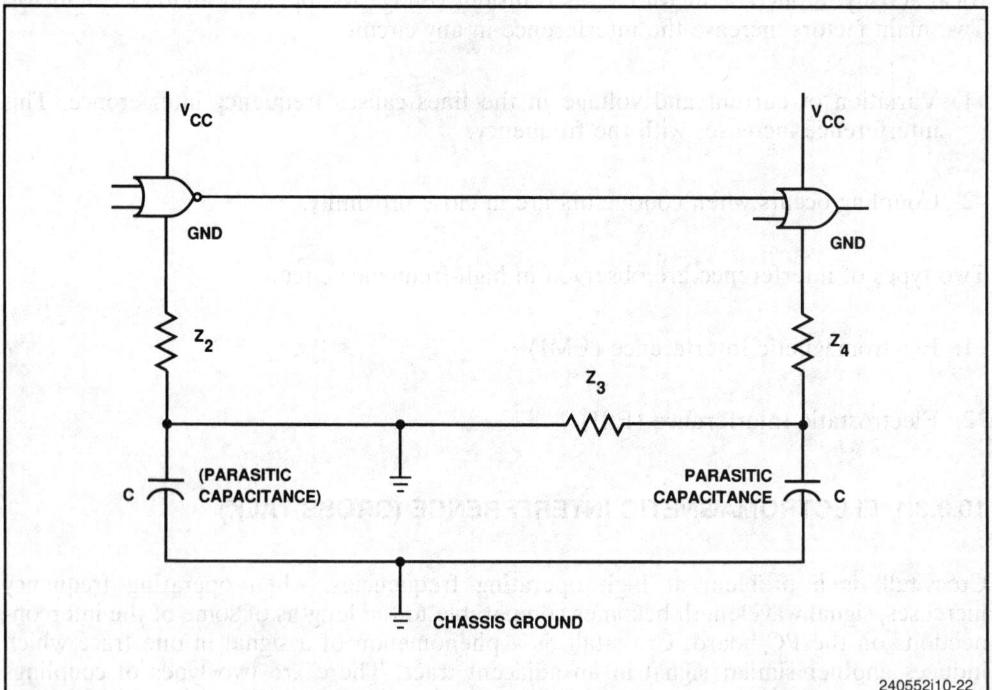

Figure 10-22. Typical Layout

(which reduces its effective impedance), this noise can be minimized. This technique also provides a secondary advantage in that it forms a shield which reduces the emissions of other circuit traces, particularly in multilayer circuit boards.

The impedances Z2 through Z4 depend upon thickness of copper pc-board foil, the circuit switching speeds and the effective lengths of the traces. The current flowing through these common impedance path radiates more noise as its value increases. The amount of voltage that is generated by these switching currents and multiplied by the impedance is difficult to predict.

An effective way of reducing EMI is to decouple the power supply by adding bypass capacitors between V_{CC} and Ground. This technique is similar to the general technique discussed earlier. (The goal of the previous technique was to maintain correct logic levels.)

The design of effective coupling and bypass schemes centers on maximizing the charge stored in the circuit bypass loops while minimizing the inductances in these loops. Some other precautions that can minimize the EMI are as folllows:

- Running a ground line between two adjacent lines. The lines should be grounded at both ends.
- The address and data busses can also be separated by a ground line. This technique may however be expensive due to large number of address and data lines.
- Removing closed loop signal paths create inductive noise as shown in Figure 10-23.

Minimizing cross-talk involves first examining the circuit's interconnection with its nearest neighbors since parallel and adjacent lines can interact and cause EMI. It is necessary to maximize the distance between adjacent parallel wires.

10.3.3.3 ELECTROSTATIC INTERFERENCE

We have discussed two types of coupling, namely inductive and radiative coupling which are responsible for creating electromagnetic interference. A third, known as capacitive coupling, occurs when two equipotential parallel traces, are separated by a dielectric and act as a capacitor. According to the standard capacitor equation, the electric field between the two capacitor surfaces varies with the permitivity of the dielectric and with the area of the parallel conductors.

Electrostatic interference (ESI) is caused by this type of coupling. The charge built on one plate of the capacitor induces opposite charge on the other. To minimize the ESI, the following steps should be taken.

- Separate the signal lines so that the effect of capacitive coupling is negated.
- Run a ground line between the two lines to cancel the electrostatic fields.

For high-frequency designs, a rule of thumb is to include ground planes under each signal layer. Ground planes limit the cross-talk caused by a capacitive coupling between small sections of adjacent layers that are at equipotentials. Additionally, when the width and the thickness of signal lines and their distance from the ground is constant, the

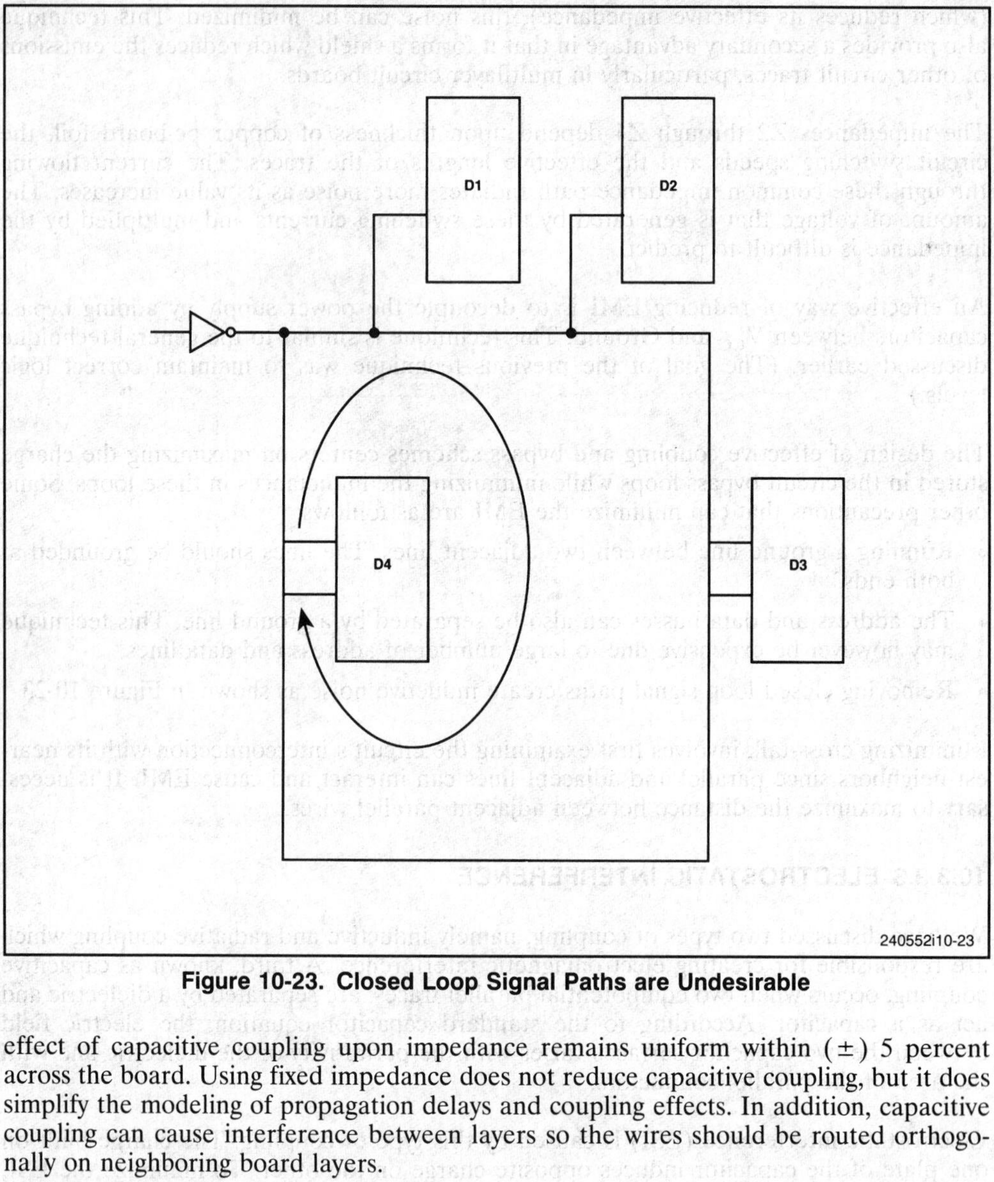

Figure 10-23. Closed Loop Signal Paths are Undesirable

effect of capacitive coupling upon impedance remains uniform within (±) 5 percent across the board. Using fixed impedance does not reduce capacitive coupling, but it does simplify the modeling of propagation delays and coupling effects. In addition, capacitive coupling can cause interference between layers so the wires should be routed orthogonally on neighboring board layers.

10.3.4 Propagation Delay

The propagation delay of a circuit is a function of the loads on the line, the impedance, and the line segments. The term propagation delay means the propagation delay in the entire circuit, including the delay in the transmission line (which is a function of the dielectric constant).

Also, the printed circuit interconnection adds to the propagation delay of every signal on the wire. These interconnections not only decrease the operating speed of the circuits, but also cause reflection, which produces undershoot and overshoot.

When the propagation delays in the circuit are significant, the design must compensate for the signal skew. Signal skew occurs when the wire lengths (and thus the propagation delays) between each source and each corresponding load are unequal.

Another negative aspect of propagation delay is that it causes a generation of race condition. This condition occurs when two signals must reach the same destination within one clock pulse of one another. To avoid race conditions, it is necessary to have the signals travel through the same length traces. But if one route is shorter, then the signals will arrive at different timings, causing race conditions.

One way to minimize this is by decreasing the length of the interconnections. Overall route lengths are shorter in multilayer printed circuit boards than in a double layer boards because ground and power traces are not present. In addition to adding ground planes, a routing program can help to shorten the routing paths.

The guide-lines discussed thus far are prominent at the higher operating frequencies. Debugging an i486 processor-based system at higher frequencies requires careful planning of the layout and the physical design. This section also covers latch-up and thermal characteristics which are system design considerations that stem from the device itself.

10.4 LATCH-UP

Latch-up is a common condition in CMOS devices which occurs when VCC becomes shorted to V_{SS}. Much attention has been directed at eliminating this phenomenon under normal conditions. It is necessary for board designers to be aware of latch-up, of its causes, and of how to prevent it.

Latch-up is triggered when the voltage limits on the I/O pins are exceeded, causing the internal PN junction to become forward-biased. The following steps ensure the prevention of latch-up.

- Observe the maximum input voltage rating of I/O pins.
- Never apply power to i486 processor pin or to any device connected to it before applying power to the i486 processor.
- Use good termination techniques to prevent overshoot and undershoot.
- Ensure a proper layout to minimize reflections and to reduce noise on the signals.

10.5 CLOCK CONSIDERATIONS

For best performance, the clock signal (CLK) for the i486 CPU must be free of noise and within the specifications listed in the i486 data sheet. The transmission line effects must also be considered for the clock paths. These paths should be suitably terminated to minimize signal reflections and prevent overshoot and undershoot.

Skew is an effect of transmission lines. This is very important in a synchronous system. Long traces add propagation delay. A longer trace or a load placed further down a trace will experience more delay than a short trace or loads very close to the source. This must be taken into account when doing the worst case timing analysis. In a system where events must occur synchronous to a clock signal, it is important to make sure the signal is available to all inputs a sufficient amount of time prior to the corresponding clock edge. When performing the component placement this is one of the considerations that must be accounted for.

To maintain proper logic levels, all digital signal outputs have a maximum load, they are capable of driving. DC loading is the constant current required by an input in either the high or the low state. It limits the ability of a device driving the bus to maintain proper logic levels. For an i486 microprocessor-based system, a careful analysis must be performed to ensure that in a worst case situation no loading limits are exceeded. Even if a bus is loaded slightly beyond its worst case limit, it might cause problems if a batch of parts whose input loading is close to maximum is encountered. Proper logic level will then fail to be maintained and unreliable operation may result. Marginal loading problems are particularly insidious, since the effect is often erratic operation and non-repetitive errors that are extremely difficult to track down. For both the high and low logic levels, the sum of the currents required by all the inputs and the leakage currents of all outputs (drivers) on the bus must be added together. This sum must be less than the output capability of the weakest driver. Since the i486 microprocessor is a CHMOS device having negligible dc loading, the main contributors to dc loading will be the TTL devices.

The AC or capacitive loading is caused by the input capacitance of each device and limits the speed at which a device driving a bus signal can change the state from high to low or low to high.

For high-frequency designs, the component and system margins are no longer available to the designer. With less than 1 ns of margin, even the amount of trace capacitance can make a circuit path critical.

A more accurate calculation of capacitive loading can be derived by modeling the device loads and system traces as a series of Transmission Lines Theory. Transmission Line Theory provides a more accurate picture of system loading in high-frequency systems. In addition, it allows new factors such as inductance and the effect of reflections upon the quality of the signal waveform to be factored into consideration.

10.5.1 Requirements

The i486 processor facilitates an easy to implement 1X clock interface. An external, TTL-compatible 25/33-MHz clock synchronizes both the internal functional blocks of the microprocessors and the external signals. Most of the i486 processor's board logic circuitry also uses this clock. The recommended i486 processor clock circuit shown in Figure 10-24 is comprised of a 25/33 MHz oscillator and a fast buffer.

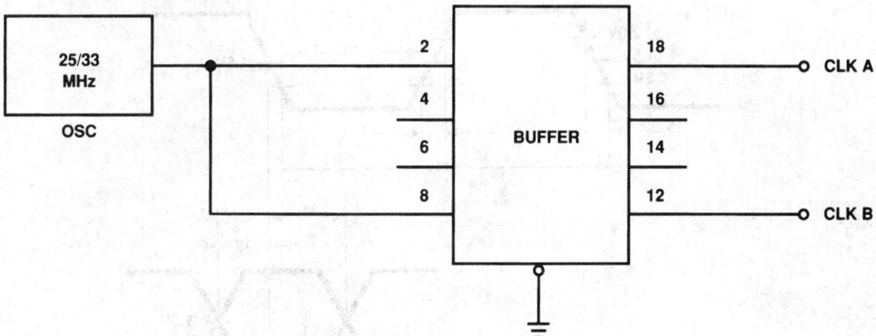

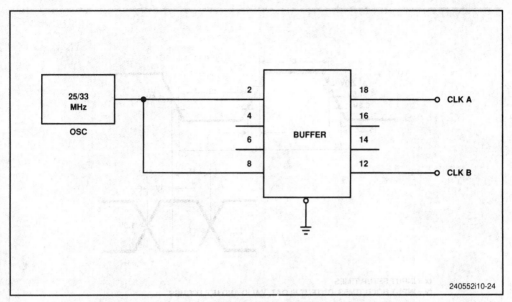

Figure 10-24. Typical i486™ Microprocessor Clock Circuit

The clock input requirements for i486 microprocessor systems are more stringent than those for many commonly used TTL devices, however. The specifications are 0.3 Volts to 0.8 volts for a logic low and 2.0 volts to V_{CC} plus 0.3 volts for a logic high.

The minimum high and low times are specified as 11 ns at 25 MHz and 5 ns at 33 MHz. The Clock timings are shown in Figure 10-25.

10.5.2 Routing

Achieving the proper clock routing around a 25/33-MHz printed circuit board is delicate because a myriad of problems, some of them subtle, can arise if certain design guidelines are not followed. For example fast clock edges cause reflections from high impedance terminations. These reflections can cause significant signal degradations in the systems operating at 25/33 MHz clock rates. This section covers some design guidelines which should be observed to properly layout the clock lines for efficient i486 processor operation.

Since the rise/fall time of the clock signal is typically in the range of 2-4 ns, the reflections at this speed could result in undesirable noise and unacceptable signal degradation. The degree of reflection depends on the impedance of the traces of the clock connections. These reflections can be optimized by using proper terminations and by keeping the length of the traces as short as possible. The preferred method is to connect all of the loads via a single trace as shown in Figure 10-26, thus avoiding the extra stubs associated with each load. The loads should be as close to one another as possible. Multiple clock sources should be used for distributed loads.

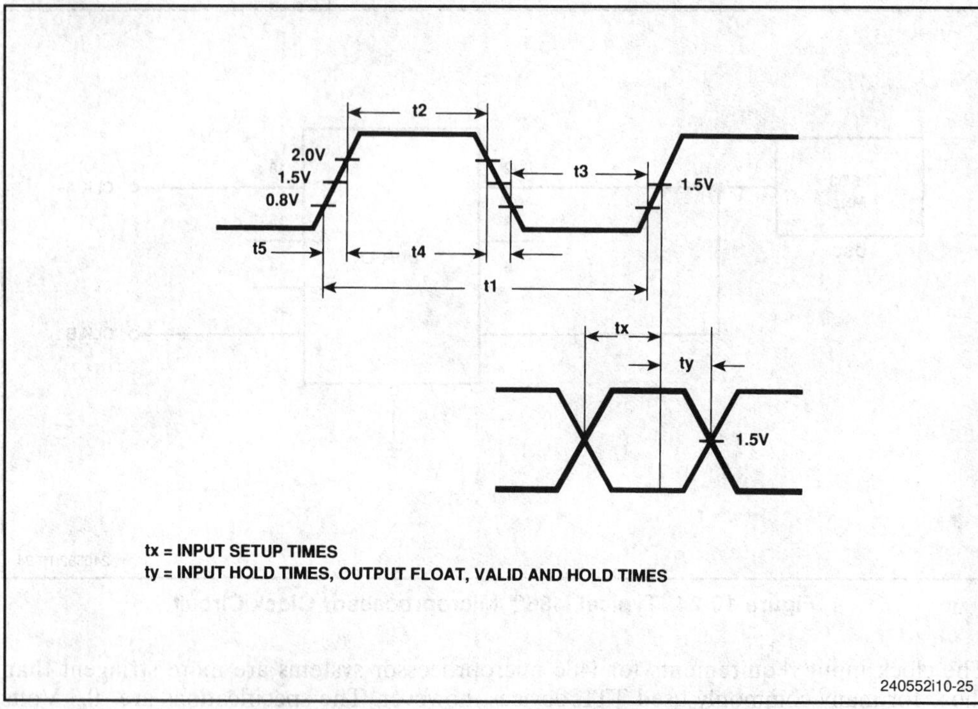

Figure 10-25. Clock Timings

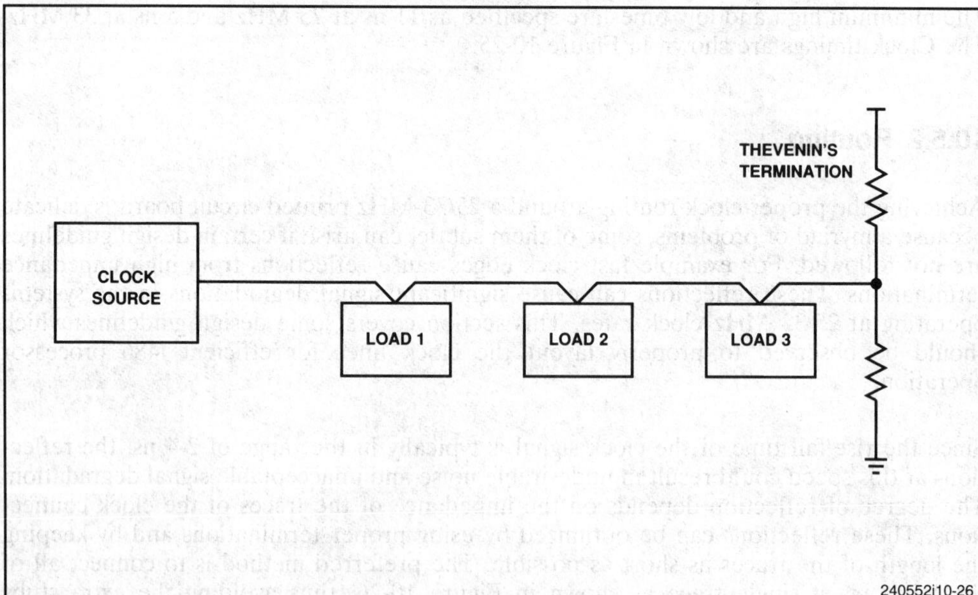

Figure 10-26. Clock Routing

Less desirable method is the star connection layout in which the clock traces branch to the load as closely as possible (Figure 10-27). In this layout, the stubs should be kept as short as possible. The maximum allowable length of the traces depends upon the frequency and the total fanout, but the length of all of the traces in the star connection should be equal. Lengths of less than one inch are recommended.

10.6 THERMAL CHARACTERISTICS

There are thermal and electrical limitations associated with all of the operating electronic devices. In an i486 processor-based system due to power dissipation concerns, these limitations must be accommodated to achieve proper system performance.

Generally, thermal and electrical characteristics are inter-related, and actual constraints depend upon the application of a particular device.

To help the user, most of the general information on case temperature (T_c), maximum current and voltage ratings, maximum thermal resistance ($theta_{ca}$) at various airflows and package thermal specifications are given in the i486 microprocessor data sheet. Despite the wealth of information presented in the data sheet, it is simply impossible to provide graphs and reference tables to cover all applications. The designer must accurately calculate several factors such as junction temperature (T_j) and total power dissipation (P_d) in particular applications.

This section explains how to perform these calculations, thereby helping to make designing with the i486 processor more simple and straight-forward.

The thermal specifications for the i486 processor are designed to ensure a tolerable temperature at the surface of the i486 chip. This temperature, called Junction Temperature (T_j), can be determined from external measurements using the known thermal characteristics of the package.

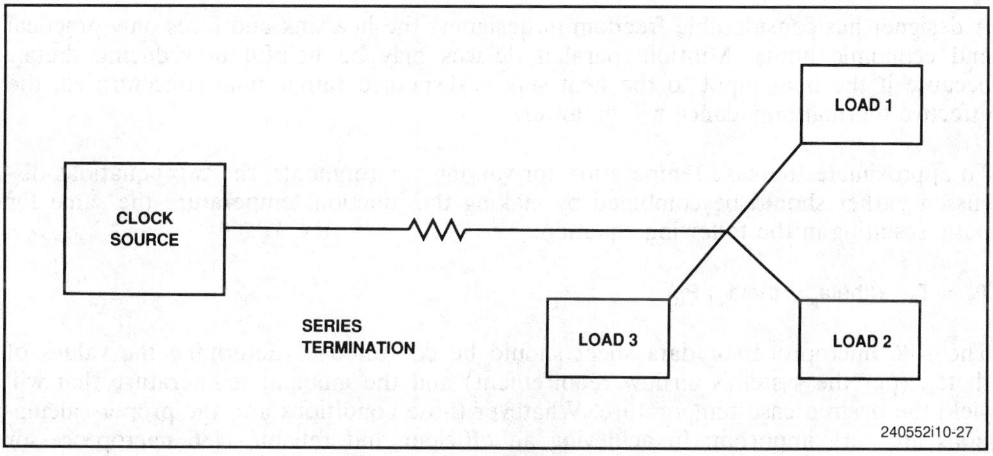

Figure 10-27. Star Connection

The following two equations facilitate the calculation of the Junction Temperature (T_j):

$T_j = T_a + (theta_{ja} * P_d)$ and
$T_j = T_c + (theta_{jc} * P_d)$ where
T_j = Junction temperature
T_a = Ambient temperature
T_c = Case temperature
$Theata_{jc}$ = Junction to Ambient temperature co-efficient
$Theta_{ja}$ = Junction to case temperature co-efficient
P_d = Power Dissipation (worst case $P_d = I_{cc} * V_{cc}$)

Given a heat sink with a thermal resistance of $theta_{sa}$ (sink to ambient), and given the thermal resistance from the junction to the case $theta_{jc}$, then the equation for calculating T_j is as follows:

$$T_j = P_d(theta_{jc} + theta_{cs} + theta_{sa}) + T_a$$

Case temperature calculations offer many advantages over ambient temperature calculations:

- Case temperature is more easily measured compared to ambient temperature because the measurement is localized to a single point (the center of the package).
- The worst case junction temperature (T_j) is lower when calculated with case temperature for two reasons. First, the junction-to-case thermal coefficient ($theta_{jc}$) is lower than the junction-to-ambient thermal coefficient ($theta_{ja}$). Therefore, the calculated junction temperature varies less with power dissipation (P_d). Second, the junction-to-case coefficient ($theta_{jc}$) is not affected by the airflow in the system, while the junction-to-ambient coefficient ($theta_{ja}$) does vary.

Given the case temperature specification, a designer can either set the ambient temperature or use fans to control the case temperature. Finned heatsinks or conductive cooling may also be used in an environment which prohibits the use of fans.

A designer has considerable freedom in designing the heatsink and faces only practical and economic limits. Multiple parallel devices may be helpful in reducing $theta_{sa}$ because if the heat input to the heat sink is dispersed rather than concentrated, the effective thermal impedance will be lower.

To approximate the case temperature for varying environments, the two equations discussed earlier should be combined by making the junction temperature the same for both, resulting in the following equation:

$$T_a = T_c \quad ((theta_{ja} \quad theta_{jc})\ P_d)$$

The i486 microprocessor data sheet should be consulted to determine the values of $theta_{ja}$ (per the system's airflow requirement) and the ambient temperature that will yield the desired case temperature. Whatever those conditions are, the proper calculations are very important in achieving an efficient and reliable i486 microprocessor system.

The i486 microprocessor is available in a 168-pin ceramic PGA. The recommended heat-sinks for the device are offered in the pin fin design that utilizes air cooling. T_a is greatly improved by adding heat sink. The heat sink is mounted on the PGA package with a frame and spring. A typical heat sink is shown in Figure 10-28a. The dimensions are shown in Figure 10-28b.

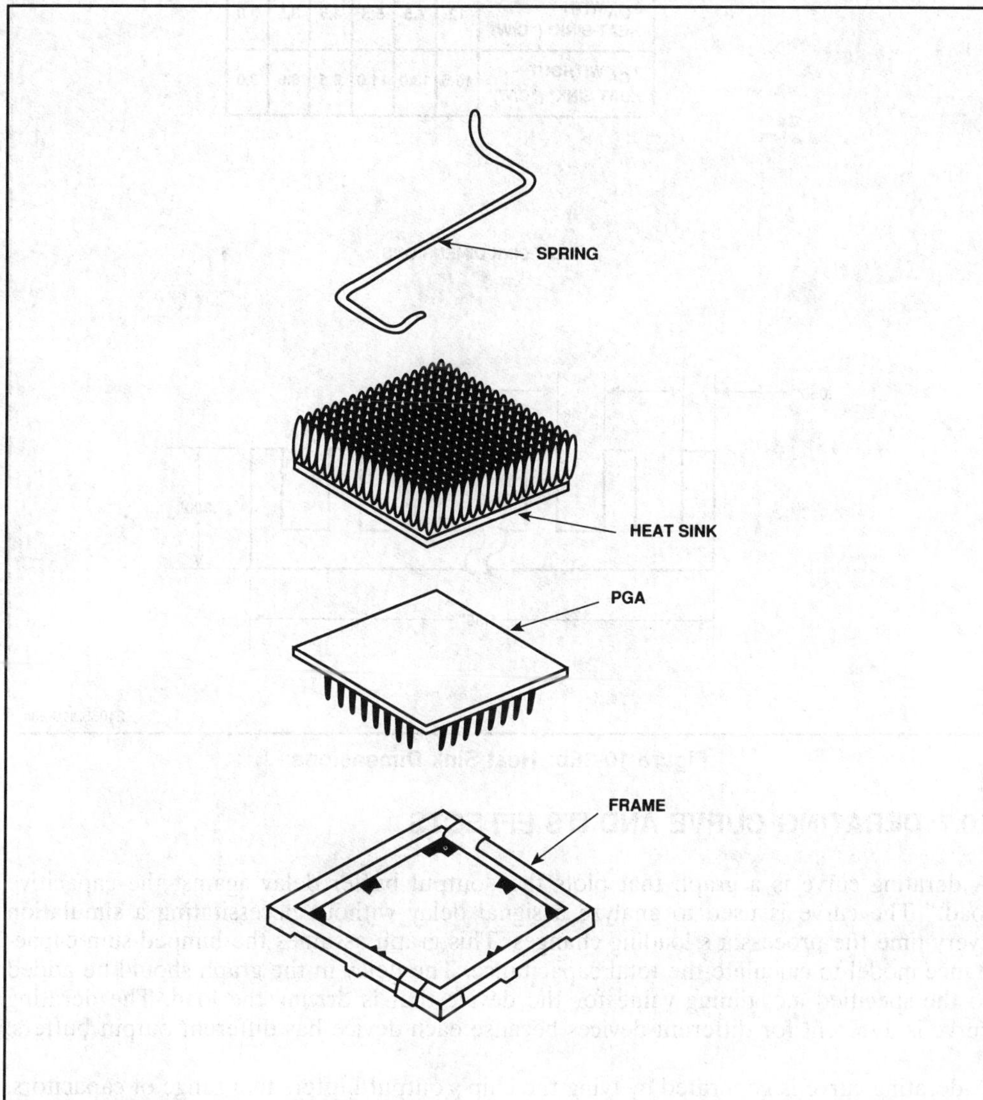

Figure 10-28a. Typical Heat Sinks

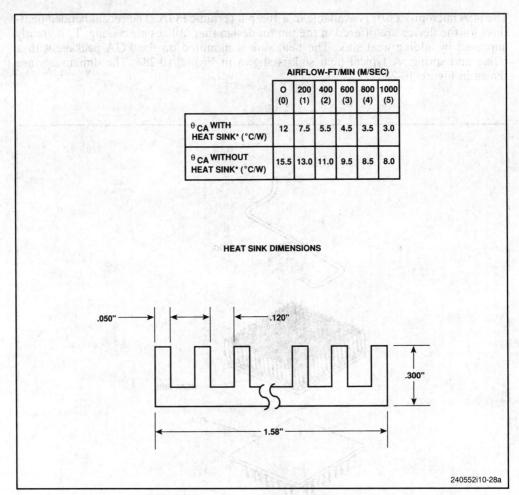

	AIRFLOW-FT/MIN (M/SEC)					
	O (0)	200 (1)	400 (2)	600 (3)	800 (4)	1000 (5)
θ CA WITH HEAT SINK* (°C/W)	12	7.5	5.5	4.5	3.5	3.0
θ CA WITHOUT HEAT SINK* (°C/W)	15.5	13.0	11.0	9.5	8.5	8.0

HEAT SINK DIMENSIONS

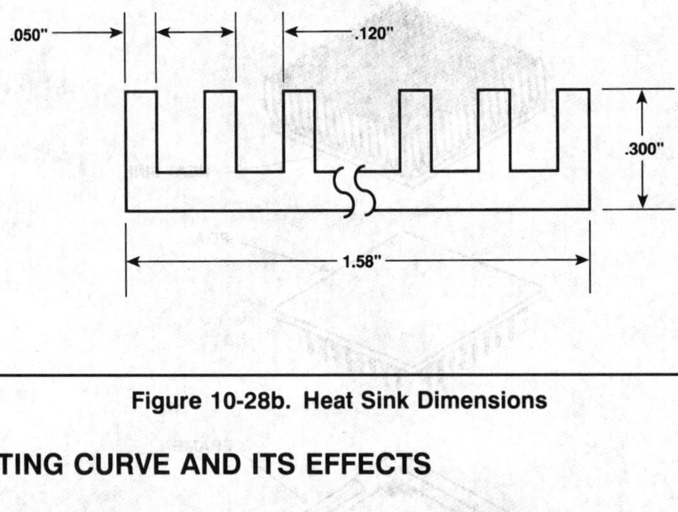

240552i10-28a

Figure 10-28b. Heat Sink Dimensions

10.7 DERATING CURVE AND ITS EFFECTS

A derating curve is a graph that plots the "output buffer delay against the capacitive load." The curve is used to analyze a signal delay without necessitating a simulation every time the processor's loading changes. This graph assumes the lumped-sum capacitance model to calculate the total capacitance. The delay in the graph should be added to the specified a.c. timing value for the device that is driving the load. The derating curve is different for different devices because each device has different output buffers.

A derating curve is generated by tying the chip's output buffers to a range of capacitors. The voltage and resistance values chosen for the output buffers are at the highest specified temperature and are rising (worst case) values. The value of the capacitors centers around the a.c. timing values for the chip. For 25 MHz and above, this is 50 pF. Since the a.c. timing specifications are measured for a signal reaching 1.5V, the output buffer delay is the time that it takes for a signal to rise from 0 to 1.5V. A curve is then drawn from the range of time and capacitance values, with 50 pF representing the average and with nominal or zero derating. These curves are valid only for a 25-150 pF load range. Beyond this range the output buffers are not well characterized. The derating curves for the i486 processor are shown in Figure 10-29. These curves use the lumped capacitance model for circuit capacitance measurements and must be modified slightly when doing

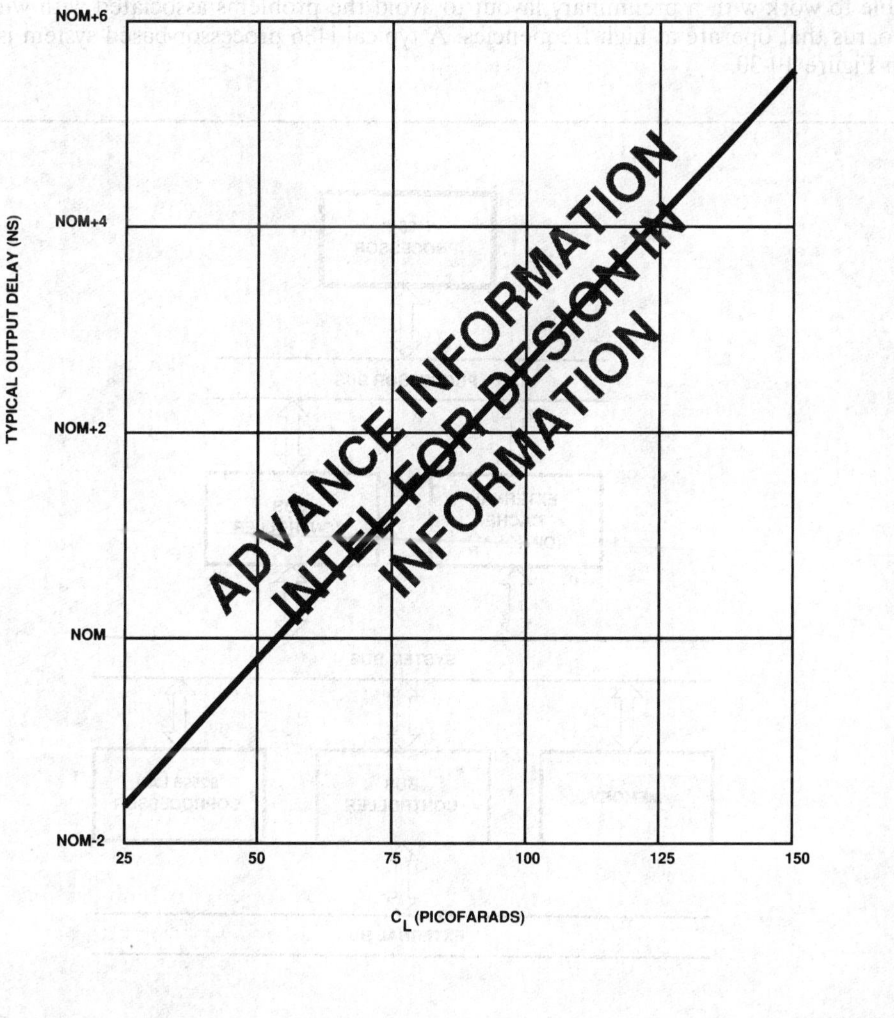

Figure 10-29. Derating Curves for the i486™ Processor

worst-case calculations that involve transmission line effects. The amount of modifications required can be calculated by performing SPICE simulation or by using other simulation packages.

10.8 BUILDING AND DEBUGGING THE i486 MICROPROCESSOR-BASED SYSTEM

While an i486 processor-based system designer should plan the entire system, it is necessary to begin building different elements of the core and begin testing them before building the final system. If a printed circuit board layout has to be done, the whole system may be simulated before generating the net list for the layout vendor. It is advisable to work with a preliminary layout to avoid the problems associated with wire wrap boards that operate at high frequencies. A typical i486 processor-based system is shown in Figure 10-30.

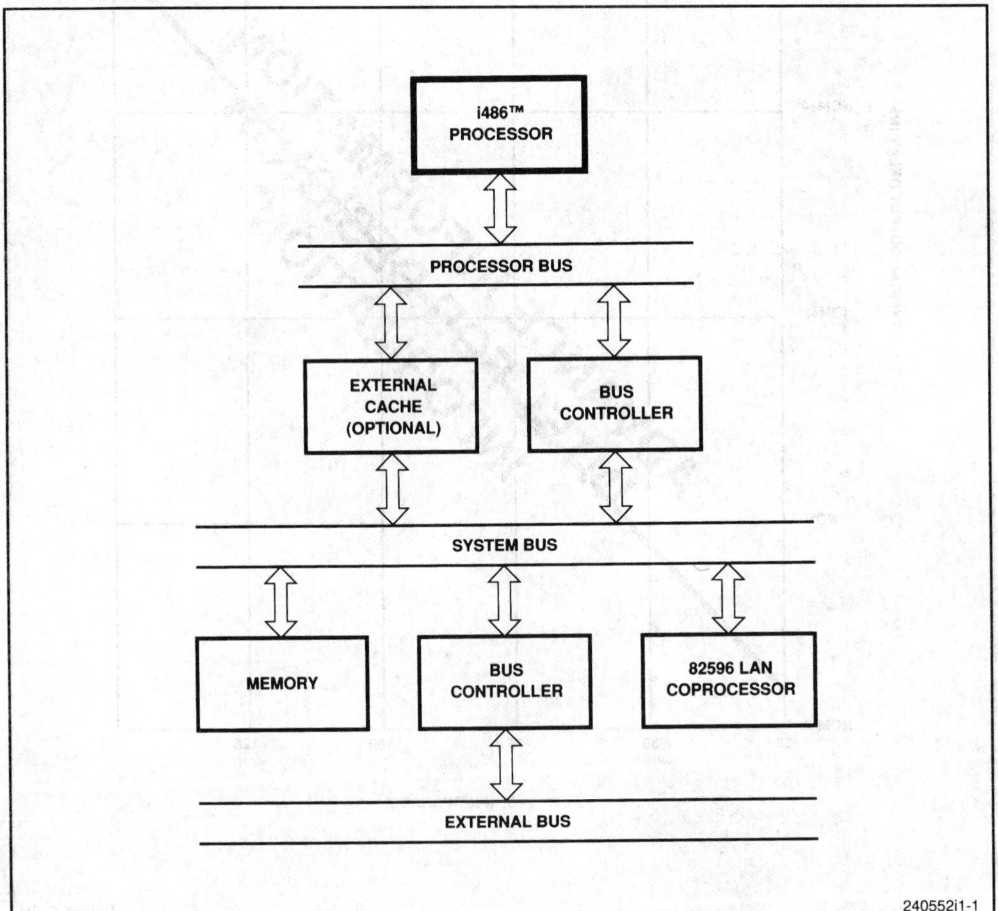

Figure 10-30. Typical i486™ Processor-Based System

An optional second-level cache can also be added to the system. The following steps are usually carried out in designing with the i486 microprocessor.

1. Clock circuitry should be using an oscillator and fast buffer. The CLK signal should be clean, without any overshoots or undershoots.

2. The reset circuitry should be designed as shown in Chapter 3. This circuitry is used to generate the RESET # signal for the i486 microprocessor. The system should be checked during reset for all of the timings. The clock continues to run during these tests.

3. The INT and HOLD pin should be tied to LOW (negated from the active state). The READY # pin is connected to HIGH so as to add additional delays (wait-states) to the first cycle. At this instance, the i486 microprocessor is reset, and the signals emitted from it are checked for the validity of the state. The i486 processor will generate the physical address 0XFFFFFF00. The address latch is connected at this time, and the address is verified.

4. The PAL implementing the address decoder should be connected to the i486 microprocessor.

10.8.1 Debugging Features of the i486 Microprocessor

The i486 microprocessor provides several features which simplify the debugging process for the system hardware designer. The device offers three on-chip debugging aids which are as follows:

- The code execution breakpoint opcode
- The single-step capability provided by the TF bit in the flag register.
- The code and data breakpoint capability as provided by the debug registers (DR0-3, DR6 and DR7).

10.8.2 Breakpoint Instruction

The i486 microprocessor provides a breakpoint instruction that can be used by software debuggers. This instruction is a single byte opcode and generates an exception 3 trap when it is executed. In a typical environment a debugger program can place the breakpoint instruction at various points in the program. The single-byte breakpoint opcode is an alias for the two-byte general software interrupt instruction, INT n where n=3. The only difference between INT 3 and INT n is that INT 3 is never IOPL-sensitive but INT n is IOPL-sensitive in Protected mode and Virtual 8086 mode.

10.8.3 Single-Step Trap

The i486 microprocessor supports X86 compatible single-step feature. If the single step-flag bit (bit8, TF) is set to 1 in the EFLAG register, a single step exception will occur. This exception is auto-vectored to exception-1 and occurs immediately after completion of next instruction. Typically a debugger sets the TF bit of the EFLAG register on the debugger's stack followed by transfer of the control to the user program. The debugger also loads the flag image (EFLAG) via IRET instruction. The single-step trap occurs after execution of one instruction of the user program.

Since the exception 1 occurs right after the execution of the instruction as a trap, the CS:EIP pushed onto the debugger's stack points to the next unexecuted instruction of the program which is being debugged, merely by ending with an IRET instruction.

10.8.4 Debug Registers

The i486 microprocessor has an advance debugging feature. It has six debug registers that allow data access breakpoints as well code access breakpoints. Since the breakpoints are indicated by on-chip registers, an instruction execution breakpoint can be placed in ROM code or in code shared by several tasks. Both of these are not supported by the INT3 breakpoint opcode.

The debug registers provides the ability to specify four distinct breakpoint addresses, control options, and read breakpoint status. When the CPU goes through reset, the breakpoints are all in the disabled state. Hence the breakpoints can not occur unless the debug resisters are programmed.

It is possible to specify up to four breakpoint addresses by writing into debug registers. The debug registers are shown in Figure 10-31. The addresses specified are 32-bit linear addresses. The processor hardware continously compares the linear breakpoint addresses in DR0-DR3 with the linear addresses generated by executing software. When the paging is disabled then the linear address is equal to the physical address. If the paging is enabled then the linear address is translated to a 32-bit address by the on-chip paging unit. Whether paging is enabled or disabled the breakpoint register will hold linear addresses.

10.8.5 Debug Control Register (DR7)

A debug control register, DR7 shown in Figure 10-31 allows several debug control functions such as enabling the breakpoints and setting up several control options for the breakpoints. There are several fields within the debug control register. These are discussed below:

LENI (breakpoint length specification bits). A 2-bit LEN field exists for each of the four breakpoints. It specifies the length of the associated breakpoint field. It is possible to have three different choices: 1 byte, 2 bytes and 4 bytes. LENi field encoding is shown in Table 10-2.

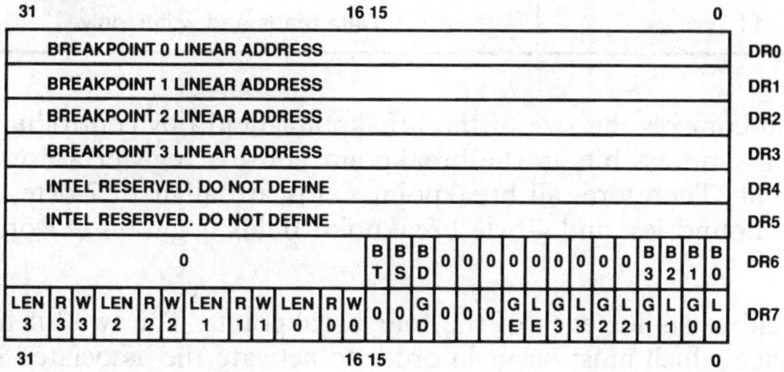

NOTE:
0 INDICATES INTEL RESERVED: DO NOT DEFINE; SEE SECTION 2.3.10

LENi ENCODING	BREAKPOINT FIELD WIDTH	USAGE OF LEAST SIGNIFICANT BITS IN BREAKPOINT ADDRESS REGISTER i, (i = 0 -3)
00	1 BYTE	ALL 32-BITS USED TO SPECIFY A SINGLE-BYTE BREAKPOINT FIELD.
01	2 BYTE	A1 — A31 USED TO SPECIFY A TWO-BYTE. WORD-ALIGNED BREAKPOINT FIELD. A0 IN BREAKPOINT ADDRESS REGISTER IS NOT USED.
10	UNDEFINED— DO NOT USE THIS ENCODING	
11	4 BYTE	A2 — A31 USED TO SPECIFY A FOUR-BYTE. DWORD-ALIGNED BREAKPOINT FIELD. A0 AND A1 IN BREAKPOINT ADDRESS REGISTER ARE NOT USED.

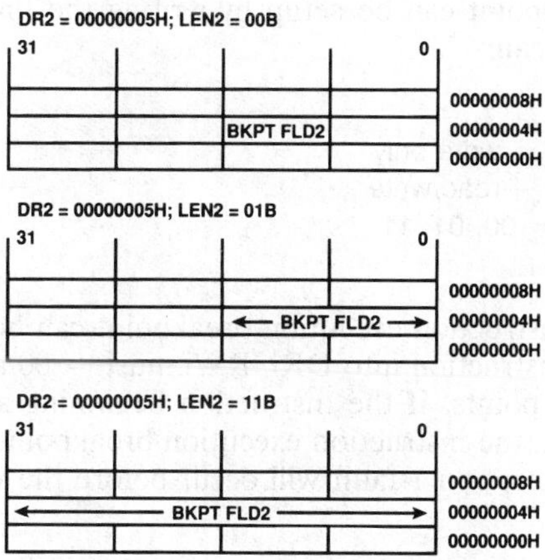

240552i10-30

Figure 10-31. Debug Registers

Table 10-2. LENi Fields

RW Encoding	Usage Causing Breakpoint
00	Instruction execution only
01	Data writes only
10	Undefined – Do not use this encoding
11	Data reads and writes only

The LENi field controls the size of the breakpoint field i by controlling whether all the low order linear address bits in the breakpoint address register are used to detect the breakpoint event. Therefore, all breakpoint fields are aligned: 2-byte breakpoint fields begin on word boundries, and 4-byte breakpoint fields begin on D word boundries.

A 2-bit RW field exists for each of the four breakpoints. The two bit field specifies the type of the usage which must occur in order to activate the associated breakpoint.

RW encoding 00 is used to setup an instruction execution breakpoint. RW encodings 01 or 11 are used to setup write only or read only or read/write data breakpoints. The data breakpoint can be setup by writing the linear address into DRi. For data breakpoints, RWi can:

= 01 – write only
= 11 – read/write
LEN = 00, 01, 11.

An instruction execution breakpoint can be setup by writing address of the beginning of the instruction into DRi. RWi must = 00 and LEN must = 00 for instruction execution breakpoints. If the instruction beginning at the breakpoint address is about to be executed, the instruction execution breakpoint has occurred, and the breakpoint is enabled, an exception 1 fault will occur before the instruction is executed.

GD (Global Debug Register access detect). The debug registers can only be accessed in real mode or at privilege level 0 in protected mode. The GD bit when set provides extra protection against any debug register access even in real mode or at privilege level 0 in protected mode. This additional protection feature is provided to guarantee that a software debugger can have full control over the debug register resources when required.

The breakpoint mechanism of the i486 microprocessor differ from that of the 386 microprocessor. The i486 microprocessor always does exact data breakpoint matching regardless of the GE/LE bit settings. Any data breakpoint trap will be reported exactly after completion of the instruction that caused the operand transfer. Exact reporting is provided by forcing the i486 microprocessor execution unit to wait for the completion of data operand transfers before beginning execution of the next instruction.

When i486 microprocessor switches to a new task, the LE bit is cleared. Thus, LE enables fast switching from one task to another task. To avoid having exact data breakpoint match enabled in the new task, the LE bit is cleared by the processor during the task switch. Note that exact data breakpoint match must be re-enabled under software control.

The GE bit supports exact data break point match that is to remain enabled during all tasks executing in the system. The i486 microprocessor GE bit is unaffected during a task switch.

Note that instruction execution breakpoints are always reported exactly.

Gi Li (breakpoint enable, global and local). Associated breakpoints are enabled when either Gi or Li are set. When this happens the i486 microprocessor detects the ith breakpoint condition, then the exception 1 handler is invoked.

Debug status register. A debug status register, DR6 allows the exception 1 handler to easily determine why it was invoked. Exception 1 handler can be invoked as a result of one of the several events as documented in the i486 microprocessor datasheet. This register contains single-bit flags for each of the possible events invoking exception 1. Some of these events are faults while others are traps.

10.8.6 Debugging

Once the i486 microprocessor-based system is designed and the printed circuit board is fabricated and stuffed. The next step is to debug the hardware in increments. The following sections provide valuable debugging concepts and techniques for writing diagnostic software. The i486 processor data sheet, programmer's reference manual and this manual provides a good start.

The design of a microprocessor based system can be subdivided into several phases. The design starts with preparation of the system specification followed by conceptual representation in the form of block diagram. Next phase is that of implementation of the design, this comprises of hardware design and the software design both occurring in parallel. Hardware debugging usually begins by testing the system with short test programs. Initially the power and ground lines are tested for opens and shorts followed by testing of reset function. After the hardware passes these programs, the hardware, software integration phase begins. The test programs are then replaced by the application software and complete system is debugged.

This can be a challenging task, since there are often hardware and software problems, and very difficult to isolate each. Several types of testing systems are available to assist in this process. The most common type is the in-circuit emulator, which plugs into the microprocessor socket and allows the operation of the system to be controlled and monitored. In-circuit emulators usually include memory that can be used in place of the prototype memory. Another useful test tool is the logic analyzer, which captures the "trace" of the bus activity and displays the sequence of bus cycles that were executed.

Most in-circuit emulators also provide this function which is invaluable for both hardware and software debugging. Another monitor which can be used for debugging is Jetmon. This requires EPROM and RAM. Test programs can be run from ICE or monitor. An example of a typical DRAM subsystem test program is shown in Figure 10-32.

```
         mov   ecx, Oh                          ;second pass, compare patt
         mov   esi, botaddr
1b300:   mov   eax,dword ptr [esi - 44h]        ; dummy read
         mov   eax, dword ptr [est + 1000h]
         cmp   eax, ecx
         db    Ofh,85h                          ;jnz
         dd    (offset 1 berr) - (offset 1b350)
1b350:   add   ecx,incrval
         add   esi,edx
         cmp   esi,topaddr
         jc    1b300
         sub   esi,topaddr - botaddr
         cmp   esi,botaddr
         jnz   1b300
```

Figure 10-32. Pattern Compare

10.9 REFERENCES

1. True K.M., "Reflection: Computations and waveforms, The Interface Handbook," Fairchild Corp, Mountain View, CA, 1975, Ch:3

2. "Packaging for high speed logic," Special report. Electronic Packaging and production. Sept 1987, pp 48-50.

3. W. Blood, "1983 MECL System Design Handbook," pp 121-145

4. "Terminate bus lines to avoid overshoot and ringing," Charles Pace

Introduction to Intel 86 Family Architecture

A

APPENDIX A
INTRODUCTION TO INTEL 86 FAMILY ARCHITECTURE

Intel's goals for the 86 family architecture have included the achievement of faster processing, simpler and lower-cost system design interfaces, and compatibility with existing software. Tradeoffs among these goals have been made to achieve continuous progress from one generation to the next since the introduction of the 8086 processor in 1978.

Externally, the duration of processor bus cycles has shortened and more functions have been integrated on-chip with each new generation. This has freed up processor bus bandwidth for other uses. The introduction of burst cycles in the i486™ processor has contributed to the performance increase. System design has become easier as the address and data buses have been de-multiplexed, the internal clock rate has been standardized at the same (1x) frequency as the external clock input, address pipelining on the processor bus has been eliminated, and the floating-point, cache, and parity logic have been integrated on-chip.

Internally, the number of clocks per executed instruction has come down with each generation and improvements have been made in protection mechanisms and in support for large multitasking applications. Continual improvements in hardware support for address computation have made execution faster. In the i486 processor, internal processing speed has increased with the on-chip availability of the cache and floating-point units.

A.1 HISTORICAL OVERVIEW

Intel introduced the world's first microprocessor – the 4-bit 4004 – in 1971. Both this and its enhanced relative – the 8-bit 8008 – formed the cornerstones of microprocessor technology. The second-generation microprocessor – the 8-bit 8080 – was introduced by Intel in 1974; it was more general-purpose than its predecessors and incorporated a larger address space (64-Kbyte) and bus arbitration. The 8085, introduced in 1976, was software-compatible with the 8080 but made system design easier.

Intel introduced the third-generation microprocessor – the 16-bit 8086 – in 1978. This was the first in the Intel 86 family architecture, shown in Tables A-1 and A-2. The 8086 processor expanded the memory address space, the instruction set, and bus operations. It introduced address-space segmentation as a protection mechanism against software errors and was object-code compatible with the 8080. Building on the extensive customer base and software libraries of the 8080, the 8086 rapidly became the leading processor for 16-bit system designs.

Table A-1. The Intel 86 Family of Processors

Processor	Year	Internal Architecture	External Bus Size	Transistors	Principle Features
8086	1978	16	16	29K	16-bit architecture, basic segmentation protection.
8088	1979	16	8	29K	Same as 8086, but with 8-bit processor bus.
80186	1982	16	16	56K	Same as 8086, but with greater integration of off-chip functions.
80188	1982	16	8	56K	Same as 80186, but with 8-bit processor bus.
80286	1982	16	16	130K	Expands segmentation protection, adds single-instruction task switching, and adds greater speed to 8086 functions.
386™ Processor	1985	32	32	275K	Adds paging, 32-bit extensions, on-chip address translation, and greater speed to 80286 functions.
386 SX	1988	32	16	275K	Same as 386, but with 16-bit processor bus.
i486™ Processor	1989	32	32	1,200K	Adds on-chip cache, floating-point unit, and greater speed to 386 functions.

Table A-2. Memory Addressing, Segmentation, and Paging

Processor	Directly Addressable Memory	Virtual Memory Size	Segment Size	Page Size
8086	1 Mbyte	none	64 Kbytes	none
80286	16 Mbytes	1 Gbyte	1 byte to 64 Kbytes	none
386™ Processor	4 Gbytes	64 Tbytes	1 byte to 4 Gbytes	4 Kbytes
i486™ Processor	4 Gbytes	64 Tbytes	1 byte to 4 Gbytes	4 Kbytes

The 16-bit 80286 processor was introduced in 1982. It supports single-instruction task switching (multitasking), protected virtual address modes (Protected Mode), 16 Mbytes of physical memory, 1 Gbyte of virtual memory, and instruction retry. Address pipelining was introduced to allow maximum address setup time before data is required by the CPU or memory. Programs could also be run on the 80286 processor in real-address mode (Real Mode), which emulates the programming environment of the 8086 processor.

The 32-bit 386 processor was introduced in 1985. In addition to adding 32-bit data types and instructions, the 386 processor added demand paging, address translation registers, Virtual-8086 operating mode (a subset of Protected Mode), and a non-pipelined option for bus cycles. The 386 processor allowed execution of DOS under UNIX or OS/2 and offered expanded testability and debugging features.

The 32-bit i486 processor was introduced in 1989. It has all of the architectural features of the 386 processor, plus on-chip cache and floating-point (numeric) processor. It does away with address pipelining on the processor bus, although instruction pipelining is done internally. It supports both 8- and 16-bit data buses, and it introduces burst cycles for fast cache line fills.

Some functions have remained constant throughout the evolution of the Intel 86 family architecture. Among them are the definition of I/O space and the manner in which interrupts are handled.

The i486 processor is object-code compatible with the Intel 86 family processors shown in Table A-3. Thus, the i486 processor can execute any software written for the 8086, 8088, 80186, 80188, 80286 or 386 processors. The reverse is not true; the i486 processor instruction set is a superset of the instruction sets of earlier processors. For example, the

Table A-3. Object-Code Compatibility

Software Source	Execution Platform							
	8086	8088	80186	80188	80286	386™	386 SX	486™
8086	–	yes	yes	yes	yes	yes	yes	yes
8088	yes	–	yes	yes	yes	yes	yes	yes
80186	yes	yes	–	yes	yes	yes	yes	yes
80188	yes	yes	yes	–	yes	yes	yes	yes
80286	no	no	no	no	–	yes	yes	yes
386	no	no	no	no	no	–	yes	yes
386 SX	no	no	no	no	no	yes	–	yes
i486	no	no	no	no	no	no	no	–

semantics of instructions which affect the segment registers are considerably different in the i486 processor than in the 8086 processor. There are also subtle differences among the processors in their shift capabilities, divide operations, use of locking, and other details.

Table A-4 shows the operating modes of the processors. The 8086 processor has two hardware modes, minimum and maximum, which use somewhat different pins. Most 8086 designs, including personal computer systems, use the maximum mode.

Each member of the Intel 86 family has an associated numerics coprocessor, shown in Table A-5. The 8087 and 80287 perform arithmetic, logical, and transcendental operations on 32-, 64- and 80-bit floating point operands, 32- and 64-bit integers, and 18-digit BCD operands. The 80387 coprocessor and the i486 processor's on-chip floating-point unit add more transcendental operations to those performed by the 8087 and 80287 coprocessors.

A.2 PROCESSOR BUS

With each new generation, the duration of bus cycles has been shortened to free up bus bandwidth for other uses. System design with the i486 processor has become easier than with earlier generations; the address and data buses have been de-multiplexed, the internal clock rate has been standardized at the same (1x) frequency as the external clock input, address pipelining on the processor bus has been eliminated (thereby reducing data latency times), and parity generation and checking have been added. Tables A-6 and A-7 show these improvements.

Bus utilization by the i486 processor is substantial improved compared with earlier generations. In the i486 processor, burst cycles fill the cache so that most subsequent read requests only access the cache and do not generate bus cycles.

Table A-8 shows the signals used for bus control and arbitration. In all four processors, bus hold by external bus masters is requested with the HOLD input and acknowledged with the HLDA output, although the 8086 processor's Maximum Mode uses the RQ#/GT#0 and RQ#/GT#1 bidirectional request/grant signals for this purpose. In the i486 processor, a refinement to bus arbitration is provided: the processor can request access

Table A-4. Operating Modes

Processor	Software Modes			Hardware Modes
	Real Mode	Protected Mode	Virtual 8086 Mode	
8086	yes	no	no	Minimum or Maximum
80286	yes	yes	no	none
386™ Processor	yes	yes	yes	none
i486™ Processor	yes	yes	yes	none

Table A-5. Numeric Coprocessors

Processor	Data Bus Width	Interface to Processor	Operations Performed	Conformance with Standard
8087	16	Synchronous	32-, 64-, and 80-bit floating point, 32- and 64-bit integers, and 18-digit BCD operands	—
80287	16	Asynchronous	Same as 8087	An early draft of the ANSI/IEEE 754
387™ Processor	32	Asynchronous	Same as 8087 and 80287 but with additional transcendental operations	ANSI/IEEE 754-1985
i486™ Processor	on-chip	on-chip	Same as 80387	ANSI/IEEE 754-1985 and ANSI/IEEE 854-1987

Table A-6. Processor Bus Features and Utilization

Processor	Data Bus Sizes Accommodated	Parity	Bus Utilization (Zero Wait States)
8086	16	none	70%
80286	16	none	80%
386™ Processor	16, 32	none	70%
i486™ Processor	8, 16, 32	Generation and Checking	50%

Table A-7. Processor Bus Clocks and Organization

Processor	Min. Clocks per Cycle at Internal Clock Rate	Frequency of Clock Input Relative to Internal Clock Rate	Address and Data Buses	Address Pipelining on the Bus
8086	4	1x	Multiplexed	Non-pipelined
80286	2	2x	Discrete	Pipelined
386™ Processor	2	2x	Discrete	Non-pipelined or Pipelined
i486™ Processor	2 (non-burst) 1 (burst)	1x	Discrete	Non-pipelined, Burst

Table A-8. Bus Control and Arbitration

Processor	Bus Hold		Bus Request		Bus Lock	Bus Backoff		Address Hold	
	Req (in)	Ack (out)	Req (out)	Ack (in)	Req (out)	Ack (in)	Req (in)	Ack (out)	Req (in)	Ack (out)
8086 (Min)	HOLD	HLDA	–	–	–	–	–	–	–	–
8086 (Max)	RQ#/GT#0, RQ#/GT#1		–	–	LOCK#	–	–	–	–	–
80286	HOLD	HLDA	–	–	LOCK#	–	–	–	–	–
386™ Processor	HOLD	HLDA	–	–	LOCK#	–	–	–	–	–
i486™ Processor	HOLD	HLDA	BREQ	–	LOCK#, PLOCK#	–	BOFF#	–	AHOLD	–

to the bus by the asserting its BREQ output; in earlier processors, there is no processor output for signalling external logic of a pending processor need for the bus. Bus locking requests are made with the LOCK# output on all processors, but the i486 processor adds a psuedo-locking (PLOCK#) output for all multiple-cycle sequences of aligned data. The bus backoff input, used to avoid bus deadlock, and the address hold input, used for invalidation of the on-chip cache by an external cache controller, are new in i486 processor.

Table A-9 shows the signals used to declare the start of a bus cycle, the definition of the cycle, the addressing of data for the cycle, and the end of the cycle. The table also shows the outputs used for segment identification in the 8086 and for page identification in the i486 processor. The segment identification feature in the 8086 processor can be used to implement memory management systems. The page identification feature in the i486

Table A-9. Bus Cycle Signals

Processor	Start of Cycle	Cycle Definition	Addresses	End of Cycle	Segment ID	Page ID	INTR Enable
8086 (Min)	ALE	M/IO#, RD#, WR#, DT/R#	A0-A19, BHE#	READY	S3#-S4#	–	S5#
8086 (Max)	ALE	S0#-S1#	A0-A19, BHE#	READY	S3#-S4#	–	–
80286	S0#-S1#	M/IO#, COD/INTA#, S0#-S1#	A0-A23, BHE#	READY#	–	–	–
386™ Processor	ADS#	M/IO#, D/C#, W/R#	A2-A31, BE0#-BE3#	READY#	–	–	–
i486™ Processor	ADS#	M/IO#, D/C#, W/R#	A2-A31, BE0#-BE3#	RDY#, BRDY#	–	PCD, PWT	–

NOTE: The encoding of M/IO#, D/C# and W/R# are different on the 386 and i486 processors.

processor tells external logic on a cycle-by-cycle basis the cacheability and write-through policy of the current page.

A.3 INTERNAL ARCHITECTURE

Internally, the number of clocks per executed instruction has decreased with each processor generation. The 8086 processor performs effective address calculation sequentially in microcode, without special hardware assistance. The 80286 processor adds hardware support for effective address calculation. The segmentation and paging units of the 386 processor can perform one address computation every two clocks and the i486 processor improves this to one address computation per clock. The i486 processor also increases speed with its on-chip cache and floating-point units; the cache can perform one access per clock. Instruction decoding throughput has increased steadily with each generation.

Tables A-10 through A-12 show the improvements in internal architecture. The biggest speed improvements in the i486 processor have been made with the addition of the on-chip cache and the improvements to address pipelining and instruction decoding.

Table A-11 lists the registers in each processor and numeric coprocessor (or, for the i486 processor, the on-chip floating-point unit). The ports listed with the general registers indicate the number of items that can be bused in or out of the general-register set in parallel. In all cases, the number of write ports is one and the remainder are read ports.

The 80286 processor's introduction of Protected Mode operation uses not only the four 16-bit segment registers of the 8086 processor (the current code, stack, and two data segments) but also four corresponding 64-bit segment descriptor registers. In the 8086 processor, segments are fixed in size at 64 Kbytes and the segment registers simply provided their contents for arithmetic calculation of physical addresses. In the 80286 processor, the 16-bit segment registers contain indices that point to 64-bit segment descriptors, the contents of which are used in the generation of physical addresses. The 386 and i486 processors add two more data segments for a total of six segment registers and six corresponding segment descriptor registers.

Table A-12 lists on-chip queues, buffers and caches.

Table A-10. Internal Speed and Throughput

Processor	Instruction Decoder Speed	Address Pipeline Throughput	Instruction Execution Speed
8086	1 byte per clock	1 clock per address	12.0 clocks
80286	1 or 2 bytes per clock (non-pipelined)	2 clocks per address	4.5 clocks
386™ Processor	1, 2 or 4 bytes per clock (non-pipelined)	2 clocks per address	4.5 clocks
i486™ Processor	1 to 7 bytes per clock (pipelined)	1 clock per address	1.8 clocks

Table A-11. Registers

Processor	General Registers	IP and FLAGS Registers	Segment Registers and Segment Descriptors	System Control Registers	Floating Point Registers
8086/8087	8 16-bit	16-bit	4 16-bit	none	8 80-bit 8 2-bit 3 16-bit 2 32-bit
80286/80287	8 16-bit	16-bit	4 16-bit 4 64-bit	1 16-bit (MSW)	8 80-bit 8 2-bit 3 16-bit 2 32-bit
386™/387™ Processor	8 32-bit	32-bit	6 16-bit 6 64-bit	4 32-bit (CR0-CR3)	8 80-bit 8 2-bit 3 16-bit 2 48-bit
i486™ Processor	8 32-bit	32-bit	6 16-bit 6 64 bit	4 32-bit (CR0-CR3)	8 80-bit 8 2-bit 3 16-bit 2 48-bit

Table A-12. On-Chip Queues, Buffers, and Caches

Processor	Write Buffers	Caches	Instruction Queue	Decoded Instruction Queue
8086	none	none	6 bytes	none
80286	none	4-entry segment descriptor cache	6 bytes	3 instructions
386™ Processor	1	6-entry segment descriptor cache 32-entry TLB	16 bytes	3 instructions
i48™ Processor	4	6-entry segment descriptor cache 32-entry TLB 8 Kbyte instruction/data cache.	32 bytes	none

A.4 TESTABILITY

Support for testing the processor has improved significantly since the 8086, as shown in Table A-13.

Table A-13. Testability

Processor	Test Registers	Debug Registers	Built-In Self Test
8086	none	none	none
80286	none	none	none
386™ Processor	2	8	Non-Random Logic, Control ROM, TLB
i486™ Processor	5	8	Non-Random Logic, Control ROM, TLB, Cache, Tristate

PLD Codes and Schematics B

APPENDIX B
PLD CODES AND SCHEMATICS

B.1 PLD DEVICES

Many design examples in this manual use PLDs (Programmable Logic Devices) which can be programmed by the user to implement random logic. A PLD device can be used as a state machine or a signal decoder, for example. The advantages of PLDs include the following:

1. PLD pinout is determined by the designer, which can simplify board layout by moving signals as required.

2. PLDs are inexpensive as compared to dedicated bus controllers.

Intel EPLDs (Erasable Programmable Logic Devices) have the following additional advantages:

1. Programmability/erasability allows EPLD functions to be changed easily, simplifying prototype development.

2. Since EPLDs are implemented in CMOS technology, they can consume an order of magnitude less power than bipolar PLDs. Power-conscious applications can benefit greatly from using EPLDs.

3. Since the EPROM cell size is an order of magnitude smaller than an equivalent bipolar fuse, EPLDs can implement more functions in the same package. This higher integration can result in a lower overall component count for a design. The added flexibility can also mean that an extremely low number of "raw" (unprogrammed) devices need to be stocked versus bipolar PLDs.

4. Once an EPLD design has been tested, plastic OTP (One-Time Programmable) versions of the device can be used in a production environment.

PLDs have the following tradeoffs:

1. Most PLDs do not have buried (not connected to outputs) registers. For some state machine applications, this means using an otherwise available output pin to store the current state.

2. The drive capability of CMOS EPLDs may be insufficient for some applications. While the trend is towards use of CMOS throughout a system, in cases where high current levels are required, some additional buffering may be required with EPLDs.

A PLD consists logically of a programmable AND array whole output terms feed a fixed OR array. Any sum-of-products equations, within the limits of the number of PLD inputs, outputs, and equation terms, can be realized by specifying the correct AND array connnections. Figure B-1 shows an example of two PLD equations and the corresponding logic array. Note that every horizontal line in the AND array represents a

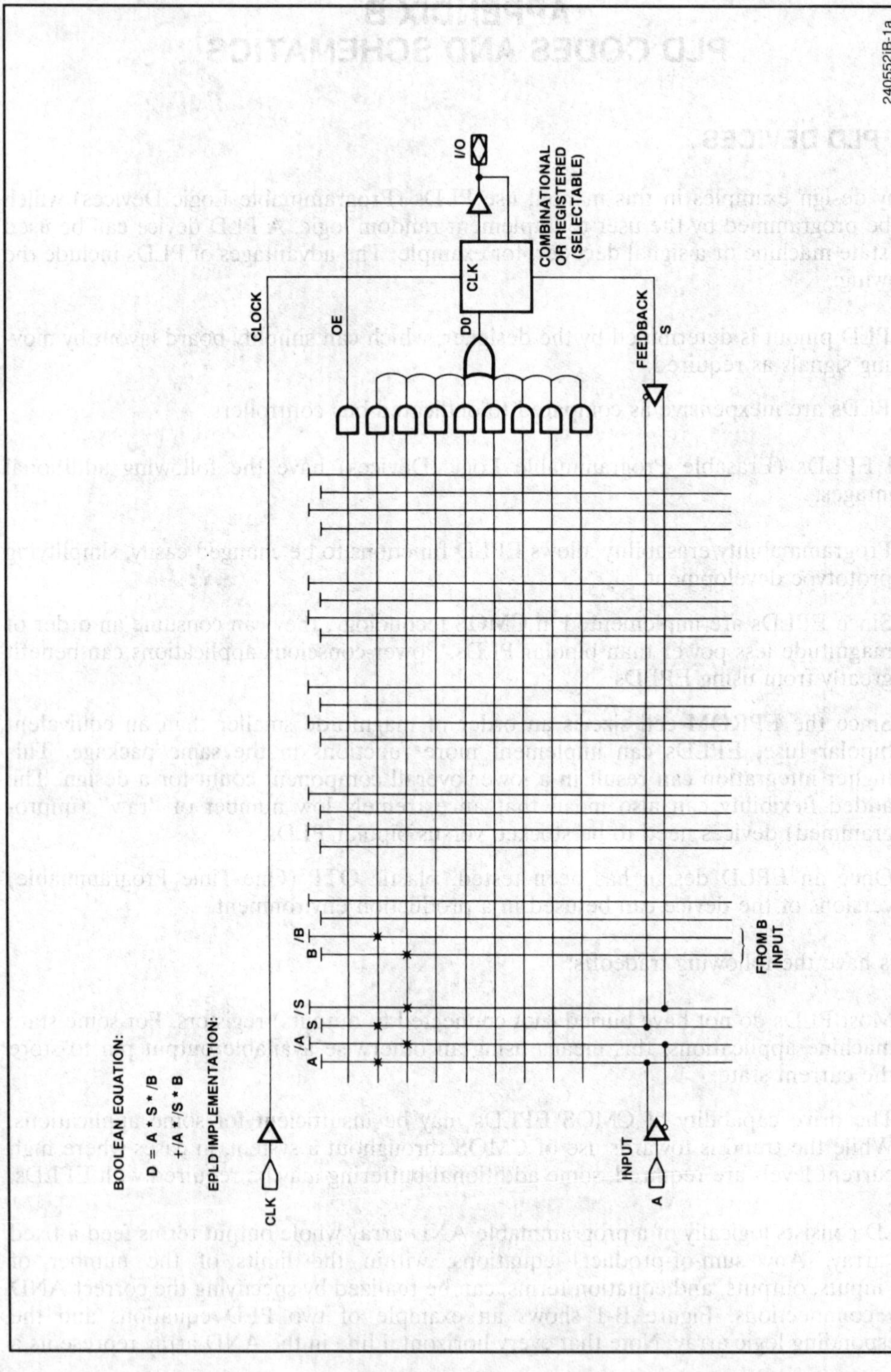

Figure B-1. PLD Equation and Device Implementation

multi-input AND gate; every vertical line represents a possible input to the AND gate. An X at the intersection of a horizontal line and a vertical line represents a connection from the input to the AND gate.

The sum-of-products is then routed to a configurable macrocell. The macrocell in Figure B-2 can be configured as a combinational output or registered output. The output can be active high or active low. A separate AND term controls the output buffer.

Designing with PLDs consists of determining where Xs must be placed in the AND array and how to configure the macrocell. This task is simplified by logic compilers, such as iPLS II (Intel's Programmable Logic Software II) or ABEL. Logic compilers accept input in the form of sum-of-product equations and translate the input into a JEDEC programming file that can be used by programming hardware/software.

Intel PLDs are described in the *Programmable Logic Handbook*. Three Intel PLDs have been used in this manual to implement state machine and decode functions. These PLDs include:

- 85C220 – fast 20-pin superset of 16x8 type bipolar and CMOS PLDs.
- 85C224 – fast 24-pin superset of 20x8 type bipolar and CMOS PLDs.
- 85C508 – fast address decode PLD with integral transparent latches.

The 85C220 and 85C224 PLDs are both available at clock speeds to support fast state-machines in i486™ systems. The 85C508 provides a fast Enable-to-Output time with a minimal system setup time.

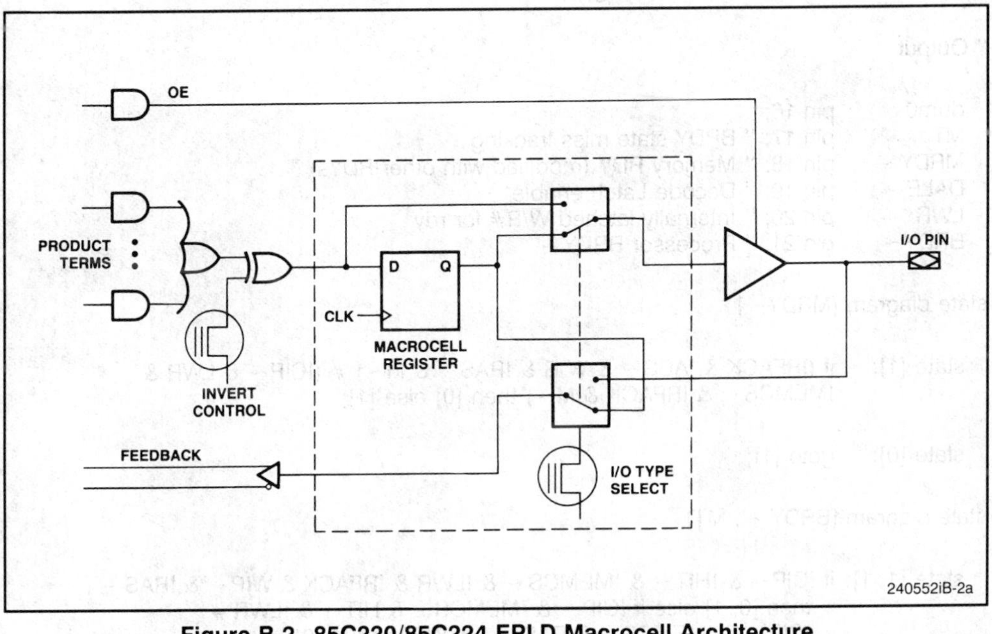

Figure B-2. 85C220/85C224 EPLD Macrocell Architecture

```
module   SC_MODE_DRAM_CTRL_4    flag '-r4'

title      'STATIC COLUMN MODE DRAM CONTROLLER - PLD 4, INTEL CORPORATION'
" This pld generates MRDY and MBRDY
" Implemented with Intel 85C224 EPLD.

  SCk  device           'E224';

  x          =   .X.;          " ABEL 'don't care' symbol
  c          =   .C.;          " ABEL 'clocking input' symbol

" Inputs

  CLK pin 1;     "P4 input CLK"
  M~             pin  2; "Miss Indicator
  CIP~           pin  3; "Cycle OK
  MEMCS~         pin  4; "Latched A2.
  HIT~           pin  5; "DRAM Page Hit Signal
  RFACK          pin  6; "Refresh acknowledge"
  ADS~           pin  7; "CPU ADS~
  W_R            pin  8; "CPU W/R
  RESET          pin  9; "System Reset
  dum1           pin 10; "Write in progress
  BOFF~          pin 11; "CPU Backoff input
  WIP~           pin 14; "CPU Burst Last output
  CAS~           pin 15; "Row Address strobe
  BLAST~         pin 22;
  RAS~           pin 23; "Any CAS# signal

" Output

  dum0           pin 16;
  MT             pin 17; " BRDY state miss tracking
  MRDY~          pin 18; " Memory RDY (modified with other RDYs)
  DALE~          pin 19; " Decode Latch enable
  LWR            pin 20; " Internally latched W/R# for rdy
  BRDY~          pin 21; " Processor BRDY~

state_diagram [MRDY~]

  state [1]:     if (!RFACK & !ADS~ & W_R & !RAS~ & M~) # (!CIP~ & LWR &
                 !MEMCS~ & !RFACK & M~) then [0] else [1];

  state [0]:     goto [1];

state_diagram [BRDY ~, MT]

  state [1, 1]: if !CIP~ & !HIT~ & !MEMCS~ & !LWR & !RFACK & WIP~ & !RAS~
                  then [0, 1] else if !CIP~ & !MEMCS~ & HIT~ & !LWR #
                  !CIP~ & !MEMCS~ & RAS~ & !LWR then [1, 0];
```

```
   state [1, 0]: if RESET then [1, 1] else
                 If WIP~ & !RFACK & !CAS~ then [0, 1];

   state [0, 1]: if RESET # !BOFF~ # !BLAST ~ then [1, 1] else [0, 1];

state_diagram [DALE~]

   state [0]:    if RESET then [0] else
                 if !ADS~ then [1] else [0];

   state [1]:    if RESET # !BOFF~ then [0] else
                 if !CIP~ then [0] else [1];

state_diagram [LWR]

   state [0]:    if RESET then [0] else
                 if !ADS~ & W_R then [1] else [0];

   state [1]:    if RESET # !BOFF~ then [0] else
                 if !ADS~ & !W_R then [0] else [1];

test_vectors

([CLK,M~,CIP~,MEMCS~,HIT~,RFACK,ADS~,W_R,RESET,WIP~,BOFF~,BLAST~]
->      [RAS~,MRDY~,DALE~,LWR,BRDY~])

" C M A M H R A W R W B B R     M D L B
" L ~ Q E I F D _ E I O L A    R A W R
" K   0 M T A S R S P F A S    D L R D
"      ~ C ~ F ~    E   F S ~    Y E   Y
"        S  K     T  ~ T           ~ ~    ~
"       ~                ~
"
"
"

  [c, x, x, x, x, x, 1, x, 1, x, x, x, x] -> [x, x, x, x];
  [c, x, 1, 1, x, x, 1, x, 1, x, x, x, x] -> [1, 0, 0, 1];
  [c, 1, 1, 1, x, 0, 1, x, 0, 0, 1, 1, 1] -> [1, 0, 0, 1];
  [c, 1, 1, 1, x, 0, 1, x, 0, 0, 1, 1, 1] -> [1, 0, 0, 1];
  [c, 1, 1, 1, x, 0, 0, 1, 0, 0, 1, 1, 1] -> [1, 1, 1, 1];
  [c, 1, 0, 0, 0, 0, 1, x, 0, 0, 1, 1, 1] -> [0, 0, x, 1];
  [c, 1, 0, 0, 0, 0, 1, x, 0, 1, 1, 1, 0] -> [1, 0, 1, 1];
  [c, 1, 1, 0, 0, 0, 0, 1, 0, 1, 1, 1, 0] -> [0, 1, 1, 1];
  [c, 1, 0, 0, 0, 0, 1, x, 0, 1, 1, 1, 0] -> [1, 0, x, 1];
  [c, 1, 1, x, 0, 0, 0, 1, 0, 1, 1, 1, 0] -> [0, 1, 1, 1];
  [c, 1, 0, 0, 0, 0, 1, x, 0, 1, 1, 1, 0] -> [1, 0, x, 1];
  [c, 1, 1, x, 0, 0, 1, x, 0, 1, 1, 1, 0] -> [1, 0, x, 1];
  [c, 1, 1, 1, x, 0, 1, x, 0, 1, 1, 1, 0] -> [1, 0, x, 1];

end SC_MODE_DRAM_CTRL_4;
```

```
module   SC_MODE_DRAM_CTRL_3   flag '-r4'

title     'STATIC COLUMN MODE DRAM CONTROLLER - PLD 3, INTEL CORPORATION'
" This PLD generates RAS
" Implemented with the Intel 85C220 EPLD.

   SC3      device      'E0320';

   x              =      .X.;                    " ABEL 'don't care' symbol
   c              =      .C.;                    " ABEL 'clocking input' symbol

" Inputs

   CLK pin   1;   "P4 input CLK"
   M~             pin  2; "Refresh Acknowledge
   CIP~           pin  3; "Cycle OK
   MEMCS~         pin  4; "Latched A2.
   HIT~           pin  5; "DRAM Page Hit Signal
   RFACK          pin  6; "Backoff input to P4"
   PCHG           pin  7; "RAS precharge count
   WIP~           pin  8; "Write in Progress
   RESET          pin  9; "System Reset
   Q1             pin 12; "RAS refresh count
" Output

   RAS2~          pin 13; "
   RAS1~          pin 14; " RAS byte 0,2
   EP             pin 15; " state variable
   EP1 pin 16; " state variable
   RAS0~          pin 17; " RAS byte 1,3
   RAS3~          pin 18; "
   CSWIP~         pin 19; "

state_diagram [RAS0~,RAS1~,EP]

   state [1, 1, 0]:     if RESET then [1, 1, 0] else
                        if !CIP~ & !CSWIP~ & !PCHG then [0, 0, 0] else
                        if RFACK & WIP~ then [1, 1, 1] else
                        [1, 1, 0];

   state [0, 0, 0]:     if RESET then [1, 1, 0] else
                        if RFACK then [0, 0, 1] else
                        if !CIP~ & HIT~ & !MEMCS~ then [1, 1, 0]
                        else [0, 0, 0];

   state [0, 0, 1]:     if RESET then [1, 1, 0] else
                        if !RFACK & !PCHG then [1, 1, 0] else
                        if RFACK & !WIP~ # !RFACK & PCHG then
                        [0, 0, 1] else if RFACK & WIP~ & !Q1 then [1, 1, 1];

   state [1, 1, 1]:     if RESET then [1, 1, 0] else
                        if !PCHG then [0, 0, 1] else [1, 1, 1];
```

```
    state [0, 1, 0]:    goto [1, 1, 0];
    state [0, 1, 1]:    goto [1, 1, 0];
    state [1, 0, 0]:    goto [1, 1, 0];
    state [1, 0, 1]:    goto [1, 1, 0];

state_diagram [RAS2~,RAS3~,EP1]

    state [1, 1, 0]:    if RESET then [1, 1, 0] else
                        if !CIP~ & !CSWIP~ & !PCHG then [0, 0, 0] else
                        if RFACK & WIP~ then [1, 1, 1] else
                        [1, 1, 0];

    state [0, 0, 0]:    if RESET then [1, 1, 0] else
                        if RFACK then [0, 0, 1] else
                        if !CIP~ & HIT~ & !MEMCS~ then [1, 1, 0]
                        else [0, 0, 0];

    state [0, 0, 1]:    if RESET then [1, 1, 0] else
                        if !RFACK & !PCHG then [1, 1, 0] else
                        if RFACK & !WIP~ # !RFACK & PCHG then
                        [0, 0, 1] else if RFACK & WIP~ & !Q1 then [1, 1, 1];

    state [1, 1, 1]:    if RESET then [1, 1, 0] else
                        if !PCHG then [0, 0, 1] else [1, 1, 1];

    state [0, 1, 0]:    goto [1, 1, 0];
    state [0, 1, 1]:    goto [1, 1, 0];
    state [1, 0, 0]:    goto [1, 1, 0];
    state [1, 0, 1]:    goto [1, 1, 0];

equations

    !CSWIP~ = (!MEMCS~ # !WIP~)& !RESET;

test_vectors

    ([CLK,M~,CIP~,MEMCS~,HIT~,RFACK,PCHG,WIP~,Q1,RESET] ->
    [RAS0~,RAS1~,EP,RAS2~,RAS3~,EP1])

"   C M A M H R P W Q R   R R E R R E
"   L ~ Q E I F C I 1 E   A A P A A P
"   K   0 M T A H P   S   S S   S S 1
"       ~ C ~ C G ~   E   0 1   2 3
"         S   K       T
"         ~
"
"
"

    [c, x, x, x, x, x, 1, x, x, 1] -> [x, x, x, x, x, x];
    [c, x, x, x, x, x, 1, x, x, 1] -> [1, 1, 0, 1, 1, 0];
    [c, x, x, x, x, x, 1, x, x, 1] -> [1, 1, 0, 1, 1, 0];
    [c, x, x, x, x, x, 1, x, x, 1] -> [1, 1, 0, 1, 1, 0];
```

```
    [c, x, x, x, x, x, 1, x, x, 1] -> [1, 1, 0, 1, 1, 0];
    [c, x, x, x, x, x, 1, x, x, 1] -> [1, 1, 0, 1, 1, 0];
    [c, x, x, x, x, x, 1, x, x, 1] -> [1, 1, 0, 1, 1, 0];
    [c, 1, 1, x, x, 0, 0, 0, 0, 0] -> [1, 1, 0, 1, 1, 0];
    [c, 1, 1, x, x, 0, 0, 0, 0, 0] -> [1, 1, 0, 1, 1, 0];
    [c, 1, 0, 0, 0, 0, 0, 0, 0, 0] -> [0, 0, 0, 0, 0, 0];
    [c, 1, 0, 0, 0, 0, 0, 0, 0, 0] -> [0, 0, 0, 0, 0, 0];
    [c, 1, 1, x, x, 0, 0, 0, 0, 0] -> [0, 0, 0, 0, 0, 0];
    [c, 1, 0, 0, 0, 0, 0, 0, 0, 0] -> [0, 0, 0, 0, 0, 0];
    [c, 1, 1, x, x, 0, 0, 0, 0, 0] -> [0, 0, 0, 0, 0, 0];
    [c, 1, 0, 0, 0, 0, 0, 0, 0, 0] -> [0, 0, 0, 0, 0, 0];
    [c, 1, 1, x, x, 0, 0, 0, 0, 0] -> [0, 0, 0, 0, 0, 0];
    [c, 1, 1, x, x, 0, 0, 0, 0, 0] -> [0, 0, 0, 0, 0, 0];
    [c, 1, 1, x, x, 0, 0, 0, 0, 0] -> [0, 0, 0, 0, 0, 0];

end SC_MODE_DRAM_CTRL_3;
```

```
module   SC_MODE_DRAM_CTRL_1   flag '-r4'

title    'STATIC COLUMN MODE DRAM CONTROLLER - PLD 1, INTEL CORPORATION
" Cycle Tracking Logic
" Implemented with Intel 85C224 EPLD.
  SCy  device     'E224';

  x            =     .X.;                    " ABEL 'don't care' symbol
  c            =     .C.;                    " ABEL 'clocking input' symbol

" Inputs

  CLK pin 1; "P4 input CLK"
  BLAST~      pin  2; "P4 BLAST output
  MEMCS~      pin  3; "Memory Chip Select
  AHOLD       pin  4; "Address HOLD input to P4"
  HIT~        pin  5; "DRAM Page Hit Signal
  BOFF~       pin  6;"Backoff input to P4"
  ADS~        pin  7; "Address Status output of P4"
  RFRQ        pin  8; "Refresh Request Signal
  RESET       pin  9; "System Reset
  BRDY~       pin 10; "Processor burst ready pin.
  MRDY~       pin 11; "Memory ready
  RAS~        pin 14; "Row Address Strobe
  EP          pin 23; "Refresh indicator - count on RAS~ low

" Output

  RFACK~      pin 15; "Refresh acknowledge
  CIP~        pin 16; " ADS~ active indicator
  M~          pin 17; " AQ0~ Miss state indicator
  CT          pin 18; " AHOLD with ADS~ indicator
  PCHG        pin 19; " Precharge state indicator
  Q1          pin 20; " Precharge state indicator
  ALD pin 21; " Address Latch Disable
  adlst~      pin 22; " ADL state variable

state_diagram [CIP~, M~]

  state [1, 1]: if RESET then [1, 1] else
                     if AHOLD # !RFACK~ # EP then [1, 1] else
                     if !ADS~ # CT then [0, 1] else [1, 1];

  state [0, 1]:      if RESET # !BOFF~ # MEMCS~
                        then [1, 1] else
                        if HIT~ & !RAS~ & !MRDY~ then [0, 0] else
                        If (!MRDY~ # (!BRDY~ & !BLAST~)) then [1, 1]
                        else [0, 1];

  state [0, 0]:      if RESET # !BOFF~ then [1, 1] else
                        if !PCHG & (CT # !ADS~) then [0, 1] else
                        if !PCHG & !CT then [1, 1] else
                        [0, 0];
```

```
  state [1, 0]: goto [1, 1];

state_diagram [PCHG, Q1]

  state [0, 0]:        if RESET then [0, 0] else
                         if !RAS~ then [1, 0] else
                         if RAS~ & !RFACK~ then [0, 1] else [0, 0];

  state [1, 0]:        if RESET then [0, 0] else
                         if RAS~ & !EP then [0, 0] else
                         if RFACK~ & EP & !RAS~ then     [1, 1] else
                         if RAS~ & EP then [0, 1] else [1, 0];

  state [0, 1]: goto [1, 0];

  state [1, 1]: goto [0, 0];

state_diagram [CT]

  state [0]:           if RESET then [0] else
                       if !ADS~ & (AHOLD # !RFACK~ # !M~ # EP) then [1] else [0];

  state [1]:           if RESET # !BOFF~ then [0] else
                       if !CIP~ & M~ then [0] else [1];

state_diagram [RFACK~]

  state[1]:            if RESET then [1] else
                       if !CIP~ & RFRQ & !MRDY~ & !HIT~ then [0] else
                       if !CIP~ & RFRQ & (!BRDY~ & !BLAST~) #
                       RFRQ & CIP~ & ADS~ then [0] else [1];

  state[0]:            if RESET # !BOFF~ then [1] else
                       if RAS~ then [1] else [0];

state_diagram [ALD, adlst~]

  state [0, 1]:        if RESET then [0, 1] else
                         if !ADS~ # !CIP~ & !MEMCS~ then [1, 0] else [0, 1];

  state [1, 0]:        if RESET then [0,1] else
                         if !CIP~ & MEMCS~ then [0, 1] else
                         if HIT~ & !MRDY~ then [1, 1] else
                         if !HIT~ & !MRDY~ then [0, 1] else
                         if !BRDY~ & !BLAST~ then [0, 1] else [1, 0];

  state [1, 1]:        if RESET then [0, 1] else
                         if !CIP~ & (!PCHG # MEMCS~) then [0, 1] else [1, 1];

  state [0, 0]: goto [0, 1];

test vectors
```

```
([CLK,BLAST~,MEMCS~,AHOLD,HIT~,BOFF~,ADS~,RFRQ,RESET] -> 
[BRDY~,MRDY~,RAS~,EP,RFACK~,CIP~,M~,CT,PCHG,Q1,ALD,adlst~])

"C B M A H B A R R B R R E   R A M C P Q A a
"L L E H I O D F E R D A P   F Q ~ T C 1 L d
"K A M O T F S R S D Y S ~   A 0     H   D l
"  S C L ~ F ~ Q E Y ~ ~     C ~     G     s
"  T S D   ~     T ~         K           t
"  ~ ~                               ~
"
"
"

[c, x, x, x, x, x, 1, x, 1, x, x, x, x] -> [1, 1, 1, 0, 0, 0, 0, 1];
[c, x, x, x, x, x, 1, x, 1, x, x, x, x] -> [1, 1, 1, 0, 0, 0, 0, 1];
[c, 1, x, 0, x, 1, 1, 0, 1, 0, 1, 1, 0] -> [1, 1, 1, 0, 0, 0, 0, 1];
[c, 1, x, 0, x, 1, 0, 0, 0, 0, 1, 1, 0] -> [1, 0, 1, 0, 0, 0, 1, 0];
[c, 1, x, 0, x, 1, 1, 0, 1, 0, 1, 1, 0] -> [1, 0, 1, 0, 0, 0, 1, 0];
[c, 1, 0, 0, 0, 1, 1, 0, 1, 0, 1, 1, 0] -> [1, 0, 1, 0, 0, 0, 1, 0];
[c, 1, 0, 0, 0, 1, 1, 0, 1, 0, 1, 0, 0] -> [1, 0, 1, 0, 1, 0, 1, 0];
[c, 1, 0, 0, 0, 1, 1, 0, 1, 0, 1, 0, 0] -> [1, 0, 1, 0, 1, 0, 1, 0];
[c, 1, 0, 0, 0, 1, 1, 0, 1, 0, 1, 0, 0] -> [1, 0, 1, 0, 1, 0, 1, 0];
[c, 1, 0, 0, 0, 1, 1, 0, 1, 0, 1, 0, 0] -> [1, 0, 1, 0, 1, 0, 1, 0];
[c, 1, 0, 0, 0, 1, 1, 0, 1, 0, 1, 0, 0] -> [1, 0, 1, 0, 1, 0, 1, 0];
[c, 0, 0, 0, 0, 1, 1, 0, 1, 0, 1, 0, 0] -> [1, 1, 1, 0, 1, 0, 0, 1];
[c, x, x, 0, x, 1, 1, 0, 1, 0, 1, 0, 0] -> [1, 1, 1, 0, 1, 0, 0, 1];

end SC_MODE_DRAM_CTRL_1;
```

```
module   SC_MODE_DRAM_CTRL_7   flag '-r4'

title  'STATIC COLUMN MODE DRAM CONTROLLER - PLD 7, INTEL CORPORATION'
" This PLD generates DATASL and WE
" Implemented with the Intel 85C220 EPLD.

   SC7   device        'E0320';

   x               =     .X.;                     " ABEL 'don't care' symbol
   c               =     .C.;                     " ABEL 'clocking input' symbol

" Inputs

   CLK pin 1; "P4 input CLK"
   BRDY~        pin  2; "Burst Ready
   CIP~         pin  3; "Cycle OK
   MEMCS~       pin  4; "memory select
   LA2 pin 5; "Latched A2.
   CAS00~       pin  6; "CAS output Bank1
   CAS10~       pin  7; "CAS output Bank1
   LW_R         pin  8; "CPU W/R latched~
   RESET        pin  9; "System Reset
   BLAST~       pin 12; "CPU BLAST~ output
   BOFF~        pin 13; "CPU Backoff input
   HIT~         pin 19;
" Output

   DATASEL      pin 14; " Bank select for reads
   RS~          pin 15; " state variable
   RALE~        pin 16; " state variable
   WE~          pin 17; " Write Enable posted writes
   BSEL         pin 18; " Selects read or write data path

state_diagram [DATASEL, RS~]

   state [1, 1]: if RESET then [1, 1] else
                   if !CIP~ & !LA2 & !LW_R & !MEMCS~ then [0, 0] else
                   if !CIP~ & LA2 & !LW_R & !MEMCS~ then [1, 0] else [1, 1];

   state [1, 0]: if RESET # !BOFF~ # (!BRDY~ & !BLAST~) then [1, 1] else
                   if !BRDY~ & BLAST~ then [0, 0] else [1, 0];

   state [0, 0]: if RESET # !BOFF~ # (!BRDY~ & !BLAST~) then [1, 1] else
                   if !BRDY~ & BLAST~ then [1, 0] else [0, 0];

   state [0, 1]: goto [1, 1];

state_diagram [WE~]

   state [1]:    if RESET then [1] else
                 if LW_R & !CIP~ & !MEMCS~ then [0] else [1];
```

```
  state [0]:    if RESET # !BOFF~ then [1] else
                if LW_R & !CIP~ & !MEMCS~ then [0] else
                if CAS00~ + CAS10~ then [1];

state_diagram [RALE~]

  state [0]:    if RESET then [0] else
                if !CIP~ & HIT~ & !MEMCS~ then [1] else [0];

  state [1]:    if RESET # !BOFF~ then [0] else
                if !HIT~ then [0] else [1];

end SC_MODE_DRAM_CTRL_7;

greg CTRACK6K ABL
greg CKPGCS0 ABL
greg CTRAST2 ABL
greg CKRDYB ABL
greg CEXMA0 ABL
greg CP4DATSL ABL
greg CKPGCS1 ABL
greg CKWE1 ABL
greg CP4WEBE1 ABL
greg CKORDY1 ABL
greg CP4DCD2 ABL
greg CEXMA1 ABL
Z
```

```
module   SC_MODE_DRAM_CTRL_11 flag '-r4'

title  'STATIC COLUMN MODE DRAM CONTROLLER - PLD 11, INTEL CORPORATION'
" This PLD generates the mux enables write enables and WIP#
" Implemented with the Intel 85C220 EPLD.

  SCw   device      'E0320';

  x          =      .X.;                     " ABEL 'don't care' symbol
  c          =      .C.;                     " ABEL 'clocking input' symbol

" Inputs

  CLK pin 1; "P4 input CLK"
  LA2 pin 2; "Latched A2.
  CIP~          pin  3; "Cycle OK
  MEMCS~        pin  4; "Memory Chip select.
  RESET         pin  5; "DRAM Page Hit Signal
  LW_R          pin  6; "latched CPU W/R#
  C01 pin 7; "Write indication Bank0
  CAS01~        pin  8; "
  C11 pin 9; "Write indication Bank1
  CAS11~        pin 19; "

" Output

  WIP~          pin 12; "New Wip signal comb
  MEN0~         pin 13; "Mux enables
  WE0~          pin 14; "
  LWIP~         pin 15; "Latched WIP~
  dum           pin 16; "
  WE1~          pin 17; "
  MEN1~         pin 18; " Mux enable Bank1

state_diagram [WE0~]

  state [1]:    if RESET then [1] else
                if !CIP~ & LW_R & !MEMCS~ & !LA2 then [0];

  state [0]:    if RESET then [1] else
                if !C01 then [0] else
                if C01 then [1];

  state_diagram [WE1~]

  state [1]:    if RESET then [1] else
                if !CIP~ & LW_R & !MEMCS~ & LA2 then [0];

  state [0]:    if RESET then [1] else
                if !C11 then [0] else
                if C11 then [1];

state_diagram [LWIP~]
```

```
  state [1]:    if !C01 # !C11 then [0] else [1];

  state [0]:    if RESET then [1] else
                if !C01 # !C11 then [0] else [1];

state_diagram [MEN0~]

  state [1]:    if RESET then [1] else
                if !CIP~ & LW_R & !MEMCS~ & !LA2 then [0];

  state [0]:    if RESET then [1] else
                if !C01 & CAS01~ then [0] else
                if !CIP~ & LW_R & !MEMCS~ & !LA2 & !CAS01~ then [0] else
                if !CAS01~ then [1];

state_diagram [MEN1~]

  state [1]:    if RESET then [1] else
                if !CIP~ & LW_R & !MEMCS~ & LA2 then [0];

  state [0]:    if RESET then [1] else
                if !C11 & CAS11~ then [0] else
                if !CIP~ & LW_R & !MEMCS~ & !LA2 & !CAS11~ then [0] else
                if !CAS11~ then [1];

equations

                !WIP~ = !LWIP~ # !C01 # !C11;

"test_vectors

"([CLK,M IO~,CIP~,MEMCS~,HIT~,RFACK,ADS~,W_R,RESET,CAS0~,BOFF~,BLAST~]
"->      [RAS~,MRDY~,DALE~,LWR,BRDY~])
"
" C M A M H R A W R C B B R  M D L B
" L _ Q E I F D _ E A O L A   R A W R
" K I 0 M T A S R S S F A S   D L R D
"   0 ~ C ~ F ~  E 0 F S ~   Y E  Y
"       S  K   T ~ ~ T      ~ ~    ~
"       ~            ~
"
"
"
"
" [c, x, x, x, x, x, 1, x, 1, x, x, x, x] -> [x, x, x, x];
" [c, x, 1, 1, x, x, 1, x, 1, x, x, x, x] -> [1, 0, 0, 1];
" [c, 1, 1, 1, x, 1, 1, x, 0, 1, 0, 1, 1] -> [1, 0, 0, 1];
" [c, 1, 1, 1, x, 1, 1, x, 0, 1, 0, 1, 1] -> [1, 0, 0, 1];
" [c, 1, 1, 1, x, 1, 0, 1, 0, 1, 0, 1, 1] -> [1, 1, 1, 1];
" [c, 1, 0, 0, 0, 1, 1, x, 0, 1, 0, 1, 1] -> [0, 0, x, 1];
" [c, 1, 0, 0, 0, 1, 1, x, 0, 1, 0, 1, 0] -> [1, 0, x, 1];
" [c, 1, 1, 0, 0, 1, 0, 1, 0, 1, 0, 1, 0] -> [0, 1, 1, 1];
" [c, 1, 0, 0, 0, 1, 1, x, 0, 0, 0, 1, 0] -> [1, 0, x, 1];
```

```
" [c, 1, 1, x, 0, 1, 0, 1, 0, 1, 0, 1, 0]  - > [0, 1, 1, 1];
" [c, 1, 0, 0, 0, 1, 1, x, 0, 1, 0, 1, 0]  - > [1, 0, x, 1];
" [c, 1, 1, x, 0, 1, 1, x, 0, 1, 0, 1, 0]  - > [1, 0, x, 1];
" [c, 1, 1, 1, x, 1, 1, x, 0, 1, 0, 1, 0]  - > [1, 0, x, 1];
"
end SC_MODE_DRAM_CTRL_11;
```

```
module   SC_MODE_DRAM_CTRL_11 flag '-r4'

title  'STATIC COLUMN MODE DRAM CONTROLLER - PLD 11, INTEL CORPORATION'
" This PLD generates the mux enables write enables and WIP#
" Implemented with the Intel 85C220 EPLD.

  SCw   device   'E0320';

  x              =      .X.;                    " ABEL 'don't care' symbol
  c              =      .C.;                    " ABEL 'clocking input' symbol

" Inputs

  CLK pin 1; "P4 input CLK"
  LA2 pin 2; "Latched A2.
  CIP~          pin   3; "Cycle OK
  MEMCS~        pin   4; "Memory Chip select.
  RESET         pin   5; "DRAM Page Hit Signal
  LW_R          pin   6; "latched CPU W/R#
  C01 pin 7; "Write indication Bank0
  CAS01~        pin   8; "
  C11 pin   9; "Write indication Bank1
  CAS11~        pin 19; "

" Output

  WIP~          pin 12; "New Wip signal comb
  MEN0~         pin 13; " Mux enables
  WE0~          pin 14; "
  LWIP~         pin 15; "Latched WIP~
  dum           pin 16; "
  WE1~          pin 17; "
  MEN1~         pin 18; " Mux enable Bank1

state_diagram [WE0~]

  state [1]:    if RESET then [1] else
                if !CIP~ & LW_R & !MEMCS~ & !LA2 then [0];

  state [0]:    if RESET then [1] else
                if !C01 then [0] else
                if C01 then [1];

state_diagram [WE1~]

  state [1]:    if RESET then [1] else
                if !CIP~ & LW_R & !MEMCS~ & LA2 then [0];

  state [0]:    if RESET then [1] else
                if !C11 then [0] else
                if C11 then [1];

state_diagram [LWIP~]
```

```
  state [1]:   if !C01 # !C11 then [0] else [1];

  state [0]:   if RESET then [1] else
               if !C01 # !C11 then [0] else [1];

state_diagram [MEN0~]

  state [1]:   if RESET then [1] else
               if !CIP~ & LW_R & !MEMCS~ & !LA2 then [0];

  state [0]:   if RESET then [1] else
               if !C01 & CAS01 ~ then [0] else
               if !CIP~ & LW_R & !MEMCS~ & !LA2 & !CAS01~ then [0] else
               if !CAS01~ then [1];

state_diagram [MEN1~]

  state [1]:   if RESET then [1] else
               if !CIP~ & LW_R & !MEMCS~ & LA2 then [0];

  state [0]:   if RESET then [1] else
               if !C11 & CAS11~ then [0] else
               if !CIP~ & LW_R & !MEMCS~ & !LA2 & !CAS11~ then [0] else
               if !CAS11~then [1];

equations

    !WIP~ = !LWIP~ # !C01 # !C11;

"test_vectors

"([CLK,M_IO~,CIP~,MEMCS~,HIT~,RFACK,ADS~,W_R,RESET,CAS0~,BOFF~]
"  ->      [BLAST~,RAS~,MRDY~,DALE~,LWR,BRDY~])
"
C M A M H R A W R C B B R   M D L B
" L _ Q E I F D _ E A O L A   R A W R
" K I 0 M T A S R S S F A S   D L R D
"   O ~ C ~ F ~   E 0 F S ~   Y E   Y
"       S  K    T ~ ~T      ~ ~   ~
"       ~            ~
"
"
"
"
" [c, x, x, x, x, x, 1, x, 1, x, x, x, x]  -> [x, x, x, x];
" [c, x, 1, 1, x, x, 1, x, 1, x, x, x, x]  -> [1, 0, 0, 1];
" [c, 1, 1, 1, x, 1, 1, x, 0, 1, 0, 1, 1]  -> [1, 0, 0, 1];
" [c, 1, 1, 1, x, 1, 1, x, 0, 1, 0, 1, 1]  -> [1, 0, 0, 1];
" [c, 1, 1, 1, x, 1, 0, 1, 0, 1, 0, 1, 1]  -> [1, 1, 1, 1];
" [c, 1, 0, 0, 0, 1, 1, x, 0, 1, 0, 1, 1]  -> [0, 0, x, 1];
" [c, 1, 0, 0, 0, 1, 1, x, 0, 1, 0, 1, 0]  -> [1, 0, x, 1];
" [c, 1, 1, 0, 0, 1, 0, 1, 0, 1, 0, 1, 0]  -> [0, 1, 1, 1];
" [c, 1, 0, 0, 0, 1, 1, x, 0, 0, 0, 1, 0]  -> [1, 0, x, 1];
```

```
" [c, 1, 1, x, 0, 1, 0, 1, 0, 1, 0, 1, 0]  - > [0, 1, 1, 1];
" [c, 1, 0, 0, 0, 1, 1, x, 0, 1, 0, 1, 0]  - > [1, 0, x, 1];
" [c, 1, 1, x, 0, 1, 1, x, 0, 1, 0, 1, 0]  - > [1, 0, x, 1];
" [c, 1, 1, 1, x, 1, 1, x, 0, 1, 0, 1, 0]  - > [1, 0, x, 1];
"

end SC_MODE_DRAM_CTRL_11;
```

```
module   SC_MODE_DRAM_CTRL_8   flag '-r4'

title  'STATIC COLUMN MODE DRAM CONTROLLER - PLD 8, INTEL CORPORATION'
" This PLD generates CAS1 (CAS for bank 1)
" Implemented with the Intel 85C220 EPLD.

    SC8   device   'E0320';

    x             =    .X.;                     " ABEL 'don't care' symbol
    c             =    .C.;                     " ABEL 'clocking input' symbol

" Inputs

    CLK pin 1; "P4 input CLK"
    RFACK       pin  2; "Refresh Acknowledge
    CIP~        pin  3; "Cycle OK
    LA2 pin 4; "Latched A2.
    HIT~        pin  5; "DRAM Page Hit Signal
    BOFF~       pin  6; "Backoff input to P4"
    LW_R~       pin  7; "
    RAS~        pin  8; "
    RESET       pin  9; "System Reset
    RDY~        pin 12; " Processor RDY#
    MEMCS~      pin 13; " Memory Chip Select
    BRDY~       pin 18; " Processor BREADY#
    BLAST~      pin 19; " Processor BLAST#

" Output

    CAS10~      pin 14; " CAS1 byte 0,2
    C1          pin 15; " state variable
    C2          pin 16; " state variable
    CAS11~      pin 17; " CAS1 byte 1,3

state_diagram [CAS10~,CAS11~,C1,C2]

    state [1, 1, 1, 1]:  if RESET # !BOFF~ then [1, 1, 1, 1] else
                            if !RFACK & !CIP~ & LA2 & LW_R~ & !MEMCS~ then
                            [1, 1, 0, 1] else if !RFACK & !CIP~ & !LW R~ & !RAS~
                            & !HIT~ & !MEMCS~ # (RFACK & RAS~) then
                            [0, 0, 1, 1] else [1, 1, 1, 1];

    state [1, 1, 0, 1]:  if RESET # !BOFF~ then [1, 1, 1, 1] else
                         if !RAS~ & RDY~ then [0, 0, 0, 0] else
                         [1, 1, 0, 1];

    state [0, 0, 0, 0]:  if RESET # !BOFF~ then [1, 1, 1, 1] else
                            if !CIP~ & LA2 & LW_R~ & !MEMCS~ then [1, 1, 0, 0] else
                            if CIP~ # (!CIP~ & (MEMCS~ # !LW_R~)) # (!CIP~ & LW_R~&
                            !LA2) then [1, 1, 1, 1] else [0, 0, 0, 0];

    state [1, 1, 0, 0]:  if !RAS~ then [0, 0, 0, 0] else [1, 1, 0, 0];
```

```
    state [0, 0, 1, 1]:  if RESET # !BOFF~ then [1, 1, 1, 1] else
                         if !BRDY~ & !BLAST~ & !RFACK then
                         [1, 1, 1, 1] else
                           if !BRDY~ & BLAST~ & LA2 then [1, 1, 1, 0] else
                           if !BRDY~ & BLAST~ & !LA2 then [0, 0, 1, 0] else
                           if RFACK then [0, 0, 1, 0] else
                           if BRDY~ & !RFACK then [0, 0, 1, 1];

    state [1, 1, 1, 0]:  if RESET then [1, 1, 1, 1] else
                           if !BOFF~ then [1, 1, 1, 0] else
                           if !BRDY~ & BLAST~ then [0, 0, 1, 1] else
                           if !BRDY~ & !BLAST~ then [1, 1, 1, 1] else
                           [1, 1, 1, 0];

    state [0, 0, 1, 0]:  if RESET # !BOFF~ then [1, 1, 1, 1] else
                           if !BRDY~ & BLAST~ then [1, 1, 1, 0] else
                           if !BRDY~ & !BLAST~ # BRDY~ then [1, 1, 1, 1];

test_vectors

    ([CLK,RFACK,CIP~,LA2,HIT,~BOFF~,LW_R~,RAS~,RESET,RDY~,MEMCS~,BRDY~]
->        [BLAST~,CAS10~,C1,C2,CAS11~])

" C R A L H B L R R R M B B     C C C C
" L F Q A I O W A E D E R L     A 1 2 A
" K A 0 2 T F R S S Y M D A     S     S
"   C ~   ~ F ~   ~ E ~ C Y S   0     0
"   K     ~       T   S   T   0   1
"                     ~     ~     ~     ~
"
"
"

    [c, x, x, x, x, x, 1, x, 1, x, x, x, x]  -> [x, x, x, x];
    [c, x, 1, 1, x, x, 1, x, 1, x, x, x, x]  -> [1, 1, 1, x];
    [c, x, 1, 1, x, 1, 1, 0, 0, 1, 0, 1, 1]  -> [1, 1, 1, 1];
    [c, 0, 1, 1, x, 1, 1, 0, 0, 1, 0, 1, 1]  -> [1, 1, 1, 1];
    [c, 0, 1, 1, x, 1, 1, 0, 0, 1, 0, 1, 1]  -> [1, 1, 1, 1];
    [c, 0, 0, 1, 0, 1, 1, 0, 0, 1, 0, 1, 1]  -> [1, 0, 1, 1];
    [c, 0, 0, 1, 0, 1, 1, 0, 0, 0, 0, 1, 1]  -> [1, 0, 1, 1];
    [c, 0, 1, 1, 0, 1, 1, 0, 0, 1, 0, 1, 1]  -> [0, 0, 0, 0];
    [c, 0, 0, 1, 0, 1, 1, 0, 0, 0, 0, 1, 1]  -> [1, 0, 0, 1];
    [c, 0, 1, x, 0, 1, 1, 0, 0, 1, 0, 1, 1]  -> [0, 0, 0, 0];
    [c, 0, 0, 1, 0, 1, 1, 0, 0, 0, 0, 1, 1]  -> [1, 0, 0, 1];
    [c, 0, 1, x, 0, 1, 1, 0, 0, 1, 0, 1, 1]  -> [0, 0, 0, 0];
    [c, 0, 1, 0, x, 1, 1, 0, 0, 1, 0, 1, 1]  -> [1, 1, 1, 1];
end SC_MODE_DRAM_CTRL_8;
```

```
module   PG_MODE_DRAM_CTRL_2   flag '-r4'

title    'PAGE MODE DRAM CONTROLLER - PLD 2, INTEL CORPORATION'
" This PLD generates CAS0
" Implemented with the Intel 85C220 EPLD.

   SC2  device  'E0320';

   x          =     .X.;                    " ABEL 'don't care' symbol
   c          =     .C.;                    " ABEL 'clocking input' symbol

" Inputs

   CLK pin 1; "P4 input CLK"
   RFACK      pin  2; "Refresh Acknowledge
   CIP~       pin  3; "Cycle OK
   LA2 pin 4; "Latched A2.
   HIT~       pin  5; "DRAM Page Hit Signal
   BOFF~      pin  6; "Backoff input to P4"
   LW_R~      pin  7; "
   RAS~       pin  8; "
   RESET      pin  9; "System Reset
   RDY~       pin 12; "Processor RDY#
   MEMCS~     pin 13; "Memory Chip Select
   BRDY~      pin 18; "Processor BREADY#
   BLAST~     pin 19; "Processor BLAST#

" Output

   CAS10~     pin 14; " CAS1 byte 0,2
   C1         pin 15; " state variable
   C2         pin 16; " state variable
   CAS11~     pin 17; " CAS1 byte 1,3

state_diagram [CAS10~, CAS11~, C1, C2]

   state [1, 1, 1, 1]:  if RESET # !BOFF~ then [1, 1, 1, 1] else
                          if !RFACK & !CIP~ & !LA2 & LW R~ & !MEMCS~ then
                          [1, 1, 0, 1] else if !RFACK & !CIP~ & !LW_R~ & !RAS~
                          & !HIT~ & !MEMCS~ # (RFACK & RAS~) then
                          [0, 0, 1, 1] else [1, 1, 1, 1];

   state [1, 1, 0, 1]:  if RESET # !BOFF~ then [1, 1, 1, 1] else
                        if !RAS~ & RDY~ then [0, 0, 0, 0] else
                        [1, 1, 0, 1];

   state [0, 0, 0, 0]:  if RESET # !BOFF~ then [1, 1, 1, 1] else
                        if !CIP~ & !LA2 & LW_R~ & !MEMCS~ then [1, 1, 0, 0] else
                        if CIP~ # (!CIP~ & (MEMCS~ # !LW_R)) # (!CIP~ & LW_R~ &
                        LA2) then [1, 1, 1, 1] else [0, 0, 0, 0];

   state [1, 1, 0, 0]:  if !RAS~ then [0, 0, 0, 0] else [1, 1, 0, 0];
```

```
state [0, 0, 1, 1]: if RESET # !BOFF~ then [1, 1, 1, 1] else
                    if !BRDY~ & !BLAST~ & !RFACK then
                    [1, 1, 1, 1] else
                      if !BRDY~ & BLAST~ & !LA2 then [1, 1, 1, 0] else
                      if !BRDY~ & BLAST~ & LA2 then [0, 0, 1, 0] else
                      if RFACK then [0, 0, 1, 0] else
                      if BRDY~ & !RFACK then [0, 0, 1, 1];

state [1, 1, 1, 0]: if RESET then [1, 1, 1, 1] else
                      if !BOFF~ then [1, 1, 1, 0] else
                      if !BRDY~ & BLAST~ then [0, 0, 1, 1] else
                      if !BRDY~ & !BLAST~ then [1, 1, 1, 1] else
                      [1, 1, 1, 0];

state [0, 0, 1, 0]: if RESET # !BOFF~ then [1, 1, 1, 1] else
                      if !BRDY~ & BLAST ~ then [1, 1, 1, 0] else
                      if !BRDY~ & !BLAST~ # BRDY~ then [1, 1, 1, 1];

test_vectors

  ([CLK,RFACK,CIP~,LA2,HIT~,BOFF~,LW_R~,RAS~,RESET,RDY~,MEMCS~,BRDY~]
  -> [BLAST~,CAS10~,C1,C2,CAS11~])

"CRALHBLRRRMBB   CCCC
"LFQAIOWAEDERL   A12A
"KA02TFRSSYMDA   S  S
"  C~  ~F~~E~CYS 0  0
"  K    ~  T  S  T  0  1
"              ~   ~   ~   ~
"
"
"

  [c, x, x, x, x, x, 1, x, 1, x, x, x, x] -> [x, x, x, x];
  [c, x, 1, 0, x, x, 1, x, 1, x, x, x, x] -> [1, 1, 1, 1];
  [c, 0, 1, 0, x, 1, 1, 0, 0, 1, 0, 1, 1] -> [1, 1, 1, 1];
  [c, 0, 1, 0, x, 1, 1, 0, 0, 1, 0, 1, 1] -> [1, 1, 1, 1];
  [c, 0, 1, 0, x, 1, 1, 0, 0, 1, 0, 1, 1] -> [1, 1, 1, 1];
  [c, 0, 0, 0, 0, 1, 1, 0, 0, 1, 0, 1, 1] -> [1, 0, 1, 1];
  [c, 0, 0, 0, 0, 1, 1, 0, 0, 0, 0, 1, 1] -> [1, 0, 1, 1];
  [c, 0, 1, 0, 0, 1, 1, 0, 0, 1, 0, 1, 1] -> [0, 0, 0, 0];
  [c, 0, 0, 0, 0, 1, 1, 0, 0, 0, 0, 1, 1] -> [1, 0, 0, 1];
  [c, 0, 1, x, 0, 1, 1, 0, 0, 1, 0, 1, 1] -> [0, 0, 0, 0];
  [c, 0, 0, 0, 0, 1, 1, 0, 0, 0, 0, 1, 1] -> [1, 0, 0, 1];
  [c, 0, 1, x, 0, 1, 1, 0, 0, 1, 0, 1, 1] -> [0, 0, 0, 0];
  [c, 0, 1, 1, x, 1, 1, 0, 0, 1, 0, 1, 1] -> [1, 1, 1, 1];
end PG_MODE_DRAM_CTRL_2;
```

```
module   SC_MODE_DRAM_CTRL_15 flag '-r4'

title  'STATIC COLUMN MODE DRAM CONTROLLER - PLD 15, INTEL CORPORATION'
" This PLD combines ready signals
" Implemented with the Intel 85C220 EPLD.

   SC15K device   'E0320';

   x          =     .X.;                    " ABEL 'don't care' symbol
   c          =     .C.;                    " ABEL 'clocking input' symbol

" Inputs

   MEMCS~     pin  1; "
   JRDY~      pin  2; "
   MRDY~      pin  3; "
   BRDY~      pin  4; "
   ALD pin 5; "
   CKEN~      pin  6; "
   SKEN~      pin  7; "
   BRDYO~     pin  8; "
   M~         pin  9; "miss indicator for CIP~
   CIP~       pin 11; " Cycle indicator

" Output

   WEN~       pin 12; "Write enable for write latches
   RDY~       pin 13; "to 486
   MRDYCS~    pin 14; "
   MALD~      pin 15; "Modified ALD for FF's
   dum10      pin 16; "
   PBRDY~     pin 17; "
   KEN~       pin 18; "
   DRDY~      pin 19; "

equations

   !MALD~ = (!MEMCS~ & !ALD);

   !RDY~ = (!MRDY~ & M~ & !MEMCS~) # !JRDY~;

   !MRDYCS~ = (!MRDY~ & M~ & !MEMCS~);

   !WEN~ = !CIP~ & M~;

   !DRDY~ = !BRDY~ # !MRDYCS~;

   KEN~ = SKEN~ & CKEN~;

   PBRDY~ = BRDY~ & BRDYO~;
"test_vectors
```

```
" ([CLK,RESET]  - >
" [RESETO])

" C R    R
" L E    E
" K S    S
"   E    E
"   T    T
"        O
"
"
"

" [c, 0]  - > [x];
" [c, 0]  - > [0];
" [c, 0]  - > [0];
" [c, 0]  - > [0];
" [c, 0]  - > [0];
"[c, 0]  - > [0];
" [c, 0]  - > [0];
" [c, 1]  - > [1];
" [c, 1]  - > [1];
" [c, 1]  - > [1];
" [c, 1]  - > [1];
" [c, 1]  - > [1];
" [c, 1]  - > [1];
" [c, 1]  - > [1];
" [c, 1]  - > [1];
" [c, 0]  - > [0];
" [c, 0]  - > [0];
" [c, 0]  - > [0];

end SC_MODE_DRAM_CTRL_15;
```

```
module   SC_MODE_DRAM_CTRL_17 flag '-r4'

title  'STATIC COLUMN MODE DRAM CONTROLLER - PLD 17, INTEL CORPORATION'
" This PLD generates the A0 signal for bank 1
" Implemented with the Intel 85C224 EPLD.

   SC17 device   'E224';

   x          =     .X.;                    " ABEL 'don't care' symbol
   c          =     .C.;                    " ABEL 'clocking input' symbol

" Inputs

   CLK pin 1; "P4 input CLK"
   BRDY~        pin  2; "Burst Ready
   CIP~         pin  3; "Cycle OK
   MEMCS~       pin  4; "memory select
   LA313        pin  5; "Latched A2.
   DATASEL      pin  6; "Refresh acknowledge"
   RAS~         pin  7; "Row address strobe
   LW_R         pin  8; "CPU W/R latched~
   RESET        pin  9; "System Reset
   BLAST~       pin 10; "CPU BLAST~ output
   A3           pin 11; "CPU Backoff input
   ALD pin 14; "Address Latch disable
   dum1         pin 15;
   WE1~         pin 22; "Write enable
   dum2         pin 23; "Address Latch disable

" Output

   B10MA0       pin 21; "Bank 1 A0
   B1A pin 20; "Burst A3 bank0
   CS0~         pin 19; " state variable
   dun pin 18; " state variable
   dum          pin 17; " Burst A3 bank1
   B11MA0       pin 16; "Bank 1 A0

 state_diagram [B1A, CS0~]

   state [1, 1]: if RESET then [1, 1] else
                   if CIP~ & !ALD & !A3 then [0, 1] else
                   if !CIP~ & !ALD & !A3 then [0, 1] else
                   if !CIP~ & !LW_R & !MEMCS~ & WE1~ then [1, 0] else [1, 1];

   state [0, 1]: if RESET then [1, 1] else
                   if CIP~ & !ALD & A3 then [1, 1] else
                   if !CIP~ & !ALD & A3 then [1, 1] else
                   if !CIP~ & !LW_R & !MEMCS~ & WE1~ then [0, 0] else [0, 1];

   state [1, 0]: if RESET # (!BRDY~ & !BLAST~) then [1, 1] else
                   if !BRDY~ & DATASEL then [0, 0] else [1, 0];
```

```
state [0, 0]: if RESET # (!BRDY~ & !BLAST~) then [1, 1] else
              if !BRDY~ & DATASEL then [1, 0] else [0, 0];

equations

!B10MA0 = !WE1~ & !LA313 # WE1~ & RAS~ & !LA313 # WE1~ & !RAS~ & !B1A;

!B11MA0 = !WE1~ & !LA313 # WE1~ & RAS~ & !LA313 # WE1~ & !RAS~ & !B1A;

end SC_MODE_DRAM_CTRL_17;
```

```
module   SC_MODE_DRAM_CTRL_6   flag '-r4'

title  'STATIC COLUMN MODE DRAM CONTROLLER - PLD 6, INTEL CORPORATION'
" This PLD generates A0 for bank 0
" Implemented with the Intel 85C224 EPLD.

   SC6   device   'E224';

   x          =     .X.;                  " ABEL 'don't care' symbol
   c          =     .C.;                  " ABEL 'clocking input' symbol

" Inputs

   CLK pin 1; "P4 input CLK"
   BRDY~       pin  2; "Burst Ready
   CIP~        pin  3; "Cycle OK
   MEMCS~      pin  4; "memory select
   LA313       pin  5; "Latched A2.
   DATASEL     pin  6; "Refresh acknowledge"
   RAS~        pin  7; "Row address strobe
   LW_R        pin  8; "CPU W/R latched~
   RESET       pin  9; "System Reset
   BLAST~      pin 10; "CPU BLAST~ output
   A3          pin 11; "CPU Backoff input
   ALD pin 14; "Address Latch disable
   dum1        pin 15;
   WE0~        pin 22; "Write enable
   dum2        pin 23; "Address Latch disable

" Output

   B00MA0      pin 21; "Bank 0 A0
   B0A pin 20; " Burst A3 bank 0
   CS0~        pin 19; " state variable
   dun pin 18; " state variable
   dum         pin 17; " Burst A3 bank1
   B01MA0      pin 16; "Bank 0 A0

state_diagram [B0A, CS0~]

   state [1, 1]: if RESET then [1, 1] else
                    if CIP~ & !ALD & !A3 then [0, 1] else
                    if !CIP~ & !ALD & !A3 then [0, 1] else
                    if !CIP~ & !LW_R & !MEMCS~ & WE0~ then [1, 0] else [1, 1];

   state [0, 1]: if RESET then [1, 1] else
                    if CIP~ & !ALD & A3 then [1, 1] else
                    if !CIP~ & !ALD & A3 then [1, 1] else
                    if !CIP~ & !LW_R & !MEMCS~ & WE0~ then [0, 0] else [0, 1];

   state [1, 0]: if RESET # (!BRDY~ & !BLAST~) then [1, 1] else
                    if !BRDY~ & !DATASEL then [0, 0] else [1, 0];
```

```
state [0, 0]: if RESET # (!BRDY~ & !BLAST~) then [1, 1] else
              if !BRDY~ & !DATASEL then [1, 0] else [0, 0];

equations

!B00MA0 = !WE0~ & !LA313 # WE0~ & RAS~ & !LA313 # WE0~ & !RAS~ & !B0A;

!B01MA0 = !WE0~ & !LA313 # WE0~ & RAS~ & !LA313 # WE0~ & !RAS~ & !B0A;

end SC_MODE_DRAM_CTRL_6;
```

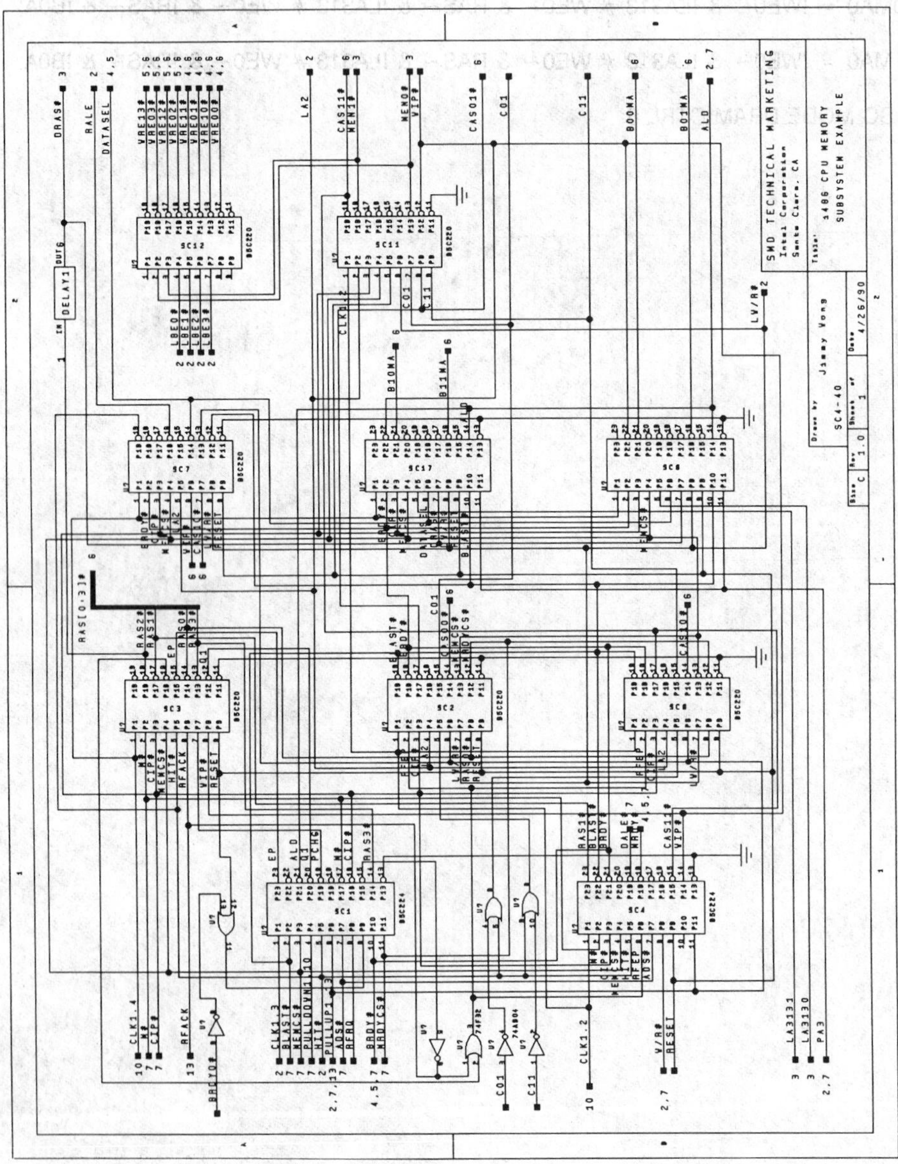
SMD TECHNICAL MARKETING
Intel Corporation
Santa Clara, CA
i486 CPU MEMORY SUBSYSTEM EXAMPLE
Jimmy Wong
4/26/90
SC4-40

240552IB-1

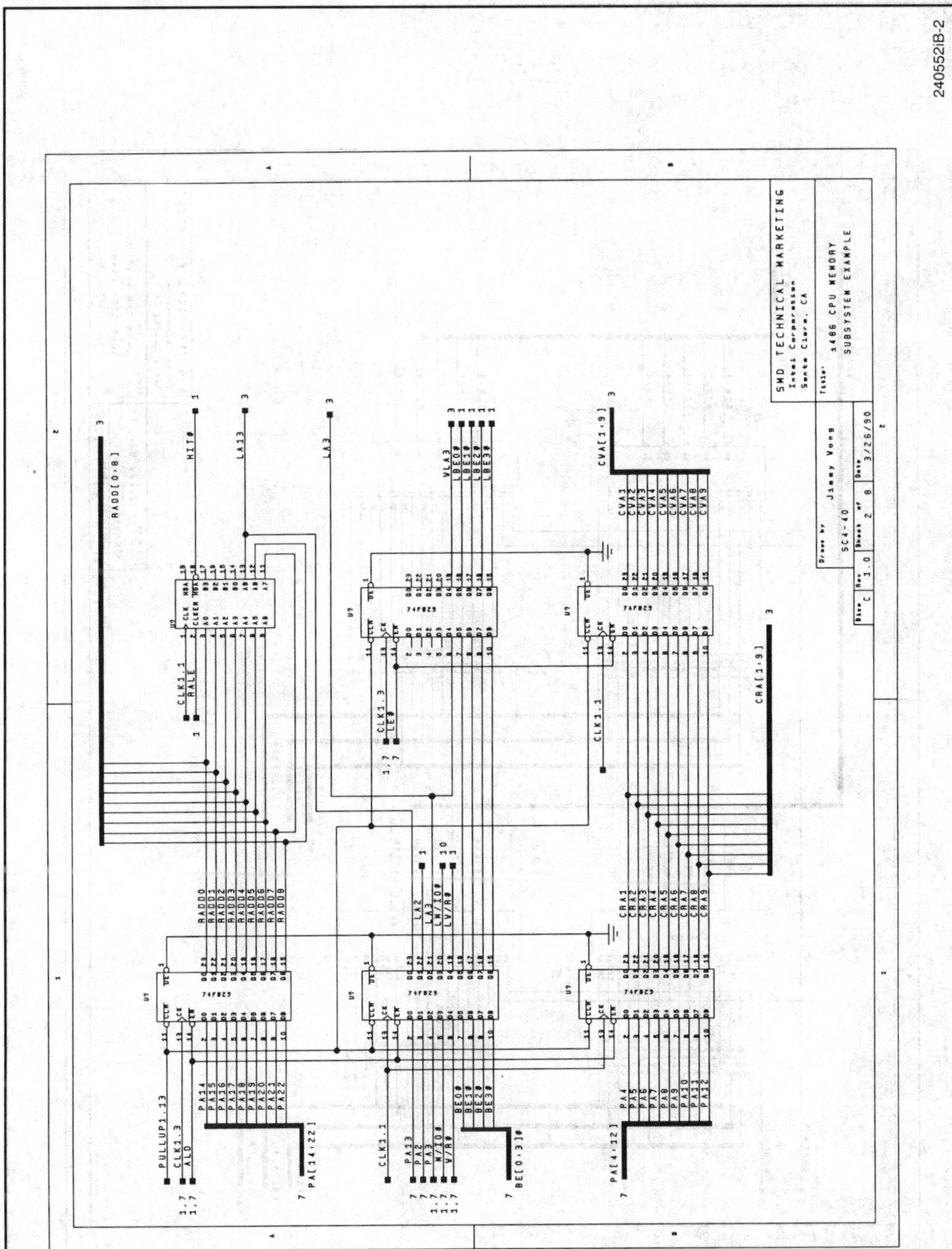
SMD TECHNICAL MARKETING
Intel Corporation
Santa Clara, CA
i486 CPU MEMORY
SUBSYSTEM EXAMPLE
Jimmy Vong
SC4-40
3/26/90
74F825
240552iB-2

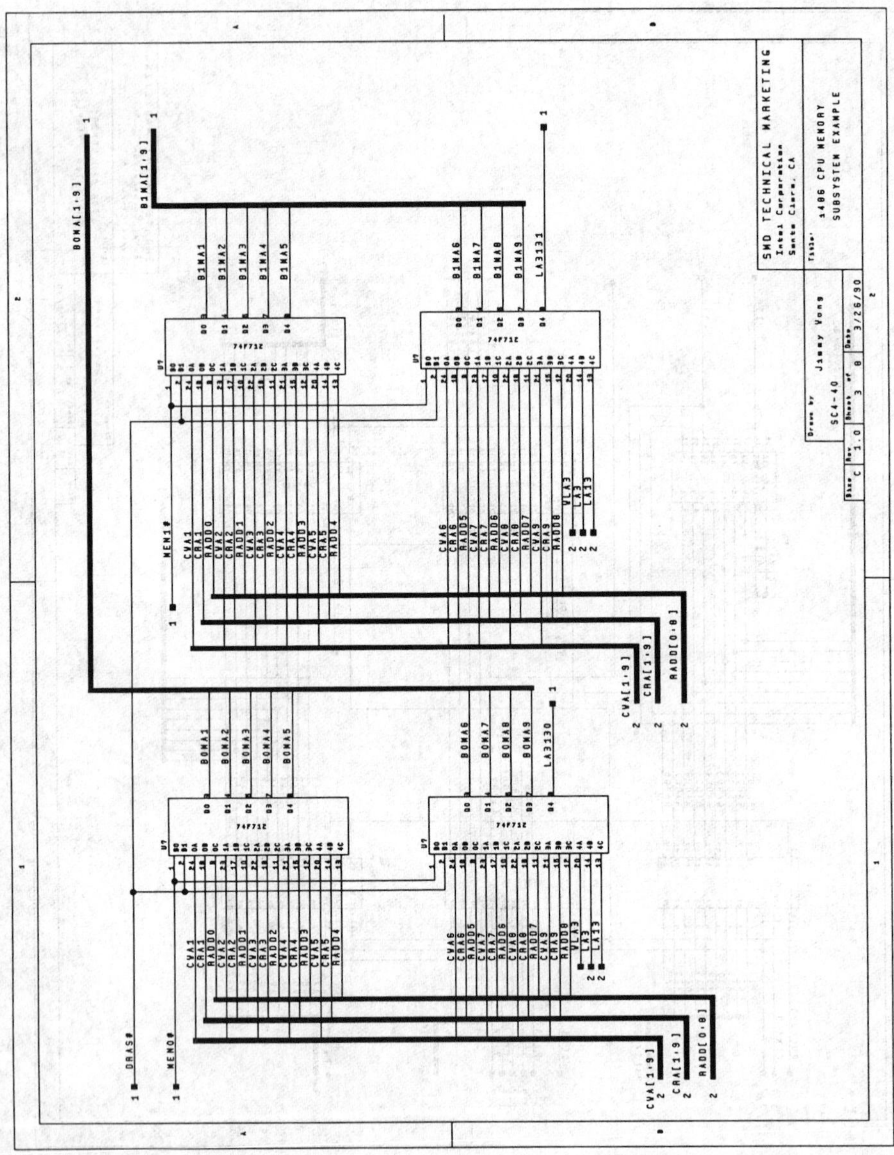
B0MA[1:9]
B1MA[1:9]
CVA[1:9]
CRA[1:9]
RADD[0:8]
DRAS#
MEM0#
MEM1#
SMD TECHNICAL MARKETING
Intel Corporation
Santa Clara, CA
i486 CPU MEMORY SUBSYSTEM EXAMPLE
Jimmy Vong
SC4-40
3/26/90

240552i8-3

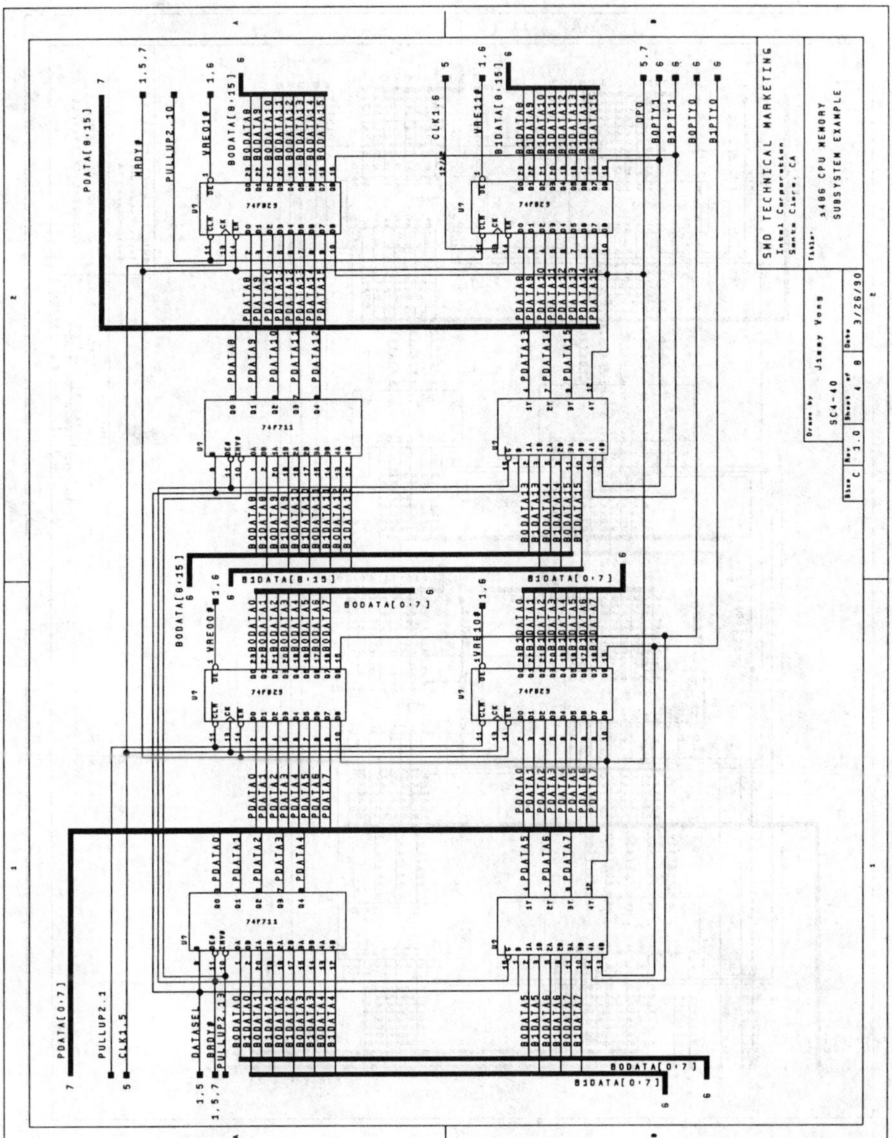
SMD TECHNICAL MARKETING
Intel Corporation
Santa Clara, CA
i486 CPU MEMORY SUBSYSTEM EXAMPLE
Jimmy Vong
3/26/90
SC4-40
74F829
74F711
PDATA[0:7]
PDATA[8:15]
B0DATA[0:7]
B1DATA[0:7]
B0DATA[8:15]
B1DATA[8:15]
DATASEL
BRDY#
PULLUP2.13
PULLUP2.1
PULLUP2.10
CLK1.5
CLK1.6
MRDY#
VRE01#
VRE00#
VRE11#
VRE10#
DP0
B0PTY1
B1PTY1
B0PTY0
B1PTY0

240552iB-4

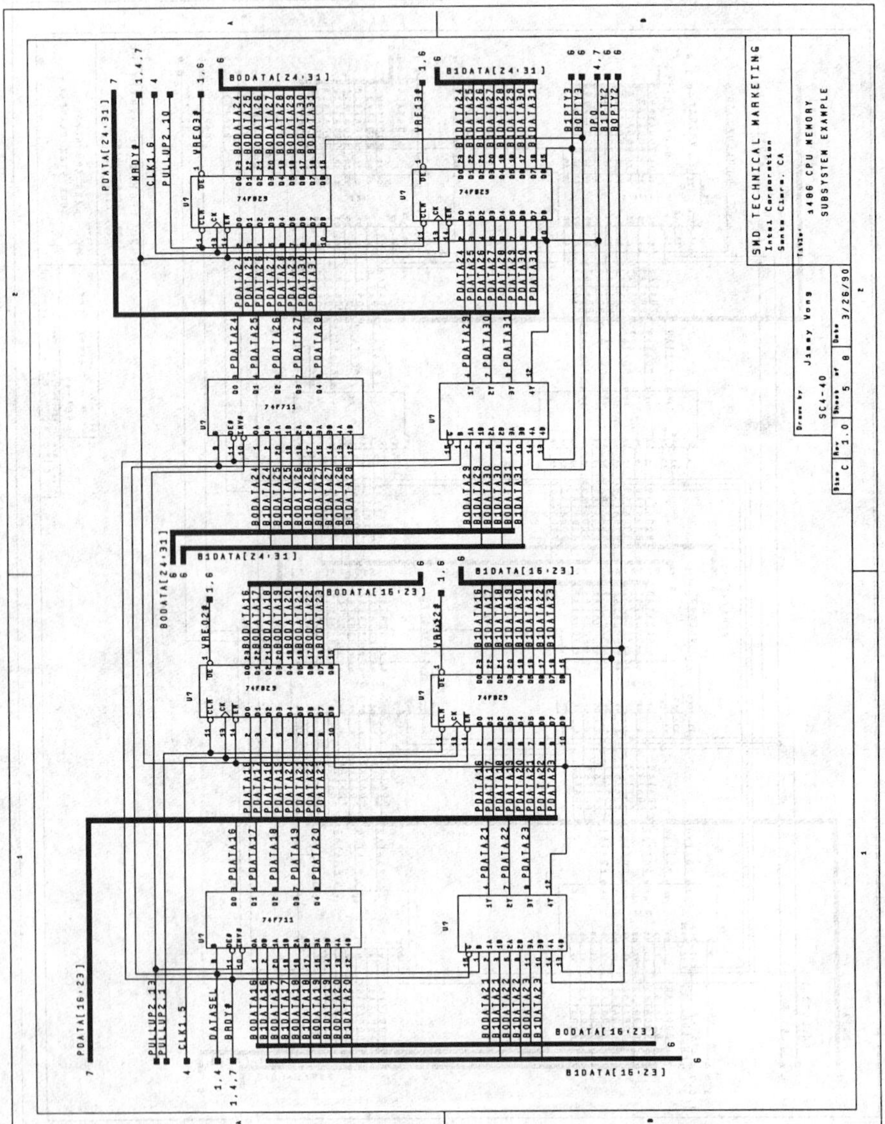
SMD TECHNICAL MARKETING
Intel Corporation
Santa Clara, CA
i486 CPU MEMORY SUBSYSTEM EXAMPLE
Jimmy Vong
SC4-40
3/26/90
74F829
74F711
PDATA[24:31]
PDATA[16:23]
B0DATA[24:31]
B1DATA[24:31]
B0DATA[16:23]
B1DATA[16:23]

240552IB-5

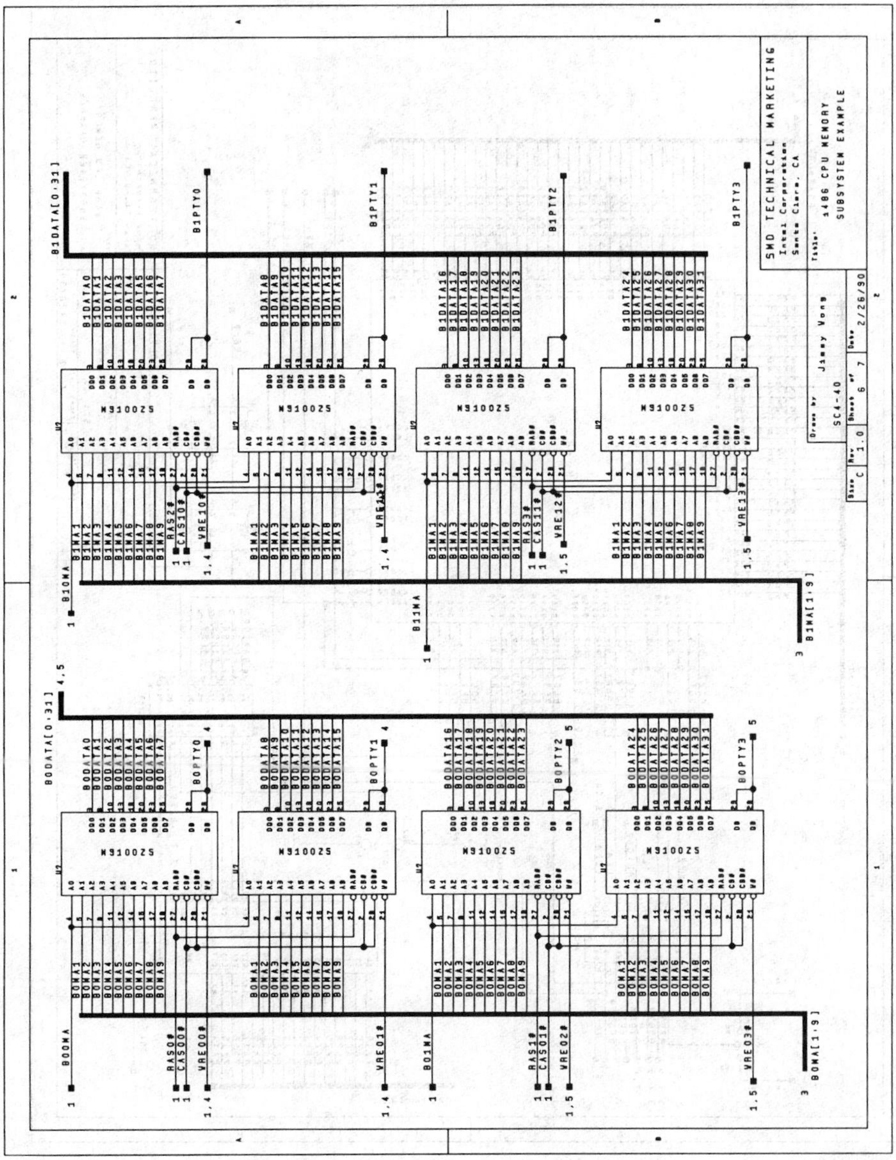

SMD TECHNICAL MARKETING
i486 CPU MEMORY
SUBSYSTEM EXAMPLE
Jimmy Vong
SC4-40
2/26/90
M5100Z5
B1DATA[0:31]
B0DATA[0:31]
B1MA[1:9]
B0MA[1:9]

240552i8-6

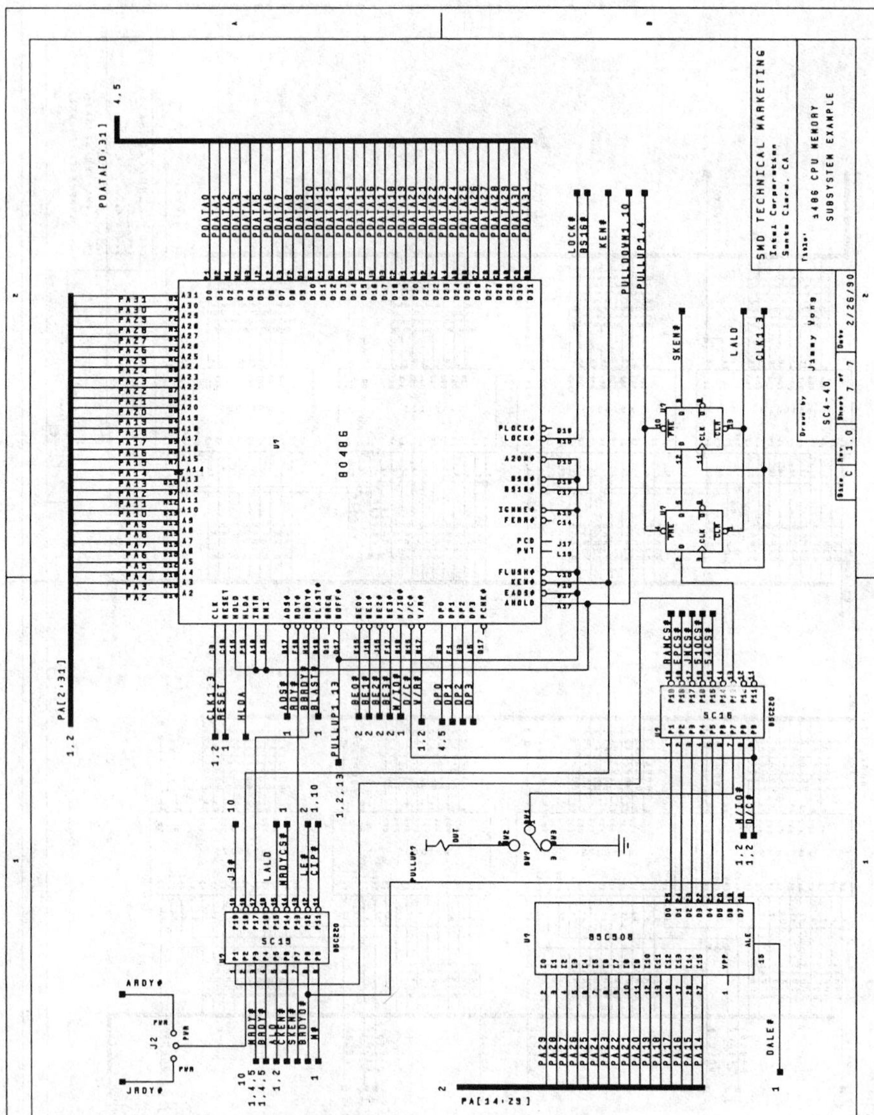
SMD TECHNICAL MARKETING
Intel Corporation
Santa Clara, CA
i486 CPU MEMORY SUBSYSTEM EXAMPLE
Jimmy Vong
SC4-40
2/26/90
80486
SC15
SC16
85C508
PDATA[0:31]
PA[2:31]
PA[14:29]

240552iB-7

240552i8-8

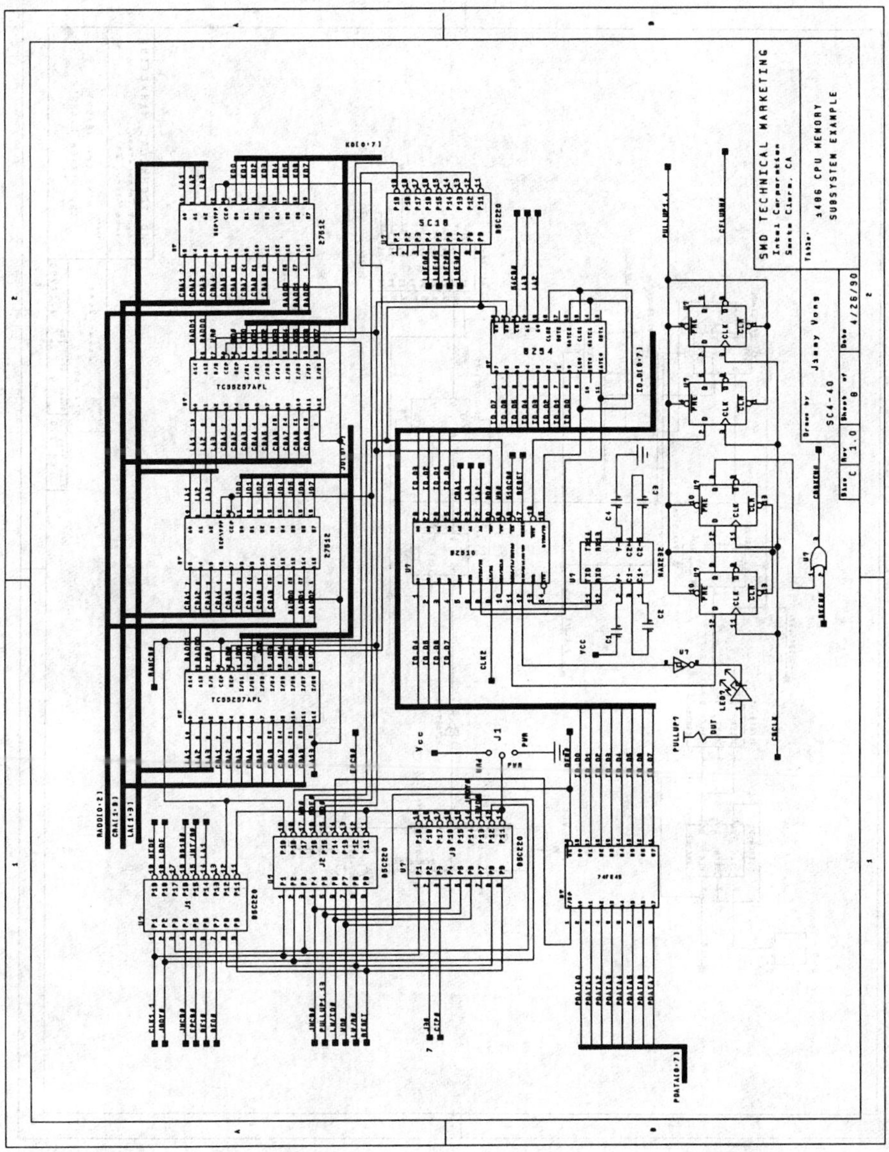
SMD TECHNICAL MARKETING
Intel Corporation
Santa Clara, CA
i486 CPU MEMORY SUBSYSTEM EXAMPLE
Jimmy Vong
4/26/90
SC4-40
TC55257APL
27512
8254
85C220
74F245
MAX232

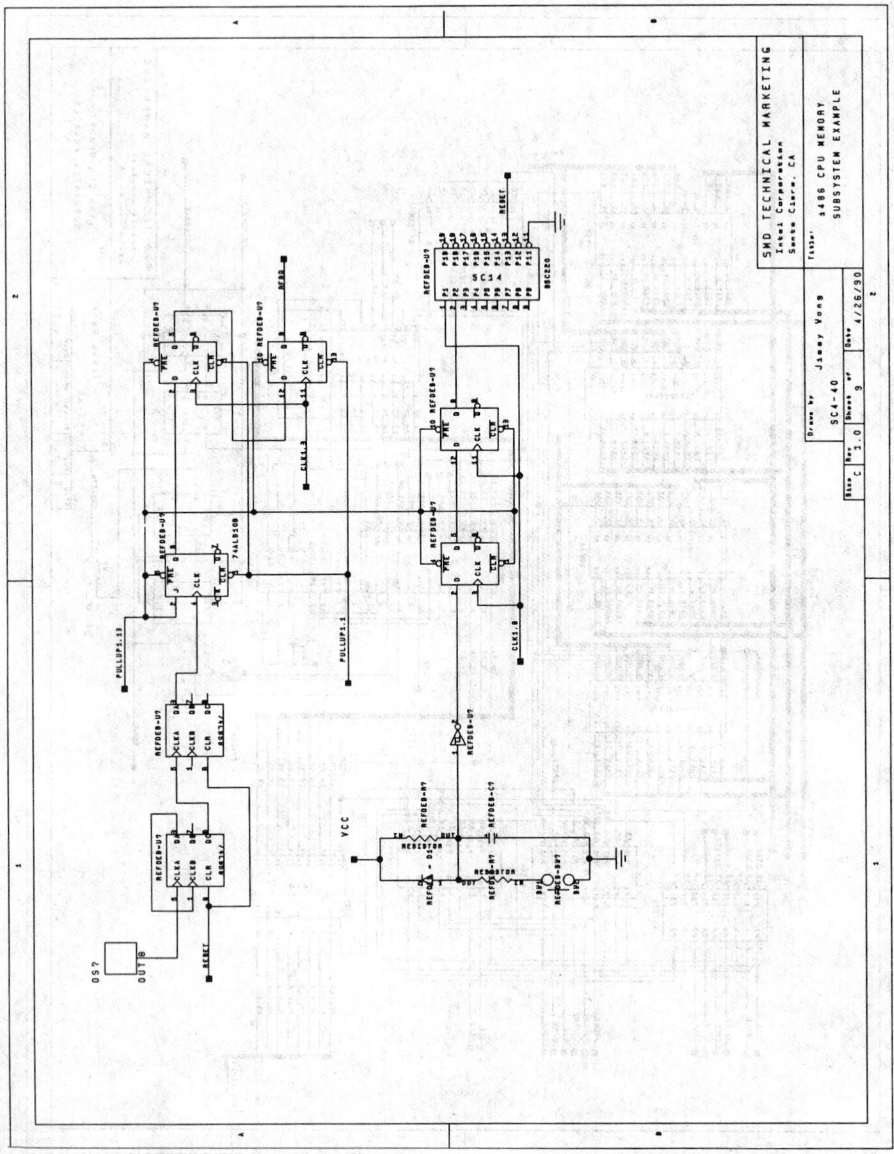
SMD TECHNICAL MARKETING
Intel Corporation
Santa Clara, CA
i486 CPU MEMORY
SUBSYSTEM EXAMPLE
Drawn by Jimmy Yong
SC4-40
Date 4/26/90
Size C
Rev 1.0
Sheet 9
SC14
VCC
RESET
CLK1.3
CLK1.0
PULLUP1.13
PULLUP1.1
74ALS109
OUT8

240552IB-9

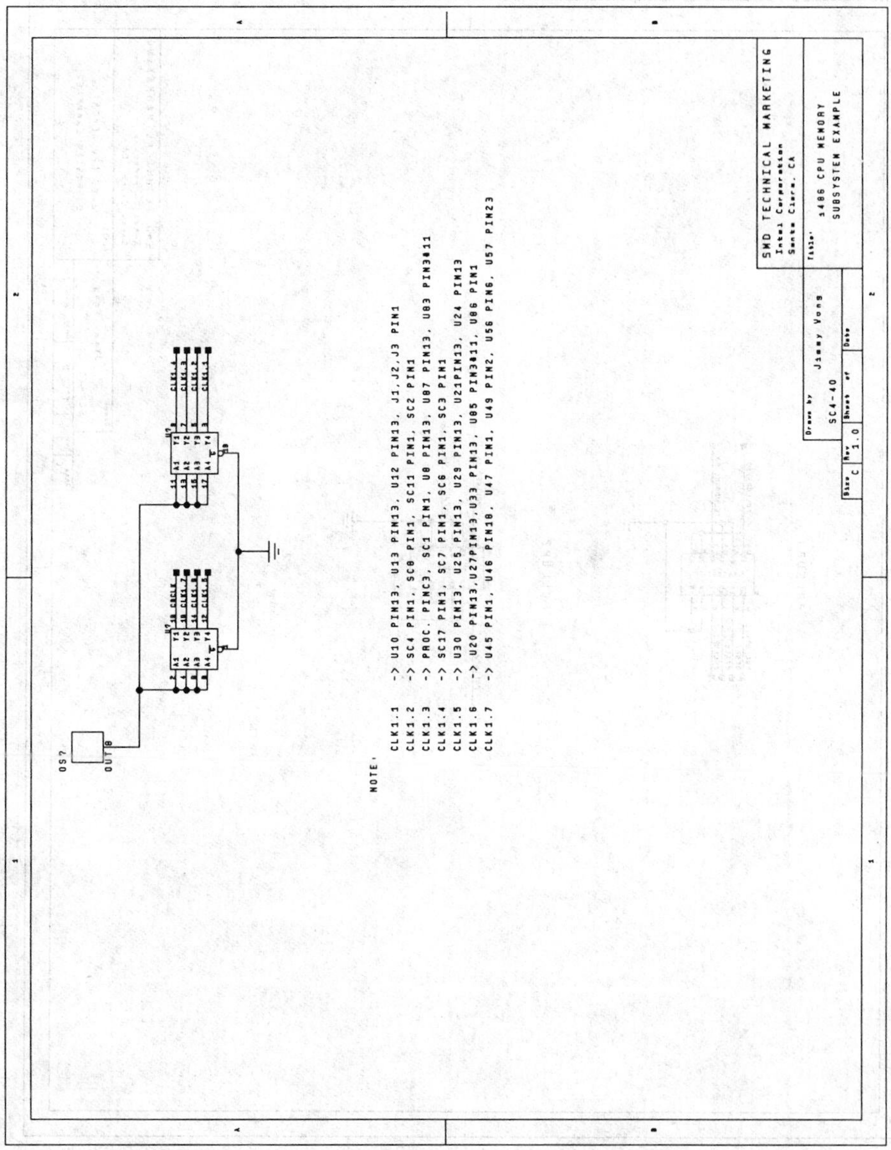
OS?
OUT8
NOTE:
CLK1.1 -> U10 PIN13, U13 PIN13, U12 PIN13, J1,J2,J3 PIN1
CLK1.2 -> SC4 PIN1, SC8 PIN1, SC11 PIN1, SC2 PIN1
CLK1.3 -> PROC. PINC3, SC1 PIN1, U8 PIN13, U87 PIN13, U83 PIN3&11
CLK1.4 -> SC17 PIN1, SC7 PIN1, SC6 PIN1, SC3 PIN1
CLK1.5 -> U30 PIN13, U25 PIN13, U29 PIN13, U21PIN13, U24 PIN13
CLK1.6 -> U20 PIN13,U27PIN13,U33 PIN13, U85 PIN3&11, U86 PIN1
CLK1.7 -> U45 PIN1, U46 PIN18, U47 PIN1, U49 PIN2, U56 PIN6, U57 PIN23
SMD TECHNICAL MARKETING
Intel Corporation
Santa Clara, CA
Title: i486 CPU MEMORY SUBSYSTEM EXAMPLE
Drawn by Jimmy Vong
SC4-40
Size C
Rev 1.0
Sheet of
Date

240552IB-10

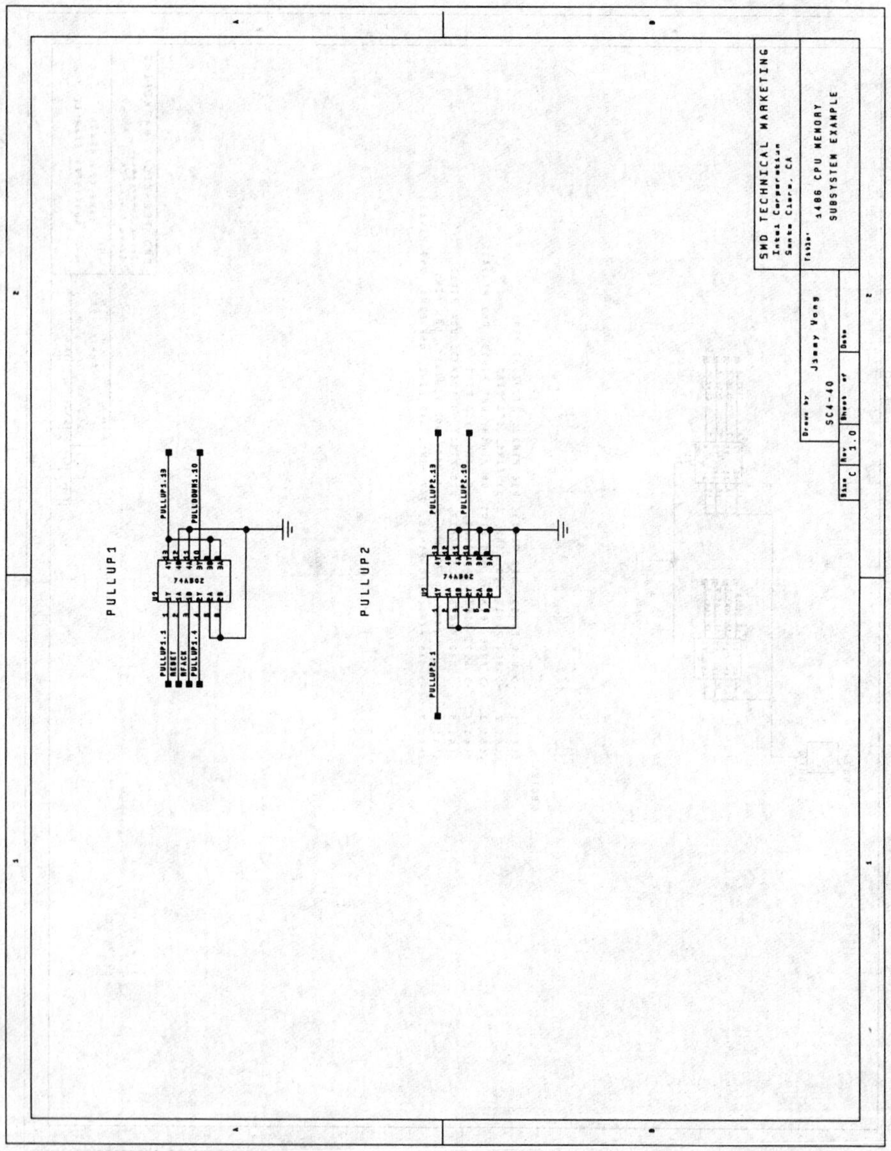
PULLUP1
74AS02
PULLUP1.1
RESET
RFACK
PULLUP1.4
PULLUP1.13
PULLDOWN1.10
PULLUP2
74AS02
PULLUP2.1
PULLUP2.13
PULLUP2.10
SMD TECHNICAL MARKETING
Intel Corporation
Santa Clara, CA
i486 CPU MEMORY
SUBSYSTEM EXAMPLE
Jimmy Wong
SC4-40
C
1.0

240552i B-11

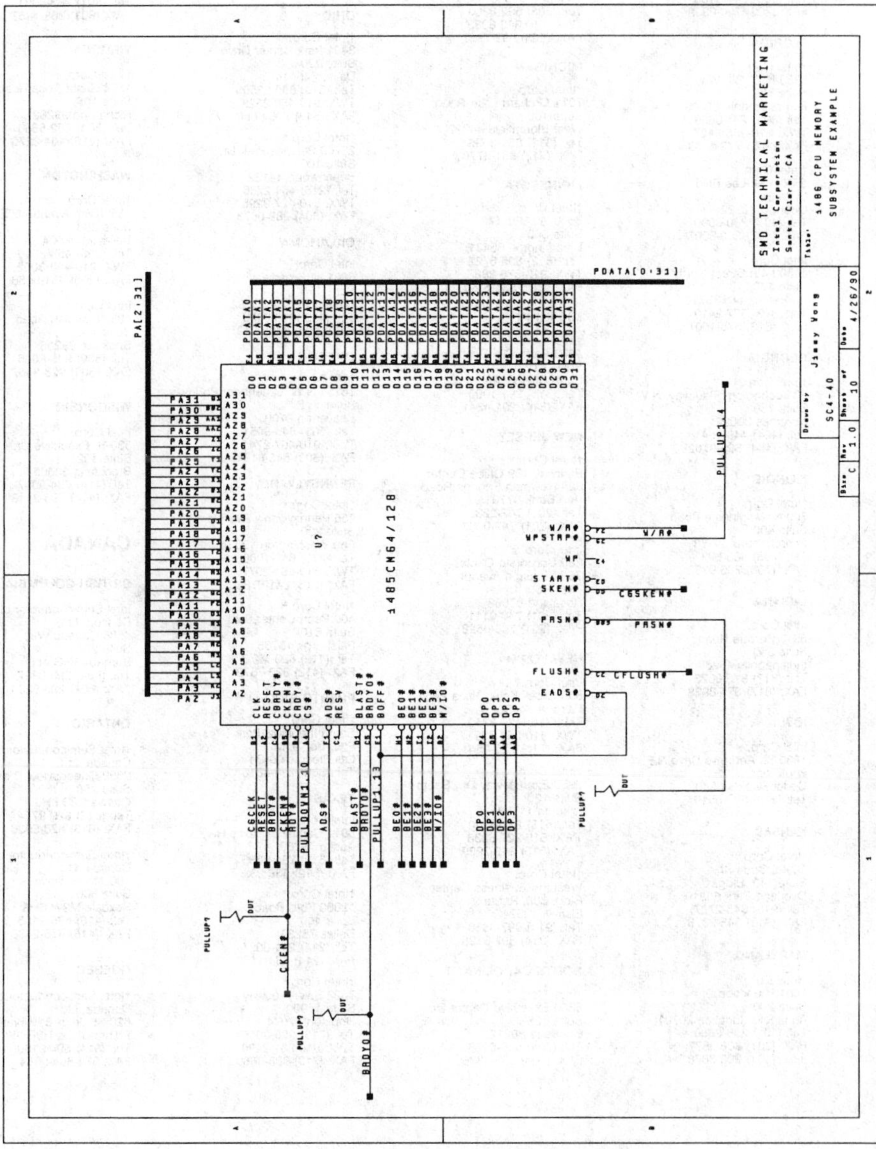
SMD TECHNICAL MARKETING
Intel Corporation
Santa Clara, CA
i486 CPU MEMORY SUBSYSTEM EXAMPLE
Jimmy Vong
4/26/90
SC4-40
PDATA[0:31]
PA[2:31]
PULLUP1.4
W/R#
CGSKEN#
PRSN#
CFLUSH#
CGCLK
RESET
BRDY#
CKEN#
RDY#
ADS#
BLAST#
BRDY0#
PULLUP1.13
BE0#
BE1#
BE2#
BE3#
M/IO#
DP0
DP1
DP2
DP3
U7

240552i8-12

intel®

DOMESTIC SALES OFFICES

ALABAMA

†Intel Corp.
5015 Bradford Dr., #2
Huntsville 35805
Tel: (205) 830-4010
FAX: (205) 837-2640

ARIZONA

†Intel Corp.
11225 N. 28th Dr.
Suite D-214
Phoenix 85029
Tel: (602) 869-4980
FAX: (602) 869-4294

Intel Corp.
7225 N. Mona Lisa Rd.
Suite 215
Tucson 85741
Tel: (602) 544-0227
FAX: (602) 544-0232

CALIFORNIA

†Intel Corp.
21515 Vanowen Street
Suite 116
Canoga Park 91303
Tel: (818) 704-8500
FAX: (818) 340-1144

†Intel Corp.
2250 E. Imperial Highway
Suite 218
El Segundo 90245
Tel: (213) 640-6040
FAX: (213) 640-7133

Intel Corp.
1 Sierra Gate Plaza
Suite 280C
Roseville 95678
Tel: (916) 782-8086
FAX: (916) 782-8153

†Intel Corp.
9665 Chesapeake Dr.
Suite 325
San Diego 92123
Tel: (619) 292-8086
FAX: (619) 292-0628

†Intel Corp.*
400 N. Tustin Avenue
Suite 450
Santa Ana 92705
Tel: (714) 835-9642
TWX: 910-595-1114
FAX: (714) 541-9157

†Intel Corp.*
San Tomas 4
2700 San Tomas Expressway
2nd Floor
Santa Clara 95051
Tel: (408) 986-8086
TWX: 910-338-0255
FAX: (408) 727-2620

COLORADO

Intel Corp.
4445 Northpark Drive
Suite 100
Colorado Springs 80907
Tel: (719) 594-6622
FAX: (303) 594-0720

†Intel Corp.*
650 S. Cherry St.
Suite 915
Denver 80222
Tel: (303) 321-8086
TWX: 910-931-2289
FAX: (303) 322-8670

CONNECTICUT

Intel Corp.
301 Lee Farm Corporate Park
83 Wooster Heights Rd.
Danbury 06810
Tel: (203) 748-3130
FAX: (203) 794-0339

FLORIDA

†Intel Corp.
6363 N.W. 6th Way
Suite 100
Ft. Lauderdale 33309
Tel: (305) 771-0600
TWX: 510-956-9407
FAX: (305) 772-8193

†Intel Corp.
5850 T.G. Lee Blvd.
Suite 340
Orlando 32822
Tel: (407) 240-8000
FAX: (407) 240-8097

Intel Corp.
11300 4th Street North
Suite 170
St. Petersburg 33716
Tel: (813) 577-2413
FAX: (813) 578-1607

GEORGIA

†Intel Corp.
20 Technology Parkway, N.W.
Suite 150
Norcross 30092
Tel: (404) 449-0541
FAX: (404) 605-9762

ILLINOIS

†Intel Corp.*
300 N. Martingale Road
Suite 400
Schaumburg 60173
Tel: (708) 605-8031
FAX: (708) 706-9762

INDIANA

Intel Corp.
8910 Purdue Road
Suite 350
Indianapolis 46268
Tel: (317) 875-0623
FAX: (317) 875-8938

IOWA

Intel Corp.
1930 St. Andrews Drive N.E.
2nd Floor
Cedar Rapids 52402
Tel: (319) 393-5510

KANSAS

†Intel Corp.
10985 Cody St.
Suite 140, Bldg. D
Overland Park 66210
Tel: (913) 345-2727
FAX: (913) 345-2076

MARYLAND

†Intel Corp.*
10010 Junction Dr.
Suite 200
Annapolis Junction 20701
Tel: (301) 206-2860
FAX: (301) 206-3677
(301) 206-3678

MASSACHUSETTS

†Intel Corp.*
Westford Corp. Center
3 Carlisle Road
2nd Floor
Westford 01886
Tel: (508) 692-0960
TWX: 710-343-6333
FAX: (508) 692-7867

MICHIGAN

†Intel Corp.
7071 Orchard Lake Road
Suite 100
West Bloomfield 48322
Tel: (313) 851-8096
FAX: (313) 851-8770

MINNESOTA

†Intel Corp.
3500 W. 80th St.
Suite 360
Bloomington 55431
Tel: (612) 835-6722
TWX: 910-576-2867
FAX: (612) 831-6497

MISSOURI

†Intel Corp.
4203 Earth City Expressway
Suite 131
Earth City 63045
Tel: (314) 291-1990
FAX: (314) 291-4341

NEW JERSEY

†Intel Corp.*
Parkway 109 Office Center
328 Newman Springs Road
Red Bank 07701
Tel: (201) 747-2233
FAX: (201) 747-0983

Intel Corp.
280 Corporate Center
75 Livingston Avenue
First Floor
Roseland 07068
Tel: (201) 740-0111
FAX: (201) 740-0626

NEW YORK

Intel Corp.*
850 Cross Keys Office Park
Fairport 14450
Tel: (716) 425-2750
TWX: 510-253-7391
FAX: (716) 223-2561

†Intel Corp.*
2950 Expressway Dr., South
Suite 130
Islandia 11722
Tel: (516) 231-3300
TWX: 510-227-6236
FAX: (516) 348-7939

†Intel Corp.
Westage Business Center
Bldg. 300, Route 9
Fishkill 12524
Tel: (914) 897-3860
FAX: (914) 897-3125

NORTH CAROLINA

†Intel Corp.
5800 Executive Center Dr.
Suite 105
Charlotte 28212
Tel: (704) 568-8966
FAX: (704) 535-2236

†Intel Corp.
5540 Centerview Dr.
Suite 215
Raleigh 27606
Tel: (919) 851-9537
FAX: (919) 851-8974

OHIO

†Intel Corp.*
3401 Park Center Drive
Suite 220
Dayton 45414
Tel: (513) 890-5350
TWX: 810-450-2528
FAX: (513) 890-8658

†Intel Corp.*
25700 Science Park Dr.
Suite 100
Beachwood 44122
Tel: (216) 464-2736
TWX: 810-427-9298
FAX: (804) 282-0673

OKLAHOMA

Intel Corp.
6801 N. Broadway
Suite 115
Oklahoma City 73162
Tel: (405) 848-8086
FAX: (405) 840-9819

OREGON

†Intel Corp.
15254 N.W. Greenbrier Parkway
Building B
Beaverton 97005
Tel: (503) 645-8051
TWX: 910-467-8741
FAX: (503) 645-8181

PENNSYLVANIA

†Intel Corp.*
455 Pennsylvania Avenue
Suite 230
Fort Washington 19034
Tel: (215) 641-1000
TWX: 510-661-2077
FAX: (215) 641-0785

†Intel Corp.*
400 Penn Center Blvd.
Suite 610
Pittsburgh 15235
Tel: (412) 823-4970
FAX: (412) 829-7578

PUERTO RICO

†Intel Corp.
South Industrial Park
P.O. Box 910
Las Piedras 00671
Tel: (809) 733-8616

TEXAS

Intel Corp.
8911 Capital of Texas Hwy.
Austin 78759
Tel: (512) 794-8086
FAX: (512) 338-9335

†Intel Corp.*
12000 Ford Road
Suite 400
Dallas 75234
Tel: (214) 241-8087
FAX: (214) 484-1180

†Intel Corp.*
7322 S.W. Freeway
Suite 1490
Houston 77074
Tel: (713) 988-8086
TWX: 910-881-2490
FAX: (713) 988-3660

UTAH

†Intel Corp.
428 East 6400 South
Suite 104
Murray 84107
Tel: (801) 263-8051
FAX: (801) 268-1457

VIRGINIA

†Intel Corp.
1504 Santa Rosa Road
Suite 108
Richmond 23288
Tel: (804) 282-5668
FAX: (216) 464-2270

WASHINGTON

†Intel Corp.
155 108th Avenue N.E.
Suite 386
Bellevue 98004
Tel: (206) 453-8086
TWX: 910-443-3002
FAX: (206) 451-9556

Intel Corp.
408 N. Mullan Road
Suite 102
Spokane 99206
Tel: (509) 928-8086
FAX: (509) 928-9467

WISCONSIN

Intel Corp.
330 S. Executive Dr.
Suite 102
Brookfield 53005
Tel: (414) 784-8087
FAX: (414) 796-2115

CANADA

BRITISH COLUMBIA

Intel Semiconductor of Canada, Ltd.
4585 Canada Way
Suite 202
Burnaby V5G 4L6
Tel: (604) 298-0387
FAX: (604) 298-8234

ONTARIO

†Intel Semiconductor of Canada, Ltd.
2650 Queensview Drive
Suite 250
Ottawa K2B 8H6
Tel: (613) 829-9714
FAX: (613) 820-5936

†Intel Semiconductor of Canada, Ltd.
190 Attwell Drive
Suite 500
Rexdale M9W 6H8
Tel: (416) 675-2105
FAX: (416) 675-2438

QUEBEC

†Intel Semiconductor of Canada, Ltd.
620 St. Jean Boulevard
Pointe Claire H9R 3K2
Tel: (514) 694-9130
FAX: 514-694-0064

†Sales and Service Office
*Field Application Location

ntel®

DOMESTIC DISTRIBUTORS

BAMA

w Electronics, Inc.
5 Henderson Road
tsville 35805
(205) 837-6955
: 205-751-1581

ilton/Avnet Electronics
0 Research Drive
tsville 35805
(205) 837-7210
: 205-721-0356

neer/Technologies Group, Inc.
5 University Square
tsville 35805
(205) 837-9300
: 205-837-9358

ZONA

ow Electronics, Inc.
4 E. Wood Street
enix 85040
(602) 437-0750
X: 910-951-1550

amilton/Avnet Electronics
S. Madison Drive
npe 85281
(602) 231-5140
: 910-950-0077

nilton/Avnet Electronics
South McKemy
andler 85226
(602) 961-6669
: 602-961-4073

le Distribution Group
1 E. Raymond
enix 85040
(602) 249-2232
X: 910-371-2871

LIFORNIA

ow Electronics, Inc.
48 Dearborn Street
atsworth 91311
: (213) 701-7500
X: 910-493-2086

row Electronics, Inc.
1 Ridgehaven Court
n Diego 92123
: (619) 565-4800
X: 619-279-8062

row Electronics, Inc.
Weddell Drive
nnyvale 94086
: (408) 745-6600
X: 910-339-9371

row Electronics, Inc.
61 Dow Avenue
stin 92680
: (714) 838-5422
X: 910-595-2860

amilton Electro Sales
70 Pullman Street
sta Mesa 92626
: (714) 641-4150
X: 910-595-2638

amilton/Avnet Electronics
75 Bordeaux Drive
nnyvale 94086
: (408) 743-3300
X: 910-339-9332

amilton/Avnet Electronics
45 Ridgeview Avenue
n Diego 92123
: (619) 571-7500
X: 910-595-2638

amilton/Avnet Electronics
150 Califa St.
oodland Hills 91376
: (818) 594-0404
X: 818-594-8233

amilton Electro Sales
950 W. Washington Blvd.
lver City 20230
: (213) 558-2458
X: 910-340-6364

amilton Electro Sales
61B West 190th Street
rdena 90248
: (213) 217-6700
X: 910-340-6364

†Hamilton/Avnet Electronics
3002 'G' Street
Ontario 91761
Tel: (714) 989-9411

†Avnet Electronics
20501 Plummer
Chatsworth 91351
Tel: (213) 700-6271
TWX: 910-494-2207

†Hamilton/Avnet Electronics
4103 Northgate Blvd.
Sacramento 95834
Tel: (916) 920-3150

Pioneer Electronics
134 Rio Robles
San Jose 95134
Tel: (408) 954-9100
FAX: 408-954-9113

Wyle Distribution Group
124 Maryland Street
El Segundo 90254
Tel: (213) 322-8100

Wyle Distribution Group
7431 Chapman Ave.
Garden Grove 92641
Tel: (714) 891-1717
FAX: 714-891-1621

†Wyle Distribution Group
2951 Sunrise Blvd., Suite 175
Rancho Cordova 95742
Tel: (916) 638-5282

†Wyle Distribution Group
9525 Chesapeake Drive
San Diego 92123
Tel: (619) 565-9171
TWX: 910-335-1590

†Wyle Distribution Group
3000 Bowers Avenue
Santa Clara 95051
Tel: (408) 727-2500
TWX: 408-988-2747

†Wyle Distribution Group
17872 Cowan Avenue
Irvine 92714
Tel: (714) 863-9953
TWX: 910-371-7127

†Wyle Distribution Group
26677 W. Agoura Rd.
Calabasas 91302
Tel: (818) 880-9000
TWX: 372-0232

COLORADO

Arrow Electronics, Inc.
7060 South Tucson Way
Englewood 80112
Tel: (303) 790-4444

†Hamilton/Avnet Electronics
9605 Maroon Circle
Suite 200
Englewood 80112
Tel: (303) 799-0663
TWX: 910-935-0787

†Wyle Distribution Group
451 E. 124th Avenue
Thornton 80241
Tel: (303) 457-9953
TWX: 910-936-0770

CONNECTICUT

†Arrow Electronics, Inc.
12 Beaumont Road
Wallingford 06492
Tel: (203) 265-7741
TWX: 710-476-0162

†Hamilton/Avnet Electronics
Commerce Industrial Park
Commerce Drive
Danbury 06810
Tel: (203) 797-2800
TWX: 710-456-9974

†Pioneer Electronics
112 Main Street
Norwalk 06851
Tel: (203) 853-1515
FAX: 203-838-9901

FLORIDA

†Arrow Electronics, Inc.
400 Fairway Drive
Suite 102
Deerfield Beach 33441
Tel: (305) 429-8200
FAX: 305-428-3991

†Arrow Electronics, Inc.
37 Skyline Drive
Suite 3101
Lake Marv 32746
Tel: (407) 323-0252
FAX: 407-323-3189

†Hamilton/Avnet Electronics
6801 N.W. 15th Way
Ft. Lauderdale 33309
Tel: (305) 971-2900
FAX: 305-971-5420

†Hamilton/Avnet Electronics
3197 Tech Drive North
St. Petersburg 33702
Tel: (813) 573-3930
FAX: 813-572-4329

†Hamilton/Avnet Electronics
6947 University Boulevard
Winter Park 32792
Tel: (407) 628-3888
FAX: 407-678-1878

†Pioneer/Technologies Group, Inc.
337 Northlake Blvd., Suite 1000
Alta Monte Springs 32701
Tel: (407) 834-9090
FAX: 407-834-0865

Pioneer/Technologies Group, Inc.
674 S. Military Trail
Deerfield Beach 33442
Tel: (305) 428-8877
FAX: 305-481-2950

GEORGIA

†Arrow Electronics, Inc.
4250 E. Rivergreen Parkway
Deluth 30136
Tel: (404) 497-1300
TWX: 810-766-0439

†Hamilton/Avnet Electronics
5825 D Peachtree Corners
Norcross 30092
Tel: (404) 447-7500
TWX: 810-766-0432

Pioneer/Technologies Group, Inc.
3100 F Northwoods Place
Norcross 30071
Tel: (404) 448-1711
FAX: 404-446-8270

ILLINOIS

†Arrow Electronics, Inc.
1140 W. Thorndale
Itasca 60143
Tel: (708) 250-0500
TWX: 708-250-0916

†Hamilton/Avnet Electronics
1130 Thorndale Avenue
Bensenville 60106
Tel: (708) 860-7780
TWX: 708-860-8530

MTI Systems Sales
1100 W. Thorndale
Itasca 60143
Tel: (708) 773-2300

†Pioneer Electronics
2171 Executive Dr., Suite 200
Addison 60101
Tel: (708) 495-9680
FAX: 708-495-9831

INDIANA

†Arrow Electronics, Inc.
7108 Lakeview Parkway West Drive
Indianapolis 46268
Tel: (317) 299-2071
FAX: 317-299-0255

Hamilton/Avnet Electronics
485 Gradle Drive
Carmel 46032
Tel: (317) 844-9333
FAX: 317-844-5921

†Pioneer Electronics
9350 Priority Way
West Drive
Indianapolis 46250
Tel: (317) 573-0880
FAX: 317-573-0979

IOWA

Hamilton/Avnet Electronics
915 33rd Avenue, S.W.
Cedar Rapids 52404
Tel: (319) 362-4757

KANSAS

Arrow Electronics
8208 Melrose Dr., Suite 210
Lenexa 66214
Tel: (913) 541-9542
FAX: 913-541-0328

†Hamilton/Avnet Electronics
15313 W. 95th
Overland Park 66215
Tel: (913) 888-8900
FAX: 913-541-7951

KENTUCKY

Hamilton/Avnet Electronics
1051 D. Newton Park
Lexington 40511
Tel: (606) 259-1475

MARYLAND

†Arrow Electronics, Inc.
8300 Guilford Drive
Suite H, River Center
Columbia 21046
Tel: (301) 995-6002
FAX: 301-381-3854

†Hamilton/Avnet Electronics
6822 Oak Hall Lane
Columbia 21045
Tel: (301) 995-3500
FAX: 301-995-3593

†Mesa Technology Corp.
9720 Patuxent Woods Dr.
Columbia 21046
Tel: (301) 290-8150
FAX: 301-290-6474

†Pioneer/Technologies Group, Inc.
9100 Gaither Road
Gaithersburg 20877
Tel: (301) 921-0660
FAX: 301-921-4255

MASSACHUSETTS

Arrow Electronics, Inc.
25 Upton Dr.
Wilmington 01887
Tel: (508) 658-0900
TWX: 710-393-6770

†Hamilton/Avnet Electronics
10D Centennial Drive
Peabody 01960
Tel: (508) 532-9838
FAX: 508-596-7802

†Pioneer Electronics
44 Hartwell Avenue
Lexington 02173
Tel: (617) 861-9200
FAX: 617-863-1547

Wyle Distribution Group
15 Third Avenue
Burlington 01803
Tel: (617) 272-7300
FAX: 617-272-6809

MICHIGAN

†Arrow Electronics, Inc.
19880 Haggerty Road
Livonia 48152
Tel: (313) 665-4100
TWX: 810-223-6020

Hamilton/Avnet Electronics
2215 29th Street S.E.
Space A5
Grand Rapids 49508
Tel: (616) 243-8805
FAX: 616-698-1831

Hamilton/Avnet Electronics
41650 Garden Brook
Novi 48050
Tel: (313) 347-4271
FAX: 313-347-4021

†Pioneer Electronics
4505 Broadmoor S.E.
Grand Rapids 49508
Tel: (616) 698-1800
FAX: 616-698-1831

†Pioneer/Michigan
13485 Stamford
Livonia 48150
Tel: (313) 525-1800
FAX: 313-427-3720

MINNESOTA

†Arrow Electronics, Inc.
5230 W. 73rd Street
Edina 55435
Tel: (612) 830-1800
TWX: 910-576-3125

†Hamilton/Avnet Electronics
12400 Whitewater Drive
Minnetonka 55434
Tel: (612) 932-0600
TWX: 910-576-2720

†Pioneer Electronics
7625 Golden Triange Dr.
Suite G
Eden Prairi 55343
Tel: (612) 944-3355
FAX: 612-944-3794

MISSOURI

†Arrow Electronics, Inc.
2380 Schuetz
St. Louis 63141
Tel: (314) 567-6888
FAX: 314-567-1164

†Hamilton/Avnet Electronics
741 Goddard
Chesterfield 63005
Tel: (314) 537-1600
FAX: 314-537-4248

NEW JERSEY

†Arrow Electronics, Inc.
4 East Stow Road
Unit 11
Marlton 08053
Tel: (609) 596-8000
FAX: 609-596-9632

†Arrow Electronics
6 Century Drive
Parsipanny 07054
Tel: (201) 538-0900
FAX: 201-538-0900

†Hamilton/Avnet Electronics
1 Keystone Ave., Bldg. 36
Cherry Hill 08003
Tel: (609) 424-0110
FAX: 609-751-2552

†Hamilton/Avnet Electronics
10 Industrial
Fairfield 07006
Tel: (201) 575-3390
FAX: 201-575-5839

†MTI Systems Sales
9 Law Drive
Fairfield 07006
Tel: (201) 227-5552
FAX: 201-575-6336

†Pioneer Electronics
14-A Madison Rd.
Fairfield 07006
Tel: (201) 575-3510
FAX: 201-575-3454

ertified Technical Distributor

intel®

DOMESTIC DISTRIBUTORS (Contd.)

NEW MEXICO

Alliance Electronics Inc.
10510 Research Avenue
Albuquerque 87123
Tel: (505) 292-3360
FAX: 505-292-6537

†Hamilton/Avnet Electronics
5659A Jefferson N.E.
Albuquerque 87109
Tel: (505) 765-1500
FAX: 505-243-1395

NEW YORK

†Arrow Electronics, Inc.
3375 Brighton Henrietta
Townline Rd.
Rochester 14623
Tel: (716) 427-0300
TWX: 510-253-4766

Arrow Electronics, Inc.
20 Oser Avenue
Hauppauge 11788
Tel: (516) 231-1000
TWX: 510-227-6623

†Hamilton/Avnet
933 Motor Parkway
Hauppauge 11788
Tel: (516) 231-9800
TWX: 510-224-6166

†Hamilton/Avnet Electronics
2060 Townline Rd.
Rochester 14623
Tel: (716) 272-2744
TWX: 510-253-5470

Hamilton/Avnet Electronics
103 Twin Oaks Drive
Syracuse 13206
Tel: (315) 437-0288
TWX: 710-541-1560

†MTI Systems Sales
38 Harbor Park Drive
Port Washington 11050
Tel: (516) 621-6200
FAX: 510-223-0846

Pioneer Electronics
68 Corporate Drive
Binghamton 13904
Tel: (607) 722-9300
FAX: 607-722-9562

Pioneer Electronics
40 Oser Avenue
Hauppauge 11787
Tel: (516) 231-9200
FAX: 510-227-9869

†Pioneer Electronics
60 Crossway Park West
Woodbury, Long Island 11797
Tel: (516) 921-8700
FAX: 516-921-2143

†Pioneer Electronics
840 Fairport Park
Fairport 14450
Tel: (716) 381-7070
FAX: 716-381-5955

NORTH CAROLINA

†Arrow Electronics, Inc.
5240 Greensdairy Road
Raleigh 27604
Tel: (919) 876-3132
TWX: 510-928-1856

†Hamilton/Avnet Electronics
3510 Spring Forest Drive
Raleigh 27604
Tel: (919) 878-0819
TWX: 510-928-1836

Pioneer/Technologies Group, Inc.
9401 L-Southern Pine Blvd.
Charlotte 28210
Tel: (919) 527-8188
FAX: 704-522-8564

OHIO

†Arrow Electronics, Inc.
6238 Cochran Road
Solon 44139
Tel: (216) 248-3990
TWX: 810-427-9409

†Hamilton/Avnet Electronics
7760 Washington Village Dr.
Dayton 45459
Tel: (513) 439-6733
FAX: 513-439-6711

†Hamilton/Avnet Electronics
30325 Bainbridge
Solon 44139
Tel: (216) 349-5100
TWX: 810-427-9452

Hamilton/Avnet Electronics
777 Brookside Blvd.
Westerville 43081
Tel: (614) 882-7004

†Pioneer Electronics
4433 Interpoint Boulevard
Dayton 45424
Tel: (513) 236-9900
FAX: 513-236-8133

†Pioneer Electronics
4800 E. 131st Street
Cleveland 44105
Tel: (216) 587-3600
FAX: 216-663-1004

OKLAHOMA

†Hamilton/Avnet Electronics
12121 E. 51st St., Suite 102A
Tulsa 74146
Tel: (918) 252-7297

OREGON

†Almac Electronics Corp.
1885 N.W. 169th Place
Beaverton 97005
Tel: (503) 629-8090
FAX: 503-645-0611

†Hamilton/Avnet Electronics
9409 S.W. Nimbus
Beaverton 97005
Tel: (503) 627-0201
FAX: 503-641-4012

Wyle Distribution Group
5250 N.E. Elam Young Parkway
Suite 600
Hillsboro 97124
Tel: (503) 640-6000
FAX: 503-640-5846

PENNSYLVANIA

Arrow Electronics, Inc.
650 Seco Road
Monroeville 15146
Tel: (412) 856-7000

Hamilton/Avnet Electronics
2800 Liberty Ave.
Pittsburgh 15238
Tel: (412) 281-4150

Pioneer Electronics
259 Kappa Drive
Pittsburgh 15238
Tel: (412) 782-2300
FAX: 412-963-8255

†Pioneer/Technologies Group, Inc.
Delaware Valley
261 Gibralter Road
Horsham 19044
Tel: (215) 674-4000
FAX: 215-674-3107

TEXAS

†Hamilton/Avnet Electronics
1807 W. Braker Lane
Austin 78758
Tel: (512) 837-8911
TWX: 910-874-1319

†Hamilton/Avnet Electronics
4004 Beltline, Suite 200
Dallas 75234
Tel: (214) 308-8111
TWX: 910-860-5929

†Hamilton/Avnet Electronics
4850 Wright Rd., Suite 190
Stafford 77477
Tel: (713) 240-7733
TWX: 910-881-5523

†Pioneer Electronics
1826-D Kramer
Austin 78758
Tel: (512) 835-4000
FAX: 512-835-9829

†Pioneer Electronics
13710 Omega Road
Dallas 75244
Tel: (214) 386-7300
FAX: 214-490-6419

†Pioneer Electronics
5853 Point West Drive
Houston 77036
Tel: (713) 988-5555
FAX: 713-982-1732

†Wyle Distribution Group
1810 Greenville Avenue
Richardson 75081
Tel: (214) 235-9953
FAX: 214-644-5064

UTAH

†Hamilton/Avnet Electronics
1585 West 2100 South
Salt Lake City 84119
Tel: (801) 972-2800
TWX: 910-925-4018

†Wyle Distribution Group
1325 West 2200 South
Suite E
West Valley 84119
Tel: (801) 974-9953

WASHINGTON

†Almac Electronics Corp.
14360 S.E. Eastgate Way
Bellevue 98007
Tel: (206) 643-9992
FAX: 206-643-9709

†Hamilton/Avnet Electronics
17761 N.E. 78th Place
Redmond 98052
Tel: (206) 881-6697
FAX: 206-867-0159

Wyle Distribution Group
15385 N.E. 90th Street
Redmond 98052
Tel: (206) 881-1150
FAX: 206-881-1567

WISCONSIN

Arrow Electronics, Inc.
200 N. Patrick Blvd., Ste. 100
Brookfield 53005
Tel: (414) 792-0150
FAX: 414-792-0156

†Hamilton/Avnet Electronics
28875 Crossroads Circle
Suite 400
Waukesha 53186
Tel: (414) 784-4510
FAX: 414-784-9509

CANADA

ALBERTA

Hamilton/Avnet Electronics
2816 21st Street N.E. #3
Calgary T2E 6Z3
Tel: (403) 230-3586
FAX: 403-250-1591

Zentronics
6815 #8 Street N.E.
Suite 100
Calgary T2E 7H
Tel: (403) 295-8818
FAX: 403-295-8714

BRITISH COLUMBIA

†Hamilton/Avnet Electronics
105-2550 Boundary
Burnaby V5M 3Z3
Tel: (604) 437-6667
FAX: 604-437-4712

Zentronics
108-11400 Bridgeport Road
Richmond V6X 1T2
Tel: (604) 273-5575
FAX: 604-273-2413

ONTARIO

Arrow Electronics, Inc.
36 Antares Dr., Unit 100
Nepean K2E 7W5
Tel: (613) 226-6903
FAX: 613-723-2018

Arrow Electronics, Inc.
1093 Meyerside, Unit 2
Mississauga L5T 1M4
Tel: (416) 673-7769
FAX: 416-672-0849

†Hamilton/Avnet Electronics
6845 Rexwood Road
Units 3-4-5
Mississauga L4T 1R2
Tel: (416) 677-7432
FAX: 416-677-0940

†Hamilton/Avnet Electronics
190 Colonnade Road South
Nepean K2E 7L5
Tel: (613) 226-1700
FAX: 613-226-1184

†Zentronics
1355 Meyerside Drive
Mississauga L59 1C9
Tel: (416) 564-9600
FAX: 416-564-8320

†Zentronics
155 Colonnade Road
Unit 17
Nepean K2E 7K1
Tel: (613) 226-8840
FAX: 613-226-6352

QUEBEC

Arrow Electronics Inc.
4050 rue Jean Talon Quest
Montreal H4P 1W1
Tel: (514) 735-5511
FAX: 514-341-4821

Arrow Electronics, Inc.
500 Boul. St-Jean-Baptiste
Suite 280
Quebec G2E 5R9
Tel: (418) 871-7500
FAX: 418-871-6816

†Hamilton/Avnet Electronics
2795 Halpern
St. Laurent H2E 7K1
Tel: (514) 335-1000
FAX: 514-335-2481

†Zentronics
520 McCaffrey
St. Laurent H4T 1N3
Tel: (514) 737-9700
FAX: 514-737-5212

†Certified Technical Distributor

EUROPEAN SALES OFFICES

NMARK

l Denmark A/S
ntevej 61, 3rd Floor
0 Copenhagen NV
(45) (31) 19 80 33
: 19567

LAND

l Finland OY
silantie 2
90 Helsinki
(358) 0 544 644
: 123332

NCE

l Corporation S.A.R.L.
ue Edison-BP 303
54 St. Quentin-en-Yvelines
lex
(33) (1) 30 57 70 00
. 699016

WEST GERMANY

Intel Semiconductor GmbH*
Dornacher Strasse 1
8016 Feldkirchen bei Muenchen
Tel: (49) 089/90992-0
TLX: 5-23177

Intel Semiconductor GmbH
Hohenzollern Strasse 5
3000 Hannover 1
Tel: (49) 0511/344081
TLX: 9-23625

Intel Semiconductor GmbH
Abraham Lincoln Strasse 16-18
6200 Wiesbaden
Tel: (49) 06121/7605-0
TLX: 4-186183

Intel Semiconductor GmbH
Zettachring 10A
7000 Stuttgart 80
Tel: (49) 0711/7287-280
TLX: 7-254826

ISRAEL

Intel Semiconductor Ltd.*
Atidim Industrial Park-Neve Sharet
P.O. Box 43202
Tel-Aviv 61430
Tel: (972) 3-548-3222
TLX: 371215

ITALY

Intel Corporation Italia S.p.A.*
Milanofiori Palazzo E
20090 Assago
Milano
Tel: (39) (02) 89200950
TLX: 341286

NETHERLANDS

Intel Semiconductor B.V.*
Postbus 84130
3099 CC Rotterdam
Tel: (31) 10.407.11.11
TLX: 22283

NORWAY

Intel Norway A/S
Hvamveien 4-PO Box 92
2013 Skjetten
Tel: (47) (6) 842 420
TLX: 78018

SPAIN

Intel Iberia S.A.
Zurbaran, 28
28010 Madrid
Tel: (34) (1) 308.25.52
TLX: 46880

SWEDEN

Intel Sweden A.B.*
Dalvagen 24
171 36 Solna
Tel: (46) 8 734 01 00
TLX: 12261

SWITZERLAND

Intel Semiconductor A.G.
Zuerichstrasse
8185 Winkel-Rueti bei Zuerich
Tel: (41) 01/860 62 62
TLX: 825977

UNITED KINGDOM

Intel Corporation (U.K.) Ltd.*
Pipers Way
Swindon, Wiltshire SN3 1RJ
Tel: (44) (0793) 696000
TLX: 444447/8

EUROPEAN DISTRIBUTORS/REPRESENTATIVES

STRIA

her Electronics G.m.b.H.
enmuehlgasse 26
0 Wien
(43) (0222) 83 56 46
: 31532

LGIUM

co Belgium S.A.
des Croix de Guerre 94
0 Bruxelles
logskruisenlaan, 94
0 Brussel
(32) (02) 216 01 60
: 64475 or 22090

NMARK

Multikomponent
erland 29
0 Glostrup
(45) (0) 2 45 66 45
: 33 355

LAND

Fintronic AB
konkatu 24A
10 Helsinki
(358) (0) 6926022
: 124224

NCE

ex
e industrielle d'Antony
rue de l'Aubepine
102
64 Antony cedex
(33) (1) 46 66 21 12
: 250067

nyn-Generim
rue des Gemeaux
: 580
53 Rungis cedex
(33) (1) 49 78 49 78
: 261585

rologie
r d'Asnieres
v. Laurent-Cely
06 Asnieres Cedex
(33) (1) 47 90 62 40
611448

Tekelec-Airtronic
Cite des Bruyeres
Rue Carle Vernet - BP 2
92310 Sevres
Tel: (33) (1) 45 34 75 35
TLX: 204552

WEST GERMANY

Electronic 2000 AG
Stahlgruberring 12
8000 Muenchen 82
Tel: (49) 089/42001-0
TLX: 522561

ITT Multikomponent GmbH
Postfach 1265
Bahnhofstrasse 44
7141 Moeglingen
Tel: (49) 07141/4879
TLX: 7264472

Jermyn GmbH
Im Dachsstueck 9
6250 Limburg
Tel: (49) 06431/508-0
TLX: 415257-0

Metrologie GmbH
Meglingerstrasse 49
8000 Muenchen 71
Tel: (49) 089/78042-0
TLX: 5213189

Proelectron Vertriebs GmbH
Max Planck Strasse 1-3
6072 Dreieich
Tel: (49) 06103/30434-3
TLX: 417903

IRELAND

Micro Marketing Ltd.
Glenageary Office Park
Glenageary
Co. Dublin
Tel: (21) (353) (01) 85 63 25
TLX: 31584

ISRAEL

Eastronics Ltd.
11 Rozanis Street
P.O.B. 39300
Tel-Aviv 61392
Tel: (972) 03-475151
TLX: 33638

ITALY

Intesi
Divisione ITT Industries GmbH
Viale Milanofiori
Palazzo E/5
20090 Assago (MI)
Tel: (39) 02/824701
TLX: 311351

Lasi Elettronica S.p.A.
V. le Fulvio Testi, 126
20092 Cinisello Balsamo (MI)
Tel: (39) 02/2440012
TLX: 352040

Telcom S.r.l.
Via M. Civitali 75
20148 Milano
Tel: (39) 02/4049046
TLX: 335654

ITT Multicomponents
Viale Milanofiori E/5
20090 Assago (MI)
Tel: (39) 02/824701
TLX: 311351

Silverstar
Via Dei Gracchi 20
20146 Milano
Tel: (39) 02/49961
TLX: 332189

NETHERLANDS

Koning en Hartman Elektrotechniek B.V.
Energieweg 1
2627 AP Delft
Tel: (31) (0) 15/609906
TLX: 38250

NORWAY

Nordisk Elektronikk (Norge) A/S
Postboks 123
Smedsvingen 4
1364 Hvalstad
Tel: (47) (02) 84 62 10
TLX: 77546

PORTUGAL

ATD Portugal LDA
Rua Dos Lusiados, 5 Sala B
1300 Lisboa
Tel: (35) (1) 64 80 91
TLX: 61562

Ditram
Avenida Miguel Bombarda, 133
1000 Lisboa
Tel: (35) (1) 54 53 13
TLX: 14182

SPAIN

ATD Electronica, S.A.
Plaza Ciudad de Viena, 6
28040 Madrid
Tel: (34) (1) 234 40 00
TLX: 42477

ITT-SESA
Calle Miguel Angel, 21-3
28010 Madrid
Tel: (34) (1) 419 09 57
TLX: 27461

Metrologia Iberica, S.A.
Ctra. de Fuencarral, n.80
28100 Alcobendas (Madrid)
Tel: (34) (1) 653 86 11

SWEDEN

Nordisk Elektronik AB
Torshamnsgatan 39
Box 36
164 93 Kista
Tel: (46) 08-03 46 30
TLX: 105 47

SWITZERLAND

Industrade A.G.
Hertistrasse 31
8304 Wallisellen
Tel: (41) (01) 8328111
TLX: 56788

TURKEY

EMPA Electronic
Lindwurmstrasse 95A
8000 Muenchen 2
Tel: (49) 089/53 80 570
TLX: 528573

UNITED KINGDOM

Accent Electronic Components Ltd.
Jubilee House, Jubilee Road
Letchworth, Herts SG6 1TL
Tel: (44) (0462) 686666
TLX: 826293

Bytech-Comway Systems
3 The Western Centre
Western Road
Bracknell RG12 1RW
Tel: (44) (0344) 55333
TLX: 847201

Jermyn
Vestry Estate
Otford Road
Sevenoaks
Kent TN14 5EU
Tel: (44) (0732) 450144
TLX: 95142

MMD
Unit 8 Southview Park
Caversham
Reading
Berkshire RG4 0AF
Tel: (44) (0734) 481666
TLX: 846669

Rapid Silicon
Rapid House
Denmark Street
High Wycombe
Buckinghamshire HP11 2ER
Tel: (44) (0494) 442266
TLX: 837931

Rapid Systems
Rapid House
Denmark Street
High Wycombe
Buckinghamshire HP11 2ER
Tel: (44) (0494) 450244
TLX: 837931

YUGOSLAVIA

H.R. Microelectronics Corp.
2005 de la Cruz Blvd., Ste. 223
Santa Clara, CA 95050
U.S.A.
Tel: (1) (408) 988-0286
TLX: 387452

Rapido Electronic Components S.p.a.
Via C. Beccaria, 8
34133 Trieste
Italia
Tel: (39) 040/360555
TLX: 460461

ld Application Location

INTERNATIONAL SALES OFFICES

AUSTRALIA

Intel Australia Pty. Ltd.*
Spectrum Building
200 Pacific Hwy., Level 6
Crows Nest, NSE, 2065
Tel: 612-957-2744
FAX: 612-923-2632

BRAZIL

Intel Semicondutores do Brazil LTDA
Av. Paulista, 1159-CJS 404/405
01311 - Sao Paulo - S.P.
Tel: 55-11-287-5899
TLX: 3911153146 ISDB
FAX: 55-11-287-5119

CHINA/HONG KONG

Intel PRC Corporation
15/F, Office 1, Citic Bldg.
Jian Guo Men Wai Street
Beijing, PRC
Tel: (1) 500-4850
TLX: 22947 INTEL CN
FAX: (1) 500-2953

Intel Semiconductor Ltd.*
10/F East Tower
Bond Center
Queensway, Central
Hong Kong
Tel: (852) 844-4555
FAX: (852) 868-1989

INDIA

Intel Asia Electronics, Inc.
4/2, Samrah Plaza
St. Mark's Road
Bangalore 560001
Tel: 011-91-812-215065
TLX: 9538452875 DCBY
FAX: 091-812-215067

JAPAN

Intel Japan K.K.
5-6 Tokodai, Tsukuba-shi
Ibaraki, 300-26
Tel: 0298-47-8511
TLX: 3656-160
FAX: 0298-47-8450

Intel Japan K.K.*
Daiichi Mitsugi Bldg.
1-8889 Fuchu-cho
Fuchu-shi, Tokyo 183
Tel: 0423-60-7871
FAX: 0423-60-0315

Intel Japan K.K.*
Bldg. Kumagaya
2-69 Hon-cho
Kumagaya-shi, Saitama 360
Tel: 0485-24-6871
FAX: 0485-24-7518

Intel Japan K.K.*
Mitsui-Seimei Musashi-kosugi Bldg.
915 Shinmaruko, Nakahara-ku
Kawasaki-shi, Kanagawa 211
Tel: 044-733-7011
FAX: 044-733-7010

Intel Japan K.K.
Nihon Seimei Atsugi Bldg.
1-2-1 Asahi-machi
Atsugi-shi, Kanagawa 243
Tel: 0462-29-3731
FAX: 0462-29-3781

Intel Japan K.K.*
Ryokuchi-Eki Bldg.
2-4-1 Terauchi
Toyonaka-shi, Osaka 560
Tel: 06-863-1091
FAX: 06-863-1084

Intel Japan K.K.
Shinmaru Bldg.
1-5-1 Marunouchi
Chiyoda-ku, Tokyo 100
Tel: 03-201-3621
FAX: 03-201-6850

Intel Japan K.K.
Green Bldg.
1-16-20 Nishiki
Naka-ku, Nagoya-shi
Aichi 450
Tel: 052-204-1261
FAX: 052-204-1285

KOREA

Intel Technology Asia, Ltd.
16th Floor, Life Bldg.
61 Yoido-dong, Youngdeungpo-Ku
Seoul 150-010
Tel: (2) 784-8186, 8286, 8386
TLX: K29312 INTELKO
FAX: (2) 784-8096

SINGAPORE

Intel Singapore Technology, Ltd.
101 Thomson Road #21-05/06
United Square
Singapore 1130
Tel: 250-7811
TLX: 39921 INTEL
FAX: 250-9256

TAIWAN

Intel Technology Far East Ltd.
8th Floor, No. 205
Bank Tower Bldg.
Tung Hua N. Road
Taipei
Tel: 886-2-716-9660
FAX: 886-2-717-2455

INTERNATIONAL DISTRIBUTORS/REPRESENTATIVES

ARGENTINA

Dafsys S.R.L.
Chacabuco, 90-6 Piso
1069-Buenos Aires
Tel: 54-1-334-7726
FAX: 54-1-334-1871

AUSTRALIA

Email Electronics
15-17 Hume Street
Huntingdale, 3166
Tel: 011-61-3-544-8244
TLX: AA 30895
FAX: 011-61-3-543-8179

NSD-Australia
205 Middleborough Rd.
Box Hill, Victoria 3128
Tel: 03 8900970
FAX: 03 8990819

BRAZIL

Elebra Microelectronica S.A.
Rua Geraldo Flausina Gomes, 78
7 Andar
04575 - Sao Paulo - S.P.
Tel: 55-11-534-9641
TLX: 55-11-54593/54591
FAX: 55-11-534-9424

CHINA/HONG KONG

Novel Precision Machinery Co., Ltd.
Flat D, 20 Kingsford Ind. Bldg.
Phase 1, 26 Kwai Hei Street
N.T., Kowloon
Hong Kong
Tel: (852) 422-3222
TWX: 39114 JINMI HX
FAX: (852) 426-1602

INDIA

Micronic Devices
Arun Complex
No. 65 D.V.G. Road
Basavanagudi
Bangalore 560 004
Tel: 011-91-812-600-631
011-91-812-611-365
TLX: 9538458332 MDBG

Micronic Devices
No. 516 5th Floor
Swastik Chambers
Sion, Trombay Road
Chembur
Bombay 400 071
TLX: 9531 171447 MDEV

Micronic Devices
25/8, 1st Floor
Bada Bazaar Marg
Old Rajinder Nagar
New Delhi 110 060
Tel: 011-91-11-5723509
011-91-11-589771
TLX: 031-63253 MDND IN

Micronic Devices
6-3-348/12A Dwarakapuri Colony
Hyderabad 500 482
Tel: 011-91-842-226748

S&S Corporation
1587 Kooser Road
San Jose, CA 95118
Tel: (408) 978-6216
TLX: 820281
FAX: (408) 978-8635

JAPAN

Asahi Electronics Co. Ltd.
KMM Bldg. 2-14-1 Asano
Kokurakita-ku
Kitakyushu-shi 802
Tel: 093-511-6471
FAX: 093-551-7861

C. Itoh Techno-Science Co., Ltd.
4-8-1 Dobashi, Miyamae-ku
Kawasaki-shi, Kanagawa 213
Tel: 044-852-5121
FAX: 044-877-4268

Dia Semicon Systems, Inc.
Flower Hill Shinmachi Higashi-kan
1-23-9 Shinmachi, Setagaya-ku
Tokyo 154
Tel: 03-439-1600
FAX: 03-439-1601

Okaya Koki
2-4-18 Sakae
Naka-ku, Nagoya-shi 460
Tel: 052-204-2916
FAX: 052-204-2901

Ryoyo Electro Corp.
Konwa Bldg.
1-12-22 Tsukiji
Chuo-ku, Tokyo 104
Tel: 03-546-5011
FAX: 03-546-5044

KOREA

J-Tek Corporation
6th Floor, Government Pension Bldg.
24-3 Yoido-dong
Youngdeungpo-ku
Seoul 150-010
Tel: 82-2-780-8039
TLX: 25299 KODIGIT
FAX: 82-2-784-8391

Samsung Electronics
150 Taepyungro-2 KA
Chungku, Seoul 100-102
Tel: 82-2-751-3985
TLX: 27970 KORSST
FAX: 82-2-753-0967

MEXICO

SSB Electronics, Inc.
675 Palomar Street, Bldg. 4, Suite A
Chula Vista, CA 92011
Tel: (619) 585-3253
TLX: 287751 CBALL UR
FAX: (619) 585-8322

Dicopel S.A.
Tochtli 368 Fracc. Ind. San Antonio
Azcapotzalco
C.P. 02760-Mexico, D.F.
Tel: 52-5-561-3211
TLX: 177 3790 Dicome
FAX: 52-5-561-1279

PSI S.A. de C.V.
Fco. Villa esq. Ajusco s/n
Cuernavaca – Morelos
Tel: 52-73-13-9412
FAX: 52-73-17-5333

NEW ZEALAND

Email Electronics
36 Olive Road
Penrose, Auckland
Tel: 011-64-9-591-155
FAX: 011-64-9-592-681

SINGAPORE

Electronic Resources Pte, Ltd.
17 Harvey Road #04-01
Singapore 1336
Tel: 283-0888
TWX: 56541 ERS
FAX: 2895327

SOUTH AFRICA

Electronic Building Elements
178 Erasmus Street (off Watermeyet Stre
Meyerspark, Pretoria, 0184
Tel: 011-2712-803-7680
FAX: 011-2712-803-8294

TAIWAN

Micro Electronics Corporation
5/F 587, Ming Shen East Rd.
Taipei, R.O.C.
Tel: 886-2-501-8231
FAX: 886-2-505-6609

Sertek
15/F 135, Section 2
Chien Juo North Rd.
Taipei 10479, R.O.C.
Tel: (02) 5010055
FAX: (02) 5012521
(02) 5058414

VENEZUELA

P. Benavides S.A.
Avilanes a Rio
Residencia Kamarata
Locales 4 AL 7
La Candelaria, Caracas
Tel: 58-2-574-6338
TLX: 28450
FAX: 58-2-572-3321

*Field Application Location